THE BIRDWATCHER'S YEARBOOK 2020

Edited by Neil Gartshore

Calluna Books

Published in 2019 by
Calluna Books
Moor Edge, 2 Bere Road, Wareham
Dorset BH20 4DD
United Kingdom

phone: 01929 552 560 ~ 07986 434 375
e-mail: enquiries@callunabooks.co.uk
website: www.callunabooks.co.uk

© Calluna Books 2019

ISBN 978-0-9933477-4-0
ISSN 2048-7258

Cover photograph: by Neil Gartshore
The Sparrowhawk *Accipiter nisus* is a common bird of prey often encountered
in our gardens - this photo of a female was taken by the editor from his office
window. Although they feed almost entirely on small birds, a Sparrowhawk in
the area is usually a sign of a healthy songbird population.

Black & white illustrations: by Dan Powell
phone: 01329 668 465
e-mail: danpowell11@btinternet.com
website: www.powellwildlifeart.com

Printed and bound in Great Britain by
Ashford Colour Press Ltd,
Gosport, Hampshire

CONTENTS

CONTENTS

PREFACE

WITH THE PUBLICATION of this *Yearbook*, the series has reached another milestone - the 40th edition. John Pemberton started the ball rolling when he saw a gap in the birdwatching market and created the first *Yearbook* (1981). I can only admire his dedication and what he achieved. Although the content has changed, and grown, somewhat since the early days, the *Yearbook* would have been much more of a monumental task to edit back then and the printing process was far more 'hands on' than today. John would have sourced information from the written word and communication would have been largely by stamped addressed envelopes (or phone calls). As computers were in their infancy, a typewriter would have been used to produce the text. In contrast, today I can use technology and I have managed to refine my methods which has helped to streamline the *Yearbook's* production. The internet has obviously been a positive help to source information (albeit frustrating at times) and, of course, e-mails make communications easier (well, sometimes). Printing is also so much easier. A 'pdf' is sent to the printers and within a couple of weeks it's back - printed and ready for sale.

There have been many comments in recent years about the demise of the printed book with the increase in digital options. To an extent this may be true but while the digital market has been levelling off, the printed market has remained healthy - this is reflected in the *Yearbook* sales and I expect that the 50th edition will be celebrated in 2030 (it remains to be seen whether by me or a new editor!)

<><><><><>

In March, my local bird club held a joint conference with the BTO. These conferences are a great way of finding out what is happening in your local area, often including work that you are unaware of. From the content of the Dorset conference I commissioned two features that I felt would be of interest to *Yearbook* readers - and could be a blueprint for projects in other parts of the country. The third feature looks at nature and our wellbeing. With the stresses & strains of modern life we all need to re-charge our batteries and nature is being promoted more and more as an effective way of doing this. The two regulars - bird news and bird books - complete the features.

My biggest task this year has been to revamp and check the Reserves Directory - the number of reserves listed has increased slightly to 380 across England, Scotland and Wales. Although there are many birding sites in each county, the directory sticks to defined reserves (and includes many of the UK's flagships). I find it quite amazing that over my birding life I have actually visited a large proportion of them (and have even worked on a few)... from Shetland to Somerset, Norfolk to North Wales. We are blessed with such a variety of reserves from the huge NNR's and RSPB sites to the smaller pockets of land managed by the Wildlife Trusts - whatever their size or location they all provide vital habitats for our birds and other wildlife. Why not use the directory to visit a few that you haven't visited before?

<><><><><>

Finally I would like to thank, as ever, all of the people who have responded to my queries over information contained in the *Yearbook* to ensure that it is as up to date and as accurate as possible. If you come across any errors, omissions or changes before the next edition please let me know (contact details on page 6).

I hope you all have some great birding in 2020.
Neil Gartshore, Wareham, September 2019

CONTACT US

The information contained in *The Yearbook* is sourced/checked in a number of ways ...websites, magazines, personal contacts, e-mails, phone calls, and so on. Once *The Yearbook* has been published there will inevitably be changes to some of the information that will not be amended until the next edition.

If someone has stepped down from a role you should be redirected to the new contact. Where we are notified of any changes we will list them on an amendments page on the Calluna Books website (go to www.callunabooks.co.uk and follow the *Yearbook* link).

If you have any comments on this edition of *The Yearbook*, corrections to advise us of or suggestions for future editions, we would be pleased to hear from you.

*****

Neil Gartshore, Moor Edge, 2 Bere Road, Wareham, Dorset BH20 4DD
phone: 01929 552 560
e-mail: enquiries@callunabooks.co.uk

The Birdwatcher's Yearbook

A limited number of back copies of *The Yearbook*
are available covering most years
from **2001** to **2019**

Please contact us for availability/prices

Martin Cade / PBO

Initiatives for farmland birds & other wildlife at Portland Bird Observatory are starting to pay dividends with the bonus of providing cover for migrants. No Pallas's Reed Bunting has turned up yet but Rustic Bunting (*Emberiza pusilla*), Pine Bunting (*E. leucocephalos*) & Aquatic Warbler (*Acrocephalus paludicola*) have.

FEATURES

PERFECTING THE MIX FOR FARM WILDLIFE AT PORTLAND BIRD OBSERVATORY (PBO) - OR JUST WISHING ON A PALLAS'S REED BUNTING?

Countryside Stewardship initaitives to improve habitats for birds and other wildlife have been around for a while. PBO Trustee James Phillips gives an insight into how the Observatory is making a difference to 'The Bill' with its own scheme.

FOR A NUMBER OF YEARS now the Portland Bird Observatory has prided itself on managing its land holdings (in particular the Crown Estate Field and Helen's Fields) to benefit migrating birds and this has been a great success. However, there has always been a thought that the Observatory could get paid to carry out this land management through a government funded agri-environment grant scheme and tailor the management further to enhance the Observatory's land holdings to deliver even more for wildlife.

In 2016 the Observatory started to look at this idea more seriously and to consider which of the agri-environment schemes would best fit its needs and at the type of land management that would most benefit migrating birds and the farm wildlife associated with Portland Bill.

Through the summer of 2016 the Observatory put together an application that we saw as the best fit and submitted this at the end of September 2016. The Observatory was accepted into the Countryside Stewardship (CS) scheme with a five-year agreement starting in January 2017.

It should be stressed that the whole process from designing a scheme to submitting an application was very much a team effort working with Martin Cade (Observatory warden), Pete Morgan (chair of Observatory trustees), Richard Newton (trustee/farming expert) and Alex Butler from the Farm Wildlife Advisory Group (FWAG) South West.

This article looks at what we are aiming to do through the Observatory's CS agreement and at some of the positive results that we are already seeing.

What is Countryside Stewardship?

Firstly, what is Countryside Stewardship (CS)? It is something we call an agri-environment grant scheme, a government scheme run by the Rural Payment Agency on behalf of Defra (Department of Environment, Farming and Rural Affairs) which provides financial incentives for land managers to look after their natural environment through activities such as conserving and restoring wildlife habitats.

The CS scheme land management options have been specifically designed to benefit England's wildlife habitats and the species associated with them. Monitoring evidence is now showing that farmland biodiversity will respond positively if the right agri-environment options are put in the right places, at the right scale and at the required quality.

Which land management options did we choose and why?

We have tailored the Observatory's CS agreement to put in place a package of land management measures to benefit the farmland birds, wild pollinators and other wildlife associated with the farmed environment at Portland Bill.

In particular we have focused on those land management options that help to provide the year-round life cycle needs that the wildlife associated with the farmed environment need in order to thrive. These are sometimes called the 'Big three' – 1. Year round food (winter food/summer chick food), 2. Shelter and 3. Nesting places. Central to the agreement was to include land management that would benefit the migrating birds that pass through Portland Bill each spring and autumn.

1. Winter bird food (wild bird seed mixes):

This option provides important food resources for farmland birds and migrating bird species, especially in autumn and winter. Pipits, thrushes, chats, warblers, finches and buntings will all benefit, with many migrants using the mixes as a valuable refuelling stop in the spring and autumn. The idea of sowing these mixes is to provide an abundant and available supply of small seeds during the autumn, winter and through into the spring.

Farmland and migrating bird species will utilise the seeds from the autumn onwards while insects including bumblebees, solitary bees, butterflies and hoverflies will use the flowers in the mix during the summer.

8

PERFECTING THE MIX FOR FARM WILDLIFE AT PBO

The mixes are sown between early March and mid-June to establish a seed mix of cereals, brassicas and other plants which produce small edible seeds to meet the autumn, winter and spring food needs of the birds. Once established the mixes last between one and two years and then are re-sown.

There is flexibility with the seed mixes we can use - so we can have more cereal based mixes or more Brassica based mixes depending on the species of birds we want to attract in. The blocks of mixes can be rotated around the Crown Estate Field and Helen's Field through the lifetime of the CS agreement.

2. Supplementary feeding the 'Hungry Gap':

This option provides important food resources for farmland birds in late winter and early spring on arable farmland, by supplementing crops of winter bird food when they have been depleted and before natural food sources become available in the late spring.

Birds that benefit will include species like Linnet and Reed Bunting and may, in time, attract in other rarer Portland species such as Yellowhammer and Corn Bunting.

The period between January and early spring is often referred to as the 'Hungry Gap' for farmland birds when food can be in very short supply and so providing this additional food source during this time period will be extremely beneficial to these species.

Tailings (the seeds and chaff removed from the harvested crop) and other small seeds including millet are used as the supplementary feed. This is spread on the ground, at least once a week from early December until the end of April.

3. Harvested low-input spring cereal:

This option is used to create an open-structured cereal crop (using wheat, barley, triticale, oats or rye) which is not too dense, which then provides summer foraging sites for localised farmland birds and habitat for rare arable plants. This will be important for wild pollinator species such as bumblebees, solitary bees, butterflies and hoverflies.

The resulting open nature of the crop will provide suitable habitat for nesting birds, such as Skylark. A range of declining arable plants and other broadleaved species will also benefit. The more weedy nature of the resulting stubble from the crop will also be beneficial, providing food for farmland birds and other migrating birds through the autumn months.

This option is also rotational and can be moved around the Observatory's land holdings each year. The Bill area holds significant breeding populations of Skylark and most of this specially managed crop will be sown in Helen Field's to help benefit these important populations.

4. Nectar flower mix:

We included this option as we wanted to provide some areas of flowering plants to boost essential food sources to benefit pollinating insects and other invertebrate species found at The Bill.

The idea is to create an abundant supply of pollen and nectar-rich flowers between early and late summer for pollinating insects such as bumblebees, solitary bees, butterflies and hoverflies and other invertebrate species.

The option works by establishing a mix of nectar-rich plants using species such as early and late flowering Red Clovers, Sainfoin, Birdsfoot Trefoil, Knapweed and Musk Mallow.

The planting of a range of suitable crops, hedgerows and scrub provides food and shelter throughout the year for a wide variety of species. Photo: James Phillips

PERFECTING THE MIX FOR FARM WILDLIFE AT PBO

The mix is established in blocks or strips between mid-March and late April or mid-July and late August. This option then remains in place for the duration of the agreement to provide a continuous long-term food source for pollinators.

As well as benefiting insects and invertebrates this habitat will also provide an important foraging habitat for breeding and migrating birds.

5. Cultivated areas for rare arable plants:

There have been historical records of rare arable plants such as Shepherd's Needle at The Bill. We added this option into the agreement to create uncropped, cultivated areas which would benefit a wide range of these scarce and declining species of plants and other species associated with cultivated arable land. This option also provides areas of less densely vegetated ground for insects and other invertebrates.

The management is simply to create fallow margins or plots annually by cultivating in the spring between February and April or in the autumn between September and November and leaving these areas in place each year. The option can be rotated and placed where we think it will be of most benefit to arable plants.

This provides the bare ground habitats to help vulnerable species of arable plants to germinate and complete their life cycle. The flowers attract foraging insects and the bare ground created provides more open foraging habitat for farmland and migrating birds.

6. Planting new hedges and areas of scrub:

We have also carried out additional capital works including planting new hedges and scrub areas in and around the Crown Estate Field. This took place in November and December 2018.

We have only used native species: Hawthorn, Blackthorn, Dogwood, Wild privet, Wayfaring tree and Spindle, all of which are characteristic to the Isle of Portland. Using this mix of species, we have planted lengths of hedgerow and scrub in and around the field to create good foraging, nesting and sheltering habitats for birds and other wildlife. This will in time also provide cover for spring and autumn migrating birds.

Much of The Bill is covered in a monoculture of 'pony paddocks'. The Observatory's planting schemes are improving the visual landscape as well as providing suitable conditions for wildlife. Photo: James Phillips

How is the wildlife responding to the land management being put in place?

The Observatory is monitoring the success of the agreement through a daily migrant census and annual breeding bird surveys of the Observatory recording area (which has been carried out each year since the mid-1960s). By doing this we will be able to track the biological responses of the bird species and other wildlife we are targeting to the land management we are putting in place.

It is early days but the response we are seeing from Portland's farm wildlife already suggests that what we are doing is starting to make a positive difference, for example:

Brown-banded Carder Bee. This rare species of bumble bee was once widespread across lowland Britain but has undergone substantial declines during the second half of the 20th century, with modern day strongholds for the species now confined to Salisbury Plain, the coast of south east and south west England and south Wales.

PERFECTING THE MIX FOR FARM WILDLIFE AT PBO

For the species to thrive it needs a good flow of nectar throughout its flight period. The areas of contiguous, well connected mosaics of flower rich limestone grassland found on Portland seem to be providing this habitat with good numbers of the species still recorded across the island. Interestingly 10-15 individuals were seen nectaring in the early summer of 2018 on the Observatory's flowering brassica-based CS wild bird seed mixes in Helen's Fields. This would suggest that this is helping to provide some much needed food at this time of year. It would be good to know just how important the Portland population is, both in a regional and national context, and how important these flowering brassica crops are to the species at this time of the year.

Four Spotted Moth. This scarce and vulnerable moth has been recorded regularly from the CS managed areas over the last two summers (2017 and 2018) and has been observed at rest and nectaring on flowers in the sown mixes and seen in association with its food plant Field Bindweed. This nationally scarce species, once widely distributed in the south is now restricted to few small populations scattered across southern England including Dorset (where it is a speciality on the Isle of Portland).

Corn Bunting. Once a common breeding bird on Portland, it has been extinct for many years now. However over the last two years observations have started to increase with spring and autumn birds now a regular feature, with records from both the Crown Estate Field and Helen's Fields. In the winter 2018/19 this included a bird being recorded from the supplementary feed areas.

Linnet. Each autumn over the last two years since the agreement started we have observed huge numbers of migrant Linnets using the wild bird seed mixes with flocks of up to 3,000 birds regularly counted feeding in the cereal and kale based mixes. This is a wonderful sight to behold for the many visitors who come to the Observatory each autumn. To date, these are the largest counts recorded for this species in Dorset. It's interesting to note how important the wild bird seed mixes are in attracting in so many Linnets in the autumn. This newly available food source must be providing a valuable fuel stop and valuable energy for the birds to help their migration as they head further south into Europe.

Tree Sparrow. In the summer of 2018 a pair bred on Portland for the first time in living memory, and reared and fledged two broods of chicks (one of six and one of five). The adults birds chose to nest in one of the nest boxes provided in Helen's Fields and were watched continually feeding in the various land management options we have put in place including collecting invertebrates to feed to the chicks.

Once the chicks fledged, the young birds were seen feeding in the various crops too. This provided us with the evidence that the mosaics of habitats and seed mixes we have put in place really did work to deliver the 'Big Three' habitats required to help this rare and declining farmland bird to thrive in 2018.

As a regular passage bird on Portland, the Tree Sparrow (*Passer montanus*) is one of the target species for the CS initaitive. photo: N.Gartshore

Other rarer species of migrant birds that have been recorded from the crops in the Crown Estate Fields in recent years have included Aquatic Warbler, Radde's Warbler, Common Rosefinch, Little, Rustic and Pine Buntings... and who knows in time this may soon include other rare migrants - we're wishing on a Pallas's Reed Bunting!

Check out the Portland Bird Observatory Website:
www.portlandbirdobs.com (see advert on page 327).

ON THE VERGE OF SUCCESS

How to help wildlife, win friends and influence people - Pete Moore explains how an initiative to save a local authority money, while increasing biodiversity along its road verges, has been a great success.

WHEN I WAS OFFERED a job as Head of Environment at Dorset County Council in 2014, I accepted with some trepidation given the number of hot potatoes in the in-tray. One of the hottest was the issue of highway verges. I don't wish to imply that the fastidious residents of suburban Dorset had nothing better to worry about than a bit of unkempt grass, but it ranked high on the list of complaints received by the Council, second only to that most heinous of social evils: inconsiderate parking.

Finding a solution for a problem

2014 became known in the cash-starved world of municipal greenspace management as 'the growing season from hell' as a warm spring followed a mild wet winter. The Council's mowers were soon creaking under the strain. A rethink was called for, a Committee was set up and it fell to my team to steer the review to a conclusion. Throwing money at it wasn't an option - and besides, we would rather spend what money we had looking after our greenspaces properly than mowing them to within an inch of their lives.

At this point I made one of my best decisions in my local government career: I asked an ecologist. Not just any old one, but Dr Phil Sterling, former Dorset County Ecologist, national micro-moth expert and now a colleague at Butterfly Conservation, the UK charity dedicated to saving butterflies, moths and the environment.

The verge network was probably the biggest single asset within the control of the Council offering the greatest opportunity to support pollinators. It also represented an extensive area of habitat and a series of wildlife corridors in its own right. Significantly, verges cover some half a million km nationally – an area equivalent to half of our remaining flower-rich grasslands and meadows.

Phil helped me understand the difference between a high nutrient verge – a monoculture of thuggish plants characterised by limited biodiversity and high maintenance – and a low nutrient verge – more diverse, attractive and much easier to manage. Sadly, many of our verges are the former. To make matters worse, when we build new roads we

tend to cover the verges in high nutrient top-soil, and leave the clippings on the verge after cutting to act as yet more fertiliser, feeding an unsustainable system.

By contrast, a low-nutrient verge needs limited management and allows a diversity of plants to coexist, making it better for pollinators and the things (like birds and, indeed, people) which depend on them. Informed by this simple but oft-forgotten insight, we turned our minds to how we could design and manage fertility out of the system.

Five-spot Burnet Moth on Pyramidal Orchid, Blandford Forum by-pass after a few years of 'cut-and-collect'

ON THE VERGE OF SUCCESS

The way forward

The strategy which emerged had three main strands. First, we simply reduced cutting when and where we didn't need to. Second, we set out to reduce the fertility of the verges where we could. And, third, we sought to communicate better with, and manage the expectations of, tax-paying residents. The key message was that, even if we wanted to, we couldn't afford to give them 'putting green' verges - but we could give them something better, and use the savings to pay for more important services.

There are various ways to reduce the vigour of a grass verge - a key one being the method known as 'cut and collect'. Under this regime, rather than leave the cuttings on the verge to act as fertiliser, we take them away. By phasing out conventional mowers and replacing them with machines capable of collecting cut grass, we found we could deliver a more efficient operation as well as a lower maintenance, more biodiverse verge. We weren't sure at the outset how quickly we would see the benefits, but they became apparent earlier than we imagined - around Blandford Forum, thanks to 'cut and collect', the number of cuts reduced from seven each year to just two in 2018 after just two years of this approach.

At the same time, we started to experiment with other interventions to reduce soil fertility. As now, local government revenue budgets were under severe pressure but there were still some capital funds available for 'invest to save' initiatives. We accessed these to conduct trials, stripping off topsoil and planting wildflower verges in prominent locations. These proved very popular with residents - so much so that it was the only time in 14 years of public administration when the compliments in my inbox outweighed complaints!

Confidence to take on large-scale initiatives

Informed by the learning from these trials, our confidence and ambition grew such that, a few years later when major resurfacing works took place on the A338 Bournemouth Spur Road, we were able to build low fertility verges into the project on a grand scale. These now require very little maintenance as well as providing valuable wildlife habitat.

Retro-fitting good grassland management was a crucial part of the strategy adopted in 2014, but some time before this an opportunity arose to work on a blank canvas. The typical

Verges on the Weymouth Relief Road, home to a stunning diversity of wildflowers and pollinating insects including 30 species of butterfly

approach on a major engineering project like the Weymouth Relief Road, built just prior to the 2012 Olympic Sailing events in Weymouth, would have been to strip back to the bare rock, put the infrastructure in place, then smother the verges in topsoil to support a nice green lawn for the day the Minister turned up to cut the ribbon. This was an anathema to Dr Sterling so, working with the council's highway design team, he specified the finest smattering of topsoil and hand sowed the slopes with locally harvested wildflower seed.

So the seeds of a new approach had been sown (literally) but we still faced two challenges from the sceptics. The first, from the accountants at County Hall, was would it really save any money?

13

ON THE VERGE OF SUCCESS

The evidence on this was compelling as, through a combination of reviewing contract spend, a more targeted approach to cutting and the efforts to reduce fertility, the council's budget for verge management reduced by about 15% (over £140,000) in the three years to 2017-18. The new cut-and-collect mowers offered payback in about five years; conventional mowers, by contrast, offered no payback at all. The cost saving on topsoil alone on the Weymouth Relief Road was around £270,000, while the ongoing annual maintenance bill came down to less than £500 p.a. compared to the standard £2,700 p.a. There were also hidden dividends as we were able to redeploy our maintenance teams onto more productive tasks such as maintaining the Rights of Way network.

The second challenge came, perhaps surprisingly, from environmentalists – would all this actually be any good for the wildlife? The experience of the Weymouth Relief Road is, again, more than encouraging: within two years of it opening in 2011, 21 species of butterfly had been recorded from what had previously been an ecologically impoverished site. That number has since risen to 30. The Small Blue butterfly colonised in 2012 and is now thought to be the largest such colony in Dorset; Adonis Blue arrived a year later; and in 2018 the first Chalkhill Blue for the site was recorded, completing a remarkable set.

So the picture was clear – by changing our mindset and our management of highway verges, there was huge potential to save public money whilst improving the roadside environment, particularly for pollinating insects. And let's face it, they need all the help they can get given the challenges they face in the wider countryside.

Looking forward to a positive future

One remarkable change over the last five years has been the apparent shift in public opinion about what a 'good' highway verge should look like. When we adopted the new policy, for every letter we got complaining we cut the wildflowers too much, we were getting at least one more saying we were not cutting enough.

A few short years later, a social media firestorm awaits the council which cuts down wildflowers too early or before the invertebrates which depend on them have completed their lifecycle. In fact, it's almost gone too far the other way with almost any cutting seen as bad - 'cutting less and doing so at a time appropriate to the habitat' is perhaps too subtle for today's keyboard warriors! But it's churlish to complain when the public mood appears to be moving away from a desire for 'tidy' verges and towards a recognition of the need for 'healthy' ones. Whether we benefitted from that change, or played a small part in it, I don't know, but it offers great hope that we are on the verge - pun intended - of something better.

Postscript: Dr Phil Sterling now leads Butterfly Conservation's 'Building Sites for Butterflies'

Dorset's wildflower verge trials proved very popular with the public

project, supported by the Patsy Wood Trust, and continues to spread the message across the UK of how creating low-fertility grasslands can help wildlife - and save money. To find out more, visit https://butterfly-conservation.org/our-work/conservation-projects/building-sites-for-butterflies

STOP FOR A MOMENT… NATURE IS ONE OF THE FINEST WELLBEING TONICS!

With the stresses & strains of modern life ever increasing, Wendy Palmer-Grove gives an insight into how nature can help improve our wellbeing.

DO YOUR SPIRITS SOAR from the delights of hearing birdsong? …maybe the iconic mew of a Buzzard overhead or the beautiful rich and fluted sound of a Blackbird dominating the evening sky.

Have you ever experienced a feeling of inner stillness whilst standing in a woodland?
…a sense of enveloped peacefulness surrounded by the sheer enormity of trees.

Do you feel mentally soothed when gazing out to sea?
…it's meditative rhythm - ebb and flow, a briny horizon with incomprehensible space.

These feelings and emotions that we experience when immersed into the natural world are Mankind's Wellbeing Tonic, helping to dissipate stresses and worries. Experiencing a sense of slowing to natures pace and feeling part of this organic wonderment is a pure boost for our wellbeing, after all to be human is to be part of nature!

Natures Wellbeing Tonic

As modern day living increases pace and pressure, the ability to access natural spaces to aid our wellbeing becomes ever more vital. Whilst technological advancements support the 'everything-in-an-instant' lifestyle, it has created a plethora of overstimulated, overloaded minds, craving to STOP for a moment.

When we are put under stress - physically or emotionally - a sequence of involuntary triggers occur to place us in fight or flight mode, a physiological, split-second change throughout the body to prepare us for 'attack'. This mode was crucial for survival in our hunter-gatherer ancestors day, however modern mankind has not evolved to manage this chemical booster or the stressors responsible.

Nature has an answer! It reduces this intense physical readiness through its many guises and importantly can activate mental slow-down or space for the mind and body to restore and recharge. The heart rate and blood pressure reduces, deeper breathing occurs aiding the removal of toxins from the body, the immune and nervous system is no longer compromised. By regularly being in nature we can start to address the impact of stress so that we improve overall wellbeing.

'Research achieved by The Woodland Trust (2013) mentioned - NHS could save billions of pounds in healthcare if more people had access to Green Spaces'

STOP FOR A MOMENT… NATURE IS ONE OF THE FINEST WELLBEING TONICS!

The Natural Effect

Many of us love nothing better than being outside with nature, some even yearn for it, but have you ever thought why we have such cravings?

Decades of scientific and physiological studies have been achieved regarding our attraction to the natural world. One proven theory is Biophilia 'our innate affinity to seek connection with nature'

'E.O. Wilson (Harvard University entomologist) developed the Biophilia theory-love of life (1984). His research proved that we subconsciously seek to be with nature, a development through biological evolution, hence the direct cognitive benefit and restorative quality we experience in nature'

Birdwatching … Nature & Nurture

When we think of Wellbeing hobbies, Birdwatching is not surprisingly a top runner, supporting both physical and mental wellbeing (NHS/Gov.uk five steps to wellbeing are: be active, connected, learning, giving, mindful).

- Birdwatching encourages a variety of outdoor activity
- Mindfully we are absorbed into our moment with nature
- Activates and reconnects our senses often stifled in modern living, such as our peripheral vision & 360° awareness
- Opportunity to escape everything square, flat and time-sapping, such as 2D screens, square box spaces, social media
- Learning-birds and nature are full of new surprises
- Feel good factor of sharing sightings, stories, laughs and company
- Supports low mood and depression-promotes positive feelings

'Scientific research via Kings College, London (2018) identified the positive impact nature has on mental wellbeing. It stated Birdsong has a stress busting action, boosting mental wellbeing for up to four hours after the experience. Even short term exposure has a measurable beneficial impact on mental Wellbeing'

Fellow Birdwatchers wellbeing thoughts on nature…

'Mental uplift! seeing beautiful, natural things helps to give me 'space' to forget worries'

'A joy to share the excitement and anticipation of birdwatching with others'

'Being in nature gives me a sense of tranquillity and brings back lovely childhood memories'

'Just 15 minutes in my garden can improve my mood and energise me for hours'

'Being in nature gives me a sense of freedom, a timelessness that often makes me smile'

'Birdwatching helps me put life stuff into perspective'

'If I'm feeling low, I walk by the river, watch birds, enjoy the seasons change …nature is so uplifting'

'I love to escape people, to be quiet and soak up everything around me in nature'

'When I'm in nature I feel relaxed, privileged and small. Mother nature continues to surprise me with its resilience and beauty'

STOP FOR A MOMENT... NATURE IS ONE OF THE FINEST WELLBEING TONICS!

Trees are medicine for the soul... and maybe much more

Without a doubt there is something quite magical about trees, they hold a regal intrigue and soothing quality, but can they also aid our wellbeing?

For many decades, research on Forest Bathing - Japanese Shinrin Yoku - has developed some remarkable results. This evidence based approach was developed to encourage people to reconnect with the natural world, predominately trees, however the physical and immunological benefits have gone beyond the initial vision.

Apart from the 'green space' benefits already identified for overall wellbeing, studies found that the natural protective chemical Phytoncide omitted by trees had a positive effect on humans. When phytoncide was absorbed through breath, a positive change of activity on a type of white blood cell called Natural Killer occurred. NK cells play an important role for our immune system by killing virus infected cells in the body and defending against such things as cancers. Whilst we wait for more of this fascinating research to unfurl, we can be assured that a walk in the woods will benefit mind, body and soul.

ReWilding the Wild Magic

Rewilding may conjure up thoughts of conservation for land or wildlife, restoring and repairing to allow nature to take care of itself. So what if we look at these same principles for ourselves to improve our wellbeing and create richer experiences.

Young children don't have the preconceived thoughts and experiences that adults share. Their ability to openly and curiously explore through their senses creates a deep, playful connection that as adults we have to learn to reconnect with.

Rewilding Ourselves

- Slow down to natures pace, immerse yourself into nature and allow yourself to be still. Become aware of all of your five senses.
- Take some slow, deep breaths. Outdoor deep breathing can be very cathartic, but also has many health benefits such as reducing heart rate & blood pressure, cleansing the body of toxins.
- **Smell:** Notice what scents and smells surround you. A coastal briny air, the smell of the Rain 'Petrichor', go beyond the obvious.
- **Touch:** Be tactile, what does nature feel like. Close your eyes as the sensation will be very different. Take a moment to notice how you feel emotionally in your green space.
- **Taste:** Often the trickiest but be patient as you explore this sense, maybe connect it with scents.

STOP FOR A MOMENT... NATURE IS ONE OF THE FINEST WELLBEING TONICS!

- **Hear:** Listen to what surrounds you, maybe bird calls, insects, water, breeze. Be curious and more adventurous than simply labelling what you already know. Listen to the tone or pitch of sounds, we develop a more intimate connection with nature when we remove the automatic identification.
- **Sight:** If we look through 'childs eyes' with a keen curiosity and sense of adventure we gain a richer experience...the vibrancy of colours, design of patterns, shape and texture ...and have fun!

... and finally seven ways to benefit from nature's elixir of life!

Immerse Yourself in a Green Space Sanctuary: Walk, sit, cycle, whatever your mode simply get outside into your garden, community space, beach, woodland... the possibilities are endless

Breath Deep and Be Still: Take a few deep breaths whilst out in nature and then be still... you'll notice how much calmer you feel

ReWild the Senses: Reconnect your senses to the natural world with adventure and curiosity, this new perspective may surprise you

Growing your own wild magic: Leave a wild space for nature in your garden and enjoy its tranquillity and diversity

Enjoy the seasons: Nature surprises us all year round. The colder months can be exhilarating and beautiful plus a boost for the immune system.

Natures spa: Plant a small sensory garden near a door or window so you can enjoy them fully to ease the mind and boost your wellbeing. Add herbs for scent and eating...and of course the wildlife will love them!

Mindful Scents: Add some natural scents to your home which are renowned to improve mental wellbeing. For stress busting qualities try Lavender, Rose, Ylang Ylang, Bergamot, Chamomile, Lemon Balm, Jasmine, Clary Sage, Orange.

Wendy is a Wellbeing Consultant, supporting mental wellbeing through her practice Coachgenie.uk and co-leader at Experience Nature. She combines her passion and knowledge for nature into her professional work, designing programmes, workshops and retreats under her banner 'Wellbeing through Nature'.

Combining expertise with her husband Ashley Grove, professional wildlife photographer, naturalist and owner of Experience Nature, they are pleased to offer, in addition to their existing portfolio of wildlife watching & photography holidays, 'Wellbeing through Nature' retreats.

To learn more about Wildlife Watching holidays or Wellbeing breaks visit W: www.experiencenature.co.uk, E: experiencenaturetours@gmail.com

To learn more about natures support for mental wellbeing contact Wendy - W: www.coachgenie.uk, E: hello@coachgenie.uk

NEWS FROM THE WORLD OF BIRDS

James Lowen offers a selection of the past year's interesting stories and titbits about wild birds from across the UK.

Rare breeders

'Long legs' (long-legged birds) were again in the news. Eurasian Bittern had a great 2018, with 188 'booming' males at 82 sites (2017: 164 at 71). The species bred for the first time on the Isle of Wight. Common Crane is doing well too, with a record-breaking 54 pairs countrywide in 2018. The total population of 180-plus birds is the highest since its return to Britain. Particular successes included 21 pairs nesting across south-west England following the release of 93 captive-reared birds by the Great Crane Project.

A pair of White Storks – thought to be free-flying feral individuals – hatched three young in Sussex as part of a reintroduction project. This event was covered by mainstream press, although birdwatchers seemed less enamoured – many arguing that the evidence for White Stork ever being a regular British breeder was flimsy. More unanimously acclaimed was the heron hotspot of RSPB Burton Mere (Cheshire). In 2019, single pairs of Cattle Egret, Great White Egret and Eurasian Spoonbill have attempted to breed within the colony of Grey Heron and Little Egret.

Corncrakes are enduring an uncertain future, with just a 2% increase in the number of calling males in Scotland during 2018 (and this was still down 31% on the peak of 1,289 in 2014). Britain's breeding waders continue to suffer. The Welsh population of Eurasian Curlew slumped by more than two-thirds between 1995 and 2017. After an absence of 45 years, European Nightjar bred at the RSPB's HQ, The Lodge, in 2018 – a reward for on-site conservation efforts. In 2019, Rutland Water's Osprey Project celebrated the 150th chick born since the first youngster fledged in 2001.

Hen Harriers

The much-loved raptor mostly remained in birdwatchers' minds for the wrong reasons – but there was some limited cause for cheer. In 2018, 34 young fledged across England – the most successful breeding season for a decade. The bumper year was thought due to landowner co-operation, reliable weather and abundant voles. One particular success was the 13 chicks that fledged on the United Utilities estate in Bowland (Lancashire) – the first successful breeding since 2015.

On the downside, a report revealed that English Hen Harriers suffer abnormally high rates of mortality compared to persecution-free Orkney. It provided compelling evidence that the most likely cause of the difference is illegal killing on and around grouse moors. Stephen Murphy from Natural England, one of the report authors, said that the study confirmed long-held suspicions "that illegal persecution is having a major impact on the conservation status of this bird". One of Natural England's solutions – 'headstarting' of captive-bred youngsters – survived a legal challenge from Mark Avery and started operations in 2019.

NEWS FROM THE WORLD OF BIRDS

Seabird success... and strife

In 2018, there was good news for Roseate Tern. Britain's sole regular colony, on Coquet Island (Northumberland), reached 118 pairs for the first time in nearly 50 years, while the species bred in Wales for the first time in a decade. Research confirmed that Coquet's population is being supported by birds moving from Co. Dublin (Ireland), where 1,633 pairs nested in 2017.

By late 2018, almost 3,000 Little Tern chicks were calculated to have fledged from 26 sites thanks to five years of EU LIFE funding, which has determined and rectify problems faced by the species. Mediterranean Gull continues its rapid population expansion. In 2018, a record 1,736 pairs bred at Hampshire's Langstone Harbour – more than double the previous year's population. Quite a way to celebrate the golden anniversary of its first British breeding attempt!

Fifteen years after the launch of a project to eradicate rats from Lundy (Devon), seabird numbers have trebled to more than 21,000 birds. Manx Shearwaters have increased from 297 pairs (2001) to 5,500, while Puffins are up to 375 individuals compared to a nadir of ten pairs. European Storm Petrel bred for the first time on the Shiants (Hebrides) in 2018, from where rats were eradicated two years earlier. On the downside, Arctic Skua breeding success in Scotland has dropped 81% in the 23 years to 2015. The decrease is thought due to depleted sandeel supplies.

Big-picture conservation

At the macro scale, there was varied news for conservation. A report by the Joint Nature Conservation Committee, a public body, found that the UK was making insufficient progress on 14 of the 20 Aichi Biodiversity Targets set by the Convention on Biological Diversity in 2010. Scottish Natural Heritage admitted that one in every five Scottish sites of European importance for wildlife remains in 'poor' condition, with the number in 'favourable' condition down by 2% since 2007.

University of Cambridge conservation biologists have suggested that 'land sparing' – farming some land more intensively while letting other areas rewild – could boost populations of some farmland birds. The UK is estimated to need a third more farmed land within 30 years – so increasing yields may provide a viable and more wildlife-friendly alternative.

A technique known as 'Natural Capital Accounting' has shown that England's National Nature Reserves provide public benefits totalling £36 million per year. Nature has become one of three top priorities at the heart of plans to distribute more than £1 billion of National Lottery Heritage Fund money over the next five years.

At the time of writing, it is unclear when and on what terms (and arguably whether...) the UK will leave the European Union. The Institute for European Environmental Policy assessed the environmental impact of various Brexit options, concluding that the worst would be a 'no-deal' scenario. The report prompted calls from conservationists for cross-party commitments to uphold wildlife standards.

NEWS FROM THE WORLD OF BIRDS

Hands-on conservation

Three rare species were given a particular helping hand this year. In spring 2019, dozens of Eurasian Curlew eggs were saved from RAF airfields (where they would have had to be destroyed), to be hand-reared by the Wildfowl and Wetlands Trust before release into the Severn Vale. Slightly earlier, one 'headstarted' Curlew – an individual reared by the UK Lowland Curlew Recovery Project in 2017 – returned to breed in Shropshire.

'Headstarting' is one measure being implemented successfully to boost numbers of Black-tailed Godwit, which has declined to 50 pairs across just a handful of sites. In 2018, 18 chicks were raised in the wild, with a further 38 bred in captivity then released by Project Godwit at the Ouse and Nene Washes. Two of the released youngsters returned to the area in spring 2019 – a sight greatly welcomed by those involved.

Despite opposition from sheep-farmers, approval was granted for White-tailed Eagles to be reintroduced to the Isle of Wight. Young Scottish birds will be translocated into Forestry England-managed woodland over the next five years. Given the UK-wide context of raptor persecution, however, what fate will await them?

Places... good news and bad

British bird observatories are collaborating on an initiative using modern tracking technology to understand the phenomenon known as 'reverse migration'. Project Yellow-browed aims to establish a network of radio-telemetry receiving stations in Britain to complement those already in Europe, and to monitor the movement of selected migrants. The observatory at Fair Isle was in the news for sad reasons, when a fire destroyed the observatory buildings in March 2019.

More positively, the RSPB significantly extended a Ribble Estuary reserve, Spurn Bird Observatory acquired new land, the Lee Valley set up a state-of-the-art 'bittern information point', Hellfield Flashes (Yorkshire) were spared development and the Welsh Government abandoned plans to build a new motorway across the Gwent Levels. There was even hope at the infamous Nightingale-threatening development at Lodge Hill (Kent), where proposals have been scaled back by 75%.

Wildlife crime

Even without accounting for Hen Harriers, wildlife crime provided disturbingly recurrent headlines. Raptors provided the main focus of illicit attention, with the RSPB's Birdcrime 2017 report revealing 68 confirmed incidents of persecution – although much criminal activity goes undetected and/or unreported. The RSPB again suggested one solution to tackle illegal persecution on grouse estates: a licensing system for driven-grouse shooting. The Government was unenthusiastic.

In mid-2019, a police scheme anticipated to stop illegal raptor persecution was launched nationally. Operation Owl aims to raise public vigilance of criminal activity and increase police surveillance checks at known blackspots. This year 'egging' sadly hit the headlines. In November 2018, prolific collector Daniel Lingham was jailed for stealing almost 5,000 wild-bird eggs – including those of Marsh Harrier and Eurasian Turtle Dove.

NEWS FROM THE WORLD OF BIRDS

View to a kill?

Quite aside from raptor persecution, the culling of birds figured prominently in the news. In December 2018, Natural England and Natural Resources Wales gave the go-ahead for Red Data Book-listed birds such as Eurasian Curlew and House Sparrow to be legitimately shot under the auspices of 'bird control'. This prompted outrage among many birdwatchers. Following a legal challenge by Wild Justice, a new organisation set up by Ruth Tingay, Mark Avery and Chris Packham, Natural England announced in April 2019 that it was revoking three general licences covering 16 bird species. This gave a stay of execution to species of goose, crow, gull and pigeon. Come June, however, three new general licences were issued, allowing shooting of ten species, including Lesser Black-backed Gull and Eurasian Jay. A wider review of general licences is underway.

Scotland was not immune to cull-related controversy. A licence permitting Ravens to be killed in Perthshire was overturned in July 2018, while studies determined a cull of Barnacle Geese on Islay (which had resulted in more than 8,000 being shot since 2015) to be founded on poor science.

#NetsDownforNature

Until 2019, say the word 'nets' to most birders and you would probably prompt thoughts of ringing. No longer. Three separate stories involving netting and birds – supermarket swallows, seaside sand martins and hedges countrywide – provoked unprecedented public indignation well beyond the birdwatching community. It was the apparently novel practice by housing developers of covering hedges and trees with giant nets – to prevent breeding by birds and other animals – that really sparked public ire. Actor Stephen Fry called it "an enraging practice", while an e-petition to making the practice illegal – shared under the social-media hashtag #NetsDownforNature – gathered 350,000 signatures. Although the Government rejected the petitioners' request, it warned developers that "netting is only appropriate where genuinely needed to protect birds from harm during development".

British list

Finally, three species were formally added to the British list: Falcated Duck, Dalmatian Pelican and White-rumped Swift – with *hutchinsii* Canada Goose and *haliomendri* Lesser Whitethroat also new at subspecies level.

The list stands at 620 species.

All Illustrations: Dan Powell

BEST BIRD BOOKS OF THE YEAR

Gordon Hamlett takes a look at the best of this year's books, ranging from birds past, to birds present and birds future.

TWENTY-ODD YEARS AGO, the RSPB's house magazine dropped through thousands of letterboxes across the country and introduced a new term to their many members. Biodiversity was the idea that birds shouldn't be considered simply on their own, but as part of a much bigger picture. The largely conservative, with a small 'c', membership was up in arms. Letters were written. The RSPB even conducted its own survey to assess what people thought of the idea. Today, nobody bats an eye about the concept.

Bird books too, it seems, are following a similar trend. Over the last few years, there have been fewer and fewer 'pure bird books' such as field guides, identification guides, monographs, where to watch guides and so on. What we are seeing instead is an increase of books that, while they feature birds to a greater or lesser extent, also include other themes. In other words, birds are just part of a bigger picture. What is new, is the diversity of some of those pictures. This year's titles range from birds and Neanderthals to birds as an aid to better health.

There is one other trend developing this year. Once upon a time, if you wanted to write a book, you had to get yourself a publisher. Then came vanity publishing, a pejorative term in which you paid someone to print your book for you. This evolved into self-publishing, a much more user-friendly term, linked to changes in book printing methods. Now, books can be printed on demand, the author just ordering a few copies at a time rather having to commit to several hundreds/thousands at once.

Now there is a new kid on the block - crowdfunding. Members of the public are invited to donate towards the cost of publishing the book in return for various rewards, anything from a simple mention in the book to days out with the author etc, depending on the amount pledged. A couple of the books featured in this article have been funded this way and we will surely see more in the next couple of years.

ID Guides & Monographs

For many readers of this article, the title **Gulls Simplified** (Dunne & Karlson, Princeton UP, £20) is the ultimate birding oxymoron. This photo-guide to North American gulls has annotated pictures of gulls in all their main plumages, often in mixed groups for comparison purposes. Many of the species detailed occur on our side of The Pond and this book will go a long way towards demystifying one of the most difficult groups of birds.

If you are happy with your ID skills, but are looking for greater insights into gull behaviour etc, then the latest New Naturalists title **Gulls** (Coulson, William Collins, £35pb, £65hb) should be on your shortlist. It is at its strongest on our commoner species, but I found sections on the scarcer gulls, for example Caspian Gulls, to be decidedly underwhelming; there are lots of 'possibles and probables' in the picture captioning when I was hoping for clarity.

Petrels, shearwaters, skuas etc are some of the most difficult species to identify, especially given the heavy seas and inclement weather of many seawatching experiences. **Oceanic Birds of the World** (Howell & Zufelt, Princeton UP, £27) arrived hours before my deadline so I haven't been able to give it as much scrutiny as I would have liked.

OCEANIC BIRDS OF THE WORLD
A Photo Guide
Steve N. G. Howell & Kirk Zufelt

This is a fast-moving area of ornithology. The taxonomy of seabirds is in a state of flux, with many island species being promoted to full species status. To put that into context, the authors point out that Harrison's classic seabird guide (published 1987) detailed 107 tubenoses.

BEST BIRD BOOKS OF THE YEAR

This guide features over 175. In all, 270 species are covered though the authors admit that some of their choices and omissions are somewhat arbitrary and there might be a bit of quibbling around the edges. For example, only 19 species of gulls and terns are included out of more than 100 species in total, the rest not considered to be sufficiently oceanic.

This photo guide contains over 2,200 pictures, annotated where necessary. There are distribution maps and brief identification, distribution and status notes to accompany the illustrations. Everything has been crammed into 360 pages so that the book will fit into larger pockets, but the overall feel is that everything is a little bit cramped; I would love to see an expanded large format edition in the future.

For example, there is a picture of a 'Bridled' Guillemot, (the authors refer to it as 'spectacled'), but no mention in the text, where you might have expected a note explaining that this form becomes more numerous the further north you go. Minor quibbles aside, if you love your seabirds, this is as up to date as you can get, and an essential purchase if you seawatch around the world.

Another deadline day delivery was **British Birds – a Pocket Guide** (Hume et al, Princeton UP, £9.99), which is essentially a cut down version of Britain's Birds which came out a couple of years ago. A photo guide, it covers 248 species plus 45 rarer vagrants over 1,600 pictures. If you use other guides, beware, considerable licence has been taken with the taxonomic order. It is the smallest field guide currently available by far, fitting easily into any coat pocket.

There are two ways you can go with a field guide aimed at beginners and improvers. You can either keep things really simple and clear, or you can try to cramasmuchinformationontoeverypageasyoupossiblycan. The publishers have gone for the second approach, which makes extracting data somewhat difficult at times.

This is a pity, as there is a lot of new stuff here, most unusual in today's field guides. For example, there are four photos showing close-ups of the tertial patterns in juvenile large gulls, an ID feature I hadn't come across before. Another photo shows which bit of the bird you are looking at but there is no mention of tertials on the bird topography page. We also discover that juvenile Caspian Gulls have 'U-shaped pale' *somethings*. We'll never know as the text in the box has been cut off.

Another page illustrates the shape of gapes in finches, buntings and sparrows, again, something new to me, but there is nothing to tell you what it all means. This is a pity as there is a lot to admire here. Too much clarity has been sacrificed in attempt to reduce the physical size of the book. It would have been better to have increased the size of the book to say that of the Collins Bird Guide and let all the information breathe.

Anyone who has taken part in either the RSPB or BTO's garden watch surveys will be interested in another New Naturalists title – **Garden Birds** (Toms, William Collins, £35pb, £65hb), which looks at the effects of putting up nest boxes and feeders, before detailing individual species accounts. As most of us feed the birds in our gardens, there is much to be learned here, including how trichomonosis caused Greenfinch populations to crash, and why you see more Siskins on your feeders when the weather is damp.

Birds of Central America (Vallely & Dyer, Princeton UP, £40) is the first field guide covering the entire region - Belize, Guatemala, Honduras, El Salvador, Nicaragua, Costa Rica and Panama. At nearly 1,200 species on 260 plates, this is a hefty tome and one for the backpack rather than the pocket.

BEST BIRD BOOKS OF THE YEAR

From a small pocket of birds in Mid-Wales, most of us are used to seeing good numbers of Red Kites when we go out birding now. Indeed, I recently counted over 100 kites in 90 minutes along the M40 corridor which I thought was brilliant until I was staggered to read that there are now over 4,000 pairs in the Chilterns alone. **The Red Kite's Year**, (Carter & Powell, Pelagic Publishing, £25) is a highly readable account of this charismatic raptor, taken to the next level by some wonderful illustrations from the palette of Dan Powell.

If you prefer waders, then I can recommend **Common & Spotted Sandpipers** (Holland, Whittles Publishing, £18.99), which tells you everything you wanted to know about one well-known summer migrant and its much rarer (on this side of The Pond) American cousin.

There are 234 bird families in the world and you might be inclined to think that one volume couldn't possibly do justice to that amount of information. Think again. **The Handbook of Bird Families** (Elphick, Natural History Museum, £20) packs a lot of information into its 400 pages, featuring all the latest research as well as hundreds of photos. If you can't run to £1,500 for the Handbook of the Birds of the World, this will serve you very well as a much, much cheaper alternative.

The second edition of **Effects of Climate Change on Birds** (ed, Dunn & Møller, Oxford UP, £37.99) is aimed at the professional ornithologist rather than the casual reader, and details the latest research in a fast-moving environment in which birds are one the easiest markers to monitor. Unfortunately, the words are too long and the pictures too few for Donald Trump to take notice.

Where the Birds Are

The Birds of Nottinghamshire (Crouch et al, Liverpool University Press, £45) is the only county avifauna to come my way this year. Covering 333 species up to 2013 (plus highlights for later records), the design is nice and clean and makes for easy browsing. As well as the many photos, a bonus is a plethora of illustrations by Michael Warren. A must buy if you live in the county or bird there regularly.

Birdwatching London (Darrell-Lambert, Safe Haven, £12.99) covers 37 sites in the metropolis, plus an extra honorary site in Southend. Written in association with the London Wildlife Trust, this is a bright cheerful book that will introduce to lots of new sites. As a non-Londoner though, I would have wished for better directions and/or some maps.

Where to Watch Birds in France (Barnagaud et al, Pelagic Publishing, £25) is definitely a guide for the 21st century. Over 450 full-colour maps detailing 312 sites will put you in the right area, but for full access, you will need to download the accompanying GPS file onto your smartphone or similar device. I didn't find the approach and layout to be particularly user-friendly, but there is an awful lot of information here and I would definitely buy a copy if visiting the country.

Covering not just birds, but insects, mammals and plants etc, **A Year in British Wildlife** (Ward, New Holland, £14,99) makes suggestions as to what you should be looking out for on a month by month basis, detailing the best weather conditions to look for. Profusely illustrated, it makes you want to get out and look for things. And you can't ask for more than that.

BEST BIRD BOOKS OF THE YEAR

Rewilding

If yesterday's word was 'biodiversity', there is little doubt as today's word: rewilding. Several books deal with this concept of reconnecting with nature directly, with several others mentioning it indirectly. The concept is still very vague though, and ranges from what you can do on a personal level to plans for regenerating huge swathes of the country to their natural state.

Scotland: A Rewilding Journey (Wright & Cairns, Scotland: The Big Picture, £25) doubles as a coffee table book. While arguing the case for redeveloping massive areas of largely sterile landscape, and re-introducing apex predators such as lynx, the book is full of stunning pictures of Scottish wildlife and landscape.

At the other end of the scale, **Rewild Yourself** (Barnes, Simon & Schuster, £14.99) discusses a variety of ways you can bring nature into your life, and so improving your well-being enormously. I disagree though with the author when he states that you have to take a boat a few miles offshore to see Gannets; they are easy to see from just about any stretch of coast in suitable conditions.

Rebirding (Macdonald, Pelagic Publishing, £19.99) is one of the most interesting books that I have read this year. Looking from a purely avian perspective, the author starts by explaining the history of our bird life as shaped by the likes of the last ice age, before going on to discuss what could be achieved in the future. These ideas make an awful lot of sense, without being too radical. Dalmatian Pelicans anybody?

In case you think that Rewilding is all a bit pie in the sky, **Rewilding** (ed. Woodfall, William Collins, £17,99) has fifty or so short, illustrated essays discussing projects, big and small, that are already taking place. We can make a difference.

For a slightly different take on things, **Green and Prosperous Land** (Helm, William Collins, £16.99) looks at the state of our countryside from an economist's point of view. Though no fan of the term 'rewilding', the author points out a series of measures that would not only improve our environment from a practical point of view, they would also cost a lot less to implement than the existing plans. I suspect that many readers would agree with his solution to the persecution of Hen Harriers: just jail a few wealthy landowners where the offences occur, a measure that will concentrate minds very quickly.

Art & Literature

A Sparrow's Life's as Sweet as Ours (Akroyd & McEwen, Bloomsbury, £20) is a total joy. Taken from a series of articles in The Oldie, you get a literature-inspired essay of a given species on one side of the page, with the corresponding Carry Akroyd print opposite.

The Worshipful Company (Medland, Brambleby Books, £28) presents a series of poems about birds of the Norfolk coast, Accompanied by a series of photographs (not all wild birds). I have to say that the poems didn't work for me at all, but as with all poetry, your views may vary.

Much more thought provoking is **Bird By Bird** (Ivimey & Blackburn, jayneivimey@gmail.com £10), the catalogue of an installation about birds on the red list. The birds are presented in a series of white clay sculptures of dead specimens of threatened British birds. Deliberately disturbing.

BEST BIRD BOOKS OF THE YEAR

Ravens feature heavily in folklore and mythology, and **A Shadow Above** (Shute, Bloomsbury, £16.99) examines man's relationship with the mightiest of the corvids from earliest times to the modern day. **A Tiding of Magpies** is the latest bird murder by Steve Burrows (Point Blank, £8.99). Set on the North Norfolk coast, you have the double whammy of trying to solve the crime and picking out the occasional birding howler.

You all know that you are cleverer and better read than the next man, but just how clever are you? Now you can test yourself with **Bird Brain** (Appleton & Gallimore, William Collins, £9.99), which features over 2,400 bird questions taken from the Rutland Water Bird Fair's quizzes over the last 15 years. There are general knowledge questions and specialist subjects, ranging from Birds in Messiaen's Music to Endemic Birds of Colombia.

Children's Books

Written by Scottish folk-singer Karine Polwart, **A Wee Bird Was Watching** (BC Books, £6.99) is a version of a folk tale about how the Robin acquired its red breast. For slightly older readers (7-9), **The Book of the Howlat** (Robertson, BC Books, £6.99) is a modern retelling of a 15th century Scottish poem about an owlet who considers himself to be too ugly and wants to change things. Both books are beautifully illustrated by Kate Leiper.

For a collection of bird-related folk tales, riddles and rhymes, take a look at **The Magpie's Nest** (The History Press, £9.99), a delightful series of tales by award-winning story teller Taffy Thomas. **The Aviary** (Merritt, Andre Deutsch, £20) is an unusual book in so much as the description of fifty interesting species are printed on thick card. The excess card around the illustrations can be removed to leave a 3-D display.

Personal Accounts

Many authors write about a journey that they have been on: fulfilling a project, seeking out a particular species, keeping a diary and so on. This is a definite growth sector, and here are some of the best titles released recently.

One of the most moving accounts is **Bird Therapy** (Harkness, Unbound, £14.99) in which the author discovers that birdwatching helps his state of mind, suicidal at times, far more than any medication ever achieved. This deserves to be read by anyone with, or looking to better understand, any form of mental illness.

Coming to terms with Asperger's Syndrome, **Blood Ties** (Crane, Head of Zeus, £20), follows in the footsteps of H is for Hawk, as the author teaches himself falconry and learns how to rehabilitate injured raptors.

The Seafarers (Rutt, Elliott & Thompson, £14.99) sees the author embark on a trip round the British coast, seeking out seabirds, everything from Kittiwakes on the Tyne to Manx Shearwaters on Skomer. **A Claxton Diary** (Jonathan Cape, £14.99) is more a series of mini essays than diary entries from Mark Cocker, one of the best nature writers in Britain today. The themes are anything to do with wildlife, set against a backdrop of the Norfolk Broads.

Most of us have birds on our lists that are dubious to say the least. When Lev Parikian finds a childhood book with 130 species ticked off, he decides to replicate the list only to find that he is having to right rather more wrongs than he expected. **Why Do Birds Suddenly Disappear?** (Unbound, £16.99) is a humorous account of rectifying the errors.

BEST BIRD BOOKS OF THE YEAR

Two books by John Lewis-Stempel take a look at a year in the life of a wood and pond. **The Wood** (Black Swan, £8.99) and **Still Water** (Black Swan, £14.99) are both beautifully written and include quotes from many literary sources. What I hadn't come across before was that as well as suggested reading lists, there are also suggested listening lists, with musical choices from a whole variety of genres. Ruth Pavey found herself buying four acres of woodland, as you do, and **A Wood of One's Own** (Duckworth, £10.99) is the story of how she developed the wood into a haven for wildlife.

Miscellaneous

Two very different history books caught my attention. **The Smart Neanderthal** (Finlayson, Oxford UP, £20) looks at archaeological finds made in Gorham's Cave, Gibraltar, and demonstrates that Neanderthals were more than capable of catching birds and using their feathers and talons for decoration.

If you enjoy biographies, the **The Wonderful Mr Willughby** (Birkhead, Bloomsbury, £25) should be on your shortlist. Dubbed the first true ornithologist, this beautifully written and illustrated account of a 17th century naturalist ends by arguing that the misnamed Honey-buzzard should be renamed Willughby's Buzzard instead.

Scotland is always a popular theme with birders and here are three titles to tempt you north of the border. **A Natural History of St Kilda** (Love, Birlinn, £20) does exactly what it says on the tin, covering accounts by naturalist dating from 1697. **A Richness of Martens** (Pullar, Birlinn, £12.99) is ideal reading for anyone visiting the wonderful Ardnamurchan peninsula. While pine martens feature prominently, there are plenty of tales about other wildlife too.

Tracking the Highland Tiger (Taylor, Bloomsbury, £16.99) also features Ardnamurchan, as well Speyside. The book alternates details about the Scottish Wildcat with the author's trip reports to both areas in search of the elusive beast. Again, this is great background reading for anyone holidaying in the area. Two of our most sought-after mammals, birds from White-tailed Eagles down and some of Britain's best scenery make for a heady mix.

Invasive Aliens (Eatherley, William Collins, £16.99) examines the impact on our environment caused by non-native species, plants, animals and birds such as Canada Geese, Ring-necked Parakeets and Mandarins. David Barrie's **Incredible Journeys** (Hodder & Stoughton, £25) discusses the latest theories of animal migration, including how birds find true north, whether they use their sense of smell to navigate and have they solved the longitude problem.

The Arctic (Sale & Michelson, Whittles Publishing, £25) is a large format, fully illustrated book covering everything from the geology, indigenous people and wildlife of one of Earth's most remote regions.

Two tiles which aren't about birds per se, but are likely to be of interest are **Evolutions** (Harman, Head of Zeus, £20), an original and thought provoking take on our origins and development from the Big Bang to the modern day, via creation myths from around the world. **The Secret Network of Nature** (Wohlleben, Bodley Head, £14.99) shows how small changes in one part of the ecosystem can have massive impacts elsewhere, such as wolves influencing the course of rivers and earthworms affecting wild boar populations. It takes us back nicely to where we began, linking biodiversity with rewilding.

Neil Gartshore

Make a date & visit the Avalon Marshes on the Somerset Levels.
The area is proving to be a paradise for breeding herons & egrets, in recent years...
Great, Cattle & Little Egrets, Night-heron, Bittern, Little Bittern & Grey Heron.
In winter, a million+ murmuration of Starlings is an experience not to be missed.

BIRDWATCHER'S DIARY 2020

EVENTS DIARY for October 2019~December 2020

The Yearbook goes to press in late-Sep so events for Oct/Dec 2019 have been listed here (and will give an indication of similar events to expect in Oct/Dec 2020). It is advisable to check the relevant website/contact the organiser to ensure that there are no changes to dates/venues.

OCTOBER 2019

26: RSPB Members' Day & AGM
QEII Centre, Westminster.
W: www.rspb.org.uk/reserves-and-events/events-dates-and-inspiration/events/agm/

24-3 Nov: Society of Wildlife Artists
The Natural Eye, 56th Annual Exhibition
Mall Galleries, Pall Mall, London SW1Y 5BD.
W: www.swla.co.uk

26: Neotropical Bird Club (with BOU/British Museum)
Flett Theatre, Natural History Museum, Cromwell Road, London SW7 5BD. Doors open 10:00am.
W: www.neotropicalbirdclub.org/events/

27-30 Oct: AFO/WOS 2019 Meeting
Association of Field Ornithologists (AFO)/
Wilson Ornithological Society (WOS)
Cape May, New Jersey, USA.
W: www.wilsonsociety.org/meetings/2019-meeting/

NOVEMBER

**5-10: Annual Meeting of the
Raptor Research Foundation**
Fort Collins Hilton, Fort Collins, CO, USA
W: www.raptorresearchfoundation.org/conferences/current-conference/

6-9: 43rd Annual Meeting of The Waterbird Society
Maryland, USA. W: www.waterbirds.org

16 Nov: Welsh Ornithological Society National Conference (30th Anniversary)
Penglais Campus, Aberystwyth University, Penbryn, SY23 3FL. W: www.birdsin.wales

16-17: North West Bird Watching Festival
WWT Martin Mere, Fish Lane, Burscough, Lancashire L40 0TA. T: 01704 895 181
W: www.wwt.org.uk/wetland-centres/martin-mere/north-west-bird-watching-festival

22-24 Nov: Scottish Ornithologists' Club AGM & Annual Conference
Atholl Palace Hotel, Pitlochry, PH16 5LY.
W: www.the-soc.org.uk/support-us/events/events/the-2019-annual-conference

DECEMBER

6-8: BTO Annual Conference
(Volunteer Value: Putting the Science into 'Citizen Science') Hayes Conference Centre, Swanwick, Derbyshire DE55 1AU. E: info@bto.org;
W: www.bto.org

JANUARY 2020

6 Jan-21 Feb: Big Schools Birdwatch (RSPB)
UK-wide event to get children interested in wild birds (first half of Spring Term). For events in your area - W: www.rspb.org.uk/fun-and-learning/for-teachers/schools-birdwatch/

25-27: Big Garden Birdwatch (RSPB)
UK-wide survey of garden birds.
W: www.rspb.org.uk/get-involved/activities/birdwatch

FEBRUARY

2: World Wetlands Day
Theme: Wetlands and Biodiversity.
Various events around the globe celebrating the importance of wetland environments.
W: www.ramsar.org

12-15: Pacific Seabird Group
47th annual meeting. Portland, Oregon, USA.
W: www.pacificseabirdgroup.org/annual-meeting/

14-21: National Nest Box Week
A BTO initiative to encourage more people to erect nestboxes. Various events – see website for details.
W: www.bto.org/how-you-can-help/nnbw
W: www.nestboxweek.com

MARCH

21: SOC/BTO
Scottish Birdwatchers' Spring Conference
Elgin Town Hall, 1 Trinity Place, Elgin, Moray IV30 1UL
W: www.the-soc.org.uk/support-us/events/events/scottish-birdwatchers-conference-2020

APRIL

7-9: BOU Annual Conference
Restoring bird populations: scaling from species to ecosystems.
Nottingham University, UK.
W: www.bou.org.uk/bou-conferences

22-26: 7th International Eurasian Ornithology Concress Symposium
Ege University, Izmir, Turkey.
www.ornithologylab.com/ieoc_2020_izmir.html

25: African Bird Club
AGM plus full programme of talks on research & conservation work in Africa.
Flett Theatre, Natural History Museum, Cromwell Road, London SW7 5BD. Doors open 10:15am.
E: info@africanbirdclub.org or
W: www.africanbirdclub.org

EVENTS DIARY for October 2019~December 2020

MAY

JUNE

27: OSME (Ornithological Society of the Middle East, Caucasus & Central Asia) Summer Meeting & AGM. BTO, The Nunnery, Thetford, Norfolk. E: secretary@osme.org; W: www.osme.org

JULY

AUGUST

6-9: BBC Countryfile Live Castle Howard, Yorkshire. W: www.countryfilelive.com

10-15: 7th North American Ornithological Congress Dan Juan, Puerto Rico. W: https://naocbirds.org/

20-23: BBC Countryfile Live Great Windsor Park, Berkshire. W: www.countryfilelive.com

21-23: British Birdwatching Fair Rutland Water Nature Reserve, Egleton, Rutland. E: callen@birdfair.org.uk; W: www.birdfair.org.uk

SEPTEMBER

11-13: Spurn Migration Festival W: www.spurnmigfest.com

12-13: Festival of Bird Art incl. National Bird Carving Championships. The Agricultural Business Centre, Agricultural Way, Bakewell, Derbyshire DE45 1AH. W: www.bdwca.org.uk

tba: **Oriental Bird Club Autumn Meeting & AGM** *(last held 21 Sep 2019).* E: mail@orientalbirdclub.org W: www.orientalbirdclub.org

tba: **2020 International Wader Study Group Annual Conference** *(last held 20-23 Sept 2019).* W: www.waderstudygroup.org

OCTOBER - DECEMBER 2020

See the Oct-Dec 2019 entries for other likely events during this period.

4-8 Oct: Annual Meeting of the Raptor Research Foundation and Neotropical Raptor Network Boise, Idaho, USA. W: www.raptorresearchfoundation.org/conferences/upcoming-conferences/

19-23 Oct: 3rd World Seabird Conference Hobart, Tasmania, Australia. W: www.worldseabirdconference.com

16-20 Nov: 15th Pan-African Ornithological Conference Victoric Falls, Zimbabwe. W: www.paoc15.org

~~~~~~~~~~

VARIOUS DATES THROUGH THE YEAR (BTO)

BTO Garden BirdWatch talks: these are given by a number of speakers to a wide variety of groups across the country.

BTO Training Courses: one day courses/residential courses - subjects include identifying birds; bird survey techniques; breeding bird survey; & bird identification/wetland bird survey.

Local Bird Club Conferences: the BTO encourage & support local bird clubs through their 'Bird Club Partnership'.

Regional Bird Ringer's Conferences: usually one-day conferences held in the different regions of the UK.

Check out the BTO's website: www.bto.org or phone: 01842 750 050 for more information on BTO-related talks, courses or conferences in 2020.

NOTE:

Due to the printing deadline of *The Yearbook* it is not always possible to confirm dates or if conferences, fairs etc will be running during the following year.

If you have, or know of, any events for 2021 & would like them mentioned in this section of *The Yearbook* then please contact us by the end of August 2020.

[See our contact details on P6.]

Conserving nature worldwide

DIARY – JANUARY 2020

[Inc. Bank Holidays for E&W = England & Wales; NI = Northern Ireland; S = Scotland and BST/time changes]

1	Wed	New Year's Day E&W, NI, S
2	Thu	Bank holiday S
3	Fri	
4	Sat	
5	Sun	
6	Mon	
7	Tue	
8	Wed	
9	Thu	
10	Fri	
11	Sat	
12	Sun	
13	Mon	
14	Tue	
15	Wed	
16	Thu	
17	Fri	
18	Sat	
19	Sun	
20	Mon	
21	Tue	
22	Wed	
23	Thu	
24	Fri	
25	Sat	
26	Sun	
27	Mon	
28	Tue	
29	Wed	
30	Thu	
31	Fri	

DIARY – FEBRUARY 2020

1	Sat	
2	Sun	
3	Mon	
4	Tue	
5	Wed	
6	Thu	
7	Fri	
8	Sat	
9	Sun	
10	Mon	
11	Tue	
12	Wed	
13	Thu	
14	Fri	
15	Sat	
16	Sun	
17	Mon	
18	Tue	
19	Wed	
20	Thu	
21	Fri	
22	Sat	
23	Sun	
24	Mon	
25	Tue	
26	Wed	
27	Thu	
28	Fri	
29	Sat	

DIARY – MARCH 2020

1	Sun	
2	Mon	
3	Tue	
4	Wed	
5	Thu	
6	Fri	
7	Sat	
8	Sun	
9	Mon	
10	Tue	
11	Wed	
12	Thu	
13	Fri	
14	Sat	
15	Sun	
16	Mon	
17	Tue	St Patrick's Day NI
18	Wed	
19	Thu	
20	Fri	
21	Sat	
22	Sun	
23	Mon	
24	Tue	
25	Wed	
26	Thu	
27	Fri	
28	Sat	
29	Sun	British Summertime begins (1 hour forwards)
30	Mon	
31	Tue	

DIARY – APRIL 2020

1	Wed	
2	Thu	
3	Fri	
4	Sat	
5	Sun	
6	Mon	
7	Tue	
8	Wed	
9	Thu	
10	Fri	Good Friday E&W, NI, S
11	Sat	
12	Sun	
13	Mon	Easter Monday E&W, NI
14	Tue	
15	Wed	
16	Thu	
17	Fri	
18	Sat	
19	Sun	
20	Mon	
21	Tue	
22	Wed	
23	Thu	
24	Fri	
25	Sat	
26	Sun	
27	Mon	
28	Tue	
29	Wed	
30	Thu	

DIARY – MAY 2020

1	Fri	
2	Sat	
3	Sun	
4	Mon	
5	Tue	
6	Wed	
7	Thu	
8	Fri	Early May bank holiday E&W, NI, S [VE Day]
9	Sat	
10	Sun	
11	Mon	
12	Tue	
13	Wed	
14	Thu	
15	Fri	
16	Sat	
17	Sun	
18	Mon	
19	Tue	
20	Wed	
21	Thu	
22	Fri	
23	Sat	
24	Sun	
25	Mon	Spring bank holiday E&W, NI, S
26	Tue	
27	Wed	
28	Thu	
29	Fri	
30	Sat	
31	Sun	

40

DIARY – JUNE 2020

1	Mon	
2	Tue	
3	Wed	
4	Thu	
5	Fri	
6	Sat	
7	Sun	
8	Mon	
9	Tue	
10	Wed	
11	Thu	
12	Fri	
13	Sat	
14	Sun	
15	Mon	
16	Tue	
17	Wed	
18	Thu	
19	Fri	
20	Sat	
21	Sun	
22	Mon	
23	Tue	
24	Wed	
25	Thu	
26	Fri	
27	Sat	
28	Sun	
29	Mon	
30	Tue	

DIARY – JULY 2020

1	Wed	
2	Thu	
3	Fri	
4	Sat	
5	Sun	
6	Mon	
7	Tue	
8	Wed	
9	Thu	
10	Fri	
11	Sat	
12	Sun	
13	Mon	Orangemen's Day NI
14	Tue	
15	Wed	
16	Thu	
17	Fri	
18	Sat	
19	Sun	
20	Mon	
21	Tue	
22	Wed	
23	Thu	
24	Fri	
25	Sat	
26	Sun	
27	Mon	
28	Tue	
29	Wed	
30	Thu	
31	Fri	

DIARY – AUGUST 2020

1	Sat	
2	Sun	
3	Mon	Summer bank holiday S
4	Tue	
5	Wed	
6	Thu	
7	Fri	
8	Sat	
9	Sun	
10	Mon	
11	Tue	
12	Wed	
13	Thu	
14	Fri	
15	Sat	
16	Sun	
17	Mon	
18	Tue	
19	Wed	
20	Thu	
21	Fri	
22	Sat	
23	Sun	
24	Mon	
25	Tue	
26	Wed	
27	Thu	
28	Fri	
29	Sat	
30	Sun	
31	Mon	Summer bank holiday E&W, NI

DIARY – SEPTEMBER 2020

1	Tue	
2	Wed	
3	Thu	
4	Fri	
5	Sat	
6	Sun	
7	Mon	
8	Tue	
9	Wed	
10	Thu	
11	Fri	
12	Sat	
13	Sun	
14	Mon	
15	Tue	
16	Wed	
17	Thu	
18	Fri	
19	Sat	
20	Sun	
21	Mon	
22	Tue	
23	Wed	
24	Thu	
25	Fri	
26	Sat	
27	Sun	
28	Mon	
29	Tue	
30	Wed	

DIARY – OCTOBER 2020

1	Thu	
2	Fri	
3	Sat	
4	Sun	
5	Mon	
6	Tue	
7	Wed	
8	Thu	
9	Fri	
10	Sat	
11	Sun	
12	Mon	
13	Tue	
14	Wed	
15	Thu	
16	Fri	
17	Sat	
18	Sun	
19	Mon	
20	Tue	
21	Wed	
22	Thu	
23	Fri	
24	Sat	
25	Sun	British Summertime ends (1 hour backwards)
26	Mon	
27	Tue	
28	Wed	
29	Thu	
30	Fri	
31	Sat	

DIARY 2020

DIARY – NOVEMBER 2020

1	Sun	
2	Mon	
3	Tue	
4	Wed	
5	Thu	
6	Fri	
7	Sat	
8	Sun	
9	Mon	
10	Tue	
11	Wed	
12	Thu	
13	Fri	
14	Sat	
15	Sun	
16	Mon	
17	Tue	
18	Wed	
19	Thu	
20	Fri	
21	Sat	
22	Sun	
23	Mon	
24	Tue	
25	Wed	
26	Thu	
27	Fri	
28	Sat	
29	Sun	
30	Mon	St Andrew's Day S

DIARY – DECEMBER 2020

1	Tue	
2	Wed	
3	Thu	
4	Fri	
5	Sat	
6	Sun	
7	Mon	
8	Tue	
9	Wed	
10	Thu	
11	Fri	
12	Sat	
13	Sun	
14	Mon	
15	Tue	
16	Wed	
17	Thu	
18	Fri	
19	Sat	
20	Sun	
21	Mon	
22	Tue	
23	Wed	
24	Thu	
25	Fri	Christmas Day E&W, NI, S
26	Sat	Boxing Day
27	Sun	
28	Mon	Bank Holiday E&W, NI, S
29	Tue	
30	Wed	
31	Thu	

DIARY 2020

YEAR PLANNER 2021

JANUARY	
FEBRUARY	
MARCH	
APRIL	
MAY	
JUNE	
JULY	
AUGUST	
SEPTEMBER	
OCTOBER	
NOVEMBER	
DECEMBER	

Neil Gartshore

The Bittern (*Botaurus stellaris*), with a growing breeding & wintering population, is a species that should be seen with a little patience at sites such as Dungeness, the Somerset Levels, Minsmere & Leighton Moss during the breeding season & in reedbeds further afield during the winter.

CHECKLISTS

CHECKLIST OF BRITISH BIRDS
Based on the British List formulated by the British Ornithologists' Union

THE OFFICIAL BRITISH LIST is maintained by The British Ornithologists' Union (BOU) which sits in judgement on which birds you can count on your list, and which you can't. The official list can change from year to year in one of two ways:

1) If someone claims to have seen a species never recorded in Britain, a panel of experts sitting on the BOU's Records Committee (BOURC) assesses the record, making sure that the identification of the bird was proved beyond all possible doubt. Then the bird's credentials are assessed, to determine whether it was a genuine vagrant, rather than one that had just hopped over the fence from the nearest zoo or aviary.

Only if the bird passes every single strenuous test does it get accepted onto the British List... a process that may take many years. Similarly, historical records may be reassessed in the light of advances in identification skills.

2) The BOU uses the International Ornithological Union's (IOU) IOC World Bird List (version 7.3) as its authority on the naming of full species and sub-species. Any changes on this list, for example a sub-species considered to be a full species or a full species considered only to be a sub-species, will result in the British List being amended accordingly.

The '9th edition' of the British List was published in December 2017 and the official British List stands (as of 1st August 2019) at 620 species. These are made up of 602 species in Category A, eight species in Category B and ten species in Category C. In addition there are two other categories (D and E) - see below for a description of the five categories.

For further information about the British List visit the BOU's website: www.bou.org.uk/british-list/

SPECIES, CATEGORIES, CODES - YOUR GUIDE TO GETTING THE BEST USE FROM THE CHECKLIST

Species Categories (column 1)

The following categories are those assigned by the British Ornithologists' Union.

A - Species recorded in an apparently natural state at least once since 1st January 1950.

B - Species recorded in an apparently natural state at least once between 1st January 1800 and 31st December1949, but not subsequently.

C - Species that, though introduced, now derive from the resulting self-sustaining populations:

C1 *(Naturalized introduced species)*
Species that have occurred <u>only</u> as a result of introduction, e.g. Egyptian Goose;

C2 *(Naturalized established species)*
Species resulting from introduction by man, but which also occur in an apparently natural state, e.g. Greylag Goose;

C3 *(Naturalized re-established species)*
Species successfully re-established by man in areas of former occurrence, e.g. Red Kite;

C4 *(Naturalized feral species)*
Domesticated species established in the wild, e.g. Rock Pigeon (Dove)/Feral Pigeon;

C5 *(Vagrant naturalized species)*
Species from established naturalized populations abroad. Currently no species in category C5;

C6 *(Former naturalized species)*
Species formerly in C1 whose naturalized populations are either no longer self-sustaining or are considered extinct, e.g. Lady Amherst's Pheasant.

D - This is for species that would otherwise appear in Category A but there is reasonable doubt that the species have ever occurred in a natural state. Species held here are regularly reviewed with a view to assigning them to either Category A or E. Species placed solely in Category D form no part of the British List, and are not included in the species totals.

E - Species that have been recorded as introductions, human-assisted transportees or escapees from captivity, and whose breeding populations (if any) are thought not to be self-sustaining. Species in Category E that have bred in the wild in Britain are designated as E*. Category E species form no part of the British List (unless already included within Categories A, B or C).

Although the majority of species usually only fall into one category, a few are placed in multiple categories, for example, those species occurring in Category A which now have naturalized populations (e.g. Red Kite).

The British List comprises only of those species placed in Categories A, B or C.

CHECKLISTS

Species List (column 2)

The *Yearbook* Checklist includes all species from categories A, B and C on the British List, based on the latest BOU listing.

Vagrants which are not on the British List, but which may have occurred in other parts of the British Isles, are not included. Readers who wish to record such species may use the extra rows provided. In this connection it should be noted that separate lists exist for Northern Ireland (kept by the Northern Ireland Birdwatchers' Association) and the Isle of Man (kept by the Manx Ornithological Society), and that Irish records are assessed by the Irish Rare Birds Committee.

The species names are those most widely used in the current field guides and each is followed by its scientific name, printed in italics.

Columns 3 to 22

These columns are for personal use and include a Life List, a 2020 list, and monthly lists from Jan to Dec. There are six columns (A-F) which could be used for a variety of reasons such as a local patch, birds in the garden, a bird race or holidays.

Generally a tick suffices in each of the columns to record a bird seen. However, added benefit can be obtained by replacing ticks with specific dates.

How you fill in these columns is a matter of personal choice. *For example:* you may want to keep your Life List up to date with the first year you saw a species - if you see your first Waxwing on 20th February 2020 it could be logged as '2/20' in the Life List column (as well as being recorded in the 2020 list as '20/2 and the February column as '20th'). As Life List entries are carried forward annually, in years to come it would be a simple matter to relocate this list into subsequent *Yearbooks*.

As space within the columns is limited, it is recommended to use a thin pointed pen or pencil.

ADDITIONAL COLUMNS, make your own list	
A	
B	
C	
D	
E	
F	

BTO species codes (column 23)

The British Trust for Ornithology two-letter species codes are shown in the fourth column from the right. Readers should refer to the BTO if more codes are needed (the other species have been allocated 5-digit codes).

Rare breeding birds (column 24)

The species monitored by the Rare Breeding Birds Panel (see National Directory) comprise of those with a sustained population of fewer than 2000 breeding pairs and rarer non-native species with fewer than 300 breeding pairs. For full details, visit: www.rbbp.org.uk

The following annotations in the charts (third column from the right) reflect the panel's categories:

A) Rare Breeding Birds in UK (Regular);
B) Rare Breeding Birds in UK (Occasional);
C) Rare Breeding Birds in UK (Potential);
D) Rare Non-native Breeding Birds in UK (Regular);
E) Rare Non-native Breeding Birds in UK (Occasional);
F) Rare Non-native Breeding Birds in UK (Potential).

Rarities (column 25)

Rarities are indicated by a capital letter 'R' (and subspecies rarities by an asterix *) in the column headed BBRC (British Birds Rarities Committee). For full details, visit: www.bbrc.org.uk

EURING species numbers (column 26)

EURING databanks collect copies of recovery records from ringing schemes throughout Europe and the official species numbers are given in the last column. As they are taken from the full Holarctic bird list there are many apparent gaps. It is important that these are not filled arbitrarily by observers wishing to record species not listed in the charts, as this would compromise the integrity of the scheme.

Similarly, the addition of a further digit to indicate sub-species is to be avoided, since EURING has already assigned numbers for this purpose. The numbering follows the Voous order of species so some species are now out of sequence following the re-ordering of the British List. For full details, visit: www.euring.org

Butterflies & Dragonflies

As most birdwatchers have an interest in other areas of natural history, checklists have been included for two of the most popular groups with a column for a Life List and another for 2020 records.

59

GEESE, SWANS, DUCKS

	Life list	2020	Jan	Feb	Mar	Apr	May	Jun	Jul	Aug	Sep	Oct	Nov	Dec	A	B	C	D	E	F	BTO	RBBP	BBRC	EU No
AE	Brent Goose	*Branta bernicla*																			BG			0168
AE*	Red-breasted Goose	*Branta ruficollis*																			EB	E	R	0169
AC2E*	Canada Goose	*Branta canadensis*																			CG		*	0166
AC2E*	Barnacle Goose	*Branta leucopsis*																			BY			0167
AE	Cackling Goose	*Branta hutchinsii*																					R	
AC2E*	Snow Goose	*Anser caerulescens*																			SJ	D		0163
AC2C4E*	Greylag Goose	*Anser anser*																			GJ			0161
AE*	Taiga Bean Goose	*Anser fabalis*																			XF	E		0157
AE*	Pink-footed Goose	*Anser brachyrhynchus*																			PG	E		0158
AE	Tundra Bean Goose	*Anser serrirostris*																			XR	E		
AE*	White-fronted Goose	*Anser albifrons*																			WG	E		0159
AE*	Lesser White-fronted Goose	*Anser erythropus*																			LC	F	R	0160
AC2	Mute Swan	*Cygnus olor*																			MS			0152
AE	Bewick's Swan	*Cygnus columbianus*																			BS	C	*	0153
AE*	Whooper Swan	*Cygnus cygnus*																			WS	A		0154
C1C5E*	Egyptian Goose	*Alopochen aegyptiaca*																			EG			0170
A	Shelduck	*Tadorna tadorna*																			SU			0173
BDE*	Ruddy Shelduck	*Tadorna ferruginea*																			UD	D	R	0171
C1E*	Mandarin Duck	*Aix galericulata*																			MN			0178
AE	Baikal Teal	*Sibirionetta formosa*																			IK		R	1830
A	Garganey	*Spatula querquedula*																			GY	A		0191
AE*	Blue-winged Teal	*Spatula discors*																			TB	E	R	0192
A	Shoveler	*Spatula clypeata*																			SV	A		0194
AC2E*	Gadwall	*Mareca strepera*																			GA			0182
	Sub total																							

	DUCKS cont.		Life list	2020	Jan	Feb	Mar	Apr	May	Jun	Jul	Aug	Sep	Oct	Nov	Dec	A	B	C	D	E	F	BTO	RBBP	BBRC	EU No
AE	Falcated Duck	Mareca falcata																							R	
AE*	Wigeon	Mareca penelope																					WN	A		0179
AE	American Wigeon	Mareca americana																					AW			0180
AC2C4E*	Mallard	Anas platyrhynchos																					MA			0186
A	Black Duck	Anas rubripes																					BD	B	R	0187
AE	Pintail	Anas acuta																					PT	A		0189
A	Teal	Anas crecca																					T.			0184
A	Green-winged Teal	Anas carolinensis																					TA	C		1842
AC2E*	Red-crested Pochard	Netta rufina																					RQ	D		0196
AE	Canvasback	Aythya valisineria																							R	0197
AE	Redhead	Aythya americana																					AZ		R	0199
AE*	Pochard	Aythya ferina																					PO	A		0198
AE	Ferruginous Duck	Aythya nyroca																					FD	B	R	0202
AE	Ring-necked Duck	Aythya collaris																					NG	B		0200
A	Tufted Duck	Aythya fuligula																					TU			0203
A	Scaup	Aythya marila																					SP	B		0204
A	Lesser Scaup	Aythya affinis																					AY	C		0205
A	Steller's Eider	Polysticta stelleri																					ES		R	0209
A	King Eider	Somateria spectabilis																					KE	C	R	0207
A	Eider	Somateria mollissima																					E.			0206
A	Harlequin Duck	Histrionicus histrionicus																					HQ	B	R	0211
A	Surf Scoter	Melanitta perspicillata																					FS			0214
A	Velvet Scoter	Melanitta fusca																					VS	C		0215
A	White-winged Scoter	Melanitta deglandi																							R	
	Sub total																									

61

DUCKS cont. GAMEBIRDS, DIVERS

	Common name	Scientific name	Life list	2020	Jan	Feb	Mar	Apr	May	Jun	Jul	Aug	Sep	Oct	Nov	Dec	A	B	C	D	E	F	BTO	RBBP	BBRC	EU No
A	Common Scoter	Melanitta nigra																					CX	A		0213
A	Black Scoter	Melanitta americana																							R	2132
A	Long-tailed Duck	Clangula hyemalis																					LN	C		0212
AE	Bufflehead	Bucephala albeola																					VH		R	0216
AE*	Goldeneye	Bucephala clangula																					GN	A		0218
AE	Barrow's Goldeneye	Bucephala islandica																							R	0217
A	Smew	Mergellus albellus																					SY	C		0220
AE	Hooded Merganser	Lophodytes cucullatus																					HO		R	2190
A	Goosander	Mergus merganser																					GD			0223
A	Red-breasted Merganser	Mergus serrator																					RM			0221
C1E*	Ruddy Duck	Oxyura jamaicensis																					RY	D		0225
C3E*	Capercaillie	Tetrao urogallus																					CP	A		0335
AE	Black Grouse	Lyrurus tetrix																					BK			0332
A	Ptarmigan	Lagopus muta																					PM			0330
A	Red Grouse	Lagopus lagopus																					RG			0329
C1E*	Red-legged Partridge	Alectoris rufa																					RL			0358
AC2E*	Grey Partridge	Perdix perdix																					P.			0367
AE*	Quail	Coturnix coturnix																					Q.	A		0370
C1E*	Pheasant	Phasianus colchicus																					PH			0394
C1E*	Golden Pheasant	Chrysolophus pictus																					GF	D		0396
C6E*	Lady Amherst's Pheasant	Chrysolophus amherstiae																					LM	D		0397
A	Red-throated Diver	Gavia stellata																					RH	A		0002
A	Black-throated Diver	Gavia arctica																					BV	A		0003
A	Pacific Diver	Gavia pacifica																							R	0033
	Sub total																									

DIVERS cont. PETRELS, ALBATROSSES, SHEARWATERS, GREBES

		Life list	2020	Jan	Feb	Mar	Apr	May	Jun	Jul	Aug	Sep	Oct	Nov	Dec	A	B	C	D	E	F	BTO	RBBP	BBRC	EU No
A	**Great Northern Diver** *Gavia immer*																					ND	C		0004
A	**White-billed Diver** *Gavia adamsii*																					VW	C		0005
A	**Wilson's Petrel** *Oceanites oceanicus*																								0050
B	**White-faced Storm Petrel** *Pelagodroma marina*																							R	0051
A	**Black-browed Albatross** *Thalassarche melanophris*																					AA	C	R	0014
A	**Atlantic Yellow-nosed Albatross** *Thalassarche chlororhynchos*																							R	0150
A	**Storm Petrel** *Hydrobates pelagicus*																					TM			0052
A	**Swinhoe's Petrel** *Oceanodroma monorhis*																							R	0056
A	**Leach's Petrel** *Oceanodroma leucorhoa*																					TL			0055
A	**Fulmar** *Fulmarus glacialis*																					F.			0020
A	**Black-capped Petrel** *Pterodroma hasitata*																							R	0029
A	**Scopoli's Shearwater** *Calonectris diomedea*																							R	
A	**Cory's Shearwater** *Calonectris borealis*																					CQ			0036
A	**Sooty Shearwater** *Ardenna griseus*																					OT			0043
A	**Great Shearwater** *Ardenna gravis*																					GQ			0040
A	**Manx Shearwater** *Puffinus puffinus*																					MX			0046
A	**Yelkouan Shearwater** *Puffinus yelkouan*																							R	
A	**Balearic Shearwater** *Puffinus mauretanicus*																								0046
A	**Barolo Shearwater** *Puffinus baroli*																						C	R	0048
A	**Little Grebe** *Tachybaptus ruficollis*																					LG			0007
A	**Pied-billed Grebe** *Podilymbus podiceps*																					PJ	B	R	0006
A	**Red-necked Grebe** *Podiceps grisegena*																					RX	B	*	0010
A	**Great Crested Grebe** *Podiceps cristatus*																					GG			0009
A	**Slavonian Grebe** *Podiceps auritus*																					SZ	A		0011
	Sub total																								

63

GREBES cont. TROPICBIRD, STORKS, SPOONBILL, BITTERNS, HERONS, FRIGATEBIRDS, GANNET

	Species	Scientific name	Life list	2020	Jan	Feb	Mar	Apr	May	Jun	Jul	Aug	Sep	Oct	Nov	Dec	A	B	C	D	E	F	BTO	RBBP	BBRC	EU No
A	Black-necked Grebe	Podiceps nigricollis																					BN	A		0012
AE	Red-billed Tropicbird	Phaethon aethereus																							R	0064
AE	Black Stork	Ciconia nigra																					OS		R	0131
AE	White Stork	Ciconia ciconia																					OR	C		0134
AE	Glossy Ibis	Plegadis falcinellus																					IB	C		0136
AE	Spoonbill	Platalea leucorodia																					NB	A		0144
A	Bittern	Botaurus stellaris																					BI	A		0095
A	American Bittern	Botaurus lentiginosus																					AM		R	0096
A	Little Bittern	Ixobrychus minutus																					LL	B	R	0098
AE*	Night-heron	Nycticorax nycticorax																					NT	E		0104
A	Green Heron	Butorides virescens																					HR		R	0107
A	Squacco Heron	Ardeola ralloides																					QH		R	0108
AE	Chinese Pond Heron	Ardeola bacchus																							R	
A	Cattle Egret	Bubulcus ibis																					EC	B		0111
A	Grey Heron	Ardea cinerea																					H.			0122
A	Great Blue Heron	Ardea herodias																							R	1230
A	Purple Heron	Ardea purpurea																					UR	B		0124
A	Great White Egret	Ardea alba																					HW	C		0121
A	Snowy Egret	Egretta thula																							R	0115
A	Little Egret	Egretta garzetta																					ET	A		0119
A	Dalmatian Pelican	Pelecanus crispus																							R	
A	Ascension Frigatebird	Fregata aquila																							R	
A	Magnificent Frigatebird	Fregata magnificens																							R	0093
A	Gannet	Morus bassanus																					GX			0071
	Sub total																									

Code	BOOBY, CORMORANTS, RAPTORS, BUSTARDS		Life list	2020	Jan	Feb	Mar	Apr	May	Jun	Jul	Aug	Sep	Oct	Nov	Dec	A	B	C	D	E	F	BTO	RBBP	BBRC	EU No
A	Red-footed Booby	Sula sula																							R	
AE	Double-crested Cormorant	Phalacrocorax auritus																							R	0078
A	Shag	Phalacrocorax aristotelis																					SA			0080
A	Cormorant	Phalacrocorax carbo																					CA			0072
AE*	Osprey	Pandion haliaetus																					OP	A		0301
BDE	Egyptian Vulture	Neophron percnopterus																							R	0247
A	Honey-buzzard	Pernis apivorus																					HZ	A		0231
A	Short-toed Eagle	Circaetus gallicus																							R	0256
B	Spotted Eagle	Clanga clanga																							R	0293
AE	Golden Eagle	Aquila chrysaetos																					EA	A		0296
A	Sparrowhawk	Accipiter nisus																					SH			0269
AC3E*	Goshawk	Accipiter gentilis																					GI	A		0267
A	Marsh Harrier	Circus aeruginosus																					MR	A		0260
A	Hen Harrier	Circus cyaneus																					HH	A		0261
A	Northern Harrier	Circus hudsonius																							R	
A	Pallid Harrier	Circus macrourus																						C	R	0262
A	Montagu's Harrier	Circus pygargus																					MO	A		0263
AC3E*	Red Kite	Milvus milvus																					KT			0239
AE	Black Kite	Milvus migrans																					KB	B		0238
AC3E*	White-tailed Eagle	Haliaeetus albicilla																					WE	A		0243
AE	Rough-legged Buzzard	Buteo lagopus																					RF	C		0290
AE*	Buzzard	Buteo buteo																					BZ			0287
AE*	Great Bustard	Otis tarda																					US	A	R	0446
A	Macqueen's Bustard	Chlamydotis macqueenii																							R	0444
	Sub total																									

65

BUSTARDS cont. RAILS, CRAKES, GALLINULES, CRANES, WADERS

	Species	Scientific name	Life list	2020	Jan	Feb	Mar	Apr	May	Jun	Jul	Aug	Sep	Oct	Nov	Dec	A	B	C	D	E	F	BTO	RBBP	BBRC	EU No
A	Little Bustard	Tetrax tetrax																							R	0442
A	Water Rail	Rallus aquaticus																					WA	A		0407
AE*	Corncrake	Crex crex																					CE	A		0421
A	Little Crake	Porzana parva																					JC		R	0410
A	Baillon's Crake	Porzana pusilla																					VC	B	R	0411
A	Spotted Crake	Porzana porzana																					AK	A		0408
A	Sora Rail	Porzana carolina																							R	0409
AE	Western Swamphen	Porphyrio porphyrio																							R	
A	Allen's Gallinule	Porphyrio alleni																							R	0425
A	American Purple Gallinule	Porphyrio martinica																							R	0426
A	Moorhen	Gallinula chloropus																					MH			0424
A	Coot	Fulica atra																					CO			0429
A	American Coot	Fulica americana																							R	0430
A	Sandhill Crane	Antigone canadensis																							R	0436
AE*	Crane	Grus grus																					AN	A		0433
A	Stone-curlew	Burhinus oedicnemus																					TN	A		0459
A	Oystercatcher	Haematopus ostralegus																					OC			0450
A	Black-winged Stilt	Himantopus himantopus																					IT	B		0455
AE	Avocet	Recurvirostra avosetta																					AV	A		0456
A	Lapwing	Vanellus vanellus																					L.			0493
A	Sociable Plover	Vanellus gregarius																					IP		R	0491
A	White-tailed Plover	Vanellus leucurus																							R	0492
A	Golden Plover	Pluvialis apricaria																					GP			0485
A	Pacific Golden Plover	Pluvialis fulva																					IF		R	0484
	Sub total																									

	WADERS cont.		Life list	2020	Jan	Feb	Mar	Apr	May	Jun	Jul	Aug	Sep	Oct	Nov	Dec	A	B	C	D	E	F	BTO	RBBP	BBRC	EU No
A	**American Golden Plover**	*Pluvialis dominica*																					ID			0484
A	**Grey Plover**	*Pluvialis squatarola*																					GV			0486
A	**Ringed Plover**	*Charadrius hiaticula*																					RP			0470
A	**Semipalmated Plover**	*Charadrius semipalmatus*																					TV		R	0471
A	**Little Ringed Plover**	*Charadrius dubius*																					LP	A		0469
A	**Killdeer**	*Charadrius vociferus*																					KL	C	R	0474
A	**Kentish Plover**	*Charadrius alexandrinus*																					KP	B		0477
A	**Lesser Sand Plover**	*Charadrius mongolus*																							R	0478
A	**Greater Sand Plover**	*Charadrius leschenaultii*																					DP		R	0479
A	**Caspian Plover**	*Charadrius asiaticus*																							R	0480
A	**Dotterel**	*Charadrius morinellus*																					DO	A		0482
A	**Upland Sandpiper**	*Bartramia longicauda*																					UP		R	0544
A	**Whimbrel**	*Numenius phaeopus*																					WM	A	*	0538
A	**Little Whimbrel**	*Numenius minutus*																							R	0536
B	**Eskimo Curlew**	*Numenius borealis*																							R	0537
A	**Curlew**	*Numenius arquata*																					CU			0541
A	**Bar-tailed Godwit**	*Limosa lapponica*																					BA	C		0534
A	**Black-tailed Godwit**	*Limosa limosa*																					BW	A		0532
A	**Hudsonian Godwit**	*Limosa haemastica*																					HU		R	0533
A	**Turnstone**	*Arenaria interpres*																					TT	C		0561
A	**Great Knot**	*Calidris tenuirostris*																					KO		R	0495
A	**Knot**	*Calidris canutus*																					KN			0496
A	**Ruff**	*Calidris pugnax*																					RU	A		0517
A	**Broad-billed Sandpiper**	*Calidris falcinellus*																					OA	C	R	0514
	Sub total																									

WADERS cont.

	Species	Life list	2020	Jan	Feb	Mar	Apr	May	Jun	Jul	Aug	Sep	Oct	Nov	Dec	A	B	C	D	E	F	BTO	RBBP	BBRC	EU No
A	Sharp-tailed Sandpiper *Calidris acuminata*																					VV		R	0508
A	Stilt Sandpiper *Calidris himantopus*																					MI		R	5150
A	Curlew Sandpiper *Calidris ferruginea*																					CV			0509
A	Temminck's Stint *Calidris temminckii*																					TK	B		0502
A	Long-toed Stint *Calidris subminuta*																							R	0503
A	Red-necked Stint *Calidris ruficollis*																							R	0500
A	Sanderling *Calidris alba*																					SS	C		0497
A	Dunlin *Calidris alpina*																					DN			0512
A	Purple Sandpiper *Calidris maritima*																					PS	A		0510
A	Baird's Sandpiper *Calidris bairdii*																					BP		R	0506
A	Little Stint *Calidris minuta*																					LX			0501
A	Least Sandpiper *Calidris minutilla*																					EP		R	0504
A	White-rumped Sandpiper *Calidris fuscicollis*																					WU			0505
A	Buff-breasted Sandpiper *Calidris subruficollis*																					BQ	C		0516
A	Pectoral Sandpiper *Calidris melanotos*																					PP	C		0507
A	Semipalmated Sandpiper *Calidris pusilla*																					PZ		R	0498
A	Western Sandpiper *Calidris mauri*																					ER		R	0499
A	Long-billed Dowitcher *Limnodromus scolopaceus*																					LD		R	0527
A	Short-billed Dowitcher *Limnodromus griseus*																							R	0526
A	Woodcock *Scolopax rusticola*																					WK			0529
A	Jack Snipe *Lymnocryptes minimus*																					JS	C		0518
A	Great Snipe *Gallinago media*																					DS	C	R	0520
A	Snipe *Gallinago gallinago*																					SN			0519
A	Wilson's Snipe *Gallinago delicata*																							R	5192
	Sub total																								

A	WADERS cont. PRATINCOLES, GULLS		Life list	2020	Jan	Feb	Mar	Apr	May	Jun	Jul	Aug	Sep	Oct	Nov	Dec	A	B	C	D	E	F	BTO	RBBP	BBRC	EU No
A	Terek Sandpiper	Xenus cinereus																					TR		R	0555
A	Wilson's Phalarope	Phalaropus tricolor																					WF	A	R	0563
A	Red-necked Phalarope	Phalaropus lobatus																					NK	A		0564
A	Grey Phalarope	Phalaropus fulicarius																					PL			0565
A	Common Sandpiper	Actitis hypoleucos																					CS			0556
A	Spotted Sandpiper	Actitis macularius																					PQ	B	R	0557
A	Green Sandpiper	Tringa ochropus																					GE	A		0553
A	Solitary Sandpiper	Tringa solitaria																					L.		R	0552
A	Grey-tailed Tattler	Tringa brevipes																					YT	A	R	0558
A	Lesser Yellowlegs	Tringa flavipes																					LY			0551
A	Redshank	Tringa totanus																					RK			0546
A	Marsh Sandpiper	Tringa stagnatilis																					MD		R	0547
A	Wood Sandpiper	Tringa glareola																					OD	A		0554
A	Spotted Redshank	Tringa erythropus																					DR			0545
A	Greenshank	Tringa nebularia																					GK	A		0548
A	Greater Yellowlegs	Tringa melanoleuca																					LZ		R	0550
A	Cream-coloured Courser	Cursorius cursor																							R	0464
A	Collared Pratincole	Glareola pratincola																							R	0465
A	Oriental Pratincole	Glareola maldivarum																					GM		R	0466
A	Black-winged Pratincole	Glareola nordmanni																					KW		R	0467
A	Kittiwake	Rissa tridactyla																					KI			0602
A	Ivory Gull	Pagophila eburnea																					IV		R	0604
A	Sabine's Gull	Xema sabini																					AB			0579
A	Slender-billed Gull	Chroicocephalus genei																					EI	C	R	0585
	Sub total																									

69

GULLS cont. TERNS

	Species	Scientific name	Life list	2020	Jan	Feb	Mar	Apr	May	Jun	Jul	Aug	Sep	Oct	Nov	Dec	A	B	C	D	E	F	BTO	RBBP	BBRC	EU No
A	Bonaparte's Gull	Chroicocephalus philadelphia																					ON		R	0581
A	Black-headed Gull	Chroicocephalus ridibundus																					BH			0582
A	Little Gull	Hydrocoloeus minutus																					LU	B		0578
A	Ross's Gull	Rhodostethia rosea																					QG		R	0601
A	Laughing Gull	Leucophaeus atricilla																					LF		R	0576
A	Franklin's Gull	Leucophaeus pipixcan																					FG		R	0577
A	Audouin's Gull	Ichthyaetus audouinii																							R	0589
A	Mediterranean Gull	Ichthyaetus melanocephalus																					MU	A		0575
B	Great Black-headed Gull	Ichthyaetus ichthyaetus																							R	0573
A	Common Gull	Larus canus																					CM			0590
A	Ring-billed Gull	Larus delawarensis																					IN	B		0588
A	Great Black-backed Gull	Larus marinus																					GB			0600
A	Glaucous-winged Gull	Larus glaucescens																							R	5960
A	Glaucous Gull	Larus hyperboreus																					GZ	B		0599
A	Iceland Gull	Larus glaucoides																					IG		*	0598
A	Herring Gull	Larus argentatus																					HG			0592
A	American Herring Gull	Larus smithsonianus																							R	26632
A	Caspian Gull	Larus cachinnans																								5927
A	Yellow-legged Gull	Larus michahellis																					YG	A	*	5927
A	Slaty-backed Gull	Larus schistisagus																							R	
A	Lesser Black-backed Gull	Larus fuscus																					LB	B	*	0591
A	Gull-billed Tern	Gelochelidon nilotica																					TG		R	0605
A	Caspian Tern	Hydroprogne caspia																					CJ		R	0606
A	Royal Tern	Thalasseus maximus																					QT		R	0607
	Sub total																										

	TERNS cont. SKUAS, AUKS		Life list	2020	Jan	Feb	Mar	Apr	May	Jun	Jul	Aug	Sep	Oct	Nov	Dec	A	B	C	D	E	F	BTO	RBBP	BBRC	EU No
A	Lesser Crested Tern	Thalasseus bengalensis																					TF	B	R	0609
A	Sandwich Tern	Thalasseus sandvicensis																					TE			0611
A	Cabot's Tern	Thalasseus acuflavida																							R	
A	Elegant Tern	Thalasseus elegans																							R	
A	Little Tern	Sternula albifrons																					AF	A		0624
A	Least Tern	Sternula antillarum																							R	
A	Aleutian Tern	Onychoprion aleuticus																							R	0617
A	Bridled Tern	Onychoprion anaethetus																							R	0622
A	Sooty Tern	Onychoprion fuscatus																							R	0623
A	Roseate Tern	Sterna dougallii																					RS	A		0614
A	Common Tern	Sterna hirundo																					CN			0615
A	Arctic Tern	Sterna paradisaea																					AE			0616
A	Forster's Tern	Sterna forsteri																					FO		R	0618
A	Whiskered Tern	Chlidonias hybrida																					WD		R	0626
A	White-winged Black Tern	Chlidonias leucopterus																					WJ			0628
A	Black Tern	Chlidonias niger																					BJ	B	*	0627
A	Great Skua	Stercorarius skua																					NX			0569
A	Pomarine Skua	Stercorarius pomarinus																					PK			0566
A	Arctic Skua	Stercorarius parasiticus																					AC	A		0567
A	Long-tailed Skua	Stercorarius longicaudus																					OG	B		0568
A	Little Auk	Alle alle																					LK			0647
A	Brunnich's Guillemot	Uria lomvia																					TZ		R	0635
A	Guillemot	Uria aalge																					GU			0634
A	Razorbill	Alca torda																					RA			0636
	Sub total																									

AUKS cont. SANDGROUSE, PIGEONS/DOVES, CUCKOOS, OWLS

	English name	Scientific name	Life list	2020	Jan	Feb	Mar	Apr	May	Jun	Jul	Aug	Sep	Oct	Nov	Dec	A	B	C	D	E	F	BTO	RBBP	BBRC	EU No
B	Great Auk (extinct)	Pinguinus impennis																								0638
A	Black Guillemot	Cepphus grylle																					TY		R	6412
A	Long-billed Murrelet	Brachyramphus perdix																							R	0645
A	Ancient Murrelet	Synthliboramphus antiquus																								
A	Puffin	Fratercula arctica																					PU			0654
A	Tufted Puffin	Fratercula cirrhata																							R	3565
A	Pallas's Sandgrouse	Syrrhaptes paradoxus																							R	0663
AC4E*	Rock Dove / Feral Pigeon	Columba livia																					DV			0665
A	Stock Dove	Columba oenas																					SD			0668
A	Woodpigeon	Columba palumbus																					WP			0670
A	Turtle Dove	Streptopelia turtur																					TD	A		0687
A	Oriental Turtle Dove	Streptopelia orientalis																							R	0689
A	Collared Dove	Streptopelia decaocto																					CD			0684
A	Mourning Dove	Zenaida macroura																							R	0695
A	Great Spotted Cuckoo	Clamator glandarius																					UK		R	0716
A	Yellow-billed Cuckoo	Coccyzus americanus																							R	0728
A	Black-billed Cuckoo	Coccyzus erythropthalmus																							R	0727
A	Cuckoo	Cuculus canorus																					CK			0724
AE*	Barn Owl	Tyto alba																					BO	C	*	0735
A	Scops Owl	Otus scops																						B	R	0739
AE	Snowy Owl	Bubo scandiacus																					SO		R	0749
A	Tawny Owl	Strix aluco																					TO			0761
A	Hawk Owl	Surnia ulula																							R	0750
C1E*	Little Owl	Athene noctua																					LO			0757
	Sub total																										

OWLS cont. NIGHTJARS, SWIFTS, KINGFISHERS, BEE-EATERS, WOODPECKERS

	Species	Scientific name	Life list	2020	Jan	Feb	Mar	Apr	May	Jun	Jul	Aug	Sep	Oct	Nov	Dec	A	B	C	D	E	F	BTO	RBBP	BBRC	EU No
A	Tengmalm's Owl	Aegolius funereus																							R	0770
A	Long-eared Owl	Asio otus																					LE	A		0767
A	Short-eared Owl	Asio flammeus																					SE	A		0768
A	Common Nighthawk	Chordeiles minor																							R	0786
B	Red-necked Nightjar	Caprimulgus ruficollis																							R	0779
A	Nightjar	Caprimulgus europaeus																					NJ			0778
A	Egyptian Nightjar	Caprimulgus aegyptius																							R	0781
A	White-throated Needletail	Hirundapus caudacutus																					NI		R	0792
A	Chimney Swift	Chaetura pelagica																							R	0790
A	Alpine Swift	Tachymarptis melba																					AI			0798
A	Swift	Apus apus																					SI			0795
A	Pallid Swift	Apus pallidus																						C	R	0796
A	Pacific Swift	Apus pacificus																							R	0797
A	White-rumped Swift	Apus caffer																							R	0799
A	Little Swift	Apus affinis																							R	0800
A	Roller	Coracias garrulus																							R	0841
A	Kingfisher	Alcedo atthis																					KF			0831
A	Belted Kingfisher	Megaceryle alcyon																							R	0834
A	Blue-cheeked Bee-eater	Merops persicus																							R	0839
A	Bee-eater	Merops apiaster																					MZ	B		0840
AE	Hoopoe	Upupa epops																					HP	B		0846
A	Wryneck	Jynx torquilla																					WY	A		0848
A	Yellow-bellied Sapsucker	Sphyrapicus varius																							R	0872
A	Lesser Spotted Woodpecker	Dryobates minor																					LS	A		0887
	Sub total																									

WOODPECKERS cont. FALCONS, PARAKEET, USA FLYCATCHERS/KINGBIRD, SHRIKES

	Species	Scientific name	Life list	2020	Jan	Feb	Mar	Apr	May	Jun	Jul	Aug	Sep	Oct	Nov	Dec	A	B	C	D	E	F	BTO	RBBP	BBRC	EU No
A	Great Spotted Woodpecker	Dendrocopos major																					GS			0876
A	Green Woodpecker	Picus viridis																					G.			0856
A	Lesser Kestrel	Falco naumanni																							R	0303
A	Kestrel	Falco tinnunculus																					K.			0304
AE	American Kestrel	Falco sparverius																							R	0305
A	Red-footed Falcon	Falco vespertinus																					FV			0307
AE	Amur Falcon	Falco amurensis																							R	3080
A	Eleonora's Falcon	Falco eleonorae																							R	0311
A	Merlin	Falco columbarius																					ML	A		0309
A	Hobby	Falco subbuteo																					HY	A		0310
AE	Gyr Falcon	Falco rusticolus																					YF	C	R	0318
AE	Peregrine	Falco peregrinus																					PE	A		0320
C1E*	Ring-necked Parakeet	Psittacula krameri																					RI			0712
A	Eastern Phoebe	Sayornis phoebe																							R	0909
A	Acadian Flycatcher	Empidonax virescens																							R	
A	Alder Flycatcher	Empidonax alnorum																							R	9023
A	Eastern Kingbird	Tyrannus tyrannus																							R	
A	Brown Shrike	Lanius cristatus																							R	1513
A	Red-backed Shrike	Lanius collurio																					ED	A		1515
A	Daurian Shrike	Lanius isabellinus																					IL		R	1514
A	Turkestan Shrike	Lanius phoenicuroides																							R	
A	Long-tailed Shrike	Lanius schach																							R	1517
A	Lesser Grey Shrike	Lanius minor																							R	1519
A	Great Grey Shrike	Lanius excubitor																					SR	C		1520
	Sub total																										

SHRIKES cont. VIREOS, ORIOLE, CORVIDS, WAXWINGS, TITS

	Species	Scientific	Life list	2020	Jan	Feb	Mar	Apr	May	Jun	Jul	Aug	Sep	Oct	Nov	Dec	A	B	C	D	E	F	BTO	RBBP	BBRC	EU No
AE	Steppe Grey Shrike	Lanius pallidirsotris																					OO		R	1523
A	Woodchat Shrike	Lanius senator																							*	1524
A	Masked Shrike	Lanius nubicus																							R	1628
A	Yellow-throated Vireo	Vireo flavifrons																							R	1631
A	Philadelphia Vireo	Vireo philadelphicus																							R	1633
A	Red-eyed Vireo	Vireo olivaceus																					EV		R	1508
A	Golden Oriole	Oriolus oriolus																					OL	A		1539
A	Jay	Garrulus glandarius																					J.			1549
A	Magpie	Pica pica																					MG			1557
A	Nutcracker	Nucifraga caryocatactes																					NC		R	1559
AE*	Chough	Pyrrhocorax pyrrhocorax																					CF	A		1560
A	Jackdaw	Coloeus monedula																					JD			1563
A	Rook	Corvus frugilegus																					RO			1567
A	Carrion Crow	Corvus corone																					C.			1567
A	Hooded Crow	Corvus cornix																					HC			1572
A	Raven	Corvus corax																					RN			1048
AE	Waxwing	Bombycilla garrulus																					WX	C		1046
AE	Cedar Waxwing	Bombycilla cedrorum																							R	1461
A	Coal Tit	Periparus ater																					CT			1454
A	Crested Tit	Lophophanes cristatus																					CI		*	1440
A	Marsh Tit	Poecile palustris																					MT			1442
A	Willow Tit	Poecile montana																					WT	A	*	1462
A	Blue Tit	Cyanistes caeruleus																					BT			1464
A	Great Tit	Parus major																					GT			
	Sub total																									

BEARDED TIT, LARKS, MARTINS, SWALLOWS, LONG-TAILED TIT, WARBLERS

	Common name	Scientific name	Life list	2020	Jan	Feb	Mar	Apr	May	Jun	Jul	Aug	Sep	Oct	Nov	Dec	A	B	C	D	E	F	BTO	RBBP	BBRC	EU No
A	Penduline Tit	Remiz pendulinus																					DT	B		1490
A	Bearded Tit	Panurus biarmicus																					BR	A		1364
A	Woodlark	Lullula arborea																					WL			0974
A	White-winged Lark	Alauda leucoptera																							R	0965
A	Skylark	Alauda arvensis																					S.			0976
AE	Crested Lark	Galerida cristata																							R	0972
A	Shore Lark	Eremophila alpestris																					SX	B		0978
A	Short-toed Lark	Calandrella brachydactyla																					VL	C		0968
A	Bimaculated Lark	Melanocorypha bimaculata																							R	0962
A	Calandra Lark	Melanocorypha calandra																							R	0961
A	Black Lark	Melanocorypha yeltoniensis																							R	0966
A	Lesser Short-toed Lark	Alaudala rufescens																							R	0970
A	Sand Martin	Riparia riparia																					SM			0981
A	Tree Swallow	Tachycineta bicolor																							R	0983
A	Purple Martin	Progne subis																							R	0989
AE	Swallow	Hirundo rustica																					SL			0992
A	Crag Martin	Ptyonoprogne rupestris																							R	0991
A	House Martin	Delichon urbicum																					HM			1001
A	Red-rumped Swallow	Cecropis daurica																					VR	C	*	0995
A	American Cliff Swallow	Petrochelidon pyrrhonota																							R	0998
A	Cetti's Warbler	Cettia cetti																					CW		R	1220
A	Long-tailed Tit	Aegithalos caudatus																					LT		*	1437
A	Wood Warbler	Phylloscopus sibilatrix																					WO			1308
A	Western Bonelli's Warbler	Phylloscopus bonelli																					IW	C	R	1307
	Sub total																									

WARBLERS cont.

	Common Name	Scientific Name	Life list	2020	Jan	Feb	Mar	Apr	May	Jun	Jul	Aug	Sep	Oct	Nov	Dec	A	B	C	D	E	F	BTO	RBBP	BBRC	EU No
A	Eastern Bonelli's Warbler	*Phylloscopus orientalis*																							R	1307
A	Hume's Warbler	*Phylloscopus humei*																							R	1300
A	Yellow-browed Warbler	*Phylloscopus inornatus*																					YB			1300
A	Pallas's Warbler	*Phylloscopus proregulus*																					PA	C		1298
A	Radde's Warbler	*Phylloscopus schwarzi*																								1301
A	Dusky Warbler	*Phylloscopus fuscatus*																					UY			1303
A	Willow Warbler	*Phylloscopus trochilus*																					WW			1312
A	Chiffchaff	*Phylloscopus collybita*																					CC			1311
A	Iberian Chiffchaff	*Phylloscopus ibericus*																						C	R	1311
A	Eastern Crowned Warbler	*Phylloscopus coronatus*																							R	12860
A	Green Warbler	*Phylloscopus nitidus*																							R	12910
A	Two-barred Greenish Warbler	*Phylloscopus plumbeitarsus*																							R	
A	Greenish Warbler	*Phylloscopus trochiloides*																					NP	C	R	1293
A	Pale-legged Leaf Warbler	*Phylloscopus tenellipes*																							R	
A	Arctic Warbler	*Phylloscopus borealis*																					AP			1295
A	Great Reed Warbler	*Acrocephalus arundinaceus*																					QW	C	R	1253
A	Aquatic Warbler	*Acrocephalus paludicola*																					AQ		R	1242
A	Sedge Warbler	*Acrocephalus schoenobaenus*																					SW			1243
A	Paddyfield Warbler	*Acrocephalus agricola*																					PY		R	1247
A	Blyth's Reed Warbler	*Acrocephalus dumetorum*																						C		1248
A	Reed Warbler	*Acrocephalus scirpaceus*																					RW			1251
A	Marsh Warbler	*Acrocephalus palustris*																					MW	A		1250
A	Thick-billed Warbler	*Iduna aedon*																							R	1254
A	Booted Warbler	*Iduna caligata*																						C	R	1256
	Sub total																									

WARBLERS cont.

	Species	Life list	2020	Jan	Feb	Mar	Apr	May	Jun	Jul	Aug	Sep	Oct	Nov	Dec	A	B	C	D	E	F	BTO	RBBP	BBRC	EU No
A	**Sykes's Warbler** *Iduna rama*																							R	12562
A	**Eastern Olivaceous Warbler** *Iduna pallida*																							R	1255
A	**Olive-tree Warbler** *Hippolais olivetorum*																							R	12580
A	**Melodious Warbler** *Hippolais polyglotta*																					ME	C		1260
A	**Icterine Warbler** *Hippolais icterina*																					IC	B		1259
A	**Pallas's Grasshopper Warbler** *Helopsaltes certhiola*																							R	1233
A	**Grasshopper Warbler** *Locustella naevia*																					GH		*	1236
A	**River Warbler** *Locustella fluviatilis*																					VW	C	R	1237
A	**Savi's Warbler** *Locustella luscinioides*																					VI	A	R	1238
A	**Lanceolated Warbler** *Locustella lanceolata*																							R	1235
A	**Fan-tailed Warbler** *Cisticola juncidis*																							R	1226
A	**Blackcap** *Sylvia atricapilla*																					BC			1277
A	**Garden Warbler** *Sylvia borin*																					GW			1276
A	**Barred Warbler** *Sylvia nisoria*																					RR			1273
A	**Lesser Whitethroat** *Sylvia curruca*																					LW			1274
A	**Western Orphean Warbler** *Sylvia hortensis*																							R	1272
A	**Eastern Orphean Warbler** *Sylvia crassirostris*																							R	
A	**Asian Desert Warbler** *Sylvia nana*																						C	R	1270
A	**Whitethroat** *Sylvia communis*																					WH			1275
A	**Dartford Warbler** *Sylvia undata*																					DW	A		1262
A	**Marmora's Warbler** *Sylvia sarda*																						C	R	1261
A	**Spectacled Warbler** *Sylvia conspicillata*																						C	R	1264
A	**Subalpine Warbler** *Sylvia cantillans*																						C	*	1265
A	**Moltoni's Subalpine Warbler** *Sylvia subalpina*																							R	
	Sub total																								

WARBLERS cont.' CRESTS; WREN, NUTHATCH, 'CREEPERS; STARLINGS, THRUSHES

	Species	Scientific name	Life list	2020	Jan	Feb	Mar	Apr	May	Jun	Jul	Aug	Sep	Oct	Nov	Dec	A	B	C	D	E	F	BTO	RBBP	BBRC	EU No
A	Sardinian Warbler	Sylvia melanocephala																						C	R	1267
A	Rüppell's Warbler	Sylvia ruppeli																							R	1269
A	Firecrest	Regulus ignicapilla																					FC	A		1315
A	Goldcrest	Regulus regulus																					GC			1314
A	Wren	Troglodytes troglodytes																					WR			1066
A	Nuthatch	Sitta europaea																					NH			1479
A	Red-breasted Nuthatch	Sitta canadensis																							R	1472
A	Wallcreeper	Tichodroma muraria																							*	1482
A	Treecreeper	Certhia familiaris																					TC		R	1486
A	Short-toed Treecreeper	Certhia brachydactyla																					TH	A	R	1487
A	Grey Catbird	Dumetella carolinensis																							R	1080
AE	Northern Mockingbird	Mimus polyglottos																							R	1067
A	Brown Thrasher	Toxostoma rufum																							R	1069
AE	Rose-coloured Starling	Pastor roseus																					OE			1594
A	Starling	Sturnus vulgaris																					SG			1582
AE	Siberian Thrush	Geokichla sibirica																							R	1171
A	White's Thrush	Zoothera aurea																							R	1170
A	Varied Thrush	Ixoreus naevius																					VT		R	1172
A	Veery	Catharus fuscescens																							R	1179
A	Grey-cheeked Thrush	Catharus minimus																							R	1178
A	Swainson's Thrush	Catharus ustulatus																							R	1177
A	Hermit Thrush	Catharus guttatus																							R	1176
A	Wood Thrush	Hylocichla mustelina																							R	1175
A	Ring Ouzel	Turdus torquatus																					RZ			1186
	Sub total																									

THRUSHES cont. FLYCATCHERS

	Common Name	Scientific Name	Life list	2020	Jan	Feb	Mar	Apr	May	Jun	Jul	Aug	Sep	Oct	Nov	Dec	A	B	C	D	E	F	BTO	RBBP	BBRC	EU No
A	Blackbird	Turdus merula																					B.			1187
A	Eyebrowed Thrush	Turdus obscurus																							R	1195
A	Black-throated Thrush	Turdus atrogularis																							R	1197
A	Red-throated Thrush	Turdus ruficollis																							R	11970
A	Naumann's Thrush	Turdus naumanni																							R	11960
A	Dusky Thrush	Turdus eunomus																							R	1196
A	Fieldfare	Turdus pilaris																					FF	A		1198
A	Redwing	Turdus iliacus																					RE	A		1201
A	Song Thrush	Turdus philomelos																					ST			1200
A	Mistle Thrush	Turdus viscivorus																					M.			1202
AE	American Robin	Turdus migratorius																					AR		R	1203
A	Rufous-tailed Scrub Robin	Cercotrichas galactotes																							R	1095
A	Spotted Flycatcher	Muscicapa striata																					SF			1335
A	Asian Brown Flycatcher	Muscicapa dauurica																							R	
A	Robin	Erithacus rubecula																					R.			1099
A	Siberian Blue Robin	Larvivora cyane																							R	1112
A	Rufous-tailed Robin	Larvivora sibilans																							R	1102
A	Bluethroat	Luscinia svecica																					BU	B		1106
A	Thrush Nightingale	Luscinia luscinia																					FN	C	R	1103
A	Nightingale	Luscinia megarhynchos																					N.		*	1104
A	White-throated Robin	Irania gutturalis																							R	1117
A	Siberian Rubythroat	Calliope calliope																							R	1105
AE	Red-flanked Bluetail	Tarsiger cyanurus																								1113
A	Pied Flycatcher	Ficedula hypoleuca																					PF		*	1349
	Sub total																									

FLYCATCHERS cont. CHATS, WHEATEARS, DIPPER, SPARROWS, ACCENTORS

	Species	Scientific name	Life list	2020	Jan	Feb	Mar	Apr	May	Jun	Jul	Aug	Sep	Oct	Nov	Dec	A	B	C	D	E	F	BTO	RBBP	BBRC	EU No
A	Collared Flycatcher	Ficedula albicollis																					FY		R	1348
A	Red-breasted Flycatcher	Ficedula parva																								1343
A	Taiga Flycatcher	Ficedula albicilla																							R	1343
A	Black Redstart	Phoenicurus ochruros																					BX	A	*	1121
A	Redstart	Phoenicurus phoenicurus																					RT			1122
A	Moussier's Redstart	Phoenicurus moussieri																							R	1127
A	Rock Thrush	Monticola saxatilis																					OH		R	1162
AE	Blue Rock Thrush	Monticola solitarius																							R	1166
A	Whinchat	Saxicola rubetra																					WC			1137
A	Stonechat	Saxicola rubicola																					SC			1139
A	Siberian Stonechat	Saxicola maurus																							R	
A	Stejneger's Stonechat	Saxicola stejnegeri																							R	1146
A	Wheatear	Oenanthe oenanthe																					W.			1146
A	Isabelline Wheatear	Oenanthe isabellina																							R	1144
A	Desert Wheatear	Oenanthe deserti																							R	1149
A	Black-eared Wheatear	Oenanthe hispanica																							R	1148
A	Pied Wheatear	Oenanthe pleschanka																					PI		R	1147
A	White-crowned Black Wheatear	Oenanthe leucopyga																							R	1157
A	Dipper	Cinclus cinclus																					DI		*	1050
A	House Sparrow	Passer domesticus																					HS			1591
A	Spanish Sparrow	Passer hispaniolensis																							R	1592
A	Tree Sparrow	Passer montanus																					TS			1598
A	Rock Sparrow	Petronia petronia																							R	1604
A	Alpine Accentor	Prunella collaris																							R	1094
	Sub total																									

ACCENTORS cont.WAGTAILS, PIPITS, FINCHES

	Species	Scientific name	Life list	2020	Jan	Feb	Mar	Apr	May	Jun	Jul	Aug	Sep	Oct	Nov	Dec	A	B	C	D	E	F	BTO	RBBP	BBRC	EU No
A	Siberian Accentor	Prunella montanella																							R	1084
A	Dunnock	Prunella modularis																					D.			
A	Yellow Wagtail	Motacilla flava																					YW		*	1017
A	Eastern Yellow Wagtail	Motacilla tschutschensis																							R	
A	Citrine Wagtail	Motacilla citreola																						C		1018
A	Grey Wagtail	Motacilla cinerea																					GL			1019
A	Pied Wagtail	Motacilla alba																					PW		*	1020
A	Richard's Pipit	Anthus richardi																					PR			1002
A	Blyth's Pipit	Anthus godlewskii																							R	1004
A	Tawny Pipit	Anthus campestris																					TI		R	1005
A	Meadow Pipit	Anthus pratensis																					MP			1011
A	Tree Pipit	Anthus trivialis																					TP			1009
A	Olive-backed Pipit	Anthus hodgsoni																					OV			1008
A	Pechora Pipit	Anthus gustavi																							R	1010
A	Red-throated Pipit	Anthus cervinus																					VP		R	1012
A	Buff-bellied Pipit	Anthus rubescens																							R	1014
A	Water Pipit	Anthus spinoletta																					WI			1014
A	Rock Pipit	Anthus petrosus																					RC			1014
AE	Chaffinch	Fringilla coelebs																					CH			1636
A	Brambling	Fringilla montifringilla																					BL	B		1638
A	Evening Grosbeak	Hesperiphona vespertina																							R	1718
A	Hawfinch	Coccothraustes coccothraustes																					HF	A		1717
AE	Pine Grosbeak	Pinicola enucleator																							R	1699
A	Bullfinch	Pyrrhula pyrrhula																					BF			1710
	Sub total																									

FINCHES cont. BUNTINGS

	Common name	Scientific name	Life list	2020	Jan	Feb	Mar	Apr	May	Jun	Jul	Aug	Sep	Oct	Nov	Dec	A	B	C	D	E	F	BTO	RBBP	BBRC	EU No
AE	Trumpeter Finch	Bucanetes githagineus																					SQ	B	R	1676
A	Common Rosefinch	Carpodacus erythrinus																					GR			1679
AE	Greenfinch	Chloris chloris																					TW			1649
A	Twite	Linaria flavirostris																					LI			1662
A	Linnet	Linaria cannabina																					FR	A		1660
A	Common Redpoll	Acanthis flammea																					LR			1663
A	Lesser Redpoll	Acanthis cabaret																					AL			1663
A	Arctic Redpoll	Acanthis hornemanni																					PC	A		1664
A	Parrot Crossbill	Loxia pytyopsittacus																					CY			1668
A	Scottish Crossbill	Loxia scotica																					CR			1667
A	Crossbill	Loxia curvirostra																					PD			1666
A	Two-barred Crossbill	Loxia leucoptera																					GO		R	1665
A	Goldfinch	Carduelis carduelis																								1653
A	Citril Finch	Carduelis citrinella																					NS		R	1644
A	Serin	Serinus serinus																					SK	B		1640
A	Siskin	Spinus spinus																					LA			1654
A	Lapland Bunting	Calcarius lapponicus																					SB	B		1847
A	Snow Bunting	Plectrophenax nivalis																					CB	A		1850
A	Corn Bunting	Emberiza calandra																					Y.			1882
A	Yellowhammer	Emberiza citrinella																					EL			1857
A	Pine Bunting	Emberiza leucocephalos																							R	1856
A	Rock Bunting	Emberiza cia																					OB		R	1860
AE	Ortolan Bunting	Emberiza hortulana																								1866
A	Cretzschmar's Bunting	Emberiza caesia																							R	1868
	Sub total																									

BUNTINGS cont.
NEW WORLD SPARROWS–WARBLERS etc

	Species	Scientific name	Life list	2020	Jan	Feb	Mar	Apr	May	Jun	Jul	Aug	Sep	Oct	Nov	Dec	A	B	C	D	E	F	BTO	RBBP	BBRC	EU No
A	Cirl Bunting	Emberiza cirlus																					CL	A		1958
A	Chestnut-eared Bunting	Emberiza fucata																							R	1869
A	Little Bunting	Emberiza pusilla																					LJ			1874
A	Yellow-browed Bunting	Emberiza chrysophrys																							R	1871
A	Rustic Bunting	Emberiza rustica																							R	1873
AE	Yellow-breasted Bunting	Emberiza aureola																						C	R	1876
A	Chestnut Bunting	Emberiza rutila																							R	
AE	Black-headed Bunting	Emberiza melanocephala																							R	1881
AE	Black-faced Bunting	Emberiza spodocephala																							R	1853
A	Pallas's Reed Bunting	Emberiza pallasi																							R	1878
A	Reed Bunting	Emberiza schoeniclus																					RB			1877
E	Song Sparrow	Melospiza melodia																							R	1835
AE	White-crowned Sparrow	Zonotrichia leucophrys																							R	1839
AE	White-throated Sparrow	Zonotrichia albicollis																							R	1840
AE	Dark-eyed Junco	Junco hyemalis																					JU		R	1842
A	Savannah Sparrow	Passerculus sandwichensis																							R	1826
A	Lark Sparrow	Chondestes grammacus																							R	1824
A	Eastern Towhee	Pipilo erythrophthalmus																							R	1798
A	Bobolink	Dolichonyx oryzivorus																							R	1897
AE	Baltimore Oriole	Icterus galbula																							R	1918
A	Red-winged Blackbird	Agelaius phoeniceus																							R	
A	Brown-headed Cowbird	Molothrus ater																							R	1899
A	Ovenbird	Seiurus aurocapilla																							R	1756
A	Northern Waterthrush	Parkesia noveboracensis																							R	1757
	Sub total																									

NEW WORLD WARBLERS cont. TANAGERS

	Species	Scientific name	Life list	2020	Jan	Feb	Mar	Apr	May	Jun	Jul	Aug	Sep	Oct	Nov	Dec	A	B	C	D	E	F	BTO	RBBP	BBRC	EU No
A	Golden-winged Warbler	Vermivora chrysoptera																							R	1722
A	Black-and-white Warbler	Mniotilta varia																							R	1720
A	Tennessee Warbler	Leiothlypis peregrina																							R	1724
A	Common Yellowthroat	Geothlypis trichas																							R	1762
A	Hooded Warbler	Setophaga citrina																							R	1771
AE	American Redstart	Setophaga ruticilla																							R	1755
A	Cape May Warbler	Setophaga tigrina																							R	1749
AE	Northern Parula	Setophaga americana																							R	1732
AE	Magnolia Warbler	Setophaga magnolia																							R	1750
A	Bay-breasted Warbler	Setophaga castanea																							R	1754
A	Blackburnian Warbler	Setophaga fusca																							R	1747
A	Yellow Warbler	Setophaga aestiva																							R	1733
A	Chestnut-sided Warbler	Setophaga pensylvanica																							R	1734
AE	Blackpoll Warbler	Setophaga striata																							R	1753
A	Yellow-rumped Warbler	Setophaga coronata																							R	1751
A	Wilson's Warbler	Cardellina pusilla																							R	1772
A	Summer Tanager	Piranga rubra																							R	1786
A	Scarlet Tanager	Piranga olivacea																							R	1788
A	Rose-breasted Grosbeak	Pheucticus ludovicianus																							R	1887
AE	Indigo Bunting	Passerina cyanea																							R	1892
	Sub total																									

85

ADDITIONAL SPECIES

	Life list	2020	Jan	Feb	Mar	Apr	May	Jun	Jul	Aug	Sep	Oct	Nov	Dec	A	B	C	D	E	F	BTO	RBBP	BBRC	EU No
Sub total																								

BRITISH BUTTERFLY CHECKLIST

SPECIES	2020 list	Life list
Chequered Skipper		
Small Skipper		
Essex Skipper		
Lulworth Skipper		
Silver-spotted Skipper		
Large Skipper		
Dingy Skipper		
Grizzled Skipper		
Swallowtail		
Wood White		
Real's Wood White		
Clouded Yellow		
Brimstone		
Large White		
Small White		
Green-veined White		
Orange-tip		
Green Hairstreak		
Brown Hairstreak		
Purple Hairstreak		
White-letter Hairstreak		
Black Hairstreak		
Small Copper		
Small Blue		
Silver-studded Blue		
Brown Argus		
Northern Brown Argus		
Common Blue		
Chalkhill Blue		
Adonis Blue		
Holly Blue		
Duke of Burgundy		
White Admiral		
Purple Emperor		
Red Admiral		

SPECIES	2020 list	Life list
Painted Lady		
Small Tortoiseshell		
Peacock		
Comma		
Small Pearl-b'dered Fritillary		
Pearl-bordered Fritillary		
High Brown Fritillary		
Dark Green Fritillary		
Silver-washed Fritillary		
Marsh Fritillary		
Glanville Fritillary		
Heath Fritillary		
Speckled Wood		
Wall		
Mountain Ringlet		
Scotch Argus		
Marbled White		
Grayling		
Gatekeeper		
Meadow Brown		
Ringlet		
Small Heath		
Large Heath		
Additional Species		
TOTAL		

CHECKLISTS

BRITISH DRAGONFLY CHECKLIST

SPECIES	2020 list	Life list	SPECIES	2020 list	Life list
Banded Demoiselle			Northern Emerald		
Beautiful Demoiselle			Brilliant Emerald		
Small Red Damselfly			Common Club-tail		
Northern Damselfly			Scarlet Darter		
Irish Damselfly			White-faced Darter		
Southern Damselfly			Broad-bodied Chaser		
Azure Damselfly			Scarce Chaser		
Variable Damselfly			Four-spotted Chaser		
Dainty Damselfly			Black-tailed Skimmer		
Common Blue Damselfly			Black-tailed Skimmer		
Red-eyed Damselfly			Keeled Skimmer		
Small Red-eyed Damselfly			Wandering Glider		
Blue-tailed Damselfly			Black Darter		
Scarce Blue-tailed Damselfly			Yellow-winged Darter		
Large Red Damselfly			Red-veined Darter		
Southern Emerald Damselfly			Banded Darter		
Scarce Emerald Damselfly			Ruddy Darter		
Emerald Damselfly			Common Darter		
Willow Emerald Damselfly					
Winter Damselfly			**Additional Species**		
White-legged Damselfly					
Southern Migrant Hawker					
Azure Hawker					
Southern Hawker					
Brown Hawker					
Norfolk Hawker					
Common Hawker					
Migrant Hawker					
Vagrant Emperor					
Emperor Dragonfly					
Lesser Emperor					
Hairy Dragonfly					
Golden-ringed Dragonfly					
Downy Emerald					
Orange-spotted Emerald			**TOTAL**		

Neil Gartshore

There are a good selection of wetland sites close to the centre of London that attract many interesting birds, often including scarce, rare and unexpected species.

RESERVES DIRECTORY

NATURE RESERVES
& BIRD OBSERVATORIES
Map of the regions

Highlands & Islands

Eastern Scotland

Central Scotland

Scottish Borders

Northern England

1. Northern Wales
2. Eastern Wales
3. Southern Wales
4. Western Wales

Central England

Eastern England

South East England

South West England

INTRODUCTION

THE RESERVES ARE listed on a regional basis (see map opposite). The aim of this directory is to give a flavour of what each county has to offer & includes many of their 'flagship' reserves.

Each entry covers:

Site name & ownership/management organisation.

Habitats: To find the greatest number of birds you will need to visit a variety of habitats - the main ones are listed for each reserve.

Birds: A small selection of birds recorded on the reserves are highlighted along with the best time of year to see them i.e. *Summer, Winter, Passage*. Those listed tend to be the main attractions of the reserve but don't forget that there will be far more 'regular' species around.

Other: Being nature reserves they offer far more than just birds. Butterflies & dragonflies are well represented & are often fairly easy to see. Mammals can be a little more elusive but with a little patience (& for some species, with a little luck!) you may see them. Spectaclar displays of flowers depend on the time of year. Rarities of individual species, of all groups, will usually depend on some knowledge of them - joining a guided walk could be a good option.

Directions: A 'sat nav' post code & grid reference are given along with a short description of how to find the reserves - use these in conjunction with a road map (unless you are happy to put your faith in your sat nav!)

Public transport: Details are noted where it is reasonably practical to get to the reserve, otherwise it is listed as 'none'. You are strongly advised to check with the transport providers noted (or via *Traveline* - see below) before travelling as services & timetables can change.

Traveline is a partnership of transport companies, local authorities & passanger groups providing a platform either by phone or online to plan your journey.

T: 0871 200 22 33 (charge of 12p/minute applies, your phone company may also add a charge).

W: www.traveline.info

Visiting: This is a catch-all section which includes information about access/opening times of the reserve & its facilities (including car parking, visitor centres, cafes, toilets, hides, viewing screens, trails, disabled access & dogs).

Wheelchair/disabled access (& pushchairs) - it is advisable to contact the reserve directly if you have any special requirements or to check the available facilities.

Dogs *(with the exception of assistance dogs)* - in many cases they are not permitted on the reserve and/or in the visitor centre or out on the reserve they may have to be kept on a (short) lead or be under 'close control'. Any dog mess should be picked up & disposed of in the bins provided... or taken offsite. Do not leave dogs unattended in cars. It is the dog owners responsibility to comply with these requests.

Contact: For each reserve a (T) telephone number & (E) e-mail address are listed &, in a few cases, a (W) website address.

<><><><><>

Although the information has been checked, some changes (under all headings) are inevitable. It may be advisable to contact the reserve or check other sources, especially if you are planning to travel a distance to get there.

We welcome feedback on this section of *The Yearbook*, including any recomendations for reserves that could be included/replaced. Please send comments to the Editor (see page 6).

Central England

Derbyshire, Gloucestershire, Leicestershire & Rutland, Lincolnshire, Northamptonshire, Nottinghamshire, Oxfordshire, Shropshire, Staffordshire, Warwickshire & West Midlands, Worcestershire

Derbyshire

FOR ITS SIZE, the county has a wide range of habitats and includes the majority of the Peak District National Park within its borders where Redstart, Pied Flycatcher and Wood Warbler can be found. A variety of waterbodies in the southern half of the county, including Carsington Water, Ogston Reservoir & Willington Gravel Pits, hold a good selection of waterfowl during the winter as well as large gull roosts that are worth checking out.

1. CARR VALE NATURE RESERVE

Derbyshire Wildlife Trust.
Habitats: Lakes, wader flashes, reedbed, sewage farm, scrub, arable fields.
Birds: Up to 150 spp. annually, long list of rarities. *Spring/autumn:* Migrants inc. pipits & thrushes. In Sep, Swallows gather in the marsh in a large roost of 1,000-2,000 birds, which often attracts Hobby. *Early summer:* Breeding birds inc. Gadwall, Skylark, Reed & Sedge Warblers, Whitethroat & Yellowhammer. *Winter:* Large numbers of wildfowl (inc. flocks of Wigeon & Teal), Water Rail. Flocks of finches & buntings.
Other: Dragonflies, Brown Hare, Harvest Mouse, Water Shrew, Grass Snake.
Directions: Sat nav: S44 6GA. SK 459 702. 0.75 mile W of Bolsover on A632 to Chesterfield. Turn L at roundabout (follow brown tourist signs) into Riverside Way. Use the County Council's Peter Fidler car park off Riverside Way.
Public transport: Bus - nos.82, 82A & 83 serve roundabout on A632 & no.83 serves Villas Road - from Chesterfield (Stephenson Place). Stagecoach.
Visiting: Open all year. Car park, coach parking on approach road, good disabled access, paths, three viewing platforms, hides. Follow footpath (waymarked) around Peter Fidler reserve. Dogs only on leads.
Contact: Derbyshire WT, T: 01773 881 188; E: enquiries@derbyshirewt.co.uk

2. CARSINGTON WATER

Severn Trent Water.
Habitats: Open water, islands, small reedbed, mixed woodland, scrub, grassland.
Birds: 220+ spp. *All year:* Willow Tit & Tree Sparrow. *Spring:* Good passage inc. Yellow & White Wagtails, Whimbrel, Black & Arctic Terns. *Summer:* Warblers & breeding waders (inc. Little Ringed Plover). Ospreys often stop-off during migration. *Winter:* Wildfowl & a large gull roost, possibility of divers & scarce grebes.

Other: Species-rich hay meadows, ancient woodlands with Bluebells, three spp. orchid, five spp. bat, 21 spp. butterflies, Water Vole.
Directions: Sat nav: DE6 1ST. SK 241 515 (visitor centre). Off B5035 Ashbourne to Wirksworth road.
Public transport: Bus - nos.110/111 (not Sun), Matlock to Ashbourne. Yourbus (T: 01773 714 013).
Visiting: Open all year (not Dec 25). Three car parks, open 7am-sunset (Apr-Oct, 7.30am in winter). Parking at visitor centre (pay-&-display) with reduced rates at Millfields & Sheepwash car parks. Visitor centre (open 10am-6pm Apr-Sep, 10am-5pm Oct-Mar): has exhibition, restaurant, four shops (inc. RSPB), play area & toilets. Good access for wheelchairs (can be borrowed at visitor centre), mobility scooters for hire. Four bird hides. Cycle & boat hire.
Contact: Carsington Water Visitor Centre, T: 0330 6780 701; E: carsingtonwater@severntrent.co.uk; W: www.carsingtonbirdclub.co.uk

92

NATURE RESERVES - CENTRAL ENGLAND

3. FOREMARK RESERVOIR & CARVER'S ROCKS NR

Severn Trent Water/Derbyshire Wildlife Trust.
Habitats: FR - open water, coniferous woodland. CR - marsh, deciduous woodland, heathland.
Birds: *All Year:* Little & Great Crested Grebes, Woodcock, Barn, Little & Tawny Owls, Kingfisher. *Passage:* waders, terns, birds of prey. *Winter:* Wildfowl (inc. Goosander) & gulls with occasional scarcer spp., Siskin, Redpoll. Occasional rarities.
Other: 27 spp. butterflies & 300 spp. moths.
Directions: Sat nav: DE65 6EG. SK 336 242. Reservoir is five miles S of Derby, W of A514 at Ticknall (signed to reservoir/Milton), Carver's Rocks at S end of reservoir.
Public transport: None.
Visiting: Open all year (not 25 Dec), dawn-8pm (last admission 5pm). Pay-&-display car park (annual permit available), toilets (inc. disabled), some paths suitable for wheelchairs. Snack kiosk open fri-sun, bank hol mondays & weekdays during school holidays.
Contact: Severn Trent Water, T: 01332 865 081; E: staunton.foremark@severntrent.co.uk
Contact: Derbyshire Wildlife Trust (Carver's Rock) - see site 1.

4. GOYT VALLEY

Forestry Commission.
Habitats: River Goyt, two reservoirs, mixed conifer/broadleaf woodland, moorland.
Birds: *Spring/summer:* Breeding Wood Warbler, Pied & Spotted Flycatchers, Tree Pipit, Redstart, Cuckoo, Nightjar on restock areas & common woodland spp., Long-eared Owl & Goshawk also present. Dipper & Grey Wagtail on river, Common Sandpiper on Errwood Reservoir. Red Grouse, Curlew, Short-eared Owl, Whinchat & Ring Ouzel breed on moorland areas.
Directions: Sat nav: SK17 6SX (Errwood Hall car park, SK 011 748) for woodland birds, Derbyshire Bridge (SK 018 716) for moorland birds. From Buxton head N on A5004 (Manchester Road), then bear L on Goyt's Lane to Errwood Hall one-way system, between Errwood car park & Derbyshire Bridge.
Public transport: Train - Whaley Bridge & Buxton, both ca.3 miles from Errwood Reservoir.
Visiting: Open all year. Toilets at Derbyshire Bridge & Bonsal Cob. Several picnic sites. Footpath between Errwood Hall & Goyt's Clough Quarry. Use Old Coach Road for walk between Derbyshire Bridge & Burbage.
Contact: Forestry Commission, T: 0300 067 4340; E: central.district@forestryengland.uk

5. HILTON GRAVEL PITS

Derbyshire Wildlife Trust.
Habitats: Ponds, lakes, fen, scrub, woodland.
Birds: *All year:* Kingfisher, 3 spp. woodpecker, Willow Tit, Tawny Owl, Bullfinch. *Spring/summer:* Great Crested Grebe, Common Tern, warblers. *Winter:* Wildfowl, Siskin, Goldcrest.
Other: 14 spp. dragonflies inc. Emperor & Red-eyed Damselfly, Great Crested Newt, bats, Black Poplar, orchids.

Directions: Sat nav: DE65 5FW (Willowpit Lane). SK 253 313. From Derby, take A516 from Mickleover W past Etwall onto A50 junction at Hilton. Turn R at first island onto Willowpit Lane. Turn L next to a large white house & park next to gate. Follow track along S side of pools.
Public transport: Bus - no.V1 to Hilton, from Derby & Burton-on-Trent. Trent Barton Villager (T: 01773 712 265).
Visiting: Open all year. Tracks, boardwalks, viewing screens (main path/viewing screen suitable for wheelchairs - entrance gate fitted with RADAR lock). Dogs only on main perimeter track, keep on lead.
Contact: Derbyshire Wildlife Trust - see site 1.

6. OGSTON RESERVOIR

Severn Trent Water/Ogston Bird Club.
Habitats: Open water, pasture, mixed woodland.
Birds: *All year:* 3 spp. woodpecker, Little & Tawny Owls, Kingfisher, Grey Wagtail. *Summer:* warblers. *Passage:* raptors (inc. Osprey), terns & waders. *Winter:* Good numbers of wildfowl, tit & finch flocks. Gull roost attracts thousands of birds inc. regular Glaucous & Iceland Gulls. Top inland site for Bonaparte's Gull & also attracts birds from Caspian/Herring Gull complex.
Directions: Sat nav: DE55 6FL. SK 374 610. From Matlock, take A615 E to B6014, just after Tansley. From A61 (Alfreton to Chesterfield road), at White Bear pub, Stretton turn onto B6014 towards Tansley, cross railway, take L fork in road & continue over hill. Reservoir is on L after hill.
Public transport: Bus - no.63/63A (not Sun) Chesterfield to Matlock, both serve N end of reservoir. Hulleys (T: 01246 582 246).
Visiting: View from roads. Three car parks on N, S & W banks. Public hide (wheelchair access) reached from west bank car park (also suitable for smaller coaches). Heronry in nearby Ogston Carr Wood (private) viewable from Ogston new road, W of reservoir. Ogston BC organises monthly guided walks (see website for details) & members have access to three hides, (two wheelchair accessible) as well as club's own 1.5ha Jim Mart Nature Reserve, three miles N of Ogston.
Contact: Jenny Marshall Club Secretary, OBC), T: 07533 973 809; E: jen.marshall@birdinformation.co.uk; W: www.ogstonbirdclub.co.uk

7. PADLEY GORGE (LONGSHAW ESTATE)

National Trust (East Midlands).
Habitats: Steep-sided valley containing largest area of sessile oak woodland in south Pennines.
Birds: *Spring/summer:* Pied & Spotted Flycatchers, Ring Ouzel, Redstart, Wheatear, Whinchat, Stonechat, Wood Warbler, Tree Pipit & common woodland spp.
Directions: Longshaw visitor centre - Sat nav: S11 7TZ. SK 267 800. From Sheffield, head SW on A625. After eight miles, turn L on B6521 to Nether Padley. Grindleford Station is just off B6521 (NW of Nether Padley) & one mile NE of Grindleford village.

Public transport: Bus - no.275 (not Sun) Sheffield to Bakewell. Hulleys (T: 01246 582 246). Train - Sheffield to Manchester Piccadilly stops at Grindleford Station.
Visiting: All year, dawn-dusk. Car parks, pay-&-display for non-NT members. Cafe, shop & toilets (inc. disabled) at Longshaw visitor centre. RADAR key needed for Hollin Bank, Hathersage toilets. Some paths are rocky - not suitable for disabled access or those unused to steep climbs. Dogs on leads only.
Contact: National Trust, High Peak Estate Office.
T: 01433 631 757; E: peakdistrict@nationaltrust.org.uk

8. WILLINGTON GRAVEL PITS

Derbyshire Wildlife Trust.
Habitats: Open water, shingle island, reedbed, grassland.
Birds: *Summer:* Lapwing, Redshank, Oystercatcher, Common Tern, Cetti's, Reed & Sedge Warblers, raptors inc. Peregrine, Kestrel, Sparrowhawk & Hobby. *Passage:* up to 20 spp. waders in spring/autumn (large nos Curlew in spring). *Winter:* Large flocks of wildfowl (inc. Wigeon, Teal, Pochard & Shoveler), Bittern & waders.

Other: Short-leaved Water Starwort. Several spp. dragonflies, occasional signs of Otter.
Directions: Sat nav: DE65 6YB (Repton Road). SK 291 276. From A50 'Toyota Island' head towards Willington & Repton. Go through village towards Repton. Just before bridge over River Trent, turn R onto un-made track (Meadow Lane). Park here & walk along lane.
Public transport: Bus - no.V3 to Willington from Derby & Burton-on-Trent. Trent Barton Villager (T: 01773 712 265). Train - stops at Willington.
Visiting: Limited parking in lane. No access on site but viewing platforms situated along Meadow Lane (steps up to platforms).
Contact: Derbyshire WT - see site 1.

Gloucestershire

LYING BETWEEN THE River Severn & the Welsh border, the Forest of Dean/Wye Valley area is a good place to see Goshawk, Hawfinch, Wood Warbler & Pied Flycatcher, & the Symonds Yat Peregrine watchpoint at worth a visit. On the east bank of the river, the wetlands of Slimbridge are well-known for their wintering geese & Bewick's Swans. The sand & gravel extractions of the Cotswold Water Park (partially shared with Wiltshire) is one of the largest man-made wetland complexes in the UK, that attracts a wide selection of wintering waterfowl & passage waders.

Visiting: Open at all times. Car park, usually restricted to reserve events, can be opened for groups by arrangment (groups should book ahead). One nature trail (1.5 miles) - can be very muddy, some limited wheelchair access. One open-backed hide, 150 yards from car park. Dogs allowed on leads.
Contact: RSPB, T: 01594 562 852;
E: highnam.woods@rspb.org.uk

1. HIGHNAM WOODS

RSPB (South West England Office).
Habitats: Ancient woodland in Severn Vale with areas of coppice, scrub.
Birds: *All year:* Buzzard, Sparrowhawk, 3 spp. woodpecker, Marsh Tit, Raven. Hawfinch possible but elusive. *Spring/summer:* Up to 20 pairs of breeding Nightingale, Spotted Flycatcher & common migrant warblers. *Winter:* Feeding site near car park good for woodland birds.
Other: Tintern Spurge in Jun-Aug. White Admiral & White-letter Hairstreak butterflies.
Directions: Sat nav: GL2 8AA. SO 778 190. Signposted on A40, three miles W of Gloucester.
Public transport: Bus - nos.24 (Mon-Sun) & no.33 (Sun) Gloucester to Cinderford stops near Highnam Woods. Stagecoach.

NATURE RESERVES - CENTRAL ENGLAND

2. NAGSHEAD

RSPB (South West England Office).
Habitats: Much of reserve is 200-year-old oak plantations, grazed in some areas by sheep, with a mixture of open areas, conifer/mixed woodland.
Birds: *All year:* Buzzard, Goshawk, Woodcock, 3 spp. woodpecker, Raven, Hawfinch. *Spring/ Summer:* Pied Flycatcher, Wood Warbler & commoner warblers, Redstart, Tree Pipit. *Winter:* Mandarin, Siskin, Crossbill (some years), other finches.
Other: Golden-ringed Dragonfly seen annually. White Admiral, Silver-washed & Small Pearl-bordered Fritillary butterflies present. Wild Boar in the area.
Directions: Sat nav: GL15 4LA. SO 606 085. In Forest of Dean, N of Lydney. Signposted immediately W of Parkend village on B4431 road to Coleford.
Public transport: Bus - no.27 (not Sun) Lydney to Parkend. Stagecoach.
Visiting: Open at all times. Car park open dawn to dusk (coach/minibus access, advise in advance). Visitor centre (with toilets) open 10am-4pm at weekends from Easter to Sep. Two two circular waymarked nature trails (one mile & 2.25 miles) - trails hilly but there is limited wheelchair access. Two woodland hides not accessible to wheelchairs. Keep dogs on leads during bird nesting season.
Contact: RSPB, T: 01594 562 852;
E: nagshead@rspb.org.uk

3. SHORNCOTE REEDBED

Cotswold Water Park Trust.
Habitats: Lakes with reedbed, marsh, ditches, islands, loafing areas. [Part of CWP, covering 40 sq. miles/150 lakes, across Wilts, Gloucs & W Oxfordshire]
Birds: *Summer:* Breeding ducks, Little Grebe, warblers, Hobby, Snipe, Sand Martin, Reed Bunting. *Winter:* Common wildfowl, Bittern, Water Rail, Snipe, Peregrine, Merlin, Stonechat & Starling flocks.
Other: Otter, Water Vole, several spp. dragonflies.
Directions: Sat nav: GL7 5US (South Cerney car park). Lakes 84, 85A & 85B, Cotswold Water Park West. From A419 Cirencester to Swindon road, take B4696 towards Cotswold Water Park West. Turn R at crossroads (station Road) towards South Cerney. Follow road through village & park in playing fields car park after sharp R bend (SU 044 970). Take footpath through playing fields, cross road & continue on path through reedbeds to small lakes & hides.
Public transport: Buses - various routes from Kemble, Cheltenham, Cirencester & Swindon. Train - Kemble station four miles.
Visiting: Open at all times. Paths flood regularly in winter, wellies essential. Two hides. Toilets, refreshments, car parking/information available from nearby Cotswold Country Park (entry charge may apply). Alternative refreshments/toilets at Gateway Centre near A419 junction.
Contact: Cotswold Water Park Trust
T: 01793 752 413; W: www.waterpark.org

4. SLIMBRIDGE

The Wildfowl & Wetlands Trust.
Habitats: Reedbed, freshwater pools, wet grassland, saltmarsh, mudflats. Captive waterfowl ponds.
Birds: 200+ spp. annually, good list of rarities. *Breeding:* Lapwing, Oystercatcher, Redshank, Little Ringed Plover, Common Tern, Kingfisher, Reed Bunting & a good range of warblers. *Passage:* Waders, terns & gulls (inc. Mediterranean & Yellow-legged). Yellow Wagtail & large passerine movements. *Winter:* 30,000 to 40,000 wildfowl esp. Bewick's Swan, White-fronted Goose, Wigeon, Teal, Pintail. Waders inc. Lapwing, Golden Plover, Spotted Redshank & Little Stint. Often large roosts of Starlings & gulls.
Other: Brown Hare, Otter, Polecat & Water Vole. 22 spp. dragonflies inc. Scarce Chaser & Hairy Dragonfly.
Directions: Sat nav: GL2 7BT. SO 723 048. On banks of River Severn, S of Gloucester. Signposted from M5 (exit Junc 13 or 14). Into Slimbridge from A38.
Public transport: Local buses stop on A38. Train - stations at Cam & Dursley (4 miles).
Visiting: Open daily (not Dec 25) at 9.30am, closes 5.30pm (5pm in winter), last entry one hour before closing. Large car park with toilets. Admission charges for non-WWT members. Restaurant, shop, toilets, gallery, cinema, discovery centre. Outdoor facilities inc. a wildfowl collection of spp. from around world, an observatory & observation tower, 13 hides. Plenty of family attractions inc. a pond zone, wader aviary, commentated swan feeds in winter, Land Rover safaris & a canoe safari trail. All paths wheelchair accessible (wheelchair hire available, book in advance). Binoculars for hire. Assistance dogs only.
Contact: The Wildfowl & Wetlands Trust,
T: 01453 891 900; E: info.slimbridge@wwt.org.uk

5. SYMONDS YAT

RSPB/Forestry Commission England.
Habitats: Cliff above the River Wye, woodland.
Birds: *Summer:* Peregrine, Buzzard, Goshawk, Sparrowhawk, Raven & woodland spp., (telescope is set up to watch nesting Peregrines).
Directions: Sat nav: HR9 6JL. SO 564 160. Hill-top site on edge of Forest of Dean, three miles N of Coleford on B4432, signposted from Coleford (brown tourist sign).
Public transport: Bus - from Coleford stops on B3342 inc. Symonds Yat car park.
Visiting: Open at all times. RSPB volunteers usually on site daily, late-Mar to early-Sep (10am-4pm). Car park (fee payable), toilets with adapted facilities for disabled visitors, picnic area, drinks & light snacks available.
Contact: RSPB, T: 01392 432 691;
E: swdatewithnature@rspb.org.uk

6. WHELFORD POOLS

Gloucestershire Wildlife Trust.
Habitats: Former gravel pit workings - two large lakes, three smaller dragonfly pools.
Birds: *Spring/summer:* Common Tern, Kingfisher, Nightingale, plus breeding Great Crested Grebe, Sedge Warbler & Reed Bunting. Artificial nesting bank for Sand Martins. *Passage:* waders. *Winter:* Wildfowl inc. Wigeon, Pochard & Tufted Ducks, occasional Bittern sightings.
Other: County's only site for Pea Mussel. Emperor, Migrant Hawker, Black-tailed Skimmer & Red-eyed Damselfly all breed.
Directions: Sat nav: GL7 4DY. SU 172 995. Lakes lie in eastern section of Cotswold Water Park between Fairford & Lechlade, from minor road S of A417.
Public transport: Cycle path from Lechlade.
Visiting: Open at all times. Car park for 12 vehicles (one disabled bay). Two bird hides. Dogs must be on leads.
Contact: Gloucestershire WT, T: 01452 383 333; E: info@gloucestershirewildlifetrust.co.uk

7. WOORGREENS

Gloucestershire Wildlife Trust.
Habitats: Former open-cast mine workings - marsh, lake and heath.
Birds: *Spring/summer:* Breeding Little Grebe, Tufted Duck, Cuckoo, possible Hobby, common woodland spp., Crossbill. *Winter:* Wildfowl (inc. Goosander, Mandarin), Snipe, Jack Snipe.
Other: Good selection of dragonflies & damselflies, Great Crested Newt, common reptile spp.
Directions: Sat nav: GL16 7EH (Speech House Woodlands car park), SO 630 127. Lake/car park lies on the B4226 between.
Public transport: Bus - no.30 Gloucester/Cinderford to Coleford, Stagecoach West (T: 01452 418 630).
Visiting: Open at all times. No car park, use Speech House Woodland car park, room for 15 vehicles. Dogs must under control.
Contact: Gloucestershire WT, T: 01452 383 333; E: info@gloucestershirewildlifetrust.co.uk

Leicestershire & Rutland

THESE ADJOINING COUNTIES are well served with reservoirs, including Swithland, Eyebrooke & Cropston - all attract wintering wildfowl & regular spring Black Tern passage. The jewel in the crown though is Rutland Water, home of the Bird Fair. Huge numbers of wildfowl & a good selection of passage waders can be found here while breeding Ospreys are the result of a successful re-introduction programme. The Wildlife Trust manages 35 nature reserves covering a broad range of habitats spread across the counties.

Visiting: There is no access to the private grounds but visiting by organised groups may be possible (contact first), otherwise view from road/roadside lay-bys. Fishing season Mar to Nov.
Contact: Eyebrook Trout Fishery,
T: 01536 770 264;
E: lodge@flyfisheyebrook.co.uk;
W: www.flyfisheyebrook.co.uk

1. EYEBROOK RESERVOIR

Corby & District Water Co.
Habitats: Open water, plantations, pasture.
Birds: *Summer:* Good populations of breeding birds with sightings of Ospreys & Red Kite regular. *Passage:* waders & Black Tern. *Winter:* Wildfowl (inc. Goldeneye, Goosander, Smew), waders & gulls (often inc. less common spp.). Tree Sparrow & Yellowhammer at a LROS feeding station (SP 848 950) also Barn & Short-eared Owls may be seen hunting at dusk near Great Easton village (close to recycling centre). A good selection of rarities have turned up.
Other: Otter, Muntjac Deer, Red Darter & Blue Damselfly, Scalloped Hazel & Riband Wave moths.
Directions: Sat nav: LE15 9JG. SP 852 963. Reservoir built 1940. S of Uppingham, from unclassified road W of A6003 to Stoke Dry.
Public transport: None.

NATURE RESERVES - CENTRAL ENGLAND

2. HICKS LODGE

Forestry Commission.
Habitats: New native woodland, rough grassland, seasonally-grazed open fields, lakes & ponds. Largest lake has two small islands, one managed for Little Ringed Plover, other ground-nesting spp.
Birds: Raptors inc. Buzzard, Red Kite, Kestrel, Hobby, Sparrowhawk & Peregrine. Common wildfowl in winter, plus a good range of finches (inc. Crossbill), buntings, tits & summer warblers. Wader records inc. Bar-tailed Godwit, Greenshank, Ringed & Little Ringed Plovers, Common Sandpiper, Oystercatcher, Temminck's Stint, Lapwing & Golden Plover. *Passage:* migrants inc. Black Tern, Cuckoo, Wheatear, Whinchat, Stonechat, Spotted Flycatcher & hirundines.
Directions: Sat nav: LE65 2UP. SK 329 155. Within National Forest, approx 0.5 miles from Moira village. Follow brown tourist signs for National Forest Cycle Centre from Moira, Ashby-de-la-Zouch & from junc 12 of A42.
Public transport: None.
Visiting: Open all year: 8am-8pm. Height barrier at main entrance is removed when open, so no vehicle restrictions. Pay-&-display car park with designated disabled bays (5). On-site forest centre with small cafe (open 9am-5pm), toilets (inc. disabled & baby-changing facilities) & bike hire. All-ability trails & cycle trails. Most birdwatching activity occurs in front of main centre, around Hicks Lodge Loop & on the ponds/lakes & open fields. Hide, Sand Martin wall.
Contact: Forestry Commission, T: 0300 067 4340; E: info_nationalforest@forestry.gsi.gov.uk

3. NARBOROUGH BOG

Leicestershire & Rutland Wildlife Trust.
Habitats: Peat bog (only substantial deposit in county), wet woodland, reedbed, dense scrub, fen meadow.
Birds: 130+ spp., inc. 3 spp. woodpecker, six spp. tit, Tawny Owl, Sparrowhawk & Kingfisher.
Other: Butterflies inc. Common Blue, Meadow Brown, Large & Small Skippers, Small Heath, Gatekeeper. Banded Demoiselle, good for moths & beetles. Harvest Mouse, Water Vole, breeding Grass Snake. Meadow Saxifrage, Common Meadow-rue, Marsh Thistle.
Directions: Sat nav: LE19 2AZ. SP 547 978. Between River Soar & M1, 5 miles S of Leicester. From city, turn L off B4114 (Leicester Road) just before going under motorway, follow track to sports club. Park near club house & walk across recreation ground to reserve entrance.
Public transport: Bus - no.X84 (not Sun) Leicester to Narborough(Abbey Rd stop), then short walk. Arriva in Midlands. Train - Narborough.
Visiting: Open at all times, keep to paths (not suitable for wheelchairs). May flood after heavy rain. Dogs on short leads only. Small bus/coach could park in sports field car park.
Contact: Leics & Rutland WT HQ, T: 0116 262 9968; E: info@lrwt.org.uk

4. RUTLAND WATER

Anglian Water/Leics & Rutland Wildlife Trust.
Habitats: Ramsar-designated reservoir, lagoons, scrapes, reedbeds, woods, meadows, plantations.
Birds: *Spring/autumn:* Outstanding wader passage, up to 28 spp. Wide range of raptors, owls, passerine flocks, terns (Black, Arctic, breeding Common, occasional Little & Sandwich). *Summer:* Ospreys among 70 breeding spp. *Winter:* Up to 28 spp. wildfowl (inc. internationally important numbers of Gadwall & Shoveler). Goldeneye, Smew, Goosander, rare grebes, Great Northern, Black & Red-throated Divers, Ruff.
Other: Otter, Badger, Fox, Weasel, stoat. Up to 20 spp. dragonflies & 24 spp. butterflies.
Directions: Two nature reserves on site.
1: Egleton Reserve (Sat nav: LE15 8BT). SK 878 075, from Egleton village off A6003 or A606 S of Oakham. Hosts British Birdwatching Fair in Aug.
2: Lyndon Reserve (Sat Nav: LE15 8RN). SK 894 058, south shore E of Manton village off A6003 S of Oakham. Follow 'nature reserve' signs to car park.
Public transport: Train - Oakham ca.two miles.
Visiting: Day permits available. Reduced admission for disabled visitors & carers.
1: The Anglian Water Bird Watching Centre - open daily (not Dec 25/26), 9am-5pm, (4pm, Nov-Jan). The centre has toilets & disabled access, mobility scooter for hire. good network of paths. 28 hides (disabled access possible to 12 of them). Badger-watching hide, book through centre. No dogs.
2: Centre open daily 9am-5pm, mid-Mar to mid-Sep - car park open to 8pm. Interpretation centre, toilets (inc. disabled), paths, use of a mobility scooter. Seven hides, four accessible to wheelchairs. Dogs on short lead only.
Contact:
1: Egleton, T: 01572 770 651;
E: julia@rutlandwater.org.uk;
2: Lyndon, T: 01572 737 378;
E: ospreys@rutlandwater.org.uk
W: www.rutlandwater.org.uk / www.ospreys.org.uk

5. SENCE VALLEY FOREST PARK

Forestry Commission.
Habitats: New forest (native broadleaf, mixed & pine), rough grassland, wildflower meadow, pools, wader scrape, River Sence.
Birds: *Spring/summer:* Artificial Sand Martin nesting wall, Wheatear, Whinchat, Redstart, Common & Green Sandpipers, Ringed & Little Ringed Plovers, Redshank. Dunlin & Greenshank frequent, possible Wood Sandpiper. Skylark, Meadow Pipit, Yellow Wagtail, Linnet, Reed Bunting. Possible Quail. Kestrel & Barn Owl seen occasionally. *Winter:* Goosander & Wigeon, Short-eared Owl, Stonechat, Redpoll.
Directions: Sat nav: LE67 6NW. SK 404 113. Within The National Forest. 10 miles NW of Leicester & two miles SW of Coalville, between Ibstock & Ravenstone. Car park is signposted from A447, northern edge of Ibstock.
Public transport: Bus - no.15 (not Sun) Coalville to Ibstock. Arriva in Midlands.

Visiting: Open all year, - pedestrians at all times. Two car parks (height barrier at main entrance) 8am-7pm (Apr-Sep), 9am-4pm (Oct-Mar), toilets (inc. disabled & baby-changing facilities), hide & viewing screen, all-abilities trails/suitable for wheelchairs. Notice required for coach or minibus visits.
Contact: Forestry Commission - see site 2.

6. SWITHLAND RESERVOIR

Severn Trent Water.
Habitats: Large reservoir divided by Great Central Railway line, small area of woodland (Buddon Wood).
Birds: Common wildfowl are regular & has produced seaduck (inc. Common Scoter, Scaup & Long-tailed Duck) & occasional divers. Black-necked Grebe seen in late summer/autumn, Mediterranean Gull is annual, BLack Tern on Spring passage. High water levels curb wader sightings but Kingfishers are regular & Ravens usually seen daily. 3 spp. woodpecker are in Buddon Wood, along with a range of woodland spp. County's best site for wintering Peregrine, also Buzzard, Sparrowhawk & Hobby (summer). Good track record of rarities in recent years.
Other: Buddon Wood along Kinchley Lane is good for Purple Hairstreak butterfly & Orange Underwing moth – look for the latter around Silver Birch.
Directions: Sat nav: LE7 7SE. SK 561 131. Lies S of Quorn, E of A6 (Leicester to Loughborough road). Use minor road between Swithland & Rothley for southern section. For northern section take Kinchley Lane along eastern shore to the dam.
Public transport: None.
Visiting: View from roads.

7. WATERMEAD COUNTRY PARK

Leicestershire County Council.
Habitats: River Soar & Grand Union Canal, 12 lakes & pools, reedbeds (one of largest in Midlands), wildflower meadow, woodland. Park stretches for nearly two miles. Wanlip Meadows can be viewed from Plover Hide.
Birds: 200 spp., inc. common wildfowl, Little Egret, Kingfisher, Water Rail, Cetti's Warbler. *Passage:* Garganey & Black Tern. Wanlip Meadows very good for waders, inc. Little Ringed Plover & is county's best site for Temminck's Stint. *Winter:* Bittern, Caspian Gull, Yellow-legged Gull, thrushes.
Other: Otters regular, but elusive. Emperor & other dragonfly spp.
Directions: LE7 1AD. SK 608 113. Located off Wanlip Road, Syston (off A46 or A607), six miles N of Leicester city centre. Watermead CP (South) is managed by Leicester City Council.
Public transport: Bus - nos.5/5A/6 from Leicester to Syston/East Goscote/Melton, regular daily. Get off at Alderton Close for south or walk from Syston for north. Arriva. Train - one mile from Syston.
Visiting: Open all year, 7am-dusk. Wanlip Road gives access to four car parks (fees payable), southern entrance in Alderton Close, Thurmaston. Wheelchair access on five miles of surfaced tracks. RADAR key needed by mobility scooter riders to negotiate kissing gates on perimeter track. Toilets, inc. disabled. Four bird hides (in nature reserve), Sand Martin nesting wall.
Contact: T: 0116 305 5000; E: countryparks@leics.gov.uk; W: www.leicscountryparks.org.uk

Lincolnshire

THIS LARGE RURAL county is relatively sparsely populated and lies between the Humber to the north & the Wash to the south-east. There are many coastal sites between the two, such as Tetney Marshes, Frieston Shore & Gibraltar Point, which attract migrants & wintering wildfowl & waders. Agricultural land dominates the interior, but there are a number of reservoirs & gravel pits here which can produce interesting birds.

1. ALKBOROUGH FLATS

North Lincolnshire Council.
Habitats: 450ha managed realignment created by breaching river defences to protect homes from flooding. Inter-tidal mudflats, reedbeds, grasslands, arable land.
Birds: 200 spp. Lying on a key migration route, geese & ducks are attracted in large numbers. Long-billed Dowitcher, Lesser Yellowlegs & Marsh Sandpiper brought site's wader total to 40 spp. *Spring/autumn:* passage waders (Avocets in autumn). *Summer:* Marsh Harriers have attempted to breed, Little Egret, Bearded Tit, Reed Warbler, Water Rail. Spoonbills are regular.

Winter: Huge flocks of Lapwings (10,000 regularly) & Golden Plover (up to 14,000 but 5,000-10,000 regular), plus Marsh & Hen Harriers, Peregrine, Merlin, Teal, Wigeon, Black-tailed Godwit. Large flock of Barnacle Geese can be seen at nearby Whitton Sands.
Other: Roe deer, Badger, Brown Hare, Water Vole, Otter, Fox. Wall Brown among butterflies & Black-tailed Skimmer among dragonflies.
Directions: Sat nav: DN15 9JN. SE 887 224, main car park. Located on S bank of Humber where Rivers Trent & Ouse meet to form the Humber. Follow brown tourist signs to Alkborough Flats from A1077 near Winterton. Reach two car parks by following the duck signs through Alkborough village. Car park at bottom of Prospect Lane is mainly for disabled visitors. Main car park off Whitton Road, just N of Alkborough village. Site also accessible via a permissive footpath from Julian's Bower, Back Street, Alkborough.
Public transport: Bus - no.60 (not Sun) Scunthorpe to Alkborough. Stagecoach.
Visiting: Open at all times. Five miles of public footpaths (two miles wheelchair-friendly), three hides, with wheelchair access.
Contact: Site Manager, T: 01724 721 269.

2. COVENHAM RESERVOIR

Anglian Water.
Habitats: 81ha concrete-sided reservoir, raised above surrounding low-lying farmland, small areas of trees.
Birds: *All Year:* Barn Owl. *Spring/Summer:* Yellow Wagtail, Wheatear, Ring Ouzel, Black Redstart possible on passage/Cuckoo, Tree Sparrow breeding but summer birds fairly limited. *Autumn:* Waders, inc. Common Sandpiper, Ruff, Curlew Sandpiper & Little Stint, more unusual waders may inc. Red-necked & Grey Phalaropes & Purple Sandpiper. Also Black-necked Grebe, Black Tern & Little Gull. *Winter:* Good variety of waterfowl inc. Goldeneye, Pochard, Pintail & regular Smew, Comon Scoter & Long-tailed Duck plus divers, grebes (inc. red-necked), gulls & occasional geese. Short-eared Owl, finch flock with occasional Brambling & Tree Sparrow. Has attracted regular rarities inc. Red-breasted Goose, American Wigeon, Ring-necked Duck & White-winged Tern.
Directions: Sat nav: LN11 0XX. TF 340 962. Five miles N of Louth. Take minor road (Pear Tree Lane) off A16 just S of Ludborough. Continue for two miles to junction - go over junction (into Bull Bank) for a further 0.5 mile to car park on R.
Public transport: None.
Visiting: Open at all times. Top of reservoir bank reached by steps from car park. Path around the top of reservoir bank.
Contact: none.

3. DONNA NOOK

Lincolnshire Wildlife Trust.
Habitats: Dunes, slacks & intertidal areas, seashore, mudflats, sandflats.
Birds: *Summer:* Little Tern, Ringed Plover, Oystercatcher. *Winter:* Brent Goose, Shelduck, Twite, Lapland Bunting, Shorelark, Linnet.
Other: One of largest & most accessible breeding colonies of Grey Seals in UK (viewing area/main car park open Oct-Dec, dawn-dusk). Badger, Stoat & Weasel, 3 spp. shrew have been identified. Common Lizard.
Directions: Sat nav: LN11 7PB. TF 422 998 (Stonebridge). Several access points off main A1031 coastal road with parking facilities at Stonebridge, Howden's Pullover (TF 449 952), Sea Lane, Saltfleet (TF 456 944) & Saltfleet Haven (TF 466 935).
Public transport: None.
Visiting: Donna Nook beach is closed on weekdays as this is an active bombing range, but dunes remain open. Some disabled access from Stonebridge car park. No dogs on viewing area.
Contact: Lincolnshire WT, T: 01507 526 667;
E: info@lincstrust.co.uk

4. EPWORTH TURBARY

Lincolnshire Wildlife Trust.
Habitats: One of few relics of raised bog in county, areas of active sphagnum bog still exist. Reed swamp & mixed fen vegetation, considerable area of birch woodland of mixed ages.
Birds: *Spring/summer:* Breeding birds inc. Woodcock, Green & Great Spotted Woodpeckers, Tree Pipit, warblers & finches. Greenshank, Green Sandpiper & Little Grebe are attracted to the wet area. Around Steve's Pond, occasional Hobby & Marsh Harrier, plus Teal, Little Grebe, Tree Pipit, Sparrowhawk & Buzzard. Willow Tit, Long-tailed Tit, Reed Bunting & Willow Warbler in the woodland areas. Occasionally Corn Buntings on the adjacent farmland. *Autumn/winter:* Large corvid flocks roost in reserve. At Pantry's Pond (winter) occasional Hen Harrier & sometimes (winter) Long-eared Owls can be observed roosting close to the path. Other birds inc. Yellowhammer, Linnet & Jay.
Other: 11 spp. breeding dragonflies. Wood Tiger Moth is well established. Plants inc. Sneezewort, Yellow & Purple Loosestrife, Meadow-rue, & Devil's-bit Scabious.
Directions: Sat nav: DN9 1EA. SE 758 036. SW of Scunthorpe. Take A18 W from Scunthorpe then A161 S to Epworth. Turn R on High Street & head towards Wroot. Entrance is near bridge over Skyer's Drain. Park inside or on verge adjoining reserve, well away from corner.
Public transport: None.
Visiting: Open at all times. Car park, two hides, way-marked trail - keep to trail paths & use hides to avoid disturbing birds on ponds.
Contact: Lincolnshire WT - see site 3.

5. FRAMPTON MARSH

RSPB (Eastern England Office).
Habitats: Saltmarsh, wet grassland, freshwater scrapes, developing reedbed.
Birds: *Summer:* Breeding Redshank, Avocet, Lapwing, Skylark, Little Ringed Plover, Ringed Plover, Sand Martin & several spp. of ducks. *Passage:* waders (inc. Greenshank, Curlew Sandpiper, Wood Sandpiper, Little & Temminck's Stints, Ruff & Black-tailed Godwit), Marsh Harrier & Hobby. *Winter:* Wildfowl (inc. Whooper Swan, dark-bellied Brent Goose & Wigeon), Hen Harrier, Short-eared Owl, Merlin, Lapwing & Golden Plover, Kingfisher, Lapland Bunting, Twite.
Other: Water Vole, Brown Hare, Stoat. Dragonflies inc. Emperor, hawkers, chasers & darters. Common butterflies inc. Wall Brown, Painted Lady & Speckled Wood. Scarce Pug, Star Wort & Crescent Striped moths on saltmarsh. Important brackish water flora & fauna inc. nationally scarce Spiral Tassleweed & several rare beetles.
Directions: Sat nav: PE20 1AY. TF 356 392. Four miles SE of Boston. From A16 follow signs to Frampton then Frampton Marsh.
Public transport: None.
Visiting: Reserve open at all times. Visitor centre, inc. toilets, open daily Nov-Feb (not Dec 25) 9.30am-4pm & Mar-Oct 9.30am-4pm weekdays/5pm weekends & bank holidays. Hot drinks & snacks available, binocular hire, plenty of information leaflets & events programmes. 60-space car park (three for disabled visitors), bicycle rack, benches, viewpoints. Footpaths & three hides open at all times, all suitable for wheelchairs.
Contact: RSPB, T: 01205 724 678;
E: lincolnshirewashreserves@rspb.org.uk

6. GIBRALTAR POINT NNR & BIRD OBSERVATORY

Lincolnshire Wildlife Trust.
Habitats: Sand dune grassland & scrub, saltmarsh & mudflats, freshwater marsh, lagoons.
Birds: Large scale visible migration during spring & autumn passage. Internationally important populations of non-breeding waders between Jul & Mar (peak Sep/Oct). Winter flocks of Brent Geese, Shelduck & Wigeon on flats & marshes with Hen Harrier, Merlin & Short-eared Owl often present. Red-throated Divers offshore (peak Feb). Colonies of Little Tern & Ringed Plover in summer. 100+ spp. can be seen in a day during May & Sep. Can be a good passage of autumn seabirds during northerly winds.
Other: Grey & Common Seal colonies, with Harbour Porpoises offshore most months. Patches of Pyramidal Orchids. Butterflies inc. Brown Argus & Green Hairstreak.
Directions: Sat nav: PE24 4SU. TF 556 580. Three miles S of Skegness, signposted from town centre.
Public transport: Train - Skegness (3.5 miles). Cycle route from Skegness.

Visiting: Open dawn-dusk all year. Charges for parking, car park closed at dusk. Free admission to reserve. Some access restrictions to sensitive sites at S end. Visitor centre & cafe open 10am-3pm (Nov-Mar) 10am-4pm (Apr-Oct), may stay open later during busy periods), toilets. shop. Public hides overlook freshwater & brackish lagoons. Wash viewpoint overlooks saltmarsh & mudflats. Four hides suitable for wheelchairs, as well as surfaced paths. Dogs on leads at all times - not permitted on beach from Apr 1st to Sep 1st. Access for coaches. Day visit groups must be booked in advance.

The Wash Study Centre Field centre is an ideal base for birdwatching/natural history groups in spring, summer & autumn. Contact Wash Study Centre for residential or day visits. T: 01754 762 763; E:gibeducation@lincstrust.co.uk

Gibraltar Point Bird Observatory.
Kev Wilson, T: 01754 898 079
E: kwilson@lincstrust.co.uk
W: http://gibraltarpointbirdobservatory.blogspot.com

Contact: Reserve & wildlife:
T: 01754 898 057; E: gibnnr@lincstrust.co.uk;
Vistor Centre: T: 01754 898 057;
E: gibvc@lincstrust.co.uk

7. WHISBY NATURE PARK

Lincolnshire Wildlife Trust.
Habitats: Flooded gravel pits with reed fringes, grassy glades, willow scrub, woodland.
Birds: *Summer:* Great Crested Grebe, Kingfisher, Sand Martin, Nightingale, Reed & Sedge Warblers. *Passage:* waders, occassional scarcer migrants. *Winter:* Wildfowl (inc. Goosander & Goldeneye), occassional Bittern, Jack Snipe & Water Rail. Grey Wagtail, Starling murmurations, finches. There is a gull roost on the adjacent Apex Pit (to east of A46) - part of the North Hykeham Pits complex - best to park at Crow Park (SK 922 660) reached off Newark Road.
Other: 500+ spp. plants.
Directions: Sat nav: LN6 9BW. SK 911 661. SW of Lincoln, to W of A46 (well signposted from A46 bypass).
Public transport: Bus - no.48 Lincoln to Witham St Hughs, alight at Thorpe on the Hill, short walk to Park. PC Executive Coaches (T: 01522 533 605).
Visiting: Open at all times, car park (charge, closed at dusk), bike racks. Nature World Visitor Centre (inc. toilets, shop, cafe) open daily Apr-Sep 9.30am-5pm, Oct-Mar 9.30am-4.30pm). Footpaths (six waymarked circular trails, several suitable for wheelchairs), seven hides. Dogs on lead.
Contact: Lincolnshire WT.
Reserve: T: 01522 500 676;
E: whisbynp@lincstrust.co.uk
Centre: T: 01522 688 868;
E: naturalworld@lincsinspire.com

Northamptonshire

MUCH OF THE BIRDING interest is found around the county's reservoirs & old mineral workings. Thrapston & Ditchford gravel pits & Stanwick Lakes Country Park in the Nene Valley, Pitsford Water & Hollowell reservoirs are good for a range of wildfowl, especially in winter. Red Kites were re-introduced near Corby &, along with Buzzards, are spreading.

1. NENE WETLANDS NATURE RESERVE

Beds, Cambs & Northants Wildlife Trust.
Habitats: Part of upper Nene valley floodplain, complex of old gravel pits, rough grassland, lakes, reed, scattered scrub, woodland. Joins up individual sites inc. Irthlingborough Lakes & Meadows, Ditchford Lakes & Meadows, Higham Ferrers Pits.
Birds: Great Crested & Little Grebes, Grey Heron, Redshank, Oystercatcher, Snipe. *Summer:* Common Tern, Cuckoo, Nightingale, Reed, Sedge & Cetti's Warblers, Swift, House Martin. *Autumn: Winter:* Wildfowl (inc. Curlew, Teal, Wigeon, Gadwall, Tufted Duck), Common Sandpiper.
Other: Hairy Dragonfly, Grass Snake, Otter. Plants inc. Marsh Woundwort, Dropwort, Great Burnet.
Directions: Sat nav: NN10 6FA. SP 938 679 (Visitor Centre). From Northampton, take A45 towards Rushden & Higham Ferrers. Take exit to Rushden Lakes Retail Park.
Public transport: Bus - nos.45, 49, 50, X46/47 from various towns inc. Northampton, Wellingborough, Kettering, Bedford to Retail Park. Stagecoach.
Visiting: Car parking at the Rushten Lakes retail park (five hrs max.). Visitor centre open daily (not Dec 25) 10am-5pm - toilets, cafe, shop. Reserve map available showing access points, inc. disabled routes. Dogs on leads.
Contact: BCN WT, T: 01933 779 587;
E: nenewetlands@wildlifebcn.org.uk

2. PITSFORD WATER

Anglian Water/Beds, Cambs & Northants Wildlife Trust.
Habitats: Open water (120 ha), marginal vegetation & reed grasses, wet woodland, grassland, mixed woodland.
Birds: Typically 165-170 spp. annually with a total list of over 250 spp. *Summer:* Breeding warblers, terns, grebes, herons. *Autumn:* Waders if water levels suitable. *Winter:* Up to 10,000 wildfowl, feeding station with Tree Sparrow & occasional Corn Bunting.
Other: 32 spp. butterflies, 392 spp. macro moths, 21 spp. dragonflies, 377 spp. flora, 404 spp. fungi, 105 spp. bryophytes. Badger, Harvest Mouse, Brown Hare.
Directions: Sat nav: NN6 9SJ. SP 787 699. Five miles N of Northampton. From A43 take turn to Holcot & Brixworth. From A508 take turn to Brixworth & Holcot.
Public transport: None.
Visiting: Reserve (N of causeway) open all year to permit holders. Wildlife Trust members can apply for free permit from HQ. Non-members can obtain day permits from fishing lodge, open mid-Mar to mid-Nov from 8am-dusk. Winter opening times variable, check in advance. No dogs. Disabled access from Lodge to first hide. Toilets available in Lodge, 15 miles of paths, eight hides & car parking.
Contact: BCN WT, T: 01604 405 285;
E:northamptonshire@wildlifebcnp.org. .
Pitsford Water Fishing Lodge, Brixworth Road, Holcot, Northampton, NN6 9SJ. T: 01604 781 350;
E: fishing@anglianwater.co.uk

3. STANWICK LAKES

Rockingham Forest Trust.
Habitats: 300ha, countryside park includes a Ramsar-designated wetland on site of former quarry, part of Nene Valley Special Protection Area, inc. reedbeds, hedgerows, grazed areas.
Birds: *All year:* Little Egret, Kingfisher, Green & Great Spotted Woodpeckers, Grey Wagtail, Cetti's Warbler & Barn Owl. *Spring/summer:* Waders inc. Oystercatcher (breeding), Little Ringed Plover, Greenshank & Green Sandpiper. Hobby, Yellow Wagtail, hirundines & migrant warblers. *Autumn/ winter:* Wildfowl inc. Pintail, Goldeneye & Goosander. Bittern, Redpoll & Siskin.
Other: Otter, Grass Snake, 150 spp. moths, dragonflies.
Directions: Sat nav: NN9 6GY. SP 967 715. Entrance off the A45, eight miles N of Wellingborough.
Public transport: None.
Visiting: Open daily (not Dec 25) 7am to 7pm (Mar & Oct), 8pm (Apr-Sep); 5pm (Nov-Feb). Visitor centre open daily (not 25/26 Dec) 10am-5pm (Mar-Oct), 10am-4pm weekdays/5pm weekends & school holidays (Nov-Feb). Charges for car & coach parking. All paths, visitor centre, gift shop, toilets & bird hide are wheelchair accessible. Disability scooter hire available.
Contact: Rockingham Forest Trust, T: 01933 625 522;
E: info@rftrust.org.uk

4. SUMMER LEYS LNR

Beds, Cambs & Northants Wildlife Trust.
Habitats: Habitats: Scrape, two ponds, lake, scrub, flood meadows, hedgerows.
Birds: *All year:* Tree Sparrow. *Spring/summer:* Common Tern, Black-headed Gull, Ringed & Little Ringed Plover, Redshank & Oystercatcher all breed. *Passage:* Whimbrel, Turnstone, Common Sandpiper. *Winter:* Large numbers of common wildfowl (inc. Goosander), Lapwing, Golden Plover & Ruff.
Other: 16 spp. dragonflies, inc. Hairy Dragonfly (check Marigold Pond). Common Blue & Brown Argus butterflies on grassland. Harvest Mouse, occassional Otter.
Directions: Sat nav: NN29 7TD. SP 886 634. Off Hardwater Road, Great Doddington, three miles from Wellingborough, accessible from A45 & A509.
Public transport: Bus - no.X47 Northampton to Great Doddington, about one mile away. Stagecoach. Train - Wellingborough.
Visiting: Open at all times, no permits required. Car park (open 5am-7.30pm Mar-Oct, 5am-4.30pm Nov-Feb); small tarmaced circular route suitable for wheelchairs. Three hides, one feeding station. No toilets, nearest are at Irchester Country Park on A509 towards Wellingborough. Dogs on leads.
Contact: BCN WT - see site 2.

5. TITCHMARSH NATURE RESERVE

Natural England (Lincs & Northants Team)/ Beds, Cambs & Northants Wildlife Trust.
Habitats: Alder/Birch/Willow wood, old duck decoy, series of water-filled gravel pits.
Birds: *Summer:* Breeding Grey Heron (no access to heronry), Common Tern, Little Ringed Plover, warblers. *Passage:* Waders. *Winter:* Good variety of wildfowl inc. nationally important numbers of Gadwall, Wigeon & Goosander, plus gulls. Migrants, inc. Red-necked & Slavonian Grebes, Hobby, Bittern & Marsh Harrier.
Other: Banded Demoiselle, Red-eyed Damselfly, Brown, Southern & Migrant Hawker Dragonflies.

Directions: Sat nav: NN14 3EE (Lowick Lane car park). TL 006 812. Seven miles E of Kettering. From A14 take A605 N. For Titchmarsh turn L at Thorpe Waterville, continue towards Aldwincle. Take first L after church (Lowick Lane) & continue to small car park on L. Take footpath to reserve.
Public transport: Bus - X16 (not Sun) Kettering to Thrapston. Centrebus (T:0116 410 5050).
Visiting: Part of the Thrapston Gravel Pits area. As well as the Aldwincle access point, there is a public footpath from lay-by on A605 N of Thrapston. Muddy conditions after heavy rain. Six hides.
Contact: BCN WT - see site 2.

6. TOP LODGE & FINESHADE WOOD

Forestry Commission.
Habitats. Ancient woodland, coniferous woodland, beech woodland, open areas, small pond.
Birds: Centre of Northants' Red Kite reintroduction scheme. *All year:* Red Kite, Buzzard, Great Spotted Woodpecker, Goshawk, Nuthatch, Crossbill, Marsh & Willow Tit, other woodland birds. *Summer:* Turtle Dove, warblers. *Winter:* Hawfinch.
Other: Adder, Grass Snake, Slow Worm, Common Lizard. Fallow Deer, Badger. Orchids inc. Greater Butterfly, Early Purple & Common Spotted, other ancient woodland flora.
Directions: Sat nav: NN17 3BB. SP 980 983. Off A43 between Stamford & Corby. Follow brown tourist signs to Top Lodge Fineshade Wood.
Public transport: None.
Visiting: Two pay-&-display car parks. Fully accessible visitor centre open daily (not Dec 25) 9.30am-4pm weekdays/9am-5pm weekends. Toilets, Top Lodge Cafe, events/activities throughout the year. Caravan & Motorhome Club site open mid-Mar to early- Nov (see C&MC website for details). Wildlife hide in wood - Smelter's Walk is an all-ability trail leading to the hide. Electric bikes available from Fineshade Cycling shop. Orienteering course. Three way-marked walking trails (one is for all abilities, two are surfaced), one horse trail, one family cycle trail with skills loops, dedicated coach & horse box parking. Sensory garden.
Contact: Forestry Commission, T: 0300 067 4340; E: sherwood.fdo@forestryengland.uk

Nottinghamshire

THE TRENT VALLEY is dominated by a series of gravel pits which can also be found in other parts of the county such as the Idle Valley NR & the RSPB's new reserve at Langford Lowfields, near Newark. Remnant pockets of heathland still hold Nightjar & Woodlark. A raptor watchpoint at Welbeck, in the heart of Sherwood Forest, may produce sightings of Honey Buzzard, Goshawk & Osprey. Hawfinch winters in Clumber Park.

1. ATTENBOROUGH NATURE RESERVE

Cement UK/Nottinghamshire Wildlife Trust.
Habitats: Disused flooded gravel workings with associated marginal & wetland vegetation.
Birds: *Spring/summer:* Breeding Common Tern (40+ pairs), Reed Warbler, Black Tern regular. *Winter:* Wildfowl, plus Bittern, Grey Heron colony, adjacent Cormorant roost.
Other: Smooth Newt, dragonflies inc. Four-spotted Chaser & Migrant Hawker. Brown Argus butterfly. 450+ spp. plants.

Directions: Sat nav: NG9 6DY. Car park at SK 515 339. In Nottingham alongside River Trent. Signposted from A6005 between Beeston & Long Eaton.
Public transport: Bus - no.510 (not Sun) Beeston to Stapleford, alight at Chilwell, walk 500 yards along Barton Lane. NottsBus (T: 0115 969 4390). Train - Attenborough, five mins walk.
Visiting: Open all year, 7am-dusk. Car park charge, coaches by prior appointment. Education & visitor centre with cafe & shop (accessible to wheelchair users) open (not Dec 25) 9am-5pm (4pm Nov-Mar), 6pm weekends & bank holidays. Paths suitable for disabled access. Nature trail (leaflet available), four hides inc. an elevated hide & innovative Sand Martin hide – a sunken hide within an artificial Sand Martin bank. Dogs on leads (guide dogs only in visitor centre).
Contact: Attenborough Nature Centre,
T: 01159 721 777;
E: enquiries@attenboroughnaturecentre.co.uk;
W: www.attenboroughnaturecentre.co.uk

2. BESTHORPE NATURE RESERVE

Nottinghamshire Wildlife Trust.
Habitats: Former gravel workings - open water with with islands, reedbeds & shingle, wildflower meadows.
Birds: *Spring/summer:* Breeding Grey Heron, Cormorant, Little Ringed Plover, Common Tern, Kingfisher, Skylark, Grasshopper Warbler. *Winter:* Large numbers of ducks (Pochard, Tufted Duck, Pintail, Wigeon) & Peregrine. Re-profiling of water margins has increased the numbers of visiting waders.
Other: Nationally rare plant community in meadows.
Directions: Sat nav: NG23 7HL. SK 818 640. Take A1133 N of Newark. Turn into Trent Lane S of Besthorpe village, reserve entrance signposted off the lane.
Public transport: Limited. Bus - Travel Wright (no.367, Phoneabus/pre-book T: 01636 703 813) along A1133 to Besthorpe village (0.75 mile away).
Visiting: Open at all times - two areas, north & south of Trent Lane. Hides, paths, boardwalks, several screens. Track around reserve wheelchair friendly with RADAR kissing gates & disabled friendly raised viewing screen overlooking Mons Pool (south). Dogs on leads. No toilets (pubs etc. in Besthorpe village).
Contact: Nottinghamshire WT, T: 01159 588 242;
E: info@nottswt.co.uk

3. COLWICK COUNTRY PARK

Nottingham City Council.
Habitats: Lakes, pools, woodlands, grasslands, new plantations, River Trent.
Birds: 220+ spp.*Summer:* 64 breeding spp., inc. warblers & Common Tern (15+ pairs). Good track record for rarities. *Winter:* Wildfowl (high concentrations of Goldeneye) & gulls. In nature reserve look for Lesser Spotted Woodpecker, Water Rail & Kingfisher. Passage migrants inc. Stonechat & Whinchat.
Other: Pool designated a SSSI for its 14 spp. breeding dragonflies. Purple & White-letter hairstreak butterflies.
Directions: Sat nav: NG4 2DW. SK 611 398. Main access from Mile End Road/River Road, off A612 two miles E of Nottingham city centre.

Public transport: Bus - no.44 Nottingham to Netherfield/Gedling, (from stop K1 on King Street), goes through Colwick.
Nottingham City Transport. th **Visiting:** Open at all times, 7am to dusk. Nature trails. Dogs on leads in designated areas.
Contact: Country Park, Mile End Road, Colwick, Nottingham, NG4 2DW.

4. IDLE VALLEY

Nottinghamshire Wildlife Trust/Tarmac/Private.
Habitats: Former sand & gravel quarries, restored gravel workings, conservation grazed areas, woodland, reedbed, river valley, farmland, scrub, willow plantations, open water.
Birds: 250+ spp. *Summer:* Gulls, terns, wildfowl & waders inc. breeding Little Ringed Plover & Redshank. *Passage:* waders, terns, passerines & raptors. *Winter:* Wildfowl, gulls, raptors. Wider valley has been good for rarities, which have inc. Broad-billed Sandpiper, Great White Egret, Baird's Sandpiper & Steppe Grey Shrike in recent times.
Directions: Sat nav: DN22 8SG. SK 689 830. S end of reserve is 0.5 mile N of Retford off A638 to Barnby Moor, via entrance to Tarmac. Rural Learning Centre is on R.
Public transport: Bus - no.27 Retford to Misson passes reserve entrance. Stagecoach.
Visiting: Open

all year, 9am-5pm. Car park (donation welcome). Idle Valley Rural Learning Centre has toilets & cafe open 10am-4pm. Four walking routes, many wheelchair accessible. Six viewing screens, two overlooking Chainbridge NR Scrape, two at Neatholme Scrape & single screens at Neatholme Fen & Neatholme Pit. Two hides in Chainbridge Wood.

Contact: Idle Valley Rural Learning Centre, Great North Road, Retford, DN22 8RQ; T: 01777 858 245; E: info@nottswt.co.uk

5. LANGFORD LOWFIELDS

RSPB Midlands Office/Lefarge Tarmac.
Habitats: RSPB/Tarmac working to create East Midlands largest reedbed. The site, inc. areas to be restored, currently covers 175ha on this sand & gravel quarry site. Mature woodland, flower-rich meadow, lake, shallow pools, islands.
Birds: *Summer:* Ten spp. warbler, inc. Cetti's, Grasshopper & regionally important numbers of Reed & Sedge. Cuckoo, Turtle Dove, Bearded Tit, Marsh Harrier, Hobby, hirundines & breeding Little Ringed Plover & Avocet *Winter:* Large waterfowl numbers, plus Bittern (can be heard booming into spring), Starling roosts & five owl spp.
Other: Badger, Brown Hare, 18+ spp. butterflies.

Directions: Sat nav: NG23 7QL. SK 821 601. Lies NE of Newark-on-Trent. From A1 take A46 (signposted to Lincoln) & then turn onto A1133 (to Collingham). After 2.5 miles turn L into Cottage Lane - gated car park 50m along the lane (height restriction 2.2m contact prior to visit if required).
Public transport: Bus - no. 367 Newark-Collingham will stop near to Cottage Lane junc. on request. Travel Wright T: 01636 703 813).
Visiting: Cottage Lane car park open dawn-dusk. Small hut open daily, if volunteers available, where two nature trails start (located 800m from car park). Viewing screen overlooking reedbed, floating bridge & boardwalk, pond dipping platform. No toilets.
Contact: RSPB, T: 01636 893 611; E: langford.beckingham@rspb.org.uk

Oxfordshire

RED KITES ARE now common place in this largely agricultural county. The Downs in the south of the county can be good for other raptors, particularly in the winter. Two outstanding birding locations are Farmoor Reservoir (for passage migrants, wintering wildfowl & rarities) & Otmoor (wildfowl numbers increase in winter & Hen Harrier, Merlin, Peregrine & Short-eared Owl are often present. The RSPB are developing wet meadows & reedbeds on the site to benefit breeding waders such as Redshank, Snipe & Lapwing).

1. ASTON ROWANT NNR

Natural England (Thames Team).
Habitats: Chalk grassland, chalk scrub, beech woodland.
Birds: *All year:* Red Kite, Buzzard, Sparrowhawk, Woodcock, Tawny Owl, Green & Great Spotted Woodpeckers, Skylark, Meadow Pipit, Marsh Tit. *Spring/summer:* Blackcap, other warblers, Turtle Dove. *Passage:* inc. Ring Ouzel, Wheatear & Stonechat. *Winter:* Brambling, Siskin, winter thrushes.
Other: Rich chalk grassland flora, inc. Chiltern Gentian, Clustered Bellflower & Frog, Bee, Pyramidal & Fragrant Orchids. Less common butterflies inc. Silver-spotted, Dingy & Grizzled Skippers, Chalkhill Blue, Adonis Blue, Green Hairstreak & Dark Green Fritillary.

Directions: Sat nav: HP14 3YL. SU 731 966 (for Beacon Hill car park). From the M40 Lewknor interchange at Junc 6, travel NE for a short distance & turn R onto A40. After 1.5 miles at the top of hill, turn R & R again into a narrow, metalled lane. Car park is signposted from A40. OX49 5HX. SU 726 958 (for Cowleaze Wood car park).
Public transport: Bus - no.275 High Wycombe to Oxford stops at Stokenchurch & Aston Rowant. Red Rose Travel (T: 01296 747 926) & no. Link40 High Wycombe to Thame, stops at Lewknor village. Carousel Buses (T: 01494 450 151). Short walks to reserve.
Visiting: Open all year. On-site parking at Beacon Hill & Cowleaze Wood - viewpoint, seats, interpretation panels. Some wheelchair access at Cowleaze Wood (contact for details).
Contact: Natural England, Aston Rowant NNR, T: 01844 351 833; E: michael.venters@naturalengland.org.uk

2. FARMOOR RESERVOIR

Thames Water.
Habitats: County's largest body of freshwater contained in two concrete basins separated by a causeway. Shallow pools in Pinkhill Reserve. Reedbed, wet grassland, pools in Shrike Meadow & Buckthorne Meadow reserves.

Birds: *Summer:* Breeding Little Ringed Plover, Common Tern & Black-headed Gull. Large numbers of hirundines, Hobby, Cuckoo. *Passage:* migrants such as White & Yellow Wagtails, Wheatear, Black Tern, Little Gull, Dunlin & Little Stint. *Winter:* Wildfowl, grebes, divers & gulls. Snipe & Water Rail at Pinkhill. A long history of rarities.

Other: Dragonflies, aquatic life-forms.

Directions: Sat nav: OX2 9NT. SP 452 061. Lies W of Oxford between A 40 & A420. Widely signposted by brown tourist signs. At mini-roundabout in Farmoor village (on B4044), turn L & look for car park at Gate 3.

Public transport: Bus - no.S1 between Oxford & Witney stop in Farmoor village (0.5 mile walk to Gate 3). Stagecoach.

Visiting: Free car parking at Gate 3. Car park off B4017. Bird hide at Pinkhill Reserve, west of reservoir.

Contact: E: hanna.jenkins@thameswater.co.uk

3. FOXHOLES RESERVE

Berks, Bucks & Oxon Wildlife Trust.

Habitats: Broad-leaved ancient woodland, grassland.

Birds: *All year:* Raven, Tawny Owl, Little Owl, Green & Greater Spotted Woodpeckers, common woodland spp. *Spring/summer:* Spotted Flycatcher, Marsh Tit & warblers. *Winter:* Redwing, Fieldfare, Woodcock.

Other: Fantastic show of Bluebells from mid-Apr & into May. Autumn fungi (200+ spp.). Silver-washed Fritillary among 23 spp. butterflies, 7 spp. bats.

Directions: Sat nav: OX7 6RW. SP 258 208. Travelling N on A424 from Burford, take R turn to Bruern. Continue past staggered crossroads towards Bruern for two miles then past R turn to Shipton-under-Wychwood. Park in lay-by after 200 yards & walk 600 yards down pot-holed track to reserve entrance - recommended not to drive along this track.

Public transport: None.

Visiting: Open all year. Car park, 1.75 mile circular wildlife walk - keep to paths (can be very muddy).

Contact: BBOWT, T: 01865 775 476; E: info@bbowt.org.uk

4. OTMOOR NATURE RESERVE

RSPB (Central England Office).

Habitats: Wet grassland, reedbed, open water, hedgerows.

Birds: *Spring/autumn passage:* Marsh Harrier, Greenshank, Green Sandpiper & Common Sandpipers, Spotted Redshank Short-eared Owl & occasional Black Tern. *Summer:* Breeding birds inc. Cetti's & Grasshopper Warblers, Lapwing, Redshank, Curlew, Snipe, Yellow Wagtail, Shoveler, Gadwall, Pochard, Tufted Duck, Little & Great Crested Grebes. Hobby breeds locally. *Winter:* Wigeon, Teal, Shoveler, Pintail, Gadwall, Pochard, Tufted Duck, Lapwing, Golden Plover, Hen Harrier, Peregrine, Merlin.

Directions: Sat nav: OX3 9TD (Otmoor Lane). SP 570 126. Car park seven miles NE of Oxford city centre. From Junc 8 of M40, take A40 W to Wheatley, then B4027. Take turn to Horton-cum-Studley, then first L to Beckley. After 0.7 mile turn R (before the Abingdon Arms public house). After 200 yards, turn L into Otmoor Lane. Car park at the end of lane (approx one mile) - if full do not park along Otmoor Lane (emergency access).

Public transport: None.

Visiting: Open dawn-dusk, no entry fee. Small car park with cycle racks, visitor trail (three mile round trip) & two screened viewpoints. Not accessible by coach & is unsuitable for large groups. No dogs allowed on reserve visitor trail (except public rights of way). In wet conditions, visitor route can be muddy & wellingtons are essential.

Contact: RSPB, T: 01865 351 163, E: otmoor.admin@rspb.org.uk

5. PORT MEADOW

Oxford City Council.

Habitats: Common land, on east bank of River Thames (adjacent to Thames Towpath & Burgess Field).

Birds: *All year:* Sparrowhawk, Little Owl, Reed Bunting. *Spring/summer/passage:* waders, hirundines, warblers, chats. *Winter:* When the area is wet, wildfowl & waders inc. (Wigeon, Teal, Gadwall, Snipe, Lapwing), plus occassional Goosander, Golden Plover, Water Rail.

Other: Butterflies, dragonflies, meadow plant spp.

Directions: Sat Nav: OX2 6ED. Lies on the NW outskirts of Oxford, accessed via Walton Well Road & Aristotle Lane in the south or Wolvercote in the north.

Public transport: Bus - no.6 from Oxford city centre (Magdalen Street, stop C3) to Wolvercote (also stops at Plantation road - short walk to south access). Oxford Bus Co.
Visiting: Open all year. Car parks off Godstow Road (north end) OX2 8PU & Walton Well Road (south end) OX2 6ED. Dogs under control.
Contact: Cutteslowe Park Offices, Harboard Road, Oxford, OX2 8ES.

6. WARBURG NATURE RESERVE

Berks, Bucks & Oxon Wildlife Trust.
Habitats: Scrub, mixed woodland, chalk grassland, ponds.
Birds: *All year:* Sparrowhawk, Red Kite, Treecreeper, Nuthatch, Tawny Owl. *Spring/summer:* Occasional Firecrest. Warblers inc. Whitethroat & Lesser Whitethroat. *Winter:* Redpoll, Siskin, sometimes Brambling, Crossbill, Woodcock.

Other: Good for orchids (15 spp.), butterflies (inc. Purple Hairstreak & Silver-washed Fritillary) & common deer spp.
Directions: Sat nav: RG9 6BJ. SU 721 878. Four miles NW of Henley-on Thames. From the A4130 turn into Bix Village. Take a L turn into Rectory Lane. Go down the steep hill & turn L at bottom, signposted Bix Bottom. Continue for about one mile until reaching car park at end of lane on R. The lane has some potholes - drive carefully.
Public transport: None.
Visiting: Open all year. Car park (not suitable for coaches) & toilets open at all times. Interpretation Centre open daily 9am-5pm, two hides (one with disabled access), children's Nature Detectives Trail, nature trail, picnic benches, leaflets. Dogs on leads. Mobility vehicle available – contact/book before visiting.
Contact: BBOWT, T: 01491 642 001; E: info@bbowt.org.uk

Shropshire

BORDERING WALES TO the west, & part of the area known as the 'Welsh Marches', the upland moorland of the South Shropshire Hills hold Red Grouse, Dipper & Ring Ouzel, while occasionally passage Dotterel may be encountered. The fertile lowland valleys, extensive farmland & mixed woodland hold a good mixture of species. The cluster of waterbodies in the north, near Ellesmere, attracts winter wildfowl & gulls, Venus Pools, Wood Lane & Chelmarsh attract passage waders.

1. CLUNTON COPPICE

Shropshire Wildlife Trust.
Habitats: One of county's largest sessile oak woodlands.
Birds: *All year:* Great Spotted Woodpecker, Buzzard, Red Kite, Peregrine, Raven. *Spring/summer:* Wide range of woodland birds, inc. Woodcock, Redstart, Wood Warbler, Spotted & Pied Flycatchers. *Winter:* Crossbill, Siskin, Redpoll.
Other: Hairy woodrush & bromerape, sessile oak woodland plants, bluebell, bilberry. Good for ferns, mosses & fungi. Dormouse, Roe Deer.
Directions: Sat nav: SY7 0HU. SO 337 806. From Craven Arms, take B4368 to Clunton village, at the crossroad go south, head straight over bridge & up the hill to small car park just before reserve sign.
Public transport: None.
Visiting: Open at all times. Limited parking in small quarry entrance on right, or opposite The Crown pub. Access along road & public rights of way only.
Contact: Shropshire WT, T: 01743 284 280; E: enquiries@shropshirewildlifetrust.org.uk

2. FENN'S WHIXALL & BETTISFIELD MOSSES

Natural England (West Midlands Team).
Habitats: 800ha, raised peatland meres & mosses.
Birds: *All year:* Kingfisher, Skylark, Linnet. *Spring/summer:* Breeding Teal, Mallard, Nightjar, Hobby, Curlew, Tree Sparrow. *Winter:* Short-eared Owl.
Other: Water Vole, Brown Hare, Polecat, Adder, 670 spp. moths, 27 spp. butterflies, nationally important for dragonflies (29 spp.), inc. White-faced Darter, 18 spp. bog moss.

Directions: Sat nav: SY13 3NY (Fenn's Bank), SJ 505 366. Four miles SW of Whitchurch, to S of A495 between Fenn's Bank, Whixall & Bettisfield. Roadside parking at entrances, car parks at Morris's Bridge, Roundthorn Bridge, World's End & a large car park at Manor House. Disabled access by prior arrangement along railway line.
Public transport: None.
Visiting: Permit required except on Mosses Trail routes. Information panels at main entrances & leaflets are available when permits are applied for. Three interlinking Mosses Trails explore the NNR & canal from Morris's & Roundthorn bridges.
Contact: Natural England, Manor House NNR Base, T: 0300 060 0269;
E: peter.bowyer@naturalengland.org.uk

3. PRIORSLEE LAKE

Severn Trent Water/Friends of Priorslee Lake.
Habitats: A man-made balancing lake, surrounded by woodland, rough grassland & three reedbeds.
Birds: 155+ spp. (41 spp. breeding). *Summer:* Warblers, inc. Reed & Sedge. *Winter:* A nearby landfill site makes Priorslee Lake a magnet for gulls & it has a good track record for Yellow-legged, Caspian & white-winged gulls. Check the wildfowl for less common spp. such as Goosander & Pintail. Bittern & Snipe in reedbeds. Finches, tits (inc. Willow), Redpoll, Siskin in woodland.
Other: Wide range of butterflies, dragonflies & other insects. Southern Marsh, Bee & Common Spotted Orchids.
Directions: Sat nav: TF2 9NS. SJ 720 095 (Teece Drive). In Telford between M54 & A5. Leave M54 going N (B5060) at Junc 4 & park in lay-by (100 yards from Junc 4) overlooking the lake. Alternatively park - without blocking gates - by Water Sports Association entrance gate at the end of Teece Drive, Priorslee, Telford. The Flash, Priorslee is a slightly smaller lake half a mile distant. Follow the stream that comes in at western end of Priorslee Lake or head for Derwent Drive, Priorslee.
Public transport: Teece Drive entrance is about two miles from Telford bus station, 1.25 miles from Telford train station.
Visiting: Open at all times. Path around lake - can be muddy when wet.
Contact: W: http://friendsofpriorsleelake.blogspot.co.uk

4. VENUS POOL

Shropshire Ornithological Society.
Habitats: 27ha, pool, several islands, open shoreline, marshy grassland, hedgerows, woodland, scrub, species-rich meadows, field growing bird-friendly crops.
Birds: Noted for wintering wildfowl, passage waders & occasional county rarities, inc. Black-necked Grebe, Purple Heron, Spoonbill, Red Kite & Woodlark.

All year: Common ducks & waterfowl, passerines, inc. Tree Sparrow. *Spring/summer:* Passage waders inc. Curlew, Ringed Plover, Dunlin, Redshank, Green & Common Sandpipers, & both godwits. Passage Black Tern, breeding Oystercatcher, Little Ringed Plover, Lapwing, warblers, hirundines. *Autumn:* Wader passage can inc. Little Stint, Greenshank, Green, Wood, Curlew & Common Sandpipers, & possible rarities. *Winter:* Occasional Bittern. Geese inc. occasional White-fronted. Ducks inc. Wigeon, Teal, Pintail, Shoveler, Pochard, Goosander (up to 50 in evening roosts) & occasional Goldeneye. Water Rail, vagrant raptors & owls, winter thrushes & large passerine flocks inc. Lesser Redpoll, Linnet, Tree Sparrow, Reed Bunting & Yellowhammer.
Directions: Sat nav: SY5 6JT. SJ 548 062. Six miles SE of Shrewsbury in angle formed by A458 & minor road leading S to Pitchford. Entrance is 0.5 mile along minor road which leaves A458, 0.5 mile SE of Cross Houses.
Public transport: Bus - no.436 Shrewsbury to Bridgnorth, stops at Cross Houses, one mile walk from Venus Pool (partly along busy main road). Arriva Midlands North.
Visiting: Car park with height barrier, also small parking area for disabled visitors close to Main Hide. Five hides (North Hide - SOS members only). Information boards. Public access inc. four hides - keep to footpaths shown on notice boards at both entrances. Wheelchair-friendly paths to two public hides & Lena's Hide overlooking feeding station. No dogs allowed.
Contact:
W: www.shropshirebirds.com/index/guide-to-birding-sites/venus-pool-reserve/

5. WOOD LANE

Shropshire Wildlife Trust
Habitats: Gravel pit restored by Tudor Griffiths Group.
Birds: 180+ spp. since 1999, 40 spp. breeding. *Summer:* Breeding Sand Martin (up to 500 pairs have bred), Lapwing, Little Ringed Plover, Yellowhammer & Tree Sparrow. Popular staging post for waders (inc. Redshank, Greenshank, Ruff, Dunlin, Little Stint, Whimbrel, Green & Wood Sandpiper). *Winter:* Large flocks of Lapwing, plus Curlew & common wildfowl.
Other: Good range of dragonflies.
Directions: Sat nav: SY12 0HY. SJ 425 329. Take the Colemere road, off A528 at Spunhill, one mile SE of Ellesmere. Car park is 0.75 mile on R.
Public transport: None.
Visiting: Open at all times. Car park signposted. Disabled access. Two hides - permit required apply to Tudor Griffiths Group, a form can be downloaded from W:
www.shropshirewildlifetrust.org.uk/nature-reserves/wood-lane
Contact: Shropshire Wildlife Trust - see site 1.

Staffordshire

THE SOUTHERN PART of Peak District National Park protrudes into the northern part of the county & has Red Grouse on the moors. In the dales and valleys, including RSPB Coombes Valley, Lesser Spotted Woodpecker, Pied Flycatcher, Redstart & other songbirds can be found. The mixed habitats of Cannock Chase are good for Nightjars, Woodlark & Goshawk, & have the occasional Great Grey Shrike in winter. Belvide, Blithfield & Croxall Lakes are the best reservoirs to find wintering wildfowl and passage waders.

1. BELVIDE

Canal & Rivers Trust/West Midland Bird Club.
Habitats: Reservoir, marsh, reedbeds, woodland, scrub.
Birds: *Breeding & passage*: waders (up to 12 spp. in a day when conditions are right) & terns. Warblers breed in reedbeds & hedgerows. *Winter*: Great Northern Diver, wildfowl inc. Bewick's Swan & Goosander. Gull roost sometimes inc. Glaucous or Iceland Gulls. Recent scarcities inc. Sabine's Gull, White-winged & Whiskered Terns & Yellow-browed Warbler.
Other: Dragonflies.
Directions: Sat nav: ST19 9LX. SJ 870 098. Entrance & car park on Shutt Green Lane, Brewood (south of A5), seven miles NW of Wolverhampton.

Public transport: Bus - no.877/878 (Mon-Fri) Wolverhampton to Brewood (walk down Shutt Green Lane). Select Bus Services (T: 01785 330 764).
Visiting: Access only by permit from WMBC (members free, non-members charged) - lock combination issued to permit holders. Parking for 25-30 cars, five hides (three with wheelchair access), hard surface paths.
Contact: Mark Rickus (West Midland Bird Club), 27 Ringmere Ave, Castle Bromwich, Birmingham, B36 9AT. T: 0121 749 5348; E: permits@westmidlandbirdclub.org.uk; non-members, groups only - no individual permits issued.

2. BLITHFIELD RESERVOIR

South Staffs Water/West Midland Bird Club.
Habitats: Large reservoir.
Birds: 250+ spp. *Winter*: Good wildfowl numbers (inc. Bewick's Swan, Goosander, Goldeneye), large gull roost (can inc. Glaucous, Iceland, Mediterrean & Caspian). *Passage*: terns (Common, Arctic, Black) & waders, esp. in autumn (Little Stint, Curlew Sandpiper, Spotted Redshank regular).
Directions: Sat nav: WS15 3PH. SK 052 250. Close to Abbots Bromley on B5013 (Rugeley/Uttoxeter road - permit holders look for signposts to Blithfield Education Centre.
Public transport: None.
Visiting: For members of WMBC only or one-off group permit, further details from the secretary. Free car park, toilets. Walk One has partial wheelchair access.
Contact: Mark Rickus - see site 1.

3. COOMBES VALLEY

RSPB (Midlands Regional Office).
Habitats: Steep-sided valley with sessile oak woodland, unimproved pasture, meadow.
Birds: *Spring*: Displaying Woodcock, drumming Great Spotted Woodpecker, Dipper & common woodland spp. joined by migrant Pied & Spotted Flycatchers, Redstart, Tree Pipit, Grey Wagtail & Wood Warbler. *Autumn/winter*: Lesser Redpoll, Siskin, winter thrushes. *Jan-Mar*: Displaying birds of prey.
Other: Bluebells, various butterflies, Slow Worm.
Directions: Sat nav: ST13 7EU. SK 009 534. Three miles SE of Leek. From Leek take A523 towards Ashbourne. After Bradnop, turn R on minor road (cross a railway line) to Apesford & follow signs to reserve.
Public transport: Bus - no.108 (not Sun) Leek to Ashbourne. 1.2 miles from reserve (take Apesford Lane) cross disused railway & continue to reserve entrance on L). Aimee's (T: 01538 385 050).
Visiting: Open daily (not Dec 25) 9am-9pm or dusk, no charge. Coach groups by prior arrangement. Information centre open daily (until 5pm) during busy periods, but may close at times in winter; toilets & refreshments. Only guide dogs allowed off public footpaths. Most trails unsuitable for disabled visitors. Three nature trails.
Contact: RSPB, T: 01538 384 017; E: coombes.valley@rspb.org.uk

4. CROXALL LAKES

Staffordshire Wildlife Trust.
Habitats: Two large lakes formed from gravel pits at junction of Rivers Tame, Trent & Mease, & shallow pools, wader scrapes, reedbeds.
Birds: *Spring/summer:* Breeding spp. inc. grebes, waders such as Redshank, Oystercatcher, Ringed Plover & Lapwing. *Winter:* Substantial numbers of wildfowl, inc. Wigeon, Teal, Goldeneye, Shoveler & occasional Smew. Between Nov & Jan, Short-eared Owls hunt over rough ground.
Other: Otter, Water Vole & Harvest Mouse present but dragonflies will be easier to see.
Directions: Sat nav: WS13 8QX. SK 189139. From Lichfield head N on A38, following signs for National Memorial Arboretum. At NMA entrance, continue over river bridge & turn L on second track into car park.
Public transport: Bus - no.812 (not Sun) Lichfield to Alrewas (1.2 miles from reserve). Midland Classic (T: 01283 500 228).
Visiting: Open at all times, except to restricted areas. Small car park (8am-5pm), two bird hides. Kissing gate at entrance wide enough for wheelchairs. Surfaced access track, leading to hide overlooking main lake. Wheelchair ramps to both hides but woodland path uneven. Restricted areas for dogs.
Contact: Staffordshire WT, T: 01889 880 100; E: info@staffs-wildlife.org.uk

5. DOXEY MARSHES

Staffordshire Wildlife Trust.
Habitats: Wet meadow habitats. Marsh, pools, reedbeds, hedgerows, reed sweet-grass swamp.
Birds: 200+ spp. (80 spp. breeding). *Spring/summer:* Breeding Lapwing, Redshank, Little Ringed Plover, Oystercatcher, Shelduck, warblers, Skylark, Water Rail. *Autumn/Winter:* Snipe, Jack Snipe, Goosander, other wildfowl. *Passage:* waders, vagrants.
Other: Otter, Harvest Mouse, Water Shrew, Noctule Bat, Musk Beetle, Reed-sweet Grass.

Directions: Sat nav: ST16 1JR. SJ 903 250. On W side of Stafford town centre, just off A5013 (Eccleshall Road) from Junc 14 on the M6. Parking options: Sainsbury's car park; car park behind Focus on GreyFriar's Industrial Estate; by play park at end of Wootton Drive/Creswell Farm Drive.
Public transport: Buses & trains to Stafford town centre, walk upstream from Sainsbury's supermarket along River Sow to reserve entrance.
Visiting: Open at all times. Flat surfaced paths, most accessible by wheelchair (unless flooded). Two hides. Dogs on leads.
Contact: Staffordshire WT - see site 4.

6. HIGHGATE COMMON

Staffordshire Wildlife Trust.
Habitats: Lowland heath with broadleaf woodland.
Birds: Cuckoo, Green Woodpecker, Tree Pipit, Skylark, Stonechat, Yellowhammer.
Other: 5,000+ spp. insects, inc. several red data book spp. bees & wasps. Glow Worm & Common Lizard.
Directions: Sat nav: DY7 5BS. SO 835 894. (Highgate Road). From A449 at Himley take B4176 towards Bridgnorth. After approx one mile, turn L at traffic lights onto Wombourne Rd, signposted towards Swindon. Continue through Swindon, along Chasepool Rd. At the T Junction turn R onto Camp Hill Road. About one mile after Camp Farm, take 1st L then R at T junction onto Highgate Rd. Take 1st entrance on R.
Public transport: None.
Visiting: Eight main car parks over the Common, network of paths. Toilets at Warden's Office, Cory Community Centre (only open when wardens on site, opening hours vary but usually 9am-4.30 pm, Mon-Sat).
Contact: Staffordshire WT - see site 4.

Warwickshire & West Midlands

WARWICKSHIRE'S RIVER VALLEYS & gravel pits are the main focus for birds. Tame Valley sites, such as Kingsbury & Ladywalk, Draycote Water & Brandon Marsh all attract wintering wildfowl & passage waders - Cetti's Warbler are well-established at the latter. In contrast to Warwickshire's largely rural setting, the West Midlands is heavily populated but Sutton Park (one of the largest urban parks in Europe) & Sandwell valley attract a good selection of birds.

1. BRANDON MARSH

Warwickshire Wildlife Trust.
Habitats: 105ha, pools, marsh, reedbeds, willow carr, scrub & small mixed woodland.
Birds: 230+ spp. *All year:* Cetti's Warbler, Kingfisher, Water Rail, Gadwall, Little Grebe, Buzzard. *Spring/summer:* Little Ringed Plover, Garden & Grasshopper Warblers, Whitethroat, Lesser Whitethroat, Hobby, Whinchat, Wheatear. *Autumn/winter:* Bittern, Dunlin, Ruff, Snipe, Greenshank, Green & Common Sandpipers, Wigeon, Shoveler, Pochard, Goldeneye, Siskin, Redpoll.
Other: 500 plant spp., Badger, Otter, Great Crested Newt. 20+ spp. butterflies & 18 spp. dragonflies. Lists on W: www.brandonbirding.co.uk

Directions: Sat nav: CV3 3GW. SP 386 758. Three miles SE of Coventry, 200 yards SE of A45/A46 junction (Tollbar End). Turn E off A45 (just after Texaco garage) into Brandon Lane. Reserve entrance signposted 1.25 miles on R.
Public transport: Bus - no.21 Coventry to Willenhall/ Tollbar End, then 1.25 miles walk. National Express, Coventry.
Visiting: Open 9.30am-4.30pm weekdays, 10am-4.30pm weekends (closes 4pm, Oct-Mar). Only Trust members can visit site outside these hours. Entrance charge (free to WT members). Visitor centre, tea-room (open 10am-4pm daily), shop, toilets, nature trails, eight hides. Wheelchair access to nature trails & Wright hide. No dogs. Parking for coaches, by arrangement.
Contact: Warwickshire WT, T: 024 7630 2912; E: enquiries@wkwt.org.uk

2. COOMBE COUNTRY PARK

Coventry City Council.
Habitats: 200ha, parkland, lake, woodland, gardens.
Birds: Heronry on lake island, many Cormorants. Common woodland spp. inc. Lesser Spotted Woodpecker & Marsh Tit.
Other: 250+ spp. plant, inc. Lesser Celandine, Foxglove, Bluebell, Red Campion & Herb Robert. Mammals inc. Wood Mouse, Muntjac.
Directions: Sat nav: CV3 2AB. SP 401 793. At Binley, five miles E of Coventry centre, on B4027 Coventry to Brinklow road.
Public transport: Bus - no.585 Coventry to Rugby, alight Coombe Abbey. Mike de Courcey Travel (T: 024 7630 2656), Stagecoach Midlands on Sun.

Visiting: Open daily, main car park (pay-&-display) available at all times, entry on foot is free. Visitor centre & cafe open daily 10am-4pm (not Dec 25/26 & Jan 1), toilets inc. disabled, gift shop. Various trails, hide, wildflower meadow (Apr-Sep).
Contact: Coombe Country Park, T: 024 7645 3720; E: coombe@coventry.gov.uk

3. DRAYCOTE WATER

Severn Trent Water.
Habitats: Large storage reservoir, surrounded by grassland, wooded areas.
Birds: *All year:* Farmland & woodland spp. in surrounding countryside. *Spring & autumn passage:* inc. waders, Black & Arctic Terns & Ospreys. *Winter:* Wide range of common wildfowl, regular sightings of less common spp. such as Smew, Scaup & Black-necked Grebe. Gull roost can number in excess of 50,000 birds, scarcer spp. often seen.
Directions: Sat nav: CV23 8AB. SP 462 685. Reservoir & 8ha country park situated near Dunchurch, 3.5 miles SW of Rugby off the A426.
Public transport: Bus - no.63 Rugby to Leamington Spa stops at Kites Hardwick/Draycote Water. Stagecoach.
Visiting: Open daily (not Dec 25) 7.30am-8pm (Apr-Sep), 7.30-dusk (Oct-Mar). Cars must stop at pay-&-display car park - disabled parking allowed at Toft, close to bird hide. Visitor centre, toilets, cafe open 10am-6pm (Apr-Sep), 4pm (Oct-Mar). Access to reservoir on foot or bicycle only. Five mile road surrounding reservoir. Paths good for wheelchairs. Dogs only in Country Park.
Contact: Draycote Water, Kites Hardwick, Warwickshire CV23 8AB; T: 01788 811 107; E: draycotewater@severntrent.co.uk; W: www.draycotebirding.co.uk

4. KINGSBURY WATER PARK

Warwickshire County Council.
Habitats: Open water, numerous small pools, some with gravel islands, gravel pits, silt beds with reedmace, reed, willow & alder, grassland, rough areas.
Birds: 230 spp. inc. Kingfisher. *Summer:* Breeding warblers (nine spp.), Little Ringed Plover, Great Crested & Little Grebes. Shoveler, Shelduck & a thriving Common Tern colony. *Winter:* Wildfowl, Short-eared Owl. *Passage:* Osprey, Hobby, waders (esp. spring).
Other: Orchids.
Directions: Sat nav: B76 0DY. SP 203 960. Signposted `Water Park' from Junc 9 M42 & A4097 NE of Birmingham.
Public transport: Bus - no.16 (not Sun) Tamworth to Kingsbury. Diamond Bus.
Visiting: Open daily (not Dec 25) generally 8am-dusk, as early as 5.30am in Jun/Jul. Pay on entry car park or annual permits in advance online. Four hides (three with wheelchair access) overlooking Cliff Pool nature reserve. Miles of flat surfaced footpaths, mobility scooters for hire. Toilets, cafe, information centre/gift shop (opening times vary during year).
Contact: Kingsbury Water Park, T: 01827 872 660; E: parks@warwickshire.gov.uk

NATURE RESERVES - CENTRAL ENGLAND

5. LADYWALK RESERVE

Eon Energy/West Midland Bird Club.
Habitats: 50ha, floodland, reedbed, woodland within a loop of River Tame.
Birds: 200+ spp. *Spring/summer:* Passage waders inc. Greenshank, Curlew, godwits & plovers, plus many hirundines & other migrants. *Winter:* Hundreds of wildfowl, inc. Wigeon, Teal, Shoveler, Goldeneye & Goosander. Water Rail & Woodcock regular & lots of small bird activity at the feeding stations. Up to four Bitterns in recent years, plus Siskin, Redpoll & winter thrushes.
Other: Five spp. orchid, inc. county's only known colony of Marsh Hellibore & locally rare Yellow Bird's Nest. Butterflies plentiful & 16 spp. dragonflies.
Directions: Sat nav: B46 2BS. SP 211 916. Site of old Hams Hall power station, in Tame Valley - 10 miles from Birmingham city centre. From Junc 9 of M42, head S on A446 to Hams Hall Distribution Centre. Follow Faraday Avenue to reserve. WMBC members can use secure car park near Sainsbury's warehouse.
Public transport: None.
Visiting: Enter site by footbridge. Reserve open only to WMBC members, but other groups can organise visits with Sec. Non-members can observe site from public footpaths east of River Tame. No easy access on site for disabled visitors. Display permits on dashboard if using secure car park. Dogs not allowed. Six bird hides, inc. elevated River Walk Hide. Other screens for close-up viewing. Circular footpath (1.6 miles).
Contact: Mark Rickus (West Midland BC Permit Sec), 27 Ringmere Ave, Castle Bromwich, Birmingham, B36 9AT. T: 0121 749 5348; E: permits@westmidlandbirdclub.org.uk; non-members, groups only - no individual permits issued.

6. MIDDLETON LAKES

RSPB (Midlands Regional Office).
Habitats: Former quarry, lakes, reedbeds, meadows, woodland.
Birds: *All year:* Barn Owls regularly seen & Cetti's Warbler frequently heard. *Spring/summer:* heronry (30+ pairs), plus common migrant warblers, Lapwing, hirundines & woodland spp. *Winter:* Lesser Spotted & Great Spotted Woodpeckers & Willow Tit on the feeders, plus peak numbers of wildfowl & waders. Raptors inc. Hen & Marsh Harriers, Merlin, Peregrine & Short-eared Owl.
Other: Bluebells & spring flowers, Grass Snake, common butterflies & moths.
Directions: Sat nav: B78 2BB. SP 192 967. Reserve lies in Tame Valley, S of Tamworth, next to Middleton Hall. Leave M42 at Junc 9 onto A446, then A4091 & finally into Bodymoor Heath Road.
Public transport: Train - Wilnecote is 2.5 miles from reserve.

Visiting: Open daily dawn/dusk. Car park for 50 - parking charge/members free, bike racks. Surfaced path from car park to Middleton Hall & heronry. Other paths are unsurfaced but generally flat. Playmeadow Trail has partial wheelchair access. Four viewing screens. Lookout hide open to view northern scrapes (see RSPB website for lock combination number). Four trails, ranging from 500 yards to two miles in length. Dogs allowed on leads on parts of site. Nearest toilets at Middleton Hall.
Contact: RSPB, T: 01827 259 454;
E: middletonlakes@rspb.org.uk

7. ROUGH WOOD CHASE LNR

Walsall Council.
Habitats: 28ha, oakwood - significant for W. Midlands. Reservoir, meadows, ponds/pools, marsh, scrubland.
Birds: *All year:* Great Crested & Little Grebes on pools in north end of Chase, common woodland spp. inc. Jay & Sparrowhawk. *Summer:* warblers.
Other: Great Crested & Smooth Newts, Water Vole, various dragonfly spp., Purple Hairstreak, Brimstone & Small Heath Butterflies.
Directions: Sat nav: WV12 5NX. SJ 981 008. Reserve composed of six sites on W edge of Walsall Borough. From Junc 10 of M6 head for Willenhall & A462. Turn R into Bloxwich Road North & R again into Hunts Lane. Car park on bend.
Public transport: Bus - nos.41 (not Sun)/69 Walsall & Willenhall (Short Heath Clinic stop). National Express, West Midlands.
Visiting: Open all year, circular nature trail linking all sites.
Contact: Environmental Improvement Team, T: 01922 653 344; E: eit@walsall.gov.uk

8. SANDWELL VALLEY COUNTRY PARK

Sandwell Metropolitan Borough Council.
Habitats: 268ha, pools, woodlands, grasslands, inc. three Local Nature Reserves.
Birds: *All year:* Grey Heron (small heronry), Great Crested Grebe, Lapwing, Reed Bunting, Great Spotted & Green Woodpeckers, Sparrowhawk, Kestrel. *Spring:* Little Ringed Plover, Oystercatcher, up to eight spp. breeding warbler, passage migrants. *Autumn:* Passage migrants. *Winter:* Goosander, Shoveler, Teal, Wigeon, Snipe.
Other: Common Spotted & Southern Marsh Orchid. Ringlet butterfly. Water Vole, Weasel.
Directions: Sat nav: B71 4BG (Sandwell Park Farm). Main entrances off Salter's Lane (SP 013 918) or Forge Lane (SP 022 930). Located approx one mile NE of West Bromwich town centre.
Public transport: Bus - nos.45/46 West Bromwich to Walsall/Great Barr. National Express, West Midlands. West Bromwich Central Metro stop (one mile).
Visiting: Car parks open 8am-sunset. Coach parking by appointment. Visitor centre, toilets, shop, cafe at Sandwell Park Farm open daily (not christmas period) 10am-4.30pm. Good footpaths around LNRs & much of the country park. Wheelchair access to Priory Woods LNR, Forge Mill Lake LNR & other parts of the country park. 8ha RSPB reserve nearby (see site 9).
Contact: Sandwell Valley CP, T: 0121 569 3070.

111

9. SANDWELL VALLEY RSPB

RSPB (Midlands Regional Office).
Habitats: Open water, wet grassland, reedbed, dry grassland, scrub.
Birds: *Summer:* Lapwing, Little Ringed Plover, Whitethroat, Sedge & Reed Warbler, Willow Tit. *Winter:* Wildfowl inc. Goosander. Water Rail, Snipe, Jack Snipe, woodpeckers, Bullfinch. *Passage:* sandpipers, Common Tern, Yellow Wagtail, chats.
Directions: Sat nav: B43 5AG. SP 035 928. Great Barr, Birmingham. Follow signs S from M6 Junc 7 via A34. Take R at 1st junction onto A4041. Take 4th L onto Hamstead Road (B4167), then R at 1st mini roundabout onto Tanhouse Avenue.

Public transport: Bus - no.16W Birmingham to West Bromwich & no.16 to Hamstead (ask for Tanhouse Avenue). Diamond. Train - Hamstead.
Visiting: Pedestrian access open al all times. Visitor centre/car park (open Tues-Sun, 10am-5pm summer (4pm winter), toilets (inc. disabled), light refreshments. Car park chage, members free/contact for coach parking. Way-marked trails, most paths accessible to assisted & powered wheelchairs with some gradients (phone for further info). Viewing screens. Hide open when staff/volunteers available (Tues-Sun, 10.30am-3pm) - hide can be hired outside of opening hours. Dogs on leads.
Contact: RSPB, T: 0121 357 7395; E: sandwellvalley@rspb.org.uk

Worcestershire

THE WILDLIFE TRUST manages more than 75 reserves covering a wide range of habitats in this largely rural county. Although it only has one sizeable reservoir (Bittell) there are excellent wetlands to explore at Upton Warren & Bredon's Hardwick. For the widest range of woodland species, including Pied Flycatcher, Wood Warbler & the more elusive Hawfinch, the best area is the Wyre Forest west of Kidderminster.

1. KNAPP & PAPERMILL

Worcestershire Wildlife Trust.
Habitats: Broadleaved woodland, unimproved grassland, fast stream, old orchard in Leigh Brook Valley.
Birds: *Summer:* Breeding Grey Wagtail & Dipper, Nuthatch & common woodland spp., Kingfisher, Spotted Flycatcher, 3 spp. woodpecker. Buzzard, Sparrowhawk & Redstart.
Other: Otters have returned recently. Good numbers of dragonflies & 30+ spp. butterflies on all three meadows inc. Holly Blue, Purple Hairstreak & White Admiral. Bluebells, Green-winged & Spotted Orchids. 11 spp. bats.
Directions: Sat nav: WR6 5HR. Take A4103 SW from Worcester, turn R at Bransford roundabout then L towards Suckley - reserve is approx three miles (do not turn off for Alfrick). Park at Bridges Stone lay-by (SO 751 522), cross road & follow path to Knapp House.
Public transport: None.
Visiting: Open dawn-dusk. Small visitor centre with toilets. Large parties should contact Warden in advance. Paths steep & uneven. Nature trail, wildlife garden, Kingfisher viewing screen. Dogs on lead at all times.
Contact: Worcestershire WT, T: 01905 754 919; E: enquiries@worcestershirewildlifetrust.org

2. MALVERN HILLS

Malvern Hills Trust.
Habitats: Grassland on hilltops, mixed woodland, scrub, quarries, small reservoirs & lakes.
Birds: Raptors inc. Buzzard, Sparrowhawk, Peregrine & Hobby. Ravens nest in quarries. Wooded areas hold all the expected common spp., breeding warblers & flycatchers, 3 spp. woodpecker & Tree Pipits on woodland edges. A few Nightingales hang on in areas of dense scrub, which also hold chats, pipits & Linnets. *Spring passage:* inc. Wheatear, Ring Ouzel (best in Happy Valley between Worcestershire Beacon & North Hill) & more rarely, Dotterel. *Autumn passage:* good range of migrants heading south. A winter highlight is Snow Bunting on the highest hills.

Other: Lesser Horseshoe & Barbastelle Bats, Polecat, 25 spp. butterflies, inc. High Brown Fritillary. Broad range of plants inc. Blinks, Crosswort & Common Spotted Orchid.
Directions: Sat nav: WR13 6DW (British Camp car park). SO 763 403. An eight mile long range of hills & commons lying S & W of Great Malvern, covering ca.1,200ha.
Public transport: None.
Visiting: Open all year. Many car parks (mainly open 6am-11pm) - charges/annual permit available. Public toilets with disabled access opposite British Camp car park (A449 Worcester Road). Two easy-access trails at Earnslaw (450 yards) & Blackhill (250 yards). Best birding areas inc. Castlemorton Common & Midsummer Hill.
Contact: Malvern Hills Trust, Manor House, Grange Road, Malvern WR14 3EY. T: 01684 892 002; E: info@malvernhills.org.uk, W: www.malvernhills.org.uk

3. TIDDESLEY WOOD NATURE RESERVE

Worcestershire Wildlife Trust.
Habitats: Ancient woodland, conifers.
Birds: *All year:* Sparrowhawk, common woodland birds, Willow & Marsh Tits. *Spring:* Cuckoo, Chiffchaff, Blackcap. *Winter:* Redwing, Fieldfare.
Other: Dragonflies inc. Club-tailed & White-legged Damselflies. Good for butterflies, inc. White Admiral, Peacock & Gatekeeper. Important invertebrates inc. nationally rare Noble Chafer Beetle.
Directions: Sat nav: WR10 2AD. SO 929 462. Take B4084 from Pershore towards Worcester. Turn L towards Besford & Croome near town boundary just before the summit of the hill (Rebecca Road). Entrance is on L after about 0.75 mile.
Public transport: Bus - no.X50 Worcester to Pershore stops close to Rebecca Road. First Bus.
Visiting: Open dawn-dusk. Car park (coaches) by arrangement. Information board. Cycles & horses only allowed on bridleway. Dogs on leads. Main ride stoney, with some potholes. Circular trail around small pathways, difficult if wet. Avoid military firing range in SW corner of wood, marked by red flags. Do not enter NE plot (private property).
Contact: Worcestershire WT - see site 1.

4. UPTON WARREN

Worcestershire Wildlife Trust.
Habitats: Fresh & saline pools with muddy islands, some woodland, scrub.
Birds: *Spring/autumn:* Passage waders, occassional Black Tern, Osprey. *Summer:* Breeding Avocet, Redshank, Little Ringed Plover, Oystercatcher, Common Tern, Cetti's, Sedge, Reed, & Grasshopper Warblers. Hobby nearby. *Winter:* Wildfowl, Bittern, Water Rail, Snipe.
Other: Saltmarsh plants, dragonflies.
Directions: Sat nav: B61 7ET. SO 936 677. Two miles S of Bromsgrove on A38. Leave M5 at Junc 5 & head N on A38, take third exit at first roundabout.
Public transport: Bus - no.144 Birmingham to Worcester passes reserve entrance. First Bus.
Visiting: Christopher Cadbury Wetland Reserve consists of Moors Pools (freshwater) & Flashes Pools (saline). Open dawn-dusk, The Flashes car park open 9am-8pm (Apr-Sep) & 9am-4pm (Oct-Mar).

Outdoor Education Centre/The Moors car parks open at all times. Non-members must obtain a day permit (Trust members - take membership card) from: Trust office, Outdoor Education Centre or volunteers on site. Six hides, maps at entrances, paths can be very muddy. Disabled access to hides at Moors Pools only by prior arrangement. Coach parking at sailing centre by arrangement. No dogs.
Contact: Worcestershire WT - see site 1.

5. WILDEN MARSH

Worcestershire Wildlife Trust.
Habitats: Dry & marshy fields with small alder & willow woods, reedbeds, many drainage ditches.
Birds: 192 spp. since 1968, about 70 spp. breed inc. Yellow Wagtail, nine spp. warbler & Redshank. *Winter:* Water Pipit, though numbers have declined recently.
Other: Plants inc. Southern Marsh Orchid, Marsh Cinquefoil, Marsh Arrow-grass, Marsh Pennywort & Lesser Water Parsnip.
Directions: Sat nav: DY13 9JT. SO 825 730. S of Kidderminster. Take A449 S from Kidderminster. At junction with A442 go straight across roundabout into Wilden Lane - very busy road with limited parking (park carefully in lay-by).
Public transport: Bus - no.15A from Kldderminster along Wilden Lane, bus stop 0.5 mile from reserve. Coniston Coaches (T: 01299 823 329).
Visiting: The reserve is complex & new visitors should consult a map. Enter over stile at gated entrance next to southern lay-by. Follow signs to leave certain areas undisturbed, no access to northern part of site. Gated entrances open at all times. Secure cattle gates at all times. Beware boggy areas, steep banks by River Stour & deep ditches.
Contact: Worcestershire WT - see site 1.

6. WYRE FOREST NNR

Natural England (West Midlands Team/Worcs Wildlife Trust.
Habitats: Ancient coppice oak woodland, conifer areas, heath heath, lowland grassland, stream.
Birds: Breeding birds inc. Redstart, Pied Flycatcher, Wood Warbler, Buzzard & Raven, with Dipper, Grey Wagtail & Kingfisher on larger streams.
Other: Mammals inc. Fallow, Roe & Muntjac Deer, Polecat, Otter, Mink, Yellow-neck Mouse, Dormouse, Water Shrew & voles. Several bat spp. inc. Pipistrelle & Daubenton's. Important for invertebrates inc. England's largest colony of Pearl-bordered Fritillary butterfly.
Directions: Sat nav: DY14 9XQ. SO 750 740 (Callow Hill/Discovery Centre). On A456 Kidderminster to Tenbury Wells road, three miles west of Bewdley.
Public transport: Bus - no.291 (not Sun) Kidderminster to Bewdley/Tenbury Wells stops at Callow Hill/DC. R&B Travel (T: 01584 890 770). Train - Kidderminster.
Visiting: Keep to paths. Toilets & refreshments (with disabled access). Several waymarked trails (some suitable for wheelchair users), regular guided walks, family cycle routes through reserve.
Contact: Wyre Forest NNR, Natural England Office, Lodge Hill Farm, Dowles Brook, Bewdley DY12 2LY; T: 01299 400 686.

Eastern England

Bedfordshire

THIS IS ONE OF England's smallest counties, with a good selection of sites scattered through it. Blows Down is one of the best southern sites to see Ring Ouzels on spring passage. The RSPB's HQ at The Lodge, Sandy, is well watched & has produced a series of excellent records, Nightjars now breed on restored heathland. A number of Country Parks in the county can be busy but attract a good range of species.

1. BLOW'S DOWNS

Beds, Cambs & Northants Wildlife Trust.
Habitats: Chalk downland, scrub & grassland - a traditional resting place for incoming spring migrants.
Birds: *Spring/autumn:* Ring Ouzel, Wheatear, Whinchat, Black Redstart, Stonechat, Willow Warbler. *Winter:* Lapwing, Meadow Pipit, Skylark.
Other: Chalkhill Blue, Brown Argus & Marbled White butterflies. Plants inc. Small Scabious, Squinancywort, Burnet-saxifrage, Great Pignut, Common Spotted & Bee Orchids.

Directions: Sat nav: LU5 4AE. TL 030 215. On boundary between Dunstable/Luton. Take A505 from W of Luton, cross M1, straight over first roundabout, L at second continue to A5 junc., turn L - after 0.6 mile turn L into Half Moon Lane (park carefully on the verge at end of lane). Can walk 0.5 mile from Dunstable centre along A5 to same entrance.
Public transport: Bus - no.B Luton-Dunstable-Downside Estate, alight Half Moon Lane stop. Centrebus (T: 0116 410 5050).
Visiting: Open all year. Steep slopes, not suitable for wheelchairs.
Contact: BCN WT, T: 01234 364 213; E: bedfordshire@wildlifebcnp.org

2. FLITWICK MOOR

Beds, Cambs & Northants Wildlife Trust.
Habitats: Important local wetland, mixture of fen, meadow, wet woodland & fragile peaty soil.
Birds: *Spring:* Lesser Spotted Woodpecker, Willow Warbler, Blackcap. *Summer:* Water Rail, Grasshopper & Garden Warblers, Cuckoo. *Autumn:* Brambling. *Winter:* Siskin, Water Rail, Great Spotted Woodpecker.
Other: Good variety of butterflies & dragonflies, plus Chimney Sweeper moth & Conehead Bush Cricket. Plants inc. 10 spp. sphagnum moss, Marsh Pennywort, Black Knapweed, Water Figwort plus Fly Agaric & Yellow Brain Fungus in autumn.
Directions: Sat nav: MK45 5BPZ TL 046 354. E of Flitwick. From Flitwick town centre (Tesco roundabout) on A5120, cross railway bridge, R at roundabout, immediately L into King's Road. After 500 yards, L into Maulden Road towards A507. After quarter mile R at Folly Farm, follow track to small car park. Also footpath to reserve from Moor Lane.
Public transport: Bus - no.2 Bedford to Flitwick (not Sun). Stagecoach. Train - Flitwick & then 0.75 mile walk.
Visiting: Open all year. Car park. Stick to public paths.
Contact: BCN WT - see site 1.

3. THE LODGE, SANDY

RSPB (Central England Office).
Habitats: 220ha, mixture of woodland, heathland & acid grassland & inc. formal gardens of RSPB's UK HQ. New areas being restored to heathland.
Birds: *All year:* Woodpeckers, woodland birds. *Spring/summer:* Hobby, Nightjar, Spotted Flycatcher, breeding common woodland species & warblers. *Winter:* Winter thrushes.
Other: Natterjack Toad, rare heathland insects. Particularly good site for fungi (600 spp.) & lichens. Garden pools good for dragonflies.
Directions: Sat nav: SG19 2DL. TL 191 485. Reserve lies one mile E of Sandy, signposted from the B1042 road to Potton.

NATURE RESERVES - EASTERN ENGLAND

Public transport: Bus - no.73 (not Sun) Bedford to Sandy, one mile from Sandy Market Place. Stagecoach. Train - Sandy (0.5 mile). Walk in part is along trail through heathland restoration.
Visiting: Reserve open daily 7am-8pm (or dusk when earlier). Gatehouse: shop (with refreshments) open 9am-5pm weekdays, 10am-5pm weekends & bank holidays. Toilets (inc. disabled). Car park charge for non-members (free if only visiting shop). Five miles of nature trails. One bridleway (0.5 mile) & gardens are wheelchair/pushchair accessible. One hide (wheelchair accessible), 50 yards from car park. Bike racks. Dogs only allowed on bridleway. Coach parking at weekends by arrangement.
Contact: RSPB, T: 01767 693 333;
E: thelodgereserve@rspb.org.uk

4. MARSTON VALE MILLENIUM COUNTRY PARK

Marston Vale Trust.
Habitats: Millenium Country Park (225ha) inc. Stewartby Lake (85ha) which attracts birds when smaller waters are frozen. Reedbeds, woodland, hawthorn scrub, ponds & wet grassland.
Birds: *Spring*: Passage waders & terns (Black, Sandwich & Arctic Terns), hirundines, Wheatear, Whinchat, Osprey & Little Gull. Yellow Wagtail & Garganey occasionally breed. *Summer*: Ten species of breeding warblers, Hobby, Turtle Dove, Nightingale, Bearded Tit, Cuckoo, Barn Owl, Marsh Harrier, Water Rail, Kingfisher & common wildfowl. *Autumn*: Passage waders & terns. *Winter*: Bittern, Peregrine, Siskin, Redpoll, Stonechat, Snipe, gulls inc. Caspian, Yellow-legged & Mediterranean Gulls, wildfowl (Gadwall, Shoveler, Pochard, Teal & Tufted Duck), Little & Great Crested Grebes. Rarer species can inc. divers, grebes, Common Scoter, Smew & Scaup. *Rarities*: Glossy Ibis, Laughing Gull, Caspian Gull, Manx Shearwater, Purple Heron & White Stork.
Other: Dingy & Grizzled Skipper butterflies, excellent for dragonflies. Also Otter & Brown Hare, plus Bee & Pyramidal Orchids & stoneworts.
Directions: Sat nav: MK43 0PS. TL 004 417. SW of Bedford off A421 at Marston Moretaine. Only five mins from Junc 13 of M1, along A421 towards Bedford. Look for brown tourist signs for the centre.
Public transport: Trains - Millbrook & Stewartby, 20 mins walk to forest centre.
Visiting: Car parking, coach parking (in advance) - charges apply - closes at 5pm. Forest Centre (cafe bar, gift shop, art gallery) open summer weekdays 9am-5pm, weekends 10am-5pm. Reduced hours in winter (closed 25/26 Dec, Jan 1). Pedestrian access to park at any time. Trails inc. a 1.25 mile Wetland Trail (entry charge, no dogs) is a level path with a compacted, loose stone surface inc. two hand gates with top latches with wheelchair & pushchair access - has four hides.
Contact: Forest Centre, T: 01234 767 037;
E: info@marstonvale.org; W: www.marstonvale.org

5. PEGSDON HILLS & HOO BIT NATURE RESERVE

Beds, Cambs & Northants Wildlife Trust.
Habitats: Chalk grassland, scrub & woodland.
Birds: *Spring*: Wheatear, Ring Ouzel, Tree Pipit, Yellowhammer. *Summer*: Turtle Dove, Grey Partridge, Lapwing, Skylark. *Winter*: Brambling, Stonechat, winter thrushes, raptors inc. Buzzard.
Other: Dark Green Fritillary, Dingy & Grizzled Skippers, Chalkhill Blue, Brown Argus & Small Heath butterflies. Glow Worm. Plants inc. Pasqueflower in spring, Fragrant & Common Spotted Orchids.
Directions: Sat Nav: SG5 3JS. TL 118 302 (lay-by). Five miles W of Hitchin. Take B655 from Hitchin towards Barton-le-Clay. Turn R to Pegsdon then immediately L & park in lay-by. Reserve entrance across B655 via footpath.
Public transport: None.
Visiting: Open at all times. Tracks/paths can be steep & uneven.
Contact: BCN WT - see site 1.

6. PRIORY COUNTRY PARK

Bedford Borough Council.
Habitats: Lakes, reedbeds, scrub & woodland, meadows adjoining River Great Ouse.
Birds: 210+ spp. Good numbers/variety of winter wildfowl, varied mix of spring passage species, with breeding warblers & woodpeckers, augmented by feeding terns, hirundines & raptors lakeside. *All year*: Cormorant, Little Egret, Grey Heron, Stock Dove, woodpeckers, Kingfisher, Grey Wagtail, Treecreeper, Goldfinch, Bullfinch. *Summer*: Hobby, Turtle Dove, Swift, hirundines, *acrocephalus* & *sylvia* warblers. *Passage*: Raptors, waders, terns, pipits. *Winter*: Grebes, Pochard, Shoveler, Gadwall, Merlin, Water Rail, gulls, thrushes, Chiffchaff, corvids, buntings.
Other: 23 spp. dragonflies, inc. Small Red-eyed Damselfly & Hairy Dragonfly. 20 spp. butterflies. Large plant list. Fox, Muntjac & Otter.
Directions: Sat nav: MK41 9DJ. TL 071 493. 1.5 miles SE from Bedford town centre. Signposted from A4280 & A421, car park on Barkers Lane.
Public transport: Bus - no.4 Bedford to Goldington, alight 1st stop on Riverfield Drive (200 yds). Stagecoach. Train - Bedford (approx 2.5 miles).
Visiting: Open daily (main one is Barkers Lane, open 5am-9pm), visitor centre, toilets, cafe (10am-4pm). Three nature trails (wheelchair accessible), hides .
Contact: Visitor Centre, Priory CP, Barkers Lane, Bedford, MK41 9DJ. T: 01234 718 012;
E: prioryrangers@bedford.gov.uk

Cambridgeshire

THE FENS, INCLUDING the Nene & Ouse Washes, are superb wetlands well known for wintering wildfowl, owls & raptors. The former offers the chance of Cranes, breeding Black-tailed Godwits, Spotted Crakes plus introduced Corncrakes in summer. The latter holds the largest inland concentration of wintering wildfowl in Britain. Grafham Water attracts plenty of scarce species, while Paxton Pits is probably the best place in the country to actually see Nightingales.

1. FEN DRAYTON LAKES

RSPB (Eastern England Office).
Habitats: Complex of lakes (former gravel workings) & traditional riverside meadows next to River Great Ouse.
Birds: At least 213 spp. have been recorded in area with 65 spp. being regular breeders, inc. Common Tern. Hobby, waders on passage. *Winter:* Nationally important numbers of Gadwall & Coot. Bitterns are now a regular sight, with Holywell Lake & Elney Lake being the favoured sites. *Rarities:* inc. Great Egret, Purple Heron, Glossy Ibis, Common Crane, Red-Footed Falcon, Honey Buzzard & Whiskered Tern.
Other: Good for butterflies, dragonflies & mammals.
Directions: Sat nav: CB24 4RB. TL 342 690. NW of Cambridge. Leave A14 at Junc 28, follow signs to Swavesey. Turn L in Boxworth End (signed to Fen Drayton). Turn R onto minor road (signed to Swavesey), then L into entrance to Fen Drayton Lakes. Follow signs to car park.

Public transport: Bus - route B between Huntingdon & Cambridge - has a request stop at reserve. Busway/Stagecoach.
Visiting: Open at all times. Ten-mile network of trails, information boards give access details/trail guides & event leaflets available from car park. Dogs only allowed on public footpaths & bridleways. Five viewing screens, one hide & three open viewing shelters.
Contact: RSPB, T: 01954 233 260;
E: fendraytonlakes@rspb.org.uk

2. FERRY MEADOWS (NENE PARK)

Nene Park Trust.
Habitats: Lakes, meadows, scrub, broadleaved woodland & small wetland nature reserve.
Birds: *All year:* Good selection of woodland & water birds, Kingfisher. *Spring:* Terns, waders, Yellow Wagtail. *Winter:* Grebes, gulls, Siskin, Redpoll, Water Rail.
Other: Bluebell, Wood Anenome, Wild Garlic in woodland.
Directions: Sat nav: PE2 6YD. TL 148 973. Three miles W of Peterborough city centre & two miles E of A1. On all major routes into city, follow brown tourist signs for Nene Park or country park symbol. Also signposted on Oundle Road (A605).
Public transport: Bus - no.X4 Peterborough to Corby stops on A605 by Notcutts Nursery. 0.5 mile walk to park. Stagecoach.
Visiting: Open daily, 6.30am-10pm (summer), 6.30am-6.30pm (winter). Car parking charges apply, height restriction. Visitor centre open 10am-5pm (Apr-Oct) & 10am-4pm (Nov-Mar), toilets (inc. disabled), cafe. Hard surface paths in park's central areas, but steep slopes in Bluebell Wood. Two wheelchair-accessible hides in nature reserve area. Electric scooters & wheelchair available - book in advance.
Contact: Nene Park Trust, T: 01733 234 193;
E: visitor.services@neneparktrust.org.uk;
W: www.neneparktrust.org.uk

3. FOWLMERE

RSPB (Eastern England Office).
Habitats: Reedbed, fen, chalk grassland, scrub.
Birds: *All year:* Water Rail, Kingfisher, Reed Bunting. *Spring/summer:* Little Grebe, Turtle Dove, ten spp. breeding warblers. *Autumn:* Yellowhammer, Corn Bunting. *Winter:* Snipe, Water Rail, raptors.
Other: Healthy population of Water Shrews & Otters. 18 spp. dragonflies.
Directions: Sat nav: SG8 6EZ. TL 406 461. Seven miles S of Cambridge. From A10, turn towards Fowlmere at Fowlmere-Shepreth crossroads (no RSPB sign); after one mile, turn R by cemetery (RSPB sign) - after another 0.6 mile, turn L into reserve.
Public transport: Bus: no.A Royston to Trumpington, alight on A10 at Shepreth, Dunsbridge Turnpike stop (one mile). Stagecoach. Walk towards Melbourn - after 300 yards, cross road & turn L on to single track road to Fowlmere (beware of traffic). After 0.75 mile, turn R into reserve (RSPB sign). Train - Shepreth, two miles.

Visiting: Open at all times. Car park, charge for non-members. Visitor reception centre staffed by volunteers (usually weekends/bank holidays). Two mile signposted nature trail, three hides, toilets inc. disabled. Space for one coach, prior booking essential.
Contact: RSPB, T: 01767 693 013;
E: fowlmere@rspb.org.uk

4. GRAFHAM WATER

Beds, Cambs & Northants Wildlife Trust.
Habitats: Open water, lagoons, reedbeds, open water, wet mud & willow carr, ancient & plantation woodland, scrub, species-rich grassland.
Birds: *All year*: Common woodland birds. *Spring/summer*: Breeding Nightingale, Reed, Willow & Sedge Warblers, Common & Black Terns. *Autumn*: Passage waders. *Winter*: Waders inc. Common Sandpiper & Dunlin, Great Crested Grebe. Wildfowl inc. large flocks of common species, plus Shelduck, Goldeneye, Goosander & Smew, gulls (can be up to 30,000 roosting in mid-winter). *Rarities*: Have inc. Wilson's Phalarope, Ring-necked Duck, Great Northern Diver, Glaucous, Iceland & Mediterranean Gulls.
Other: Bee, Common Spotted & Early Purple Orchids, Common Twayblade (in woods), Cowslip. Common Blue & Marbled White butterflies, dragonflies inc. Broad-bodied Chaser, voles, Grass Snake.
Directions: Sat nav: PE28 0BX. TL 143 671. Follow signs for Grafham Water from A1 at Buckden or A14 at Ellington. Follow B661 road towards Perry & Staughtons to West Perry. As you leave village, Anglian Water's Mander car park is signposted on R.
Public transport: Bus - no.400 (Mon-Fri) Huntingdon Circular to West Perry. Go-Whippet (T: 01954 230 011).
Visiting: Open all year (not Dec 25). Use Plummer car park for lagoons, Marlow car park for dam area (good for waders/vagrants) - pay-&-display, disabled parking. Visitor centres at Mander & Plummer car parks with restaurants, shops & toilets. Six bird hides in nature reserve: three in bird sanctuary area, two in wildlife garden accessible to wheelchairs, further hide overlooks islands/scrapes in settlement lagoons. Cycle track through reserve also accessible to wheelchairs. No dogs in wildlife garden, on leads elsewhere.
Contact: Grafham Water Nature Reserve,
T: 01480 811 075; E: grafham@wildlifebcn.org

5. THE GREAT FEN

BC&N Wildlife Trust/Natural England (East Anglia Team)/Environment Agency/Hunts District Council.
Habitats: Pools formed from clay pits at Ramsey Heights; extensive birch forest (largest in lowland Britain) & reedbed at Holme Fen; mixed woodland, open waters, fen & grassland at Woodwalton.
Birds: Wide variety of common wildfowl plus Kingfisher, Grey Heron, Bittern & wintering Goosander on meres. Marsh Harriers breed in reedbed, along with Bearded Tit & Cetti's Warbler. Hen Harriers visit in winter. Common Crane observed in recent years. Wet meadows at Darlow's Farm attractive to breeding Lapwing, Snipe & Redshank & wintering Whooper & Bewick's Swans.

Other: Great Crested Newt & rare beetles at ramsey heights. Otter, Brown Hare, deer spp., Water Vole. Scarce Chaser dragonfly, Small Copper & White Admiral butterflies. Wide variety of bog & heath plants.
Directions: Sat nav: PE26 2RS. TL 245 848 (Ramsey Heights), plus Holme Fen NNR & Woodwalton NNR (Chapel Road, Ramsey Heights), S of Peterborough, lying between A1 in west & Ramsey. B660 runs through centre of Great Fen.
Public transport: Bus - no.31 (Mon-Sat) Peterborough to Ramsey stops at end of Chapel Road, 0.5 mile from Countryside Centre. Stagecoach.
Visiting: Open at all times, views over farmland linking sites - Ramsey Heights Nature Reserve, Woodwalton Fen NNR, Holme Fen NNR & New Decoy Farm. Great Fen will eventually occupy 3,700ha. All have waymarked trails - grassy paths mostly level. Countryside Centre at Ramsey Heights (open 9am-4pm), toilets. Hides at Woodwalton & Holme Fen. Dogs on leads.
Contact: Great Fen Team, T: 01487 710 420;
E: info@greatfen.org.uk; W: www.greatfen.org.uk

6. NENE WASHES

RSPB (Eastern England Office).
Habitats: Wet grassland with ditches - often flooded.
Birds: *Spring/early summer*: Corncrake release scheme, plus Spotted Crake. UK's top site for breeding Black-tailed Godwit. Other breeding waders inc. Lapwing, Redshank & Snipe. Duck (inc. Garganey), Marsh Harrier, Hobby, Yellow Wagtail & Tree Sparrow. *Autumn/winter*: Waterfowl in large numbers (inc. Bewick's Swan, Pintail, Shoveler), Barn & Short-eared Owls, Hen Harrier, Common Crane, roost of up to 20 Marsh Harriers.
Other: Water Vole, Otter, Water Violet, Flowering Rush & Fringe Water Lily.
Directions: Sat nav: PE7 2DD. TL 318 991. Reserve is eight miles E of Peterborough & NE of Whittlesey. Car park at end of Eldernell Lane, N off A605 east of Coates.
Public transport: Bus - no.33 (not Sun) Peterborough to Chatteris runs on A605, alight at Coates, walk down Eldernell Lane (ca. one mile). Stagecoach.
Visiting: Open at all times along South Barrier Bank, accessed at Eldernell. Small car park at end of Eldernell Lane - one coach max so group visits along central path by arrangement. No access to fields or for wheelchairs along bank. Nene Valley Way path offers elevated views over reserve.
Contact: RSPB, T: 01733 205 140;
E: charlie.kitchin@rspb.org.uk

7. OUSE FEN

RSPB (Eastern England office)/Hanson.
Habitats: A working sand & gravel quarry being developed into a vast nature reserve with open water, grassland & potentially the UK's largest reedbed.
Birds: *Spring/summer*: Breeding Great Crested Grebe, Skylark, Marsh Harrier, Black-headed Gull, Reed Bunting, Bearded Tit & incoming migrants inc. Reed & Sedge Warblers, hirundines, Black-tailed Godwit, Ruff, Garganey, Common Tern & Hobby.

Autumn: Passage waders inc. Green Sandpiper, increasing numbers of common wildfowl & incoming winter thrushes. *Winter:* Good numbers of Mute Swan, Gadwall, Tufted Duck, Wigeon & Pochard & regular sightings of Smew. Large number of Little Egret, plus flocks of tits, finches & buntings. Barn Owl & Bittern regular, Short-eared Owl, Hen Harrier & Peregrine occasional.
Other: Brown Hare, Roe & Muntjac Deer. Wide range of butterflies & dragonflies.
Directions: Sat nav: PE27 4TA. TL 348 726. Located at Needingworth, near St Ives. Leave Junc 26 of A14 onto A1096 London Road. Go straight over three roundabouts. At fourth, take third exit (A1123). Cross over next roundabout & take next R onto Bluntisham Road. After 400 yards, turn L into reserve.
Public transport: Bus - no.21 (Mon-Fri, limited service) St Ives to Needingworth. Dews Coaches (T: 01487 740 241). From village bus stop follow Bluntisham Road east for 0.75 mile until signpost for reserve on R.
Visiting: Open at all times. Car park (free)), height barrier - no coaches. Two waymarked visitor trails, two viewpoints (one screened).
Contact: RSPB, T: 01954 233 260; E: ousefen@rspb.org.uk

8. OUSE WASHES

RSPB (Eastern England Office).
Habitats: Lowland wet grassland, seasonally flooded. Open pool systems in front of some hides, particularly Stockdale's hide.
Birds: *Summer:* 70 spp. breed inc. Black-tailed Godwit, Lapwing, Redshank, Snipe, Shoveler, Gadwall, Garganey & Spotted Crake. Also Hobby & Marsh Harrier. *Autumn:* Passage waders inc. Wood & Green Sandpipers, Spotted Redshank, Greenshank, Little Stint, plus terns & Marsh & Hen Harriers. *Winter:* Large number of wildfowl (up to 100,000 birds) inc. Bewick's & Whooper Swans, Wigeon, Teal, Shoveler, Pintail, Pochard. Tree Sparrow.
Other: Good range of dragonflies, butterflies & fenland flora.
Directions: Sat nav: PE15 0NF. TL 471 860. Between Chatteris & March on A141, take B1093 to Manea. Reserve signposted from Manea. Reserve office & visitor centre located off Welches Dam.
Public transport: None to reserve entrance. Buses & trains stop at Manea, three miles from reserve.
Visiting: Open at all times. Car park (inc. two disabled bays, groups welcome - space for two small 36-seat coaches, large coaches can't pass final bend to reserve). Access reserve from visitor centre (open daily 9am-5pm, not Dec 25/26), toilets, hot drinks. Ten hides (open at all times) overlook reserve - Welches Dam hide (with disabled access) 350 yards from visitor centre, rest up to 1.8 miles away. Welches Dam to public hides approached by marked paths behind boundary bank. Boardwalk over pond is good for dragonflies in summer. Dogs on leads.
Contact: RSPB, T: 01354 680 212; E: ouse.washes@rspb.org.uk

9. PAXTON PITS NATURE RESERVE

Huntingdonshire District Co./Friends of Paxton Pits.
Habitats: 77ha, lakes, riverside, reedbed, meadows, scrub, woodland.
Birds: 235 spp., 70 spp. breed. *Spring/summer:* Nightingale, Kingfisher, Common Tern, Sparrowhawk, Hobby, Grasshopper, Sedge & Reed Warblers, Lesser Whitethroat. Large Cormorant colony. *Winter:* Wildfowl inc. Smew, Goldeneye, Goosander, Gadwall, Pochard.
Other: Wildflowers, 27 spp. butterflies & 21 spp. dragonflies are in abundance. Common Spotted Orchids along meadow trail, Bee Orchids around car park. Otters use reserve.
Directions: Sat nav PE19 6ET. TL 196 629. Access from A1 at Little Paxton, two miles N of St Neots. Reserve signposted from edge of Little Paxton.
Public transport: Bus - no.66 (not Sun) St Neots & Huntingdon to Little Paxton. Stagecoach. Train - St Neots (two miles - can walk along Ouse Valley Way.)
Visiting: Open at all times. Car park - coaches/groups by arrangement, bike racks. Wheelchair-accessible visitor centre/toilets, small shop - books, bird feeders/seed etc, & light refreshments. Open 10am-4.30pm (not Dec 25) - subject to volunteer availability. Three hides (always open), marked nature trails. Many paths suitable for wheelchairs, but muddy when wet. Dogs must be under control.
Contact: The Rangers, Paxton Pits Nature Reseve, High Street, Little Paxton, St Neots, Cambs PE19 6ET. T: 01480 406 795; W: www.paxton-pits.org.uk; E: paxtonpits@huntingdonshire.gov.uk

10. WICKEN FEN NNR

The National Trust.
Habitats: Internationally important wetland, inc. open fen meadows, sedge fields, grazing marsh, partially flooded wet grassland, reedbed, scrub, woodland.
Birds: *Spring:* Passage waders & passerines. *Summer:* Marsh Harriers, Hobbies, waders & warblers. *Winter:* Wildfowl, Hen Harriers roost on Sedge Fen, Marsh Harrier, Bittern, Black-tailed Godwit, Barn & Short-eared Owls, Cetti's Warbler.
Other: 9,000+ spp. recorded inc. 21 spp. dragonflies, 27 spp. butterflies, 1,200+ spp. moths. Water Vole, Otter.
Directions: Sat nav CB7 5XP. TL 564 706. Lies 17 miles NE of Cambridge & ten miles S of Ely. From A10 drive E along A1123 to Wicken, turn R in village (signposted).
Public transport: None.
Visiting: Open daily dawn-dusk daily (not Dec 25). Disabled parking in main car park (close to visitor centre), coach parking limited (groups need to book). Parking/entry fee for non-NT members. Visitor centre, shop & cafe open daily (10am-5pm/dusk in winter). Toilets (inc. disabled), nine hides (three equipped for wheelchairs), boardwalk (suitable for wheelchairs), footpaths, cycle route (NCN Route 11 passes through reserve). National Dragonfly Centre open weekends during summer.
Contact: Wicken Fen Visitor Centre, T: 01353 720 274; E: wickenfen@nationaltrust.org.uk

Essex

THE COUNTY HAS a wide range of habitats - the Wildlife Trust manages 87 nature reserves throughout this huge county. The RSPB's coastal reserves at Rainham Marshes & Old Hall Marshes both attract a wide range of species including wintering raptors. The coast (including the Naze & Bradwell, where there is a Bird Observatory) attracts migrants, including rarities. Try seawatching along the Thames off Southend Pier. Away from the coast, Abberton Reservoir holds important numbers of wintering wildfowl & wader passage can be good. The ancient woodland of Epping Forest lies close to London.

1. ABBERTON RESERVOIR

Essex Wildlife Trust.
Habitats: 25ha on edge of expanding 485ha reservoir, with wader-friendly muddy margins.
Birds: *Spring:* Passage waders, terns, birds of prey. *Summer:* Tree-nesting Cormorant colony, raft-nesting Common Tern. Hobby, Yellow Wagtail, warblers, Nightingale, Turtle Dove, Skylark, Corn Bunting. *Autumn:* Red-crested Pochard, waders, rarities. *Winter:* Nationally important for Coot, Mallard, Teal, Wigeon, Shoveler, Gadwall, Pochard, Tufted Duck, Goldeneye. Smew, Bittern & Goosander regular. Golden Plover & Lapwing flocks on surrounding fields.
Other: Dragonflies inc. Broad-bodied Chaser, Small Red-eyed damselfly. Butterflies inc. Brown Argus & Purple Hairstreak. Roesel's Bush-cricket. Brown Hare, Smooth Newt, Wasp Spider.
Directions: Sat nav: CO2 0EU. TL 962 177. Six miles SW of Colchester on B1026 (Colchester to Maldon). Follow signs from Layer-de-la-Haye or Great Wigborough.
Public transport: None.

Visiting: Open daily (not Dec 25/26) 9am-5pm (4pm Nov-Jan). Ample parking, inc. disabled & coach bays. Visitor centre inc. toilets, viewing verandah, cafe & shop. Electric wheelchair for hire. Outdoor play area. Good viewing where roads cross reservoir. Nature trails with panoramic views, three hides - two overlook water, one in woodland.
Contact: Essex WT, T: 01206 738 172;
E: abberton@essexwt.org.uk

2. ABBOTT'S HALL FARM

Essex Wildlife Trust.
Habitats: 280ha coastal farm - saltmarsh, saline lagoons, grazing marsh, farmland, woodland, freshwater lakes & ponds.
Birds: Skylark, Grey Partridge, Corn Bunting & other farmland species. Passage migrants & summer warblers. *Winter:* Waders & wildfowl, large roost of Little Egret.
Other: Range of butterflies, reptiles, newts, Water Vole.
Directions: Sat nav: CO5 7RZ. TL 962 146. On Blackwater estuary, seven miles SW from Colchester. Turn E off B1026 (Colchester-Maldon road) towards Peldon. Entrance, near Great Wigborough, is 0.5 mile on R.
Public transport: None.
Visiting: Wildlife Trust HQ & a working farm - take care. Weekdays (9am-5pm). Toilets, three hides (two with wheelchair ramps), information boards. Many footpaths through farmland areas. Guided walks, factsheets available. Dogs only in designated area.
Contact: Essex WT, T: 01621 862 960;
E: admin@essexwt.org.uk

3. BRADWELL BIRD OBSERVATORY/SHELL BANK

Essex Birdwatching Society/Essex Wildlife Trust.
Habitats: Mudflats, saltmarsh, 12ha of shellbank. Mouth of Blackwater estuary.
Birds: *Spring/autumn:* good passage of migrants. *Summer:* Small breeding population of terns & other estuarine species, Yellow Wagtail, Reed Bunting & Linnet. *Winter:* Wildfowl (inc. Red-throated Diver, Brent Geese, Red-breasted Merganser), large numbers of waders (up to 20,000), small numbers of Twite, Snow Bunting & occasional Shore Lark on beaches. Hen Harrier, Merlin & Peregrine.
Other: Variety of dragonflies inc. Hairy Dragonfly & Scarce Emerald Damselfly.
Directions: Sat nav: CM0 7PN.
TM 031 085. BBO is located on edge of Bradwell Shell Bank nature reserve, 100 yards S of St Peter's Chapel, Bradwell-on-Sea. Parking at end of East End Road.
Public transport: Bus - no.D1 (not Sun) from Maldon. Hedingham (T: 01206 769 778). No.DaRT4 (not Sun) from Burnham-on-Couch. Essex & Suffolk DaRT (T: 01621 874 411).
Visiting: Open all year. Car park. Keep to seawall in breeding season to prevent disturbance.
Contact: Graham Smith (BBO Sec), 48 The Meads, Ingatestone, Essex CM4 0AE. T: 01277 354 034;
E: silaum.silaus@tesco.co.uk; Essex WT - see site 2.

4. FINGRINGHOE WICK

Essex Wildlife Trust.
Habitats: Old gravel pit, large lake, many ponds, sallow/birch thickets, young scrub, reedbeds, saltmarsh, gorse heathland.
Birds: 200 spp. recorded. *Spring/summer:* 25+ male Nightingales. Marsh Harrier, Hobby, Turtle Dove, Cuckoo, Green & Great Spotted Woodpeckers & good variety of warblers in scrub/thickets. *Autumn/winter:* Brent Goose, waders (inc. Avocet & Golden Plover), Peregrine, Merlin, Hen Harrier, Little Egret. Little Grebe, Mute Swan, Teal, Wigeon, Shoveler, Gadwall.
Other: Swathes of Sea Lavender in summer among 350 plant spp. Numerous dragonflies & butterflies.
Directions: Sat nav: C05 7DN. TM 048 192. Reserve signposted from B1025 to Mersea Island, five miles S of Colchester.
Public transport: Nearest buses to Fingringhoe (then 45 min walk along Gravel Pit Trail to reserve.
Visiting: Open daily (not Dec 25/26) 9am-5pm (4pm Nov-Jan). Car park. Voluntary entrance donation. Visitor centre - toilets (inc. baby changing facilities, easy access toilet), shop, light refreshments, observation room with displays overlooking saltmarsh. One wheelchair available. Seven hides, nature trails. Dogs on leads, limited to dog walk area at edge of reserve.
Contact: Fingringhoe Wick Visitor Centre, T: 01206 729 678; E: fingringhoe@essexwt.org.uk

5. HANNINGFIELD RESERVOIR

Essex Wildlife Trust/Essex & Suffolk Water.
Habitats: 45ha, mixed woodland with grassy glades & rides, adjoining 352ha Hanningfield Reservoir.
Birds: *Spring:* Good numbers & mix of woodland warblers. *Summer:* Vast numbers of Swifts, Swallows & martins feeding over the water. Hobby & Osprey. *Winter:* Good numbers & mix of waterfowl. Large gull roost.
Other: Spectacular displays of Bluebells in spring. Dragonflies around ponds. Grass Snake & Common Lizard sometimes bask on rides.
Directions: Sat nav: CM11 1WT. TQ 725 971. Three miles N of Wickford. Exit off Southend Road (Old A130) at Rettendon onto South Hanningfield Road. Follow this for two miles until reaching the T-junction with Hawkswood Road. Turn R - entrance to visitor centre & reserve is one mile on R.
Public transport: Bus - no.14 (not Sun) Chelmsford to Wickford. First Essex. Alight at Downham village & walk 0.5 mile down Crowsheath Lane.
Visiting: Open daily (not Dec 25/26) 9am-5pm (4pm Nov-Jan). Voluntary entrance donation. car park with disabled & coach parking. Visitor centre, shop, refreshments, toilets, education room. Picnic area, four bird hides (one adapted), nature trails. No dogs. No cycling.
Contact: Hanningfield Reservoir Visitor Centre, T: 01268 711 001; E: hanningfield@essexwt.org.uk

6. OLD HALL MARSHES

RSPB (Eastern England Office).
Habitats: 630ha, coastal grazing marsh, reedbed, open water, saline lagoon, saltmarsh & mudflat.
Birds: *Summer:* Breeding Avocet, Redshank, Lapwing, Pochard, Shoveler, Gadwall, Marsh Harrier, Bearded Tit & Barn Owl. *Passage:* All expected waders inc. Spotted Redshank, Green Sandpiper & Whimbrel. Yellow Wagtail, Whinchat & Wheatear. *Winter:* Large numbers of wildfowl inc. Brent Goose (ca. 4,000), Wigeon, Teal, Shoveler, Goldeneye, Red-breasted Merganser, waders, Merlin, Hen Harrier, Short-eared Owl & Twite.
Other: Brown Hare, Water Vole, Hairy Dragonfly, Scarce Emerald Damselfly, Ground Lackey moth, Cream Spot Tiger, White-letter Hairstreak among 24 spp. butterflies, Yellow Meadow Ant.
Directions: Sat nav: CM9 8TP. TL 959 122. Overlooks River Blackwater, SW of Colchester. From A12 take B1023, via Tiptree to Tolleshunt D'Arcy. Turn L at village maypole then R into Chapel Road (back road to Tollesbury). After approx 1 mile, turn L into Old Hall Lane. Continue up Old Hall Lane, through iron gates & follow signs straight ahead to car park.
Public transport: Bus - no.95 (not Sun) Maldon to Tollesbury (then two mile walk along seawall). Hedingham (T: 01206 769 778).
Visiting: Open 9am-5pm/dusk if earlier when car park gates locked. No coaches. Do not park in the lane. Two trails - three miles & 6.5 miles. Viewing screens overlooking saline lagoon area at E end of reserve. No wheelchair access or facilities. Dogs under control allowed on footpaths. Nearest toilets in Tiptree, six miles away.
Contact: RSPB, T: 01621 869 015; E: oldhallmarshes@rspb.org.uk

7. RAINHAM MARSHES

RSPB (Eastern England office).
Habitats: Former MoD shooting range, largest area of lowland wetland remaining along the Thames.
Birds: *Spring:* Marsh Harrier, Hobby, Wheatear, hirundines & other migrants. *Summer/autumn:* Many waders, inc. Black-tailed Godwit, Whimbrel, Greenshank, Snipe, Lapwing, Avocet. Yellow-legged Gull. Hunting Merlin & Peregrine. *Winter:* Waders, wildfowl, Water Pipit, Short-eared Owl, Little Egret. Penduline Tit most winters.
Other: 21 spp. dragonfly, inc. Hairy Dragonfly, Scarce Emerald & Small Red-eyed Damselfly. Marsh Frog, Water Vole, Water Shrew, Fox, Stoat, Weasel, 32 spp. butterflies, & 13 spp. orthoptera. Deadly Nightshade, Flowering Rush.
Directions: Sat nav: RM19 1SZ. TQ 547 787. Off New Tank Hill Road (A1090) in Purfleet, just off A1306 between Rainham & Lakeside. This is accessible from Aveley, Wennington & Purfleet junction of A13 & Junc 30/31 of M25.
Public transport: Bus - no.44 Grays to Lakeside. Ensignbus (T: 01708 865 656)/Arriva (on Sun). Train - Purfleet. Reserve is 20 mins walk along riverside path (signposted).

Visiting: Open 9.30am-5pm (Feb-Oct), 9.30am-4.30pm Nov-Jan (not Dec 25/26). Entry fee for non-RSPB members. Car park (four Blue Badge spaces). Award-winning visitor centre with disabled toilets, shop, cafe (10am-to 30 mins before reserve closes), picnic area, wildlife garden & children's playground. Four hides. Three signposted trails, suitable for wheelchairs & pushchairs. Guided walks - check RSPB website for details. Dogs allowed only on Thames riverside path.
Contact: RSPB, T: 01708 899 840;
E: rainham.marshes@rspb.org.uk

8. THURROCK THAMESIDE NATURE PARK

Essex Wildlife Trust/Cory Environmental Trust.
Habitats: 48ha, reclaimed landfill site covering overlooking Mucking Flats SSSI & Ramsar-designated Thames estuary. Saltmarsh, grassland, woodland, ponds & reedbed.
Birds: *All year:* Kingfisher, Barn Owl, Reed Bunting, Bearded Tit, Cetti's Warbler & Skylark. *Winter:* Wildfowl, Internationally important numbers of Ringed Plover & Avocet & nationally significant numbers of Grey Plover, Dunlin, Redshank & godwits. Short-eared Owl.
Other: Water Vole, Harvest Mouse, Shrill Carder Bee, Great Crested Newt, Adder.
Directions: Sat nav: SS17 0RN. TQ 696 806. From Basildon head SW on A13 towards Stanford-le-Hope. Take A1014 exit & follow signs for Walton Hall Farm Museum. Past museum entrance turn R into Mucking Wharf Road & take single lane entrance road to visitor centre.
Public transport: None.
Visiting: Open daily (not Dec 25/26) 9am-5pm, 4pm Nov-Jan). Visitor centre with rooftop viewing platform, toilets (inc. disabled), cafe, shop. Good access for wheelchair users to visitor centre, toilet & paths. Bird hide overlooks mudflats. Dogs on leads.
Contact: Essex WT, T: 01375 643 342;
E: ttnp@essexwt.org.uk

9. TOLLESBURY WICK MARSHES

Essex Wildlife Trust.
Habitats: Estuary with fringing saltmarsh & mudflats with some shingle. Extensive freshwater grazing marsh, brackish borrowdyke & small reedbeds.
Birds: *Summer:* Avocet, Redshank, Lapwing, Little Tern, Reed & Sedge Warblers, Reed Bunting, Barn Owl. *Passage:* Spotted Redshank, Green Sandpiper, Whimbrel.

Winter: Large numbers of wintering wildfowl & waders, particularly Brent Geese & Wigeon, Lapwing & Golden Plover. Short-eared Owl, Hen & Marsh Harriers.
Other: Plants inc. Spiny Restharrow, Grass Vetchling, Yellow Horned-poppy, Slender Hare's-ear. Hairy Dragonfly, Roesel's & Great Green Bush-crickets. Brown Hares. Occasional Common Seals seen from sea wall.
Directions: Sat nav: CM9 8TB. TL 970 103. On Blackwater Estuary eight miles E of Maldon. Follow B1023 to Tollesbury via Tiptree, leaving A12 at Kelvedon. Then follow Woodrolfe Road S towards marina. Use small public car park at Woodrolfe Green (500 yards before reserve entrance on sea wall - suitable for mini-buses & small coaches.
Public transport: Bus - no.91 (Mon-Fri) from Witham, no. 92 (not Sun) from Colchester & no.95 (not Sun) from Maldon, all to Tollesbury. Hedingham (T: 01621 869 778).
Visiting: Open all times along exposed sea wall footpath. Motorised wheelchair access possible to Block House Bay. Hide. Public toilets at Woodrolfe Green car park.
Contact: Essex WT - see site 2.

10. WRABNESS NATURE RESERVE & MARSH

Essex Wildlife Trust.
Habitats: 24ha, grazed grassland & open scrub overlooking wader & wildfowl feeding grounds in Jacques Bay.
Birds: *Spring/summer:* Nightingale, Whitethroat, Turtle Dove, Bullfinch, Yellowhammer. *Winter:* Internationally important species inc. Brent Goose, Shelduck, Wigeon, Pintail, Black-tailed Godwit, Grey Plover, Dunlin, Turnstone & Curlew. Short-eared & Barn Owls hunt over grassland.
Other: Wildflowers, plus good range of butterflies & dragonflies.
Directions: Sat nav: CO11 2TD. TM 167 314. Lies on southern bank of Stour estuary. From B1352 between Bradfield & Wrabness turn down Whitesheaf Lane to the reserve. Car park is on L just beyond railway bridge.
Public transport: Bus - no.103 Colchester to Harwich, (not Sun) alight Wrabness. First Essex. Train - Wrabness - one mile walk from reserve on public footpath.
Visiting: Open all year. Car park, hide. Hard-surfaced path around site suitable for wheelchairs (RADAR NKS key required for gates).
Contact: Essex WT - see site 2.

Hertfordshire

FAMOUS FOR BRITAIN'S first breeding record of Little Ringed Plover (1938) & England's first breeding record of Black-necked Grebe (1919), the Tring Reservoirs are still one of the best sites in the county. The Wildlife Trust manages over 40 nature reserves offering residents of this urbanised Home County a welcome taste of the countryside. The wetland habitats of the Lee Valley have regular wintering Bittern and other interesting species can turn up here.

1. AMWELL NATURE RESERVE

Herts & Middlesex Wildlife Trust.
Habitats: Disused gravel pit with reedbeds & woodland.
Birds: *Spring/summer:* Ringed Plover, Little Ringed Plover, Lapwing, Common Tern. *Winter:* Bittern, Smew, Gadwall Shoveler, Snipe, Siskin.
Other: Best county site for dragonflies (21 spp. recorded), Otter, nationally scarce Marsh Dock, plus Early & Southern Marsh Orchids.

Directions: Sat nav: SG12 9SS. TL 376 127. In Lee Valley near Ware. From A10, leave at junction signposted A414 to Harlow. At first roundabout, take B181 to St Margarets & Stanstead Abbotts. On entering St Margarets, just before railway, turn L on Amwell Lane (park on lane). Reserve is on R (signposted).
Public transport: Bus - no.310 Hertford to Waltham Cross, alight St Margarets. Arriva. 5 mins walk. Train - St Margarets (0.75 mile from reserve). Walk E along B181 to towpath of River Lee Navigation, then walk N for 0.5 mile to reserve.
Visiting: Open all year. Two hides, several viewing areas. Dragonfly Trail boardwalk (May-Sep).
Contact: Herts & Middlesex WT, T: 01727 858 901; E: info@hmwt.org

2. KINGS MEAD

Herts & Middlesex Wildlife Trust.
Habitats: Largest remaining area of grazed riverside flood meadow in Hertfordshire.
Birds: 119 spp. recorded. *Summer:* Yellow Wagtail, Skylark, seven species of breeding warblers, Reed Bunting. *Winter/spring:* Gadwall, Shoveler, Wigeon, Teal, Snipe, gulls, waders, Siskin, Redpoll.
Other: 265 spp. wildflowers, 18 spp. dragonflies. Significant population of Short-winged Conehead.
Directions: Sat nav: SG12 9XD. TL 349 136. From Ware head SE on A1170 High Street, turn R into Burgage Lane shortly after Ware Museum. Park in public car park. From here pedestrian access is via the River Lee, go over the bridge, turn R & walk 250 yards. Turn L into reserve.
Public transport: Bus - no.310 Waltham Cross to Hertford, alight Hertford Regional College. Arriva in Herts & Essex. Train - Ware. Both five mins walk to reserve.
Visiting: Open all year.
Contact: Herts & Middlesex WT - see site 1.

3. MAPLE LODGE

Thames Water/Maple Lodge Conservation Society.
Habitats: Man-made wetland habitat formed from two gravel pits & a sludge settlement area. Two lakes & a reedbed. Mixed broadleaf plantation on eastern side.
Birds: *All year:* Wildfowl (esp. winter), Sparrowhawk, Red Kite, Buzzard, Water Rail 3 spp. woodpecker, Kingfisher, Tawny Owl, variety of finches, thrushes & woodland species. *Summer:* Hobby, migrant warblers. *Passage:* Snipe, Green & Common Sandpipers. .
Other: 250 spp. moths, plus many butterflies & aquatic insects. 125 spp. wildflowers. Seven of nine bat spp. found in Herts have been recorded.
Directions: Sat nav: WD3 9SF. TQ 036 925. S of Rickmansworth, close to village of Maple Cross. From M25 Junc 17 drive towards Denham/ Uxbridge, turn L at traffic lights. Drive down Maple Lodge Close & park in social club car park on R.
Public transport: Bus - nos.432 & 724 from Rickmansworth to Maple Cross. Arriva. Train - Maple Cross.

Visiting: Restricted to members of MLCS but visits by non-members & groups can be arranged in advance. Site can be boggy, keep to designated paths. Information centre, toilets, nine hides (two wheelchair-friendly & two more when ground dry). Winter feeding stations.
Contact: Maple Lodge Conservation Society, T: 07580 535 986; E: enquiries@maplelodgenaturereserve.org; W: www.maplelodge.org

4. RYE MEADS

RSPB/Herts & Middlesex Wildlife Trust.
Habitats: Beside River Lee - marsh, willow scrub, pools, scrapes, lagoons & reedbed.
Birds: *Summer:* Breeding Water Rail, Tufted Duck, Gadwall, Common Tern, Kestrel, Kingfisher, Little Ringed Plover, nine species of warblers. Hobby. *Autumn:* Birds on passage inc. Green Sandpiper, Teal & Snipe. *Winter:* Bittern, Shoveler, Goldeneye, Teal, Water Rail, Snipe, Jack Snipe, Redpoll & Siskin. Occasional rarities.
Other: Fen vegetation, invertebrates & reptiles.
Directions: SG12 8JS. TL 389 103. Take Hoddesdon turn off A10 & follow brown duck signs. Near Rye House railway station.
Public transport: Bus - no.410 (not Sun) Harlow to Waltham Cross alight Rye Road/Rye Park, 0.5 mile. Trustybus. Train - Rye House, 0.4 mile.
Visiting: Open daily (not Dec 25/26) 9am-5pm/dusk if earlier. Gates are locked when the reserve is closed. Car park (charge for non-members), visitor centre - staffed reception, drinks machine, classrooms - toilets. Nature trails, picnic area, bird feeding area seven hides. Visitor cente, toilets & trails have disabled access. RSPB reserve has close-circuit TV on nests in summer. No dogs, except guide dogs. Access to the HMWT site.
Contact: RSPB, T: 01992 708 383; E: rye.meads@rspb.org.uk Herts & Middlesex WT - see site 1.

5. THERFIELD HEATH LNR

Conservators of Therfield Heath.
Habitats: Natural chalk/grass downland.
Birds: Noted stop-off site for migrants such as Ring Ouzel & Wheatear. *Spring/summer:* Breeding Skylark, Meadow Pipit, Willow Warbler, Whitethroat, Lesser Whitethroat & Grey Partridge. Good selection of raptors seen regularly, inc. Red Kite.
Other: 26 spp. butterflies inc. increasingly rare Chalkhill Blue. Several orchid spp., Pasqueflower & variety of chalk grassland flowers.
Directions: Sat nav: SG8 9NT. TL 335 400. Common land SSSI lies west & south of Royston & is accessed from A505 (Baldock Road).
Public transport: Train - Royston, two mins walk from heath.
Visiting: Open at all times. Open downland walks, golf course & sports fields.
Contact: Conservators of Therfield Heath,
E: clerk@therfieldheath.org.uk
W: www.therfieldheath.org.uk

6. TRING RESERVOIRS

Canals & Rivers Trust/Herts & Middlesex Wildlife Trust. [Water Treatment Works lagoon – Thames Water].
Habitats: Four reservoirs with surrounding woodland, scrub & meadows. Two of reservoirs have extensive reedbeds. WTW Lagoon with islands & dragonfly scrape, surrounding hedgerows & scrub.

Birds: *Spring/summer:* Breeding water birds Common Terns & heronry. Regular Hobby, Black Terns & Red Kite, warblers inc. Cetti's. Occasional Marsh Harrier, Osprey. *Autumn/winter passage:* Waders, occasional White-winged Tern. *Winter:* Gull roost, large wildfowl flocks, bunting roosts, Bittern.
Other: Black Poplar trees, locally rare plants in damp areas. 18 spp. dragonflies inc. Black-tailed Skimmer, Ruddy Darter & Emerald Damselfly. Holly Blue & Speckled Wood butterflies. Chinese Water Deer, Daubenton's, Natterer's & both spp. Pipistrelle bats.
Directions: Sat nav: HP23 4NW. SP 904 134. Reservoirs two miles NW of Tring, all accessible from B489 which crosses A41 Aston Clinton by-pass. NB: exit from by-pass only southbound.
Public transport: Bus - no.164 (not Sun) Aylesbury to Tring (circular), alight Tringford Road. (0.9 miles to Wilstone, 0.4 miles to Startops). Redline Buses (T: 01296 426 786). Train - Tring (3.8 miles to Wilstone, 2.7 miles to Startops).
Visiting: Reservoirs, Marsworth / Startops End / Tringford / Wilstone, open at all times. Coaches can only drop off & pick up, contact for advice. Car parks: at Wilstone (free, height barrier), at Startop's End (pay-&-dispaly). Hides on all reservoirs. Disabled access from car park at Startops/Marsworth Reservoirs, as well as WTW Lagoon Hide.
Contact: Herts & Middlesex WT - see site 1.

Norfolk

THE COUNTY IS REGARDED as the UK's best birding area & with such iconic sites as Cley, Titchwell, The Broads & Breckland this is hard to dispute. Its east coast location ensures that no matter what time of the year you visit you will always find a wide variety of birds. During spring/autumn migration these may include common, scarce & rare species & a 'first for Britain' wouldn't be unexpected. With breeding Bittern, Crane & Stone Curlew, passage waders & large numbers of wintering geese there is something for everyone.

1. CLEY MARSHES NNR

Norfolk Wildlife Trust.
Habitats: Reedbeds, salt & freshwater marshes, pools/scrapes & shingle ridge with international reputation as one of finest birdwatching sites in Britain.
Birds: *Breeding:* Avocet, Marsh Harrier, Spoonbill, Bearded Tit. Spring/Autumn: waders - most common species & regularly less common spp. inc. Ruff, Wood Sandpiper, Spotted Redshank & Temminck's & Little Stint. Common/scarce passage migrants and rarities can turn up at anytime. *Winter:* large numbers of wintering wildfowl inc. Wigeon, Teal, Pintail & Brent Goose. Offshore - divers, grebes, seaduck.

Directions: Sat nav: NR25 7SA. TG 054 440. Situated four miles N of Holt on A149 coast road, 0.5 mile E of Cley-next-the-Sea. Visitor centre & car park on inland side of road.
Public transport: Bus - Coastliner CH4 service Cromer-Sheringham-Wells stops at Cley. Sanders Coaches (T: 01263 712 800). Connections for train & bus services at Sheringham.
Visiting: Open dawn-dusk. Visitor Centre open daily, (not Dec 24/25) 10am-5pm/4.30 (Nov-Feb). Environmentally-friendly visitor centre (wheelchair accessible) incorporates observation area, interactive interpretation inc. remote controllable wildlife camera, toilets, cafe (closes 30 mins before centre) & sales area. Free admission to visitor centre, entrance fee charged for reserve (NWT members/children free). Five hides (three with wheelchair access), boardwalk & information boards, audio trail. Wildlife detective bumbags for children, free to hire. Reserve leaflet, regular events. No dogs on reserve but can walk Beach Road, along shingle bank & East bank.
Contact: NWT Cley Marshes Visitor Centre,
T: 01263 740 008;
Norfolk WT, T: 01603 625 540;
E: info@norfolkwildlifetrust.org.uk

2. HICKLING BROAD NNR

Norfolk Wildlife Trust.
Habitats: The largest & wildest of the Norfolk Broads with open water, reedbed, den, grazing marsh & woodland.
Birds: *All year:* Bittern, Pochard, Water Rail, Cetti's Warbler, Bearded Tit. *Nov-Feb:* raptor roost at Stubb Mill, provides excellent views of raptors flying in to roost. Likely spp. inc. Marsh & Hen Harriers, Merlin, Crane & Pink-footed Goose. *Autumn/winter:* Wildfowl inc. Shoveler, Teal & Goldeneye.
Other: Swallowtail butterfly, Norfolk Hawker dragonfly, Marsh Orchid.
Directions: Sat nav: NR12 0BW. TG 428 222. Approx four miles SE of Stalham, just off A149 Yarmouth Road. From Hickling village, follow brown badger tourist signs into Stubb Road at Greyhound Inn. Follow Stubb Road for another mile & turn R at end for nature reserve.
Public transport: Bus - no.34 Stalham to North Walsham - stops in Hickling village. Sanders Coaches (T: 01263 712 800). 25 mins walk to reserve.
Visiting: Open daily dawn-dusk, groups welcome. Visitor centre open daily 10am-5pm from Apr-Oct & 11am-4pm Nov-Mar (weekends, Dec 26 & Jan 1). Entrance fee charged for reserve, NWT members/children free. Shop, refreshments, toilets. Picnic area, boardwalk trail through reedbeds to open water, hides - disabled access to broad, boardwalk & toilets. Dogs only allowed on Weaver's Way footpath. Water trail boat trips May to Sep (additional charge - booking advisable).
Contact: Hickling Broad Visitor Centre, T: 01692 598 276; Norfolk WT - see site 1.

3. HOLKHAM NNR

Holkham Estate/Natural England (East Anglia Team).
Habitats: 4,000 ha, sandflats, dunes, marshes, pinewoods, reclaimed saltmarsh.
Birds: *All year:* Marsh Harrier, Grey Heron, Lapwing, Barn Owl, Kestrel. *Summer:* Breeding Little Tern, Snipe, Oystercatcher & Ringed Plover. *Passage:* Migrants, inc. Yellow Wagtail, Wheatear, Cuckoo & many unusual species. *Winter:* Wildfowl, inc. Brent (7,000), Pink-footed (20,000) & White-fronted Geese, up to 13,000 Wigeon. Shorelark, Twite & Snow Bunting.
Other: Seablite bushes, attractive to incoming migrant birds, Sea Aster & Sea Lavender. Antlion.
Directions: Sat nav: NR23 1RH. TF 890 447. Three miles W of Wells on A149. From Holkham village turn down Lady Ann's Drive (opposite entrance to Holkham Hall) to park. More parking at end of Wells Beach Road in Wells & at Burnham Overy.
Public transport: Bus - Coastliner 36 King's Lynn-Hunstanton-Fakenham stops at Holkham. Lynx Bus (T: 01553 611 955).

Visiting: Unrestricted, keep to paths & off grazing marshes/farmland. Pay-&-display parking, two hides. Disabled access.
Contact: Holkham Estate, Holkham Nature Reserve T: 01328 800 730; E: j.fiennes@holkham.co.uk

4. HOLME OBSERVATORY

Norfolk Ornithologists' Association (NOA).
Habitats: Set in a 5ha reserve of pine & scrub covered dunes between shore & Broad Water (reed-fringed lagoon) making this a migration hotspot.
Birds: 300+ spp., over 150 spp. ringed. *Spring/ Autumn:* paassage migrants inc. rarities which have inc. Red-flanked Bluetail, Red-breasted Flycatcher, Yellow-browed, Pallas's, Subalpine, Arctic & Barred Warblers, Alpine Accentor, Little Bunting. *Winter:* Wildfowl & waders, Merlin, Snow Bunting, Twite.
Other: Moth trap run Mar-Oct, migrant moths & butterflies recorded annually.
Directions: Sat nav: PE36 6LQ. TF 713 449. E of Hunstanton, signposted from A149. Access from Broadwater Road, Holme. Reserve & visitors centre are beyond White House at end of track.
Public transport: Bus - Coastliner 36 service King's Lynn-Hunstanton-Fakenham stops at Holme. Lynx Bus (T: 01553 611 955).
Visiting: Open daily dawn-dusk (members) & 9am-5pm to non-members by permit from Observatory. Parties by prior arrangement. Car park, visitor centre & several hides (seawatch hide reserved for NOA members), access to beach & coastal path. Dogs on leads. Accredited Bird Observatory operating all year for bird ringing, MV moth trapping & other scientific monitoring.
Contact: Sophie Barker, Holme Bird Observatory, Broadwater Road, Holme, Hunstanton, Norfolk PE36 6LQ. T: 01485 525 406; E: info@noa.org.uk; W: www.noa.org.uk

5. NUNNERY LAKES

British Trust for Ornithology.
Habitats: Flood meadows, scrape, flooded gravel pits, heathland, scrub & wet woodland.
Birds: 60 spp. breed. *All year:* Grey Heron, Egyptian Goose, Kingfisher, Green Woodpecker. *Spring:* Passage waders, hirundines, Swift, passerines. *Summer:* Warblers, Cuckoo, Oystercatcher, Lapwing, Hobby. *Winter:* Goosander, Teal, Water Rail, Snipe, Siskin.
Other: Otter, Brown Hare, Muntjac, Grass Snake, Common Lizard. Emperor Dragonfly, Red-eyed Damselfly. Speckled Wood & Orange-tip butterflies. Mossy Stonecrop.
Directions: Sat Nav: IP24 2PU. TL 873 815. On S edge of Thetford, adjacent to BTO's headquarters at The Nunnery. Main access point is via Nun's Bridges car park (off A134), cross pedestrian bridge at TL 874 821.
Public transport: Regular services to Thetford. Bus - station 0.5 mile. Train - station one mile.
Visiting: Open dawn-dusk, public access permitted on waymarked paths. Boardwalk through wet woodland, information panels, hide. Toilets on Nunnery Place at back of BTO, available office hours. Call reception in advance to arrange wheelchair access to lakes & hide. Pre-booked coaches can park in grounds. Dogs on leads at all times.
Contact: British Trust for Ornithology, The Nunnery, Thetford, Norfolk IP24 2PU. T: 01842 750 050; E: info@bto.org

6. SCULTHORPE MOOR

Hawk & Owl Trust.
Habitats: Wetland reserve, fen containing saw sedge (European priority habitat), reedbed, wet woodland, pools, ditches & riverbank.
Birds: 90 spp. inc. breeding Marsh Harrier, Barn Owl & Tawny Owl. Buzzard, Goshawk, Hobby, Kestrel, Osprey, Sparrowhawk. Water Rail, Kingfisher, Marsh & Willow Tits, Lesser Spotted Woodpecker. Winter finches, thrushes.
Other: Otter, Water Vole, Roe Deer, Glow Worm, 19 spp. dragonflies, butterflies inc. White Admiral.
Directions: Sat nav: NR21 9GN. TF 900 305. In Wensum Valley, just W of Fakenham, on A148 to King's Lynn. Nature reserve signposted opposite village of Sculthorpe. Follow Turf Moor Road to visitor centre.
Public transport: Bus - no.X29 Fakenham to King's Lynn stops at end of Turf Moor Road. First Norfolk & Suffolk (T: 08456 020 121).
Visiting: Open daily (not Dec 25), 8am-5pm Apr-Oct, (4pm Nov-Mar). Late opening THurs until 8.30pm or dusk. Coach parking available. Entrance by suggested donation for adults (children & members free). Visitor centre, with adapted toilets, hot drinks, interpretive displays & live CCTV coverage from around reserve. Reserve & two hides accessible to wheelchairs & buggies via a mile of boardwalk. Bark chipping path to other hides. Guide dogs only.
Contact: The Hawk & Owl Trust, Turf Moor Road, Sculthorpe, Fakenham NR21 9GN. T: 01328 856 788; E: sculthorpe@hawkandowl.org; W: www.hawkandowltrust.org/reserves

7. SNETTISHAM

RSPB (Eastern England Office).
Habitats: Intertidal mudflats, saltmarsh, shingle beach, brackish lagoons, & unimproved grassland/scrub. Highest tides best for good views of waders.
Birds: *Summer:* Breeding Mediterranean Gull, Ringed Plover, Redshank, Avocet, Common Tern. Marsh Harrier regular. *Autumn/winter/spring:* Waders - particularly Knot, Bar & Black-tailed Godwits, Dunlin, Grey Plover. Wildfowl - particularly Pink-footed (40,000) & Brent Geese, Wigeon, Gadwall, Goldeneye. Peregrine, Merlin, Hen Harrier, Short-eared owl. Passage migrants in season.
Other: Yellow Horned Poppies & other shingle flora along the beach.
Directions: Sat nav: PE31 7RA. TF 650 328. Car park two miles along Beach Road, signposted off A149 S of Hunstanton, opposite Snettisham village.
Public transport: Bus - Coastliner 36 service King's Lynn-Hunstanton-Fakenham stops at Snettisham. Lynx Bus (T: 01553 611 955).
Visiting: Open at all times. Car park (charge to non-members), three trails, two hides. Coach groups by prior arrangement (contact Titchwell Reserve). Dogs on lead.
Contact: RSPB, T: 01485 210 779; E: snettisham@rspb.org.uk

8. STRUMPSHAW FEN

RSPB (Eastern England Office).
Habitats: Reedbed/reedfen, wet grassland, woodland.
Birds: *Summer:* Bittern, Little Egret, Bearded Tit, Marsh Harrier, Hobby, Kingfisher, Cetti's Warbler & other reedbed birds. *Winter:* Bittern, wildfowl, Marsh & Hen Harrier.
Other: Rich fen flora - six spp. orchid, inc. Marsh Helleborine & Narrow-leaved Marsh Orchid. Otter, Chinese Water Deer & Water Vole. Swallowtail, White Admiral & Small Heath butterflies, Norfolk Hawker, Scarce Chaser & Variable Damselfly among 20 dragonfly spp.
Directions: Sat nav: NR13 4HS. TG 341 065. Six miles E of Norwich. Approach off A47 Great Yarmouth road - take roundabout to Brundell and continue on same road towards Strumpshaw. Just after Strumpshaw sign turn R into Stone Road & R again into Low Road. Car park 0.3 mile on R.
Public transport: Bus - nos.15 &15A from Acle/Linwood-Norwich-Wymondham. - stops 0.5 mile from reserve. First Norfolk & Suffolk (T: 08456 020 121). Train: Brundall, ca.1.5 miles from reserve.
Visiting: Open daily (not Dec 25), dawn-dusk. Entry fee for non-RSPB members. Reception hide & information centre open 9.30am-5pm Apr-Sep, 10am-4pm Oct-Mar, drinks/snacks available. Toilets, two other hides, trails. Guide dogs only. Limited wheelchair access - phone for advice.
Contact: RSPB, T: 01603 715 191; E: strumpshaw@rspb.org.uk

9. TITCHWELL MARSH

RSPB (Eastern England Office).
Habitats: Freshwater reedbed & fresh water lagoons, extensive salt marsh, dunes, sandy beach with associated exposed peat beds.
Birds: *Spring/summer:* Breeding Avocet, Bearded Tit, Bittern, Marsh Harrier, Reed Sedge & Cetti's Warbler, Redshank, Ringed Plover & Common Tern. *Summer/ autumn:* Passage waders inc. Knot, Wood & Green Sandpiper, Little Stint, Spotted Redshank, Curlew Sandpiper & many more. *Winter:* Brent Goose, Hen/ Marsh Harrier roost, Snow Bunting. Offshore Common & Velvet Scoter, Long-tailed Duck, Great Northern & Red-throated Divers.
Other: 25 spp. butterflies, inc. all the common spp., plus Essex Skipper & annual Clouded Yellow. 21 spp. dragonflies, inc. Small Red-eyed Damselfly. Good diversity of saltmarsh plants inc. Shrubby Sea-blite & three spp. Sea Lavender.
Directions: Sat nav: PE31 8BB. TF 750 438. E of Hunstanton, signposted off A149.
Public transport: Bus - Coastliner 36 service King's Lynn-Hunstanton-Fakenham stops at Titchwell. Lynx Bus (T: 01553 611 955).
Visiting: & public toilets always open. Car park charge for non-RSPB members, limited coach parking. Visitor centre open daily (not Dec 25/26) 9.30am-5pm (4pm Nov-Feb), information desk, cafe, shop - large selection of optics, birdfood & books. Four hides. Three signposted trails, suitable for wheelchairs, but beach not accessible (wheelchairs available, no charge). Groups by appointment. Dogs on leads only on west bank path (public path).
Contact: RSPB, T: 01485 210 779;
E: titchwell@rspb.org.uk

10. WEETING HEATH

Norfolk Wildlife Trust.
Habitats: Breckland grass & lichen heath.
Birds: *Spring/summer:* Stone Curlew (main attraction), Lapwing, Little Owl, Hobby, Woodlark, Tree Pipit, Spotted Flycatcher, Crossbill.
Directions: Sat nav: IP26 4NQ. TL 757 881. W of Brandon on Norfolk/Suffolk border. Head N from Brandon on A1065 to Mundford. Cross railway line on outskirts of town, then turn L to Weeting & Methwold. In Weeting, turn L to Hockwold cum Wilton - reserve is signpost off this road.
Public transport: Bus - no.40 from Brandon to Weeting (Thetford-Brandon-King's Lynn. Limited services Mon-Fri, only one on Sat). Coach Services (T: 01842 821 509). Train - Brandon.

Visiting: Open daily mid-Mar to end Jul (9.30am-4pm). Car park with coach parking (groups welcome but book first). Entrance fee for non-members, members & children free. Visitor centre open daily toilets, shop, refreshments, hides, live webcam. Disabled access to visitor centre & hides. Reserve/visitor centre opening extended into Aug if Stone Curlews still nesting.
Contact: Weeting Heath Visitor Centre, T: 01842 827 615; Norfolk WT - see site 1.

11. WELNEY WETLAND CENTRE

The Wildfowl & Wetlands Trust.
Habitats: 400ha, washland reserve, spring damp meadows, winter wildfowl marsh (SPA, Ramsar site, SSSI, SAC). Additional 80ha of recently created wetland habitat next to visitor centre.
Birds: *All year:* Local Cranes regularly seen, esp. post-breeding birds. *Spring/summer:* Common Tern, Avocet, Lapwing, Black-tailed Godwit, House Martin, occasional rarities. *Autumn:* waders inc Little Stint, Ruff & Curlew Sandpiper. *Winter:* Bewick's & Whooper Swans, wintering wildfowl.
Other: Purple Loosestrife, Meadow Rue, mixed grasses. Dragonflies inc. Scarce Chaser, Emperor, Banded Demoiselle, Small Red-eyed damselfly. 400 spp. moths inc. Goat Moth. Butterflies inc. Brown Argus.
Directions: Sat nav: PE14 9TN. TL 546 944. Hundred Foot Bank, 12 miles N of Ely, signposted from A10 & A1101. Check if A1101 is flooded in winter before setting off.
Public transport: None.
Visiting: Open daily (not Dec 25). Free car & coach parking. 9.30am-5pm (last entry 4.30pm) Mar-Oct, 10am-5pm (last entry 4.30pm) Mon-Wed & 10am-8pm (last entry 6.30pm) Thurs-Sun Nov-Feb). Entrance fee - WWT members free. Visitor centre (wheelchair-friendly), Blue Badge parking, wheelchairs for hire (electric scooter/manual chairs), lifts, disabled toilets, ramps. Large, heated observatory & five hides. Cafe open, 9.30am-4.30pm Mar-Oct, 10am-4.30pm Mon-Wed & 10am-6pm Thurs-Sun Nov-Feb. Access roads & paths to remote hides may be flooded so check before visiting. No dogs allowed.
Contact: WWT Welney, T: 01353 860 711;
E: info.welney@wwt.org.uk

Suffolk

THE COASTAL HOTSPOTS tend to get most attention from visiting birders, & rightly so. The county, in particular the RSPB reserve at Minsmere, has always been the stronghold of iconic birds like the Bittern, Marsh Harrier & Avocet, now all more widespread in the UK. Away from the coast the Suffolk Brecklands are worth a visit & there are other inland sites good for birds among the Wildlife Trust's 51 reserves.

1. BENACRE BROAD NNR

Natural England (East Anglia Team).
Habitats: 393ha, coastal, woodland, saline lagoons, reedbeds & heathland.
Birds: 100 spp. of breeding birds, inc. Marsh Harrier, Bearded Tit, Water Rail & wildfowl. Bittern breeds irregularly. Woodlark, Hobby & Wheatear breed on heathland areas & Little Terns fish off the coast. *Winter:* Shorelark possible on cliff-top areas, winter thrushes.
Other: Lagoon Shrimp, Starlet Sea-anemone, Yellow-horned Poppy, Grey Hair Grass.
Directions: Sat nav: NR34 7JW. TM 522 820. (Covehithe). On coast S of Kessingland. From A12 at Wrentham take minor road to Covehithe. Park near Covehithe church.
Public transport: None.
Visiting: Open at all times on permissive paths. Clifftop from Covehithe unstable, proceed with care. Elevated bird hide on southern edge of Broad - if sea has breached sandbar it is not possible to reach hide from north. Dogs on lead. Telescope needed for best views.
Contact: Natural England, T: 01502 676 171.

2. BOYTON & HOLLESLEY MARSHES

RSPB (Eastern England Office).
Habitats: 57ha, coastal grazing marsh & saltmarsh on the lower Alde-Ore estuary.
Birds: *Spring:* Breeding waders & wildfowl, inc. Lapwing, Avocet, Shoveler & Gadwall. Migrants inc. Yellow Wagtail & Whitethroat. Barn & Little Owls. *Autumn:* Wildfowl arriving inc. Teal & Wigeon. Migrating waders inc. Whimbrel, Black-tailed Godwit & Greenshank. *Winter:* Wildfowl & waders, inc. Wigeon, Teal, Curlew, Dunlin & Redshank. Marsh & Hen Harriers, Short-eared Owl.
Other: Grassland butterflies such as skippers, Wall & Meadow Browns & dragonflies.
Directions: Sat nav: IP12 3LR. TM 387 475. Seven miles E of Woodbridge. Follow B1084 to Butley. Turn R & follow to Capel St. Andrew before turning L towards Boyton village. Approx 0.25 mile before village, bear L down concrete track on sharp right-hand turn to car park.

Public transport: None.
Visiting: Open at all times. Car park at Boyton (eight spaces), for Hollesley, park at Shingle Street. Entrance free, donations welcome. Information boards. Public footpaths not suited to wheelchair use. Dogs only on public footpaths.
Contact: RSPB, T: 01394 450 732;
E: havergate.island@rspb.org.uk

3. CARLTON MARSHES

Suffolk Wildlife Trust.
Habitats: 141ha, meadows, wet grassland, reedbeds, marsh & woodland (together with Oulton Marsh).
Birds: 150+ spp. inc. wide range of wetland & Broadland birds, inc. Grasshopper, Reed, Sedge & Cetti's Warblers, Bearded Tit, Barn Owl, Hobby & Marsh Harrier. Breeding Lapwing & Redshank.
Other: Water Vole, 22 spp. dragonflies inc. Norfolk Hawker & rare Fen Raft Spider. Plants inc. Common Spotted & Southern Marsh Orchids, Water Soldier.
Directions: Sat Nav: NR33 8HU. TM 508 920 (Carlton). (NR32 3JP Oulton). W of Lowestoft, at W end of Oulton Broad. From Lowestoft, take A146 towards Beccles continue to Carlton Colville. Turn L off A146 down Burnt Hill Lane (signposted).
Public transport: Bus - nos. X21/X22 Norwich to Lowestoft, alight Carlton Colville. First Eastern Counties. Train - Oulton Broad South. Both within walking distance.
Visiting: Open dawn-dusk, free car park - suitable for coaches. Education centre with disabled toilet. Keep to marked paths. Firm path around part of marsh, inc. easy access gates. Disabled access route along river wall from Oulton Broad to Carlton Marshes. Dogs allowed in some areas, on leads at all times.
Contact: Suffolk WT, T: 01502 564 250;
E: info@suffolkwildlifetrust.org

4. HAVERGATE ISLAND

RSPB (Eastern England Office).
Habitats: Small island: shallow brackish water, lagoons with islands, mudflats, saltmarsh. Part of Orfordness-Havergate Island NNR on Alde/Ore estuary.
Birds: *Summer:* Breeding gulls, Common & Sandwich Terns, Avocet, Shelduck & Oystercatcher. Flock of Spoonbills present from mid-Jul onwards. *Winter:* Wildfowl & waders inc. Wigeon, Teal, Pintail, Shoveler, Avocet, Lapwing & Black-tailed Godwit. Barn & Short-eared Owls, Marsh Harrier.
Other: Brown Hare.
Directions: Sat nav: IP12 2B. TM 425 495. Orford is 10.5 miles NE of Woodbridge, signposted off A12.
Public transport: None.
Visiting: Pre-booked 20-min boat crossings (for max. 12 people) from Orford Quay - leaves at 10am, returns at ca. 3.20pm on first Sat of month (not May/Jun/Jul) & special event weekends (see RSPB website). Bookings made via RSPB website or search Havergate Island on Eventbrite. Reduction for RSPB members. Park in Orford's pay-&-display car park next to quay. On the island: Compost toilet with alcohol handwash - no running water, picnic area, five hides, one viewing screen, visitor trail (approx 1.25 miles).
Contact: RSPB - see site 2.

5. HEN REEDBED NNR

Suffolk Wildlife Trust.
Habitats: Reedbed, grazing marsh, scrape & estuary.
Birds: *Spring/summer:* Marsh Harrier, Bittern, Hobby, Lapwing, Snipe, Avocet, Black-tailed & Bar-tailed Godwits, Reed & Sedge warblers, Bearded Tit. *Passage:* Wood & Green Sandpipers. *Winter:* Large flocks of waders on estuary, inc. Golden & Grey Plovers, Black & Bar-tailed Godwits, Avocet & Dunlin.
Other: Otters & Water Voles regularly seen. Four-spotted Chaser & Hairy Dragonfly, occasional Norfolk Hawker. Brown Argus butterfly colony close to car park.
Directions: Sat nav: IP18 6SH. TM 471 771. Three miles from Southwold. Turn off A12 at Blythburgh & follow A1095 for two miles to signposted car park. The reserve forms part of the Suffolk Coast NNR.
Public transport: Bus - no.99A Halesworth-Southwold. First Norfolk & Suffolk (T: 08456 020 121).
Visiting: Open at all times. Viewing platforms & hides, waymarked trails. Wheelchair access to platform near car park. Dogs on lead.
Contact: Suffolk WT, T: 01473 890 089;
E: info@suffolkwildlifetrust.org

6. LACKFORD LAKES NATURE RESERVE

Suffolk Wildlife Trust.
Habitats: Restored gravel pit with open water, lagoons, islands, willow scrub, reedbeds.
Birds: *Spring/autumn:* Migrants, raptors inc. Osprey. *Summer:* Breeding Shelduck, Little Ringed Plover & reedbed warblers. Nightingale, Turtle Dove, Hobby. *Winter:* Bittern, Water Rail, Bearded Tit. Large gull roost. Wide variety of wildfowl (inc. Goosander, Pochard, Tufted Duck, Shoveler) & waders.

Other: Otter. 17 spp. dragonflies inc. Hairy & Emperor. Early Marsh & Southern Orchid.
Directions: Sat nav: IP28 6HX. TL 801 706. Five miles NW of Bury St Edmunds. Access via track off N side of A1101, between Lackford & Flempton.
Public transport: Bus - no.16 Bury St Edmunds to Mildenhall stops at Lackford - walk from church. Stephensons of Essex (T: 01440 704583).
Visiting: Open daily, dawn-dusk. Car park, coaches by arrangement. Visitor centre open 10am-5pm - viewing area upstairs, refreshments (to 4.30pm), shop, toilets. Eight hides, five trails. Wheelchair access -visitor centre, Kingfisher Trail & four hides. Limited access for dogs.
Contact: Lackford Lakes Visitor Centre,
T: 01284 728 706;
E: lackford.centre@suffolkwildlifetrust.org

7. LAKENHEATH FEN

RSPB (Eastern England Office).
Habitats: Reedbed, riverside pools, poplar woods.
Birds: *Spring/summer:* Bittern, Marsh Harrier, Cuckoo, Turtle Dove, Hobby (up to 40), Grasshopper, Reed & Sedge Warblers. *Autumn:* Harriers, Bearded Tit. *Winter:* Wildfowl inc. occassional Whooper Swan, Common Crane, Peregrine, Barn Owl, Kingfisher.
Other: 15+ spp. dragonflies & damselflies, inc. Hairy Dragonfly & Scarce Chaser. Range of fenland plants inc. Water Violet, Common Meadow-rue & Fen Ragwort. Roe Deer, Otter & Water Vole.
Directions: Sat nav: IP27 9AD. TL 724 865. W of Thetford, straddling the Norfolk/Suffolk border. From A11, head N on B1112 to Lakenheath & then two miles further. Entrance is on L, after level crossing.
Public transport: Bus - nos.200/201 Thetford-Brandon stop at Lakenheath, then two mile walk to reserve. Coach Services. Train - weekends-only some trains on Norwich-Ely service stop in Lakenheath (path links station to Visitor Centre).
Visiting: Reserve open daily dawn-dusk. Entrance fee for non-RSPB members (free if just visiting visitor centre), group bookings welcome - coaches must book oin advance. Visitor centre & toilets (inc. disabled) open 9am-5pm daily (not Dec 25-26). Events programme. Four viewpoints, one hide, picnic area, four nature trails of varied terrain - okay for wheelchairs. Dogs restricted to public footpaths.
Contact: RSPB, T: 01842 863 400;
E: lakenheath@rspb.org.uk

8. LANDGUARD BIRD OBSERVATORY

Landguard Conservation Trust.
Habitats: Adjoining LNR, composed of close grazed turf, raised banks with holm oak, tamarisk, etc.
Birds: Common, scarce and occassionally rare migrants passs through area, esp. in spring & autumn. Mediterranean Gull regular on beach. In summer/autumn check for seabird & wildfowl movements offshore.
Other: 18 spp. dragonflies & 29 spp. butterflies. Several small mammal spp. plus sightings of seals & cetaceans off-shore. Nationally rare Stinking Goosefoot.

Directions: Sat nav: IP11 3TW. TM 283 317. On Landguard peninsula, off View Point Road S of Felixstowe town centre. Housed in wartime emplacements alongside Languard Fort.
Public transport: Buses & trains to Felixstowe town centre (1.5 miles away).
Visiting: Open all year providing there is a member on site to give access - contact in advance to make arrangements. Migration watch point & ringing station.
Contact: Landguard Bird Observatory, View Point Road, Felixstowe, IP11 3TW. T: 01394 673 782; E: landguardbo@yahoo.co.uk (enquiries or to arrange a visit); W: www.lbo.org.uk

9. MINSMERE

RSPB (Eastern England Office).
Habitats: Coastal lagoons, 'the scrape', freshwater reedbed, grazing marsh, vegetated dunes, heathland, arable reversion & woodland.
Birds: *All year:* Marsh Harrier, Bearded Tit, Bittern, Cetti's & Dartford Warblers, Little Egret, Green & Great Spotted Woodpeckers. *Summer:* Breeding Hobby, Avocet, Lapwing, Redshank, Common, Sandwich & Little Terns, Mediterranean Gull, Sand Martin, warblers, Nightingale, Nightjar, Woodlark, Stone Curlew (sometimes visible). *Autumn/spring:* Passage waders inc. Black-tailed Godwit, Spotted Redshank, Ruff. Regular Wryneck, Red-backed Shrike, Yellow-browed Warbler. *Winter:* Wildfowl inc. White-fronted Goose, Bewick's Swan, Smew, Hen Harrier (scarce), Water Pipit, Siskin.
Other: Red & Muntjac Deer, Otter, Water Vole, Badger. Dragonflies inc. Emperor, Norfolk Hawker & Small red-eyed Damselfly. 27 spp. butterflies inc. Purple & Green Hairstreaks & Brown Argus. Adder. Antlion. Marsh Mallow, Southern Marsh Orchid.
Directions: Sat nav: IP17 3BY. TM 473 672. Six miles NE of Saxmundham. From A12 at Yoxford or Blythburgh. Follow brown tourist signs via Westleton village. Car park is two miles from village.
Public transport: Train - Saxmundham or Darsham (five miles) then demand-responsive bus will meet local buses/trains 7am-7pm, Mon-Sat. Suffolk Links Blyth (T: 01728 635 938) - book before day of travel.
Visiting: Car park & hides open daily (not Dec 25/26) dawn-dusk. Coaches by appointment only. Visitor centre/shop open 9am-5pm (4pm Nov-Jan), cafe open 9.30am-4.30pm (3.30pm Nov-Jan). Visitor centre (free entry) - entry fee for non RSPB members to visit reserve. Car park, seven hides & viewing platform, toilets (inc. disabled). Volunteer guides, guided walks & family events (see RSPB website for details). Limited access for dogs.
Contact: RSPB, T: 01728 648 281; E: minsmere@rspb.org.uk

10. NORTH WARREN

RSPB (Eastern England Office).
Habitats: Grazing marsh, heath, reedbed, woodland.
Birds: *Spring/summer:* Breeding Bittern, Hobby, Marsh Harrier, Nightjar, Woodlark, Nightingale, Dartford Warbler. *Winter:* White-fronted Goose, Tundra Bean Goose, Wigeon, Shoveler, Teal, Gadwall, Pintail, Snow Bunting.

Other: Hairy Dragonfly, Norfolk Hawker & Red-eyed Damselfy, Green & Purple Hairstreak butterflies & Southern Marsh Orchid.
Directions: Sat nav: IP15 5BH. TM 467 576. Directly N of Aldeburgh on Suffolk coast. Take A1094 to Aldebugh then follow Thorpe Road towards Thorpeness. Use signposted main car park on beach.
Public transport: Bus - no.64 Saxmundham to Aldeburgh. First Norfolk & Suffolk (T: 08456 020 121). Train - Saxmundham (six miles).
Visiting: Open at all times. Pay-&-display car parks in Aldeburgh & Thorpeness (coach spaces at the latter) Toilets in Aldeburgh & Thorpeness. Various viewing points & viewing platform adjacent to old railway line overlooking the marshes. Several circular walks on public rights of way. Beach area suitable for disabled access. Dogs only on public footpaths/bridleways.
Contact: RSPB - see site 9.

11. REDGRAVE & LOPHAM FENS

Suffolk Wildlife Trust.
Habitats: Calcareous fen with open water areas, wet acid heath, river corridor, scrub & woodland.
Birds: *All year:* Water Rail, Snipe, Teal, Shelduck, Gadwall, Woodcock, Sparrowhawk, Kestrel, Great Spotted & Green Woodpeckers, Tawny, Little & Barn Owls, Kingfisher, Bearded Tit, Willow & Marsh Tits, Reed Bunting. *Summer:* Hobby, warblers inc. Reed, Sedge & Grasshopper, Spotted Flycatcher,plus large Swallow & Starling roosts. *Winter/ occcasionals on passage:* Marsh Harrier, Greenshank, Green Sandpiper, Shoveler, Pintail, Garganey, Jack Snipe, Bittern, Little Ringed Plover, Oystercatcher, Wheatear, Stonechat & Whinchat.
Other: Otter, Water Vole, Roe, Muntjac & Chinese Water Deer, Stoat, Pipistrelle & Natterer's Bats. Great Crested Newt, Grass Snake, Adder, Slow Worm, Common Lizard. 300+ spp. flowering plants. 27 spp. butterflies inc. Purple & Green Hairstreaks & Brown Argus. 20+ spp. dragonfly inc. Emperor, Hairy Dragonfly, Black-tailed Skimmer & Scarce Emerald Damselfly. Fen Raft Spider.
Directions: Sat nav: IP22 2HX. TM 052 803. Five miles from Diss, signposted & easily accessed from A1066 & A143, car park on minor road off the B1113.
Public transport: Bus - no.304 (Mon-Sat) Diss to Bury St Edmunds stops at Redgrave. Simonds (T: 01379 647 300).
Visiting: Open all year. Car park with coach space, area for bikes. Education Centre, toilets (inc. disabled). Five waymarked circular trails (wheelchair-accessible gates on 'spider' trail) - trails can be muddy after heavy rain (not wheelchair accessible), boardwalk & viewing platform. Dogs on short leads.
Contact: Suffolk WT, T: 01379 687 618; E: info@suffolkwildlifetrust.org

Northern England

Cheshire & Wirral

SITES ALONG THE DEE & Mersey estuaries provide a spectacular wader experience at passage time & during the winter. North-westerly gales in autumn bring Leach's Petrels to the tip of the Wirral peninsula, probably the best place in Britain to see them away from their breeding sites. To the east the county border abuts the Peak District.

1. DEE ESTUARY (BURTON MERE WETLANDS)

RSPB (Northern England).
Habitats: Former farm & fishery now converted to freshwater wetland, mixed farmland & woodland.
Birds: *All year:* Little Egret. Great Spotted & Green Woodpecker. *Spring/summer:* Avocet, Grasshopper Warbler, Lesser Whitethroat & other commoner warblers, passage Black-tailed Godwit, Spotted Redshank & regular Mediterranean Gull. Hobby, Marsh Harrier, Spoonbill. *Autumn:* Passage waders (inc. Little Stint, Ruff, Spotted Redshank, Green, Curlew & Wood Sandpipers). *Winter:* Whooper & Bewick's Swans, Teal, Water Rail, Hen Harrier, Fieldfare, Redwing, Linnet, Brambling.

Other: Extensive butterfly list. Pipistrelle, Noctule, Daubenton's Bats, Water Vole, wide array of orchids. Red-eyed Damselfly.
Directions: Sat nav: CH64 5SF. SJ 319 739. Located on the Wirral. From Chester High Road (A540) follow signs for Burton Mere Wetlands. Turning down Puddington Lane, reserve's entrance is just outside Burton Village.
Public transport: Bus - no.487 Liverpool (Whitechapel) to nearest bus stop at Ness Botanic Gardens, 1.5 miles from reserve. Arriva in North West.
Visiting: Open daily 9am-9pm/dusk if earlier. Large car park, not suitable for coaches/larger minibuses (groups should ring for advice). Visitor centre open 9.30am-5pm (4.30pm Nov-Jan). Admission charge for non-RSPB members. Refreshments, toilets inc. disabled. Three hides & three viewing screens overlooking pools & wetland area, picnic tables. Signposted trails -wheelchair access to footpaths & hides. Guided walks & binocular hire. Guide dogs only.
Contact: RSPB, T: 0151 353 2720;
E: deeestuary@rspb.org.uk

2. DEE ESTUARY (HESWALL)

Wirral Council.
Habitats: Saltmarsh & mudflats.
Birds: *Autumn/winter:* Large passage & winter wader roosts (Redshank, Curlew, Black-tailed Godwit, Oystercatcher, Golden Plover, Knot), Shelduck, Teal, Red-breasted Merganser, Peregrine, Merlin, Hen Harrier, Short-eared Owl. Smaller numbers of Pintail, Wigeon, Bar-tailed Godwit, Greenshank, Spotted Redshank, Grey & Ringed Plovers, Whimbrel, Curlew Sandpiper, Little Stint, occasional Scaup & Little Egret.

Directions: Sat nav: CH60 9JS. SJ 255 815. Leave A540 Chester to Hoylake road at Heswall & head downhill (one mile) to free car park at shore end of Banks Road. Heswall is 30 mins from South Liverpool & Chester by car.
Public transport: Buses - nos.175 & 181 from Heswall bus station to Banks Road car park. A2B Travel (T: 0151 609 0600).
Visiting: Open all times. Best viewpoint 600 yards along shore N of Banks Road arrive 2.5 hours before high tide. Coach parking available, information board. No disabled access along shore, but good birdwatching from bottom of Banks Road. Sheldrakes Restaurant, end of Banks Road, has outside terrace overlooking foreshore.
Contact: Wirral Country Park Visitor Centre, Station Road, Thustaston, Wirral CH61 0HN. T: 0151 648 4371; E: wcp@wirral.gov.uk

3. DEE ESTUARY (PARKGATE)

RSPB (Northern England).
Habitats: Estuary, saltmarsh, pools, mud, sand. Best viewed at high tide.
Birds: *Spring/summer/autumn:* Little Egret, Greenshank, Spotted Redshank, Curlew Sandpiper, Skylark, Reed Bunting. *Winter:* Pink-footed Goose, Shelduck, Teal, Wigeon, Pintail, Oystercatcher, Black-tailed Godwit, Curlew, Redshank, Merlin, Peregrine, Water Rail, Short-eared Owl, Hen Harrier.
Other: On very high tides, incoming water displaces several mammal spp. inc. Pygmy Shrew, Water Shrew, Harvest Mouse, Weasel & Stoat.
Directions: Sat nav: CH64 6RL. SJ 273 789. On W side of Wirral, S of Birkenhead. View high tide activity from Old Baths car park near Boathouse pub, Parkgate, off B5135.
Public transport: Bus - no.487 Liverpool (Whitechapel) to Parkgate. Arriva in North West. Train - station at Neston, two miles from reserve.
Visiting: Open at all times. Shared car park (closes 8pm summer/5pm winter). Toilets at Parkgate village opposite the Square. Viewing from public footpaths & car parks - don't walk on saltmarsh (dangerous tides/ nesting birds). Picnic area, group bookings, guided walks, special events, wheelchair access. Dogs only on footpaths.
Contact: RSPB - see site 1.

4. FRODSHAM MARSH

Manchester Ship Canal Company.
Habitats: Saltmarsh, mudflats, embanked tanks to hold river dredgings, reedbeds, farmland & river.
Birds: 20+ spp. wader, inc. large flocks of Redshank, Black-tailed Godwit, Dunlin. *Summer:* Breeding Oystercatcher, Ringed & Little Ringed Plovers, Grasshopper, Sedge & Reed Warblers. *Autumn:* Hobbies hunt. *Winter:* Wildfowl, inc. Whooper Swan, Pinkfeet, Shelduck, Pochard, Pintail, Wigeon & other common species, Raven, Short-eared Owl, Hen Harrier, Peregrine. Passage migrants inc. wagtails, pipits, terns, Garganey, Wheatear & Whinchat.

Directions: Sat nav: WA6 7BN. SJ 511 779 (Marsh Lane), SJ 520 785 (Weaver Bend/Ship Street). Large area of mixed habitat lying alongside Manchester Ship Canal, SW of Runcorn. Close to Frodsham town centre. Take Ship Street, off High Street, turn L into Weaver's Lane & cross over M56 (to access Weaver's Bend). Take Marsh Lane, off Main Street, take R fork at Marsh Green Cottages & cross over M56. (to access main marsh).
Public transport: None.
Visiting: Open at all times. Park just before concrete bridge, walk along grassy track to barrier gates & then towards vantage points overlooking Rivers Mersey & Weaver. Wheelchair access difficult.
Contact: None.
W: https://frodshammarshbirdblog.wordpress.com/

5. HILBRE ISLAND LNR

Wirral Council.
Habitats: Sandflats, rocky shore & open sea.
Birds: *Late summer/autumn:* Seabird passage inc. Gannets, terns, skuas, shearwaters & after NW gales good numbers of Leach's Petrel. *Passage:* migrants. *Winter:* Wader roosts at high tide, Purple Sandpiper, Turnstone, sea ducks, divers, grebes.
Other: Nationally scarce Rock Sea-lavender & Sea Spleenwort. Field Vole, Grey Seal. Whales & dolphins.
Directions: Sat nav: CH48 0QG. SJ 208 866 (Dee Lane, West Kirby). SJ 184 880 (main island). Three tidal islands in mouth of Dee Estuary. Park in West Kirby on A540 Chester to Hoylake road. Follow brown Marine Lake signs to Dee Lane pay-&-display car park (or free parking along promenade). Coach parking available in West Kirby.
Public transport: Bus - no.437 Liverpool (Union Court) to West Kirby, within 0.5 mile of Dee Lane slipway. Arriva in North West. Train - West Kirby.
Visiting: Two mile walk across sands from Dee Lane slipway - DO NOT cross either way within 3.5 hours of high water - tide times & suggested safe route on noticeboard at slipway. No disabled access. Permit required for groups of six or more (apply to Wirral Country Park Visitor Centre). Composting toilets on main island (Hilbre) & at Wirral Sailing Centre (end of Dee Lane, West Kirby). Leaflets & tide times available at Visitor Centre. Visits to Hilbre Bird Observatory by prior appointment only.
Contact: Wirral Country Park Visitor Centre - see site 2. Hilbre Island Bird Obs,
E: secretary@hilbrebirdobs.org.uk;
W: http://hilbrebirdobs.blogspot.co.uk

6. MOORE NATURE RESERVE

FCC Environment.
Habitats: 80ha, woodland, meadows, lakes & ponds.
Birds: 130+ spp. annually, inc. occasional rarities.
Spring/summer: Breeding wildfowl & waders,
warblers. *Autumn/winter*: Wide variety of wildfowl,
Bittern. Also good for gulls, woodpeckers, owls (all
five UK spp. recorded) & raptors.
Other: Wildfowers inc. rarities. Great crested newt.
Directions: Sat nav: WA4 6XE. SJ 577 854. SW of
Warrington, off A56 Warrington to Chester road. At
traffic lights at Higher Walton, follow signs for Moore.
Take Moore Lane over swing bridge to reserve.
Public transport: Bus - nos.62 (Mon-Fri) & 62A
Warrington to Runcorn stop in Moore, less than 0.75
mile from reserve. Warrington's Own Buses
(T: 01925 634 296) & Halton Transport (T: 0151 423 3333).
Visiting: Open all year. Car park, coaches by prior
arrangement, paths, hides, bird feeding area. One
hide suitable for wheelchairs, other parts of site
unsurfaced or gravel paths.
Contact: Moore Nature Reserve, T: 01925 444 689;
W: www.fccenvironment.co.uk/waste-processing/
landfill/arpley-landfill/moore-nature-reserve/

7. NORTH WIRRAL COASTAL PARK

Wirral Council.
Habitats: Saltmarsh.
Birds: Important as a feeding & roosting site for
passage & wintering flocks of waders, wildfowl, terns &
gulls inc. wintering Knot (20,000+), Bar-tailed Godwit
(2,000+) & Dunlin (10,000). Redshank (1,000+) &
Turnstone (500+) feed on the rocky shore at Perch Rock
& on rocky sea walls. Oystercatcher (500+), Curlew,
Grey Plover & Black-tailed Godwit regularly roost here
in relatively high numbers. Small numbers of wildfowl,
inc. Common Scoter, Scaup & Goldeneye, Red-throated
Diver & Great Crested Grebe also frequently winter.
Other: Sea Holly, Marram Grass, Storksbill, Burnet
Rose & rarities like the Isle of Man Cabbage. One of
two known sites in world for very rare British sub-
species of Belted Beauty moth.
Directions: Sat nav: CH46 4TA. SJ 241 909. Located
between outer Dee & Mersey Estuaries. From Moreton
take A553 E. then A551 N. Turn L onto Tarran Way
South then R onto Lingham Lane. Parking available by
lighthouse. Foreshore can be viewed from footpath
which runs alongside.
Public transport: Bus - routes along Leasowe Road,
Pasture Road & Harrison Drive. Train - area served by
Grove Road (Wallasey), Leasowe, Moreton, & Meols
Merseyrail Stations.
Visiting: Open at all times. Various car parks, toilet
blocks, picnic areas, extensive network of footpaths
& public bridleways. Wirral Country Park Visitor
Centre open daily (not Dec 25) 10am-4.45pm, located
Heswall & West Kirby, off A540 - has toilets, hide,
cafe, kiosk (all wheelchair accessible).
Contact: Wirral Country Park Visitor Centre
- see site 2.

8. TRENTABANK RESERVOIR

Cheshire Wildlife Trust.
Habitats: Reservoir surrounded by coniferous
plantation. [Other reservoirs in area (viewable from
roads) & further access into Macclesfield Forest.]
Birds: Small heronry. *All year:* Raven, Crossbill,
common coniferous woodland spp. *Spring/autumn:*
(when water levels expose the banks) Green
Sandpiper, Little Ringed Plover. *Summer:* Common
Sandpiper, Woodcock (roding). *Winter:* Wildfowl inc.
Goldeneye, Goosander.
Other: Red Deer, variety of butterflies & dragonflies.
Directions: Sat Nav: SK11 0NS. SJ961711. Three miles
SE of Macclesfield. Head out of Macclesfield on A537
Buxton Road, take minor road signposted Tegg's Nose
Country park. After 0.7 miles turn R & continue to
Langley, turn L at T-junction. After another 0.8 miles
turn R (by Ridgegate Reservoir) & then L for 250 yards
to reservoir car park/visitor centre.
Public transport: None.
Visiting: Open all year. The woodland trail & heronry
viewpoint is opposite car park entrance. Access to
reservoir itself is by permit only. Visitor centre may
be open on selected weekends. Toilets. Dogs on leads.
Contact: Cheshire WT, T: 01948 820 728;
E: info@cheshirewt.org.uk

9. WOOLSTON EYES

Woolston Eyes Conservation Group.
Habitats: Wetland, marsh, scrubland, wildflower
meadow areas.
Birds: 230 spp. *Breeding:* Black-necked Grebe, variety
of duck, good number of warblers (inc. Grasshopper),
raptors (Merlin, Peregrine, Marsh Harrier). *Passage:*
waders. *Winter:* wildfowl, winter thrushes.
Other: 24 mammal spp. inc. four spp. bat. 241 spp.
lepidoptera inc. wide variety of butterflies. 21 spp.
dragonflies. Notable plants inc. Marsh & Bee Orchids,
Helleborine, Snakeshead Fritillary & Cowslip.
Directions: Sat Nav: WA4 1PD. SJ 654 888. E of
Warrington between River Mersey & Manchester Ship
Canal. Off Junc. 21 of M6, take New Manchester Road
(A57), take 2nd L into Weir Lane (footpath only) - do
not park at bottom end of Weir Lane. Vehicle access
via Thelwall Lane, Latchford - permit & key required.
Sat Nav: WA4 1NN. SJ 638 873.
Public transport: Buses - from Warrington Bus
Interchange. (Weir Lane) no.3 to Martinscroft. (Thelwall
Lane) nos.1 or 2 to Westy (Whitley Ave) & walk to east
end of Thelwall Lane. Warriington's Own Buses
(T: 01925 634 296).
Visiting: Open all year from 8am dusk. Permits
required - contact via website for details. Hides &
raised platform. Dogs on lead - pick up watse & take
away with you.
Contact: E: via website; W: www.woolstoneyes.com

Cumbria

WINTERING WILDFOWL, INCLUDING Barnacle & Pink-footed Geese, reach into their thousands on The Solway. The Lake District can still offer a typical range of upland birds & there is an Osprey watchpoint at Lake Bassenthwaite. A small seabird colony at St Bees Head holds a few Black Guillemots & Puffins. Walney, with its bird observatory, is a good place to pick up passage migrants, including occasional rarities.

1. CAMPFIELD MARSH

RSPB (Northern England).
Habitats: Saltmarsh/intertidal areas, open water, raised peat bog, farmland, wet grassland.
Birds: *Spring/summer*: Breeding Lapwing, Curlew, Redshank, Snipe, Tree Sparrow & warblers. *Spring & autumn*: Passage waders inc. Black-tailed Godwit, Whimbrel. Look for Pomarine, Arctic, Great & Long-tailed Skuas over the Solway. *Winter*: Waders (up to 10,000 Oystercatchers among large roosting wader flocks). Wildfowl inc. Barnacle & Pink-footed Geese, Shoveler, Scaup, Grey Plover. Hen Harrier.
Other: Roe Deer, Brown Hare. Bog Rosemary, Bog Asphodel, sundews & cotton grass. Large numbers of dragonflies (inc. Azure & Emerald Damselflies & Four-spotted Chaser).

Directions: Sat nav: CA7 5AG. NY 197 615. At North Plain Farm, on S shore of Solway estuary, W of Bowness-on-Solway. Signposted on unclassified coast road from B5307 from Carlisle.
Public transport: Bus - no.93 from Carlisle terminates at reserve's eastern end, 1.5 mile walk to North Plain Farm. Stagecoach.
Visiting: Open at all times. Car park at North Plain Farm. Disabled visitors can drive to wheelchair-friendly hide to view high-tide roosts. Small visitor centre - 'Solway Wetlands Centre' - open 10am-4pm, manned most weekends. One hide, several viewing screens overlooking wetland areas, three trails (grass paths, can be muddy). Roadside lay-bys overlook wader roosts.
Contact: RSPB, T: 01697 351 330;
E: campfield.marsh@rspb.org.uk

2. DRUMBURGH MOSS NNR

Cumbria Wildlife Trust.
Habitats: One of four raised bogs south of Solway (rated best in England), woodland, wet heath, grassland.
Birds: *Summer*: Breeding Curlew, Redshank & Grasshopper Warbler. *Winter*: Geese from Solway, Short-eared Owl.
Other: Large Heath butterfly, Emperor Moth, Adder & lizards, Roe Deer, Brown Hare. Specialist plants inc. 13 spp. of sphagnum moss, sundews, cotton grass & Bog Rosemary.
Directions: Sat nav: CA7 5DR. NY 255 586. From Carlisle city centre, head W on B5307 to Kirkbride. After about one mile, turn R to Burgh by Sands. Follow road for 7.5 miles to Drumburgh village. Turn L by post box, continue down track & park on R past Moss Cottage.
Public transport: Bus - no. 93 Carlisle to Bowness-on-Solway (not Sun), stops in Drumburgh. Stagecoach.
Visiting: Open all year. Difficult terrain, so it is best to walk on paths or waymarked routes. Viewing platform. Dogs on leads.
Contact: Cumbria WT, 01228 829 570;
E: mail@cumbriawildlifetrust.org.uk

3. HAWESWATER

RSPB (Northern England)/United Utilities.
Habitats: Fells with rocky streams, steep oak & birch woodlands.
Birds: *Upland breeders*: Peregrine, Raven, Ring Ouzel, Curlew, Redshank, Snipe. *Woodlands*: Pied Flycatcher, Wood Warbler, Tree Pipit, Redstart, Buzzard, Sparrowhawk. Breeding Goosander & Dipper around lake. *Winter*: Large gull roost.
Other: Red Deer, Red Squirrel.
Directions: Sat nav: CA10 2QT. NY 469 108, (Haweswater car park). For old eagle viewpoint, go to Bampton village, 10 miles S of Penrith & five miles NW of Shap. From Bampton, head S towards Haweswater reservoir. Drive down unclassified road alongside Haweswater reservoir, road ends at a car park - walk from here.

Public transport: None.
Visiting: Majority of site is open access. Small car park at south end of Hawswater reservoir (managed by United Utilities).
Contact: RSPB, T: 01931 713 376;
E: haweswater@rspb.org.uk

4. ST BEES HEAD

RSPB (Northern England).
Habitats: Three miles of sandstone cliffs, up to 300 feet high.
Birds: *Spring/summer:* Largest seabird colony on W coast of England: Fulmar, Cormorant, Guillemot, Razorbill, Puffin, Kittiwake & England's only breeding pairs of Black Guillemot (around Fleswick Bay). Linnet, Stonechat, Whitethroat & Rock Pipit along cliff-top heath areas.
Directions: Sat nav: CA27 0ETN NX 959 118. S of Whitehaven via B3545 to St Bees village. Car park at end of Beach Road.
Public transport: Train - St Bees (0.75 mile).
Visiting: Open at all times. Pay-&-display car park, toilets next to reserve entrance. Three viewpoints overlook seabird colony - access via three mile cliff-top coast-to-coast footpath (steep in parts). Dogs only on public footpaths.
Contact: RSPB, T: 01697 351 330;
E: stbees.head@rspb.org.uk

5. SMARDALE GILL NNR

Cumbria Wildlife Trust.
Habitats: Limestone grassland, river, ancient semi-natural woodland, quarry.
Birds: *All year:* Usual woodland birds, Buzzard, Sparrowhawk, Raven, Green Woodpecker & Dipper. *Summer:* Redstart, Pied Flycatcher & commoner woodland species.
Other: Scotch Argus, Northern Brown Argus, Common Blue & Dark Green Fritillary butterflies. Fragrant Orchid, Common Rockrose, Bluebell & Bloody Cranesbill. Red Squirrel.
Directions: Sat nav: CA17 4HG. NY 742 083 (Smardale car park). Approx 2.5 miles NE of Ravenstonedale on A685 or 0.5 mile S of Kirkby Stephen station. Take turning signed to Smardale. Cross over railway & turn L to junction, ignoring turn to Waitby. Cross over railway & turn L at junction ignoring sign for Smardale. Cross disused railway, turn L immediately & L again to car park. Alternative parking - Sat Nav: CA17 4NY. NY 703 053 Newbiggin-on-Lune parking area).
Public transport: Bus - no.S5 Kirby Stephen to Kendal, alight Newbiggin-on-Lune. New Western Dales Bus (T: 01539 620 125). Train - Kirkby Stephen.
Visiting: NNR occupies a 3.75 miles stretch of disused railway between Tebay & Darlington. Railway line open to all, non-members should obtain a permit before visiting other parts of reserve. Dogs on lead.
Contact: Cumbria WT, 01539 816 300;
E: mail@cumbriawildlifetrust.org.uk

6. SOUTH WALNEY

Cumbria Wildlife Trust.
Habitats: Shingle, lagoon, sand dune, saltmarsh.
Birds: 250 spp. *Spring/autumn:* Passage migrants inc. Wheatear, Redstart, Goldcrest & Willow Warbler. *Summer:* 14,000 breeding pairs of Herring, Greater & Lesser Black-backed Gulls, Shelduck, Eider. Arctic, Little & Sandwich Terns offshore. *Winter:* Teal, Wigeon, Goldeneye, Redshank, Greenshank, Curlew, Oystercatcher, Knot, Dunlin, Merlin, Short-eared Owl, Tree Sparrow, Twite.
Other: 450 spp. of flowering plants. Grey Seal colony.
Directions: Sat nav: LA14 3YQ. SD 225 620. Six miles S of Barrow-in-Furness. From Barrow, cross Jubilee Bridge onto Walney Island, turn L at lights. Continue through Biggar village to South End Caravan Park. Follow road for one mile to reserve.
Public transport: Bus - no.1 Barrow-in-Furness to Biggar, 3.5 mile walk to South End/reserve car park (along coast road). Stagecoach.
Visiting: Open daily (10am-5pm, 4pm in winter) - entrance fee, members free. Coach parking available. Toilets, nature trails, hides (two wheelchair accessible), 200 yard boardwalk. Mobility tramper for hire. No dogs, except assistance dogs.
Contact: Cumbria WT, T: 01229 471 066;
E: mail@cumbriawildlifetrust.org.uk

7. TALKIN TARN COUNTRY PARK

Carlisle City Council.
Habitats: Natural glacial tarn, mature oak/beech woodland, orchid meadow (traditionally managed), wet mire & farmland.
Birds: *Spring/summer:* Spotted Flycatcher, Redstart, Chiffchaff, Wood Warbler. *Winter:* Grebes, swans, Goosander, Gadwall, Wigeon, occasional Smew & Long-tailed Duck. Brambling.
Other: Common Blue Damselfly, Common Darter, Small Copper butterfly, Otter, Red Squirrel.
Directions: Sat nav: CA8 1HN. NY 543 590. Nine miles E of Carlisle. From A69 E at Brampton, go S on B6413 for two miles (signposted). Talkin Tarn is on L just after level crossing.
Public transport: Train - Brampton Junction, one mile along footpath.
Visiting: Open at all times. Car park charges, coaches welcome. Tearoom, shop open 10.30am-4pm daily from easter to Oct half term then Sat/Sun & school holidays until easter. Toilet. Wheelchair access around tarn. Watersport activities can cause some disturbance to water birds.
Contact: Talkin Tarn Country Park, Tarn Road, Brampton, Cumbria, CA8 1HN. T: 01228 817 200;
E: talkintarn@carlisle.gov.uk
W: www.carlisle.gov.uk/talkintarn/

8. WALNEY BIRD OBSERVATORY

Habitats: Estuarine, maritime, dunes, freshwater & brackish pools, scrub & farmland. Observatory is located in south but covers whole island.
Birds: *Spring/autumn:* Migrants - island has a proven pedigree for attracting rare & unusual species. *Summer:* Renowned Eider & gull colonies at south end. Winter: wildfowl & wader spectacular across island.
Other: Famed for Walney Geranium, but also important for coastal shingle species such as Sea Holly, Sea Rocket & Sea Kale. 500+ spp. moths inc. sand dune specialities such as Coast Dart & Sand Dart. Natterjack Toad at North Walney.

Directions: See site 6.
Public transport: See site 6.
Visiting: Access to several areas, notably golf course/airfield, is restricted but island's narrow width means most sites are viewable from road or footpaths. Monitoring & ringing of breeding birds/migrants, with ringing opportunities for qualified visitors. For availability contact Walney Bird Obs.
Contact: Walney Bird Observatory, Coastguard Cottages, Walney Island, Barrow-in-Furness, Cumbria LA14 3YQ.
E: walneyobs@gmail.com;
W: http://walneybo.blogspot.co.uk

Durham

THE COAST AROUND the Teesmouth area pulls in rarities & regular migrants during spring & autumn passage & large numbers of wintering wildfowl & waders. Away from the coast, Upper Teesdale still holds Black Grouse & breeding waders while the Derwent Valley has a good mixture of habitats & birds.

1. DERWENT WALK COUNTRY PARK & DERWENTHAUGH PARK

Gateshead Council.
Habitats: Mixed woodland, river, ponds, meadows.
Birds: *All year:* Kingfisher. *Summer:* Red Kite, Grasshopper Warbler, Lesser Whitethroat, Dipper, Great Spotted & Green Woodpeckers, Blackcap, Garden Warbler, Nuthatch. *Winter:* Teal, Tufted Duck, Goosander, Marsh Tit, Brambling, Bullfinch, Siskin.

Other: Otter, Roe Deer, Badger, woodland flowers.
Directions: Sat nav: NE39 1AU. NZ 178 604 (Thornley Woodlands Visitor Centre, near Rowlands Gill). Sat Nav: NE16 3BN. NZ 199 621 (Swalwell Visitor Centre, on B6317 beside Blaydon Rugby Club). Along River Derwent, four miles SW of Newcastle & Gateshead. Several car parks along A694. Derwent Walk follows old railtrack for 11 miles from Swalwell to Consett.
Public transport: buses - various services from Newcastle/Gateshead to Swalwell/Rowlands Gill. Bus stop Thornley Woodlands Centre. Go North East (T: 0191 420 5050).
Visiting: Open at all times. Two visitor centres. Thornley Woodlands, open daily 10am-4pm. Parking, toilets, cafe, ranger service. Swalwell, open 10am-3pm Mon-Fri only (not xmas-new year or bank holidays). Parking, toilets, information - open subject to staff availability. Hides at Far Pasture Ponds & Thornley feeding station - keys from Thornley. Derwent Walk & Derwenthaugh Parks both accessible to wheelchairs from Swalwell.
Contact: Thornley Woodlands Centre, T: 01207 545 212; Swalwell Visitor Centre, T: 0191 414 2106;
E: countryside@gateshead.gov.uk;
W: www.gateshead.gov.uk/article/4393/Derwent-Walk-Country-Park-and-Derwenthaugh-Park

2. HAMSTERLEY FOREST

Forestry Commission.
Habitats: Commercial mixed & broadleaved woodland.
Birds: *All year:* Goshawk, Dipper, Green Woodpecker. *Spring/summer:* Chiffchaff, Willow & Wood Warblers, Redstart, Tree Pipit, Pied Flycatcher. *Winter:* Crossbill, Redwing, Fieldfare.
Other: Hay meadows have wide variety of plants inc. Globe Flower.
Directions: Sat nav: DL13 5NL (Forest Drive car park). NZ 092 312. Ten miles W of Bishop Auckland. Main entrance is five miles from A68, S of Witton-le-Wear & signposted through Hamsterley village & Bedburn.
Public transport: None.

Visiting: Open all year, dawn-dusk. Forest drive & car park open 9am-5pm - daily toll charge, higher during bank holidays. Visitor centre (main car park), information point open 9am-4pm, cafe open 10am-4pm (5pm weekends & school holidays). Toilets, shop, access for disabled. Visitors should not enter fenced farmland.
Contact: Forestry Commission, T: 01388 488 312; E: enquiries.hamsterley@forestryengland.uk

3. HAWTHORN DENE NATURE RESERVE

Durham Wildlife Trust.
Habitats: Extensive area of semi-natural habitat situated on magnesian limestone escarpment. Steep-sided ravine woodland & limestone grassland.
Birds: *Summer:* Green Woodpecker, Sparrowhawk, Kestrel, Skylark (important conservation site), Twite, Linnet, Yellowhammer, Whitethroat, Blackcap, Grasshopper Warbler, Tree Sparrow, Reed Bunting. *Passage:* Wheatear, Fieldfare, Redwing, Waxwing, Buzzard, Ringed Plover, Dunlin, Knot, Lapwing. *Winter (coast/offshore):* Wide variety of waders inc. Turnstone, Purple Sandpiper, Redshank, Curlew, Oystercatcher. Common Scoter, Red-throated Diver, Guillemot, Cormorant & Great Crested Grebe.
Other: Good variety of butterflies. Snowdrops, Bluebells & numerous spp. orchid, inc. Early Purple, Bird's Nest, Lesser Butterfly & Bee. Roe Deer, Badger & Brown Hare.
Directions: Sat nav: SR7 8SH. NZ 424 459. Hawthorn Dene Meadow located between Easington & Seaham on Durham coast. Leave A19 at Easington or Seaham & join B1432 to Hawthorn village. From N end of village, follow minor road E, signposted 'Quarry Traffic'. After 0.25 mile, road ends at two metal gates. Park on grass verge on opposite side to gate. Follow track through gate for 350 yards, turn R onto trail into wood.
Public transport: Bus - nos.22/23 Sunderland to Durham/Hartlepool, pass through Hawthorn. Arriva Durham County. Short walk to reserve entrance.
Visiting: Open all year, footpaths. Dogs on leads.
Contact: Durham WT, T: 0191 584 3112; E: mail@durhamwt.co.uk

4. SALTHOLME

RSPB (Northern England).
Habitats: Wet grasslands, reedbeds, pools with tern islands, wader scrapes.
Birds: *All year:* Lapwing, Peregrine, Water Rail. *Spring/summer:* Breeding Great Crested Grebe, common wildfowl, hirundines, Snipe, Skylark, Yellow Wagtail, large colony of Common Terns. *Autumn:* Various waders inc. Black-tailed Godwits & Green Sandpipers, occasional rarer species. *Winter:* Large numbers of wildfowl & waders, inc. impressive flocks of Golden Plover & Lapwing. Starling murmuration.
Directions: Sat nav: TS2 1TP. NZ 506 231. N of River Tees between Middlesbrough & Billingham. From A19, take A689 north of Stockton & then A1185. After four miles join A178 at mini roundabout. Take third exit & reserve is 250 yards on R.
Public transport: Bus - no.1 Middlesborough-Hartlepool stops outside reserve. Stagecoach.

Visiting: Open daily (not Dec 25) 9.30am-5pm Apr-Oct (4pm Nov-Mar). Large car park, inc. Blue Badge spaces & coach parking - charge for non-members. Visitor centre, tea-room & shop open 9.30am-4pm (3.30pm winter). Toilets (inc. disabled), picnic area, bound gravel surfaces to five trails, four hides (wheelchair users may need assistance to reach them). Dogs only allowed in small exercise area.
Contact: RSPB, T: 01642 546 625; E: saltholme@rspb.org.uk

5. SHIBDON POND

Durham Wildlife Trust/Gateshead Council.
Habitats: Pond, marsh, scrub & damp grassland.
Birds: *Summer:* Reed & Sedge Warblers, Lesser Whitethroat, Grasshopper Warbler, Water Rail. Roosts of terns & Cormorants. *Autumn:* Passage waders & wildfowl, Kingfisher. *Winter:* Large numbers of wildfowl, Water Rail, occasional white-winged gulls.
Other: 17 spp. butterfly, inc. Dingy Skipper. Nine spp. dragonflies inc. Ruddy Darter, Migrant Hawker. Otter, Great Crested Newt.
Directions: Sat nav: NE21 5LU. NZ 192 628. E of Blaydon, S of Scotswood Bridge, close to A1. Car park at Blaydon swimming baths. Open access from B6317 (Shibdon Road).
Public transport: Buses - various services from Newcastle/Gateshead to Blaydon (take another short bus journey to Blaydon Baths/Shibdon Road - short walk from here). Go North East (T: 0191 420 5050).
Visiting: Open at all times. Hide (disabled access) in SW corner of pond (key required, see site 1/Thornley Woodlands Visitor Centre). Dogs on lead.
Contact: Durham WT - see site 1.

6. TEESMOUTH NNR

Natural England (North East Team).
Habitats: Grazing marsh, dunes, intertidal sand & mudflats.
Birds: *Spring/summer:* Breeding Ringed Plover, Lapwing, Oysterctacher, Redshank & Snipe. *Passage:* terns & skuas in late summer, scarce passerine migrants & rarities. *Winter:* Internationally important numbers of waterbirds, inc. divers, grebes, waders & Shelduck. Merlin, Peregrine, Short-eared Owl, Snow Bunting, Twite.
Other: Northern area has large Marsh Orchid populations in damp grassland. Colony of Common Seals at Seal Sands (pups born in late-Jun).
Directions: Two areas - North Gare, centred on Sat Nav: TS25 2DT, NZ 535 276 & Seal Sands - centred on Sat Nav: TS25 2BY, NZ 530 260. Three & five miles S of Hartlepool, E of A178. Access to northern area from car park at NZ 533 282, 0.5 mile E of A178. Access to southern area from A178 bridge over Greatham Creek at NZ 509 254. Car park adjacent to A178 at NZ 508 251. Both car parks can accommodate coaches.
Public transport: Bus - no.1 Middlesborough-Hartlepool. Stagecoach. Train - Seaton Carew is 1.25 miles from North Gare car park.

Visiting: Open at all times. Northern area - no restrictions over most of dunes & North Gare Sands (avoid golf course, dogs must be kept under close control). Southern area - easy-access path to public hides at NZ 516 255 & NZ 516 252 (no other access). Nearest toilets at Seaton Carew, one mile to N & RSPB Saltholme (one mile to S). Interpretive panels & leaflet. Teesmouth Field Centre, T: 01429 853 847, W: www.teesmouthfieldcentre.org.uk
Contact: Natural England,
T: 01429 853 325 or 07803 228 394;
E: northumbria.hub@naturalengland.org.uk

7. WASHINGTON

The Wildfowl & Wetlands Trust.
Habitats: Wetlands, woodland & meadows.
Birds: *Spring/summer*: Nesting colony of Grey Heron, other breeders inc. Common Tern, Avocet, Oystercatcher, Lapwing. *Winter*: Goldeneye & other wildfowl. Bird-feeding station visited by Willow Tit, Siskin, Redpoll, Brambling, Bullfinch & Sparrowhawk.

Other: Wildflower meadows hold Cuckoo Flower, Bee Orchid & Yellow Rattle. Dragonfly & amphibian ponds.
Directions: Sat nav: NE38 8LE. NZ 330 564. On N bank of River Wear, four miles E of A1(M), sign-posted from A195, A19, A182 & A1231.
Public transport: None.
Visiting: Open daily (not Dec 25) 9.30am-5.30pm Apr-Oct (4.30pm Nov-Mar) - last admission one hour before closing. Admission fee for non-members, WWT members free. Good disabled access. Visitor centre, shop (open 9.30am) & cafe (open 10am), toilets, parent & baby room, four hides, woodland feeding station. Guide dogs only.
Contact: Washington Wetland Centre,
T: 0191 416 5454; E: info.washington@wwt.org.uk

Lancashire & North Merseyside

THE COUNTY'S NUMEROUS estuaries attract tens of thousands of wintering waders & the Mosses hold huge numbers of wintering Pink-footed Geese & Whooper Swans. Leighton Moss is one of the RSPB's flagship reserves, Bittern are regular. Seaforth Docks has a good reputation for rare gulls. Inland, Pendle Hill attracts regular Dotterel on spring passage.

1. BROCKHOLES

Wildlife Trust for Lancashire, Manchester & N. Merseyside.
Habitats: Created from disused gravel pits, alongside River Ribble now features open water, reedbeds, wet grassland & woodland.
Birds: *Spring/summer*: Breeding Great Crested Grebe, Lapwing, Redshank, Skylark, Reed & Sedge Warblers, Reed Bunting. *Passage*: waders inc. Turnstone, Grey Plover, Greenshank, Whimbrel, Curlew, Wood, Green & Curlew Sandpipers & Black-tailed Godwit. *Winter*: Good for wildfowl, inc. Pochard, Pintail, Goldeneye & Teal.

137

Other: Brown Hawker & Emperor dragonflies.
Directions: Sat nav: PR5 0AG. SD 588 306. Site in
Preston New Road, Samlesbury, adjacent to Junc 31
of M6. From S take A59 towards Blackburn & then
first exit, signposted to reserve, & follow under
southbound slip road north of River Ribble.
Public transport: Buses run close to entrance but no
safe pedestrian route to reserve.
Visiting: Gates to recerve open 6am-9pm - car park
charges, inc. members. Visitor Village open 10am-
5pm Apr-Oct, 10am-4pm Wed to Sun, Nov-Mar (not
Dec 25/26). The village - is a cluster of buildings
made from sustainable materials with a village store
& shop, cafe, adapted toilets. Most paths are level &
surfaced - wheelchair-friendly (for larger wheelchairs
a refundable deposit required for keys to access gates
bypassing kissing gates), hides, Sand Martin wall,
children's play area. Guided tours available, booking
required. No dogs.
Contact: WT for Lancashire, Manchester & N. Merseyside;
T: 01772 872 000; E: info@brockholes.org

2. HEYSHAM NR & BIRD OBSERVATORY

Wildlife Trust for Lancashire, Manchester & N. Merseyside
/EDF Energy Estates.
Habitats: Wetland, acid grassland, alkaline grassland,
foreshore.
Birds: 170+ spp annually. *Summer:* Good variety of
breeding birds (inc. eight spp. warbler on reserve).
Passage: Passerines when conditions right - two or
three scarce land-birds annually, esp. Yellow-browed
Warbler. Good seabird passage in spring, esp. Arctic
Tern. Storm Petrel & Leach's Petrel during strong
onshore (SW-WNW) winds in mid-summer & autumn
respectively.
Other: Notable area for dragonflies - Red-veined
Darter has bred for several years at nearby Middleton
Community Woodland main pond SD 418 592 (mid-Jun
to mid-Jul). Bee Orchid.
Directions: Sat nav: LA3 2UW. SD 407 601. W of
Lancaster. Take A683 to Heysham port. Turn L at
traffic lights by Duke of Rothesay pub, then first R
after 300 yards.
Public transport: Buses from Lancaster to various
Heysham sites within walking distance (ask for
nearest stop to the harbour). Train services connect
with nearby Isle of Man ferry terminal.
Visiting: Pedestrian access at all times, car park open
9am-6pm or dusk if earlier - map in car park. Limited
disabled access. No dogs on main reserve but extensive
off-lead area nearby. No manned visitor centre or toilet
access, but someone usually in reserve office in morning
(next to main car park).
Contact: WT for Lancashire, Manchester & N. Merseyside;
Reserve Warden, Heysham Nature Reserve,
T: 01524 855 030; E: rneville@lancswt.org.uk
Check out observatory's blogpot for virtually daily
updates & detailed map at bottom of page.
http://heyshamobservatory.blogspot.co.uk/

3. LEIGHTON MOSS

RSPB (Northern England).
Habitats: Reedbed, shallow meres, woodland & scrub.
Saltmarsh pools approx one mile.
Birds: *All year:* Bittern, Bearded Tit, Water Rail,
Shoveler, Gadwall, Marsh Tit, Little Egret. *Summer:*
Breeding Marsh Harrier, Reed & Sedge Warbler. Avocet
at saltmarsh pools. *Passage:* Black-tailed Godwits in
spring (good numbers), Greenshank, Ruff & godwits
in autumn. *Winter:* Large flocks of Starlings roosting,
hunting Peregrine & Merlin terrorise overwintering
wildfowl.
Other: Otter, Red Deer.
Directions: Sat nav: LA5 0SW. SD 478 750. Four miles
NW of Carnforth, Lancs. Leave M6 at Junc 35. Take A6
N towards Kendal & follow brown signs for Leighton
Moss off A6.
Public transport: Train - Silverdale station is 250 yards
from reserve (on Manchester Airport to Barrow line).
Visiting: Open daily, dawn-dusk. Entry fee for
non-members (half-price if arriving by bike or public
transport). Visitor centre/cafe (free entry) open
9.30am-5pm/4.30pm Dec-Jan (not Dec 25) - shop,
cafe (stairlift available), toilets (inc. disabled),
binoculars for hire. Three signposted nature trails,
seven hides (some wheelchair access). Dogs restricted
to Causeway public footpath.
Contact: RSPB, T: 01524 701 601;
E: leighton.moss@rspb.org.uk

4. LUNT MEADOWS

Wildlife Trust for Lancashire, Manchester & N. Merseyside
Habitats: Open water/pools, reedbeds, grassland,
small orchard - along the River Alt.
Birds: *All year:* Marsh Harrier, Peregrine, Barn Owl,
Kingfisher, Bearded Tit, Reed Bunting. *Spring/summer:*
Shelduck, Oystercatcher, Avocet, Little Ringed &
Ringed Plovers. Hobby, Grasshopper, Reed & Sedge
Warblers. *Passage:* Common & Green Sandpipers, Ruff,
Greenshank, Black-tailed Godwit, Black Tern. *Winter:*
Wildfowl & waders, Short-eared Owl.
Other: Water Vole.
Directions: Sat Nav: L29 8YA. SD 355 021. Lies just to
W of Maghull. From A59/M57/M58 interchange take
A5758. At roundabout, turn L (A565) then L at traffic
lights towards Netherton (Green Lane). Continue to
T-junction, turn L (B5422 to Maghull). In Sefton turn
L into Bridge Lane (brown sign to The Punchbowl)
continue on this road (1 mile) to reserve entrance on R.
Public transport: Bus - no.133 from
Waterloo Interchange-Kirkby, stops at Lunt village.
Cumfybus (T: 0151 236 7676 - Merseytravel network).
Visiting: Open at all times. Car park (free) open
9.30am-6.30pm (summer), 9.30am-4.30pm
(winter) - if locked, park by entrance gate - do not
park in surrounding lanes to access reserve. Paths
(unsurfaced, can be rough), viewing screens, hide.
Dogs on lead.
Contact: WT for Lancashire, Manchester & N. Merseyside;
Reserve Warden, T: 01519 203 769;
E: agraham@lancswt.org.uk

NATURE RESERVES - NORTHERN ENGLAND

5. MARSHSIDE

RSPB (Northern England).
Habitats: Coastal grazing marsh & lagoons.
Birds: *All year:* Black-tailed Godwit. *Spring:* Breeding waders, inc. Avocet & wildfowl, Garganey, migrants. *Autumn:* Migrants. *Winter:* Wildfowl inc.Pink-footed Goose, waders inc. Golden Plover, raptors inc. Merlin, Peregrine, Kestrel & Sparrowhawk.
Other: Brown Hare, various plants inc. Marsh Orchid, Migrant Hawker dragonfly.
Directions: Sat nav: PR9 9PJ. SD 353 205. From Southport, follow minor coast road Marine Drive N (1.5 miles from Southport Pier) to small car park by sand works.
Public transport: Bus - no.44 Southport to Crossens, alight at Marshside, Elswick Road stop. Walk 0.5 mile (towards the coast) to reserve entrance. Arriva in North West.
Visiting: Open all year 8.30am-5pm (dusk if earlier), car park charge for non-members - coach parties should book in advance. Visitor centre, toilets (inc. disabled), two hides (both glazed, one doubling as visitor centre), trails accessible to wheelchairs, two viewing screens, one raised viewing platform. Dogs not permitted on path to Nel's hide or in the hides, keep on leads elsewhere.
Contact: RSPB, T: 01704 211 690; E: Ribble.reserves@rspb.org.uk

6. MARTIN MERE

The Wildfowl & Wetlands Trust.
Habitats: Open water, wet grassland, moss, copses, reedbed, parkland.
Birds: *Spring:* Ruff, Shelduck, Little Ringed & Ringed Plovers, Lapwing, Redshank. *Summer:* Marsh Harrier, Garganey, hirundines, Tree Sparrow. Breeding Avocet, Lapwing, Redshank, Shelduck. *Autumn:* Pink-footed Goose, waders on passage. *Winter:* Whooper & Bewick's Swans, Pink-footed Goose, various ducks, Ruff, Black-tailed Godwit, Peregrine, Hen Harrier, Tree Sparrow.
Other: Whorled Caraway, Golden Dock, Tubular Dropwort, 300 spp. moth.
Directions: Sat nav: L40 0TA. SD 428 145. Off Fish Lane, Burscough, six miles N of Ormskirk via Burscough Bridge (A59). 20 miles from Liverpool & Preston. Signposted from: Junc 8 M61, Junc 3 M58, Junc 27 M6.
Public transport: Train - Burscough Bridge (2.5 miles) or Burscough Junction (three miles - walk to Burscough Bridge station first). New Lane Station (1.2 miles - no safe footpath, have to walk along a road).
Visiting: Open daily (not Dec 25) 9.30am-6pm Apr-Oct (4.30pm Nov-Mar), last admission one hour before closing. Entrance fee for non-WWT members (discount if arrive by public transport or bike), coach park available - special rates for coach parties. Visitor centre, toilets, shop, cafe, education centre, play area, nature reserve/nature trails, hides, waterfowl collection, sustainable garden. Full disabled access, hides suitable for wheelchairs. Special dawn & evening events. Guide dogs only.
Contact: WWT Martin Mere Wetland Centre, T: 01704 895 181; E: info.martinmere@wwt.org.uk

7. MERE SANDS WOOD

Wildlife Trust for Lancashire, Manchester & N. Merseyside.
Habitats: 40ha, freshwater lakes, mixed woodland.
Birds: 170 spp., 60 spp. have bred. *All year:* Lesser Spotted Woodpecker, Willow Tit, Treecreeper, Nuthatch. *Summer:* Kingfisher. *Passage:* Most years - Osprey, Crossbill, Green Sandpiper, Greenshank. *Winter:* Regionally important for Teal & Gadwall, good range of waterfowl inc. Mandarin & Goosander. Feeding stations attract Tree Sparrow, Bullfinch, Reed Bunting, Water Rail.
Other: 18 spp. dragonflies recorded annually, Broad Bucker Fern, 200+ spp. fungi. Red Squirrel, Stoat, Water Vole.
Directions: Sat nav: L40 1TG. SD 449 161. 12 miles from Southport, 0.5 mile off A59 Preston to Liverpool road, in Rufford along B5246 (Holmeswood Road).
Public transport: Bus - no.347 Southport-Chorley (Presrton Bus) & no.2B Preston-Ormskirk (Stagecoach) stop in Rufford, 0.5 mile walk. Train: Preston-Ormskirk service stops at Rufford station, one mile walk.
Visiting: Reserve & car park open at all times (car park charge). Visitor centre open 9.30am-4.30pm Tues-Sun/bank-holiday Mons, exhibition room, shop, toilets (inc. disabled). Six viewing hides (wheelchair accessible), three trails - three miles of wheelchair-accessible footpaths, latest sightings board. Feeding stations. Guided walks for groups can be arranged. Two motorised buggies - booking essential.
Contact: WT for Lancashire, Manchester & N. Merseyside; Reserve Manager, Mere Sands Wood NR, T: 01704 821 809; E: lbeaton@lancswt.org.uk

8. MORECAMBE BAY (HEST BANK)

RSPB (Northern England).
Habitats: Saltmarsh, estuary.
Birds: *Winter:* 250,000 waders & wildfowl winter on Britain's second-most important estuary site. Wildfowl inc. Pintail, Shelduck, Wigeon. Important high tide roost for waders inc.Oystercatcher, Curlew, Redshank, Dunlin & Bar-tailed Godwit.
Directions: Sat nav: LA2 6HN. SD 467 666. Two miles N of Morecambe at Hest Bank. Access car park from Hest Bank level crossing off A5105.
Public transport: Bus - no.5 runs between Carnforth & Morecambe. Stagecoach. Train - nearest station is Morecambe.
Visiting: Open at all times - do not go onto saltmarsh or intertidal area (dangerous channels & quicksands). Viewpoint & toilets at local council car park. Paths from car park too rough for wheelchairs. Dogs allowed. Guided walks programme.
Contact: RSPB- see site 3.

9. RIBBLE ESTUARY NNR

Natural England (Greater Manchester, Merseyside & Cheshire Team).
Habitats: One of England's largest areas of saltmarsh, & mudflats.
Birds: *Winter:* High water wader roosts of Knot, Dunlin, Black-tailed Godwit, Oystercatcher & Grey Plover are best viewed from Southport, Marshside, Lytham St Annes. Pink-footed Geese & wintering swans are present in large numbers from Oct-Feb on Banks Marsh & along River Douglas respectively. Banks Marsh can be viewed from public footpath which runs along sea defence embankment from Crossens Pumping Station to Hundred End. Large flocks of Wigeon, for which site is renowned, can be seen on high tides from Marshside but feed on saltmarsh areas at night. Good numbers of raptors.
Directions: Sat Nav: PR4 6XH. SD 380 240 (S side). Lies approx 4.5 miles W of Preston, stretching on both sides of River Ribble as far as Lytham St Anns (N side) & Crossens (S side). Take A584 & minor roads for north bank, A59/A565 & minor roads for south bank.
Public transport: Bus - no.2 Preston to Southport & no.68 Preston to Lytham St Anns. Stagecoach.
Visiting: Public footpaths open at all times, no access to saltmarsh itself. Ribble Discovery Centre at Fairhaven Lake (3.2 miles from Lytham). RSPB Marshside, adjacent to NNR - see site 5.
Contact: Natural England, T: 01704 578 774;
E: dave.mercer@naturalengland.org.uk

10. SEAFORTH NATURE RESERVE

Wildlife Trust for Lancs, Manchester & N Merseyside.
Habitats: Saltwater & freshwater lagoons, scrub grassland & small reedbed.
Birds: Major roosting site for waders (38 spp. have been recorded) & seabirds, noted for Little Gull on passage (Apr) & seabirds, noted for Little Gull on passage (Apr), Roseate, Little & Black Terns. *Breeding/passage:* Common Tern (Apr-Sep). *Passage/winter:* waders & gulls – 15 spp. of gulls recorded, with Ring-billed annual & Mediterranean seen almost daily. Passage passerines, esp. White & Yellow Wagtails, pipits, Wheatear, & a sprinkling of vagrants.
Directions: Sat nav: L21 1JD. SJ 318 971. Five miles from Liverpool city centre. From M57/M58 take A5036 to docks. Enter via Liverpool Freeport entrance in Crosby Road South.
Public transport: Buses - to dock gates from Liverpool. Train - to Waterloo or Seaforth stations from Liverpool.
Visiting: Open at all times. Permit required (visitor & vehicle passes) - members only, apply for them directly from Port Police 0151 949 6144. Organised groups must contact reserve office (below) at least seven days in advance of planned visit.
Contact: WT for Lancashire, Manchester & N. Merseyside; Reserve Warden, T: 0151 920 3769;
E: seaforth@lancswt.org.uk

Manchester (Greater)

DESPITE BEING A LARGELY urban area, there are good places for birdwatching. The former colliery workings of Pennington & Wigan Flashes are the area's best all-round birding sites with a wide range of species, including rarities from time to time. Etherow CP has Dipper & a good selection of woodland birds including Pied Flycatcher.

Public transport: Metrolink - Sale Water Park.
Visiting: Open dawn-dusk. Sale Water Park visitor centre car park off Rifle Road. Walk to reserve by following track behind visitor centre. Small concrete hide. No paths within reserve, view from perimeter paths.
Contact: MVCWS, T: 0161 906 1100;
E: info@merseyvalley.org.uk

1. BROAD EES DOLE (SALE WATER PARK)

Mersey Valley Countryside Warden Service.
Habitats: Wetland site with water levels managed to provide feeding & breeding opportunities for spp. such as herons, Kingfisher, Little Ringed Plover & Lapwing.
Birds: Important site for migratory species & waders inc. Snipe & Jack Snipe. *Winter:* wildfowl inc. Mallard, Gadwall, Teal, Coot, Moorhen in LNR, wider variety on main lake of Water Park.
Other: Spotted Orchid, Smooth & Great Crested Newts. Variety of fish on main lake in Sale Water Park.
Directions: Sat nav: M33 2LX. SJ 804 926. Local Nature Reserve located close to visitor centre in Sale Water Park, Trafford. Access from Junc 6 of M60, following signs for Trafford Water Sports Centre.

2. ETHEROW COUNTRY PARK

Stockport Metropolitan Borough Council.
Habitats: River Etherow, woodlands, marshy area, ponds & surrounding moorland.
Birds: 100+ spp. inc. Sparrowhawk, Buzzard, Woodcock, 3 spp. woodpecker, Dipper, warblers inc. Wood & Garden, Pied Flycatcher, *Winter:* Brambling, Siskin, Water Rail. Frequent sightings of Merlin & Raven over hills.
Other: 200 spp. of plants.
Directions: Sat nav: SK6 5JD. SJ 965 908. Site lies at halfway point on 12-mile Valley Way Footpath linking Stockport & Woolley Bridge. Situated at Compstall on B6104 near Romiley, Stockport.
Public transport: Bus - nos.383 & 384 Stockport, Marple/Romiley circular - alight at Compsall. Stagecoach. Train - Romiley & Marple Bridge.
Visiting: Parkland open at all times - permit required for conservation area (contact first for info). Pay-&-display car park. Visitor centre open (not Dec 25) 11am-4pm (when possible), cafe (10am-4pm summer, 10am-3pm winter) & toilets. One hide, nature trail, Keep to paths. Motorised wheelchairs available (free), book in advance.
Contact: Etherow Country Park Visitor Centre, T: 0161 427 6937.

3. HOLLINGWORTH LAKE

Hollingworth Lake/Rochdale MBC.
Habitats: Lake (47ha, inc. 17.5ha nature reserve), woodland, streams, marsh, willow scrub.
Birds: *All year:* Great Crested Grebe, Cormorant, Lapwing, Kingfisher, Little Owl, Bullfinch. Occasional Peregrine, Sedge Warbler, Water Rail, Snipe. *Spring/ autumn:* Passage waders, wildfowl, Kittiwake. *Summer:* Reed Bunting, Dipper, Common Sandpiper, Curlew, Oystercatcher, Black Tern, 'Commic' Tern, Grey Partridge, Blackcap. *Winter:* Goosander, Goldeneye, Golden Plover, Siskin, Redpoll.
Directions: Sat nav: OL15 0AQ. SD 939 153 (visitor centre). On outskirts of Littleborough, four miles NE of Rochdale, signposted from A58 Halifax Road & Junc 21 of M62 (B6225 to Littleborough).
Public transport: Bus nos.455 & 458 from Rochdale stop at Hollingworth Lake. Transport for Greater Manchester (T: 0161 244 1000). Train - Littleborough or Smithy Bridge (ca 10 mins to Lake).
Visiting: Open access to lake & surroundings. Car parks, coaches by prior arrangement. Visitor centre open 10am-3pm, Fri to Tues, toilets (disabled/baby changing facilities) & cafe open at 9.30am. Hide, trails. Education service, free wheelchair hire, fishing.
Contact: Hollingworth Lake Country Park & Visitor Centre, T: 01706 373 421.

4. PENNINGTON FLASH COUNTRY PARK

Wigan Council
Habitats: Lowland lake, ponds & scrapes, fringed with reeds, rough grassland, scrub & woodland.
Birds: 240+ spp. inc. many county firsts & rarities. *All year:* Waterfowl. Feeding station attracts Willow Tit, Stock Dove & up to 40 Bullfinches. *Spring/ autumn passage:* waders (14+ spp.) & terns (4+ spp.). *Summer:* Breeding inc. Common Tern, Ringed & Little Ringed Plover, nine spp. warbler. *Winter:* Peregrine, Merlin, large gull roost (with occasional white-winged gulls), Siskin, Brambling.
Other: Several spp. orchid, inc. Bee Orchid. Wide variety of butterflies & dragonflies.
Directions: Sat nav: WN7 3PA. SJ 640 990. One mile from Leigh town centre & well signposted from A580 East Lancashire Road. Main entrance on A572 (St Helens Road).
Public transport: Bus - one mile from Leigh bus station, nos. 589 & 590 stop on St Helens Road near entrance to park. Transport for Greater Manchester (T: 0161 244 1000).
Visiting: Park open at all times. Main car park pay-&-display (coach parking/group visits available if booked in advance) Toilets (inc. disabled) & information point open 9am-dusk (not Dec 25), catering. Main paths flat, suitable for disabled. Seven hides, nature trails. Site leaflet available.
Contact: Wigan Council, T: 01942 489 007

5. WIGAN FLASHES

Wildlife Trust for Lancs, Manchester & N Merseyside/ Wigan Council.
Habitats: Open water, reedbed, fen, rough grassland, wet woodland & scrub.
Birds: 200+ spp. *Summer:* Nationally important for Willow Tit. Common Tern, Water Rail, Reed, Sedge, Cetti's & Grasshopper Warblers, Kingfisher. *Passage:* Black Tern. *Winter:* Bittern, wildfowl, especially diving duck & Gadwall.
Other: Interesting orchids, six spp. inc. Marsh & Dune Helleborine. One of UK's largest feeding assemblage of Noctule Bats. Water Vole. 18 spp. dragonflies, has inc. Red-veined Darter.
Directions: Sat nav: WN3 5NY. SD 585 030. Leave M6 at J25 head N on A49, turn R on to Poolstock Lane (B5238) - car park 0.75 mile on R. Also parking on Welham Road - after turning into Poolstock Lane turn R (0.3 mile) into Carr Lane then L into Welham Road, just before school. Can access reserve from banks of Leeds & Liverpool Canal.
Public transport: Bus - no.607 bus Wigan to Ashton Heath passes along Poolstoiock Lane. Diamond Bus North West (T: 01942 888 893).
Visiting: Open at all times. Poolstock Lane car park has 300 spaces - access for coaches, contact reserve manager. Network of footpaths, areas suitable for wheelchairs. Six hide screens.
Contact: WT for Lancashire, Manchester & N. Merseyside; T: 01942 233 976; E: mchampion@lancswt.org.uk

Northumberland

THE COUNTY OFFERS a lot of variety with a fantastic range of habitats. The seabird colonies on the Farne Islands & Coquet Island are teeming with birds that can be seen at close quarters. Coastal sites, such as Holy Island (Lindisfarne), Budle Bay & East Chevington, attract spring & autumn migrants, & large numbers of wintering birds. Kielder Forest is good for Crossbills & raptors, including Goshawk & Osprey, while the nearby moors hold a good selection of upland species.

1. DRURIDGE POOLS & CRESSWELL POND

Northumberland Wildlife Trust.
Habitats: 1 (Druridge): Deep lake & two wet meadows with pools behind dunes. 2 (Cresswell): Shallow brackish lagoon behind dunes fringed by saltmarsh & reedbed, some mudflats.
Birds: 1: Especially good in spring. Winter & breeding wildfowl (mostly Wigeon & Teal); passage & breeding waders. 2: Good for waders, esp. on passage. Wildfowl inc. Pinkfooted Geese in winter.
Other: Sheltered sunny banks good for a range of butterflies & dragonflies in summer at Druridge Pools. Otters often seen by lakes.
Directions: Two sites lying on coast between Amble & Newbiggin, off A1068. 1: Sat nav: NE61 5EG for Druridge Pools (NZ 275 963). Roadside parking next to National Trust's Druridge Links site. 1.9 miles N of Cresswell. 2: Sat nav: NE61 5EH for Cresswell Pond (NZ 283 944). Use car park to northern end of reserve, 0.6 mile N of Cresswell & walk S along road Blakemoor Farm track.
Public transport: Bus - 1: no.X18 Alnwick to Morpeth alight Widdrington (two miles). 2: no.1 to Cresswell (Blyth to Widdrington). Arriva in North East.
Visiting: 1: Access along public footpath or short path to screen, two hides. 2: Access along short path from farm track. Wheelchair users can view northern part of Cresswell Pond from public footpath or roadside. Hide. Dogs on leads.
Contact: Northumberland WT, T: 0191 284 6884; E: mail@northwt.org.uk

2. EAST CHEVINGTON

Northumberland Wildlife Trust.
Habitats: Ponds & reedbeds created from former open cast coal mine. Areas of scrub & grassland.
Birds: Summer: Breeding Skylark, Stonechat, Reed Bunting, Reed, Sedge & Grasshopper Warblers. Marsh Harrier. Winter: Large numbers of wildfowl, inc. Greylag & Pinkfooted Geese. Short-eared Owl, Tree Sparrow, Twite.Capable of attracting rarities at any time.
Other: Coastal wildflowers & in grassland, Dyer's Greenweed.
Directions: Sat nav: NE61 5BX. NZ 270 990. Near Red Row, overlooking Druridge Bay, off A 1068 between Amble & Widdrington - park at Druridge Bay Country Park (signposted).
Public transport: Bus - X18 to Red Row (one mile). Arriva in North East.

Visiting: Main access from overflow car park at Druridge Bay Country Park (walk S). Four hides, plant ID boards.Cafe, toilets & information at Country Park (County Council).
Contact: Northumberland WT - see site 1.

3. FARNE ISLANDS

The National Trust.
Habitats: 15-28 maritime islands, depending on tide.
Birds: *Spring/summer:* ca.23 breeding spp./100,000 pairs of seabirds - Common, Arctic & Sandwich Terns, Puffin, Razorbill, Guillemot, Kittiwake, Eider, Shag. Shearwaters, skuas offshore. Rarities often turn up but usually difficult to see as a visitor.
Other: Large Grey Seal colony, breed late-Oct/early Dec.
Directions: Sat nav: NE68 7TA. NU 219 322 (Seahouses). Access by boat from Seahouses Harbour, reached from A1.
Public transport: Bus - no.X18 Berwick to Alnwick (few services on Sun). Arriva Northumbria. No.418 (not Sun) Alnwick to Belford. Travelsure (T: 01665 720 955). Trains: Alnmouth & Berwick (then use bus).
Visiting: Four boat companies run trips out of Seahouses. Islands open: Apr, Aug-Sep: Inner Farne 10.30am-5pm. May-Jul: Staple Island 10.30am-1.30pm & Inner Farne: 1.30pm-5pm. Disabled access possible on Inner Farne, contact Property Manager for details. NT charge to land on islands (free to members) - these DO NOT include boatmen's fees. Toilets on Inner Farne. Dogs may be allowed on boats (check with boatman) but NOT allowed on islands.
Contact: The National Trust, The Farne Islands, Seahouses, NE68 7SR. T: 01289 389 244; E: farneislands@nationaltrust.org.uk

4. KIELDER WATER & FOREST PARK

Forestry Commission.
Habitats: Commercial coniferous/broadleaved woodland.
Birds: Successful Osprey breeding programme since 2009. *All year:* Dipper, Great Spotted & Green Woodpeckers, Tawny Owl, Song Thrush, Jay, Nuthatch, Goldcrest, Siskin. *Spring/summer:* Goshawk, Raven, Chiffchaff, Willow Warbler, Redstart. *Winter:* Crossbill & winter thrushes.
Other: Impressive display of Northern Marsh Orchids at entrance to Kielder Castle. Red Squirrel, Badger, Otter, Roe Deer, seven bat spp.
Directions: Sat nav: NE48 1ER. NY 632 934 (Kielder Castle). The Castle is situated at N end of Kielder Water, NW of Bellingham, 30 miles from Hexham.
Public transport: Bus - no.880 (Mon-Sat) Hexham to Kielder Castle. Snaith's Travel (T: 01830 520 609) & Tyne Valley Coaches (T: 01434 602 217). No.714 (Sun/bank hol - limited, Newcastle to Kielder Castle. Arriva.
Visiting: Forest open all year, car parks open dawn-dusk. Car parking facilities at Kielder Castle & overflow behind Angler's Arms pub (24-hr parking ticket required) - transferable for all car parks on south shore. Toll charge for 12-mile forest drive (rough surface), closed Nov to end-Apr due to conditions.

Kielder Castle Information Centre, free exhibition, licensed Kielder Castle Cafe with live wildlife viewing screens, access for disabled & toilets inc. baby changing facilities. Many walking/mountain biking trails start from here, ask staff for more info. Kielder Cycle Centre & bike wash, post office/local shop, Angler's Arms pub, youth hostel, camp site, No.27 B&B & 24 hour (pay by card) garage. One mile multi-access Duke's Trail inc. arboretum & hide where red squirrels can usually be seen. Bakethin Nature Reserve has dipping pond.
Contact: Forestry Commission, T: 01434 250 209; E: kieldercastle@forestryengland.uk
Ospreys: W: www.kielderospreys.wordpress.com
W: www.visitkielder.com

5. LINDISFARNE NNR

Natural England (North East Team).
Habitats: Dunes, sand, mudflats & saltmarsh, rocky shore & open water.
Birds: *Passage & winter:* Wildfowl & waders, inc. Pale-bellied Brent Goose, Red-breasted Merganser, Long-tailed Duck & Whooper Swan. Divers, grebes, Merlin. Common, scarce & rare migrants.
Other: Butterflies inc. Dark Green Fritillary & Grayling, nine spp. orchid inc. Coralroot & Lindisfarne Helleborine. Grey Seal.
Directions: Sat nav: TD15 2SS. NU 094 430. Island access lies two miles E of A1 at Beal, signposted to Holy Island, 10 miles S of Berwick-on-Tweed.
Public transport: Bus - no.477 limited service to Holy Island from Berwick. Border Buses (T: 01289 308 719). WT2 'Lindisfarne Hoppa' service Haggerston/Beal to Holy Island. Woody's Taxis T: 01289 547009. Both mainly summer, services fit in with safe crossing times.
Visiting: NOTE - causeway to Holy Island floods at high tide, check safe crossing times BEFORE crossing. Some restricted access (bird refuges). On island - car & coach parking, toilets & visitor centre in village, hide & self-guided trail. New hide with disabled access at Fenham-le-Moor (on mainland).
Contact: Natural England, T: 01289 381 470.

6. PRESTWICK CARR

Northumberland Wildlife Trust.
Habitats: Lowland raised mire, woodland, farmland.
Birds: A noted raptor watchpoint: 2010's White-tailed Eagle became 14th bird of prey spp. recorded since 1990s. *All year:* Water Rail, Kingfisher, Stonechat, Whinchat & Willow Tit. Barn, Little, Long-eared & Tawny Owls breed. *Summer:* migrants, inc. Grasshopper Warbler. *Passage:* waders occur in large numbers if carr is flooded. *Winter:* Hen Harrier are regular between Oct-Jan. Merlin & Peregrine, Short-eared Owl.
Directions: Sat nav: NE20 9UD. NZ 192 733. Seven miles NW of Newcastle city centre between Dinnington & Ponteland. Take A696 from A1 western bypass for three miles, then minor road to Prestwick hamlet. Park on minor roads north of Prestwick & Dinnington.
Public transport: Bus - no.45 runs between Newcastle Haymarket & Dinnington (0.75 mile walk to carr's eastern end). Arriva Northumbria.

Visiting: Restricted to minor roads & bridleway across carr. No access to northern section when military firing range in use (between Prestwick Mill Farm & Berwick Hill). Viewing platform & interpretation.
Contact: Northumberland WT - see site 1.

7. WHITELEE MOOR

Northumberland Wildlife Trust.
Habitats: Blanket bog & heather moorland.
Birds: The River Rede & its tributaries add to habitat & bird diversity. Notable breeding spp. inc. Merlin, Hen Harrier, Peregrine, Red Grouse, Dunlin, Curlew, Golden Plover, Skylark, Meadow Pipit, Stonechat. Dipper & Ring Ouzel regularly visit reserve.
Other: Otters often hunt along the Rede & herd of feral Goats may be seen.
Directions: Sat nav: TD8 6PT. NT 698 068. (Carter Bar) Reserve located at head of Redesdale, S of A68 Newcastle to Jedburgh road where it crosses Scottish Border at Carter Bar.
Public transport: None.
Visiting: Remote & wild, so hill-walking experience needed if attempting long walks. Park at tourist car park at Carter Bar & on lay-bys on forest track at reservoir end. Public footpath along old track to Whitelee Limeworks - then southwards extends to site's southern boundary - eastwards to link up with bridleway from White Kielder Burn to Chattlehope Burn. Additional access on foot via Forestry road near eastern corner of reserve. Dogs on lead.
Contact: Northumberland WT - see site 1.

Yorkshire (East Riding)

THE COAST DOMINATES the birding here - the headlands at Flamborough Head & Spurn Point are a magnet for migrants - they regularly turn up rarities, especially in the autumn. Bempton Cliffs is probably the best mainland seabird colony in England, where you can get close to Puffins & Gannets. An autumn boat trip from Bridlington is worth taking to see passing shearwaters & skuas.

1. BEMPTON CLIFFS

RSPB (Northern England).
Habitats: Largest mainland seabird colony in UK & only Gannet colony in England. Sea cliffs, farmland, grassland, coastal scrub.
Birds: Breeding numbers in excess of 200,000 between Apr-Jun inc. Kittiwake, Gannet, Puffin, Guillemot, Razorbill & Fulmar, some spp. start returning to cliffs in Jan. Breeding Tree Sparrow & Corn Bunting. *Passage:* skuas, shearwaters, terns & passerine migrants.
Other: Harbour Porpoise & Grey Seal regularly offshore. Bee & Northern Marsh Orchids.
Directions: Sat nav: YO15 1JF. TA 197 738. Near Bridlington. Take Cliff Lane N from Bempton village off B1229 to car park & visitor centre.
Public transport: Train - Bempton station 1.25 miles from reserve.
Visiting: Entrance charge for non-members, coaches/ minibuses (in advance, or drop off only). Seabird Centre open daily (9.30am-5pm Mar-Oct, 9.30am-4pm Nov-Feb). Toilets (inc. disabled), light refreshments, shop, picnic area, binoculars for hire. Cliff-top public footpath with five observation points (two wheelchair accessible). Four miles of stunning chalk cliffs, highest in county. Short farmland footpath. Dogs on leads.
Contact: RSPB, T: 01262 422 212;
E: bempton.cliffs@rspb.org.uk

2. BLACKTOFT SANDS

RSPB (Northern England).
Habitats: Second largest tidal reedbed in UK, saline lagoons, lowland wet grassland, willow scrub.
Birds: 270 spp. *Summer:* Breeding Bittern, Avocet, Marsh Harrier, Bearded Tit, Reed & Sedge Warblers, Tree Sparrow. *Passage:* waders (exceptional list inc. rarities). *Winter:* Wildfowl, Hen Harrier, Merlin, Peregrine.
Other: Water Vole. Dragonflies & damselflies inc. Black-tailed Skimmer, Four-spotted Chaser, Large Red Damselfly. Marsh Sow Thistle easily seen from footpaths in summer. Rare Brown-veined Wainscot moth.
Directions: Sat nav: DN14 8HR. SE 843 232. Eight miles E of Goole. Follow brown tourist signs on minor road between Ousefleet & Adlingfleet.
Public transport: Bus - no.360/361 from Goole stops at reserve entrance. East Yorkshire Motor Services (Busline: T: 01482 592 929).
Visiting: Open daily (not Dec 25) 9am-9pm/dusk if earlier. Charge for non-members. Car park, toilets. Reception hide open daily 9am-5pm Apr-Sep, weekends 10am-4pm Oct-Mar. Light refreshments, binocular hire. Six hides with wheelchair spaces, one viewing screen, footpaths suitable for wheelchairs. Assistance dogs only.
Contact: RSPB, T: 01405 704 665;
E: blacktoft.sands@rspb.org.uk

3. FLAMBOROUGH CLIFFS

Yorkshire Wildlife Trust.
Habitats: Coastal cliffs, species-rich rough grassland & scrub, farmland.
Birds: *Summer:* Breeding Puffin, Guillemot, Razorbill, Kittiwake, Shag, Fulmar, Skylark, Meadow Pipit, Linnet, Whitethroat, Yellowhammer, Tree Sparrow, occasional Corn Bunting. Thornwick reedbeds hold Reed & Sedge Warblers & Reed Bunting. *Passage migrants:* thrushes, warblers, finches, buntings & occasional rarities such as Wryneck & Red-backed Shrike. *Autumn:* Passage divers, grebes & seaduck.
Other: Pyramidal & Northern Marsh Orchids, Harebell, Thrift on cliff tops. Migrant butterflies such as Small Skipper & Painted Lady.
Directions: Sat nav: YO15 1BJ. Car parks: North Landing - TA 238 71920 & Thornwick Bay - TA234 719. Reserve is part of Flamborough headland, approx four miles NE of Bridlington. From Bridlington take B1255 to Flamborough & follow signs for North Landing.
Public transport: Bus - no.14 Bridlington to North Landing (not Sun). East Yorkshire Motor Services, (Busline: T: 01482 592 929).
Visiting: Open all year. Pay-&-display car parks at North Landing?thornwick Bay gives access to trails on reserve. Paths not suitable for wheelchairs. Cafe at North Landing (open Apr-Oct, 10am-5pm), toilets.
Contact: Yorkshire WT,
T: 01904 659 570;
E: info@ywt.org.uk

4. HORNSEA MERE

Wassand Hall.
Habitats: Yorkshire's largest body of freshwater, 0.6 mile inland from coast, edged by reedbeds & woodland.
Birds: *All year:* common wildfowl. *Spring/autumn passage:* Marsh Harrier, Osprey, Little Gull, terns, White & Yellow Wagtails, Wheatear, maybe rarer spp.
Winter: common wildfowl with a chance of divers, grebes, Long-tailed Duck, Goosander & Pintail.
Directions: Sat nav: HU11 5RJ .TA 174 460 (Hall). 12 miles E of Beverley, Wassand is between Seaton & Hornsea on A1035. Mere can also be viewed from Hornsea - enter town, onto Southgate then take signposted road to car park at Kirkholme Point.
Public transport: Bus - no.246 Hull-Beverley-Hornsea - ask to stop by Wassend Hall. East Yorkshire Motor Services, (Busline: T: 01482 592 929).
Visiting: Mere is owned by nearby Wassand Hall (which is open to public on selected days through year). Cafe on site (limited winter opening), toilets. Hide & woodland trail open daily (not Dec 25) - see notices for closing times. Hide - charge for electronic code, available from 10.30am at East Lodge, first house after Wassand Estate entrance on R (parking at Hall). Dogs on leads.
Contact: Warden, T: 01964 532 251 or 07972 05841; W: www.wassand.co.uk
W: https://hornseamere.wordpress.com/

5. LOWER DERWENT VALLEY NNR

Natural England (Yorkshire Team)/ Yorkshire Wildlife Trust/Carstairs Countryside Trust.
Habitats: Flood meadows, pastures, swamp, open water & alder/willow woodland.
Birds: 80+ spp. *Spring/summer:* Breeding wildfowl & waders, inc. Garganey & Snipe. Grey Partridge, Spotted Crake, Barn Owl & warblers. *Passage:* waders, inc. Whimbrel. *Winter/spring:* Bittern, 20,000+ waterfowl inc. Whooper Swan, wild geese, Teal & Wigeon. Large gull roost. Merlin, Hen Harrier, Peregrine, finches, buntings.
Other: Pocklington Canal is particularly good for wide range of aquatic plants & animals. Noctule, Daubenton's & Pipistrelle bats regularly recorded. Water Vole, Pygmy Shrew & Brown Hare.
Directions: Sat nav: YO19 6FE (Bank Island). Six miles SE of York, stretching 5 miles S along River Derwent from Newton-on-Derwent to Wressle & along Pocklington Canal. Three main accsess points: Bank Island (SE 691 448), North Duffield Carrs (SE 697 367) & Wheldrake Ings YWT (SE 691 444 - see site 9).
Public transport: Buses (not Sun) - no.18 York to Wheldrake/North Duffield. East Yorkshire Motor Services, (Busline: T: 01482 592 929). No.36 York to Wheldrake. Pullman (T: 01904 622 992).
Visiting: Open all year. Car parks at all sites, bike stands Bank Island & North Duffield Carrs. Bank Island - RADAR key toilets, two hides, viewing tower, sightings board. North Duffield Carrs - two hides, wheelchair access. Thorganby - viewing platform. No dogs.
Contact: Natural England, T: 07917 088 021; E: craig.ralston@naturalengland.org.uk

6. NORTH CAVE WETLANDS

Yorkshire Wildlife Trust.
Habitats: Former gravel pits converted into various lagoons for wetland birds, inc. reedbed, scrub & hedgerows, wet grassland. A developing site.
Birds: 200+ spp. *Summer:* Breeding spp. inc. Great Crested Grebe, Gadwall, Pochard, Common Tern, Sparrowhawk, Avocet, Little Ringed & Ringed Plover, Oystercatcher, Sedge Warbler & Reed Bunting. Large numbers of Sand Martins feed over reserve in summer.
Winter: wildfowl & waders inc. Golden Plover, Dunlin, Ruff & Redshank. Tree Sparrow.
Other: Water Vole, dragonflies, several butterfly spp. inc. small colony of Brown Argus.
Directions: Sat nav: HU15 2LY. SE 886 328. NW of North Cave village, approx 10 miles W of Hull. From Junc 28 of M62, follow signs to North Cave on B1230. In village, turn L & follow road to next crossroads, then go L, & park in Dryham Lane.
Public transport: Bus - nos.X55 (not Sun), 155 to North Cave from Hull/Goole. East Yorkshire Motor Services, (Busline: T: 01482 592 929).
Visiting: Open all year, car park 7.30am to dusk, toilet on site. Wild Bird Cafe (mobile trailer, Wed-Sun, 7.15am-1.15pm) on Dryham Lane, adjacent to reserve. Part of circular footpath is suitable for all abilities, five hides, four wheelchair accessible. No dogs.
Contact: Yorkshire WT - see site 3.

7. SPURN NNR

Yorkshire Wildlife Trust.
Habitats: Sand dunes with marram & sea buckthorn scrub. Mudflats around Humber Estuary.
Birds: *Spring:* Many migrants on passage, inc. scarce spp. inc. Red-backed Shrike, Bluethroat. *Summer:* Little Terns feed offshore. *Autumn:* Passage migrants & rarities inc. Wryneck, Pallas's Warbler. *Winter:* Large numbers of waders, Shelduck, Brent Goose, Merlin, Peregrine, Snow Bunting.
Other: Unique habitats & geographical position makes Spurn an interesting site for butterflies (25 spp.) & moths.
Directions: Sat nav: HU12 0UH. TA 419 149. 26 miles from Hull. Take A1033 from Hull to Patrington then R on B1445 to Easington & continue along minor road to Kilnsea. Turn R at crossroads towards Spurn Discovery Centre.
Public transport: None.
Visiting: Open all year - inclement weather may result in reserve being closed. Pay-&-display car park (open dawn-dusk) on approach road to reserve, opposite Spurn Discovery Centre (members & Easington parish residents/with permit free). Coaches - book in advance. Centre open 9am-6pm (cafe 10am-5pm), toilets, shop. Cycle hire. Hides. Limited access for dogs.
Contact: Spurn Discovery Centre, Spurn Road, Kilnsea, Hull, HU12 0UH. T: 01964 650 144; E: spurn@ywt.org.uk

8. TOPHILL LOW NATURE RESERVE

Yorkshire Water.
Habitats: Open water (two reservoirs), marshes, wet grassland, wader scrapes, woodland & thorn scrub.
Birds: 270 spp., 160 spp. annually. *Spring/early summer:* Hirundines, Black Tern & Black-necked Grebe. Breeding Little Ringed Plover, Common Tern, Kingfisher & Barn Owl with variety of warblers. *Late summer/autumn:* Up to 20 spp. of passage wader. *Winter:* wildfowl, one of UK's largest Black-headed & Common Gull roosts. Regular Bittern & Smew. Feeding station - Marsh & Willow Tit.
Other: 400+ spp. flora, 365+ spp. fungi, 16 spp. odonata inc. Hairy Hawker. Grass Snake, Otter, Water Vole, Great Crested Newt & Roe Deer.
Directions: Sat nav: YO25 9RH. TA 071 482. Located SE of Driffield & signposted (four miles) from A164 at Watton.
Public transport: None.
Visiting: Open daily (9am-6pm), other times by reserve membership only. Entrance fee, concessions available -from car park ticket machine. Coaches welcome. Toilets (inc. disabled) open daily. 12 hides (seven with wheelchair access), paths (disabled access), sightings board. No dogs.
Contact: Warden, Tophill Low NR, Watton Carrs, Hutton Cranswick, Driffield, East Yorkshire YO25 9RH. T: 01377 270 690;
E: richard.hampshire@yorkshirewater.co.uk;
W: www.tophilllow.blogspot.com

9. WHELDRAKE INGS

Yorkshire Wildlife Trust.
Habitats: Flooded meadows & pools, riverside vegetation.
Birds: *All year:* Kingfisher, Little & Barn Owl.
Spring passage: Garganey, Little Gull, terns & Wheatear. *Summer:* Breeding waders, plus Turtle Dove, Yellow Wagtail, hirundines & migrant warblers.
Autumn: Passage waders, Hobby & wildlfowl. *Winter:* large numbers wildfowl, inc. Shelduck, Pintail & Goldeneye among commoner species. Hen Harrier, Whooper & Bewick's Swans, Little Egret.
Other: Internationally important community of meadow plants. Brown Hare.
Directions: Sat nav: Y019 6AX. SE 690 446. Eight miles SE York, four miles E of A19. From York by-pass (A64) head S on A19 towards Selby for 1.2 miles, then turn L on Wheldrake Lane. Drive through Wheldrake village & turn sharp R to reach Natural England's Bank Island car park. Alternatively continue another 250 yards, just past the water compound to Ings Lane on L - park on stoney area next to bridge over river (can be flooded).
Public transport: See site 5.
Visiting: Open all times. Paths (inc. link between car parks), hides (not suitable for wheelchairs). No dogs.
Contact: Yorkshire WT - see site 3.

Yorkshire (North)

Seawatching IN THE AUTUMN from Filey Brigg can produce a range of skuas & shearwaters, with divers & grebes becoming more noticeable as the season progresses. The North York Moors hold breeding waders, chats, raptors & Red Grouse. The Lower Derwent Valley has great birding throughout the year.

1. COATHAM MARSH

Tata Steel/Tees Valley Wildlife Trust.
Habitats: 54ha, freshwater pools, lakes, reedswamp.
Birds: *Spring/autumn:* Wader passage (inc. Greenshank & Wood Sandpiper). *Summer:* Passerines (inc. Sedge Warbler, Yellow Wagtail). *Winter:* Large numbers of common ducks (plus Smew). *Occasional:* Water Rail, Great White Egret, Avocet, Bearded Tit & Bittern.
Other: Lime-rich soil good for wildflowers, inc. Northern Marsh Orchid. Insects inc. Migrant Hawker dragonfly.
Directions: Sat nav: TS10 5BQ. NZ 586 247. Located on W edge of Redcar, off A1085. At crossroads with Kirkleatham Lane, turn L continue over railway bridge to next mini roundabout. Turn L onto York Road/Tod Point Road. Reserve is on L.

Public transport: Bus - nos. X3/X3A (not Sun), X4, 62/62A Redcar to Middlesbrough stop in Coatham, 0.5 mile from reserve. Arriva Durham County. Train - Redcar Central station one mile from reserve.
Visiting: Open dawn-dusk. Keep to permissive footpaths only, section along The Fleet prone to winter flooding. Nearest toilets on Redcar seafront.
Contact: Tees Valley WT, T: 01287 636 382;
E: info@teeswildlife.org

2. FILEY BIRD OBSERVATORY & GROUP

FBOG/Yorkshire Wildlife Trust (The Dams).
Habitats: Five reserves owned/managed in area inc. wetland, woodland, scrub - attractive to migrants.
Birds: The Dams: Breeding & wintering water birds, breeding Sedge Warbler, Reed Warbler & Tree Sparrow.
The Tip: Important for breeding Skylark, Meadow Pipit, common warblers & Grey Partridge. *Winter:* Buntings, inc. Lapland. **Seawatching Hide:** *(Jul-Oct)* All four skuas, shearwaters, terns. *Winter:* Divers & grebes. **Parish Wood:** Common woodland residents & summer migrants inc. Grasshopper Warbler, Lesser Whitethroat. Scarce/rare migrants possible at all sites.
Directions: The Observatory recording area lies between coast & A165, centred around Filey town in N & as far as Reighton in S.

Filey Dams & East Lea: Sat nav: YO14 0DG. TA 106 807.
The Old Tip: Sat nav: YO14 9NU. TA 112 818.
Parish Wood: Sat nav: YO14 9NU. TA 112 815.
Rocket Pole Field: Sat nav: YO14 9ES. TA 121 818.
Public transport: Filey bus & train stations are within
walking distance (one mile) from each site.
Visiting: Open at all times. Park at end of Wharfedale
Road (Dams/East Lea), Sycamore Avenue (Parish
Wood/The Old Tip) or North Cliff Country Park
(Rocket Pole Field & Filey Brigg). Toilets in Country
Park (Apr-Oct) & town centre. Two open-access hides
at The Dams (wheelchair access to Main Hide), one
hide on The Brigg (for FBOG members only). Nature
trails at The Dams, Parish Wood/Old Tip. Cliff top
walk for seabirds along Cleveland Way. Dogs only in
Parish Wood & The Old Tip (on lead). Events held.
Contact: Bird Observatory,
E: membership.fbog@gmail.com; W: www.fbog.co.uk
Yorkshire WT, T: 01904 659 570; E: info@ywt.org.uk

3. FYLINGDALES MOOR CONSERVATION AREA

Strickland Estate/Fylingdales Moor ESS Co Ltd.
Habitats: Heather moorland (former grouse moor),
with scattered trees, wooded valleys & gulleys. Now
managed for wildlife & archaeological remains.
Birds: 80+ common spp. inc. Kestrel, Lapwing,
Snipe, Cuckoo, Meadow Pipit, Grey Wagtail & Wood
Warbler. Peregrine regular. Scarce breeding spp.
inc. Hen Harrier, Merlin, Golden Plover, Red Grouse,
Curlew, Wheatear, Stonechat, Whinchat, Skylark,
Marsh & Willow Tit, Linnet, Bullfinch, Reed Bunting &
Yellowhammer.
Other: Otter, Roe Deer, Brown Hare, stoat, Weasel &
Badger, important for Water Vole. Three spp. heather,
plus Cranberry, Cowberry, Moonwort and, in wetter
parts, Bog Myrtle, Lesser Twayblade, Bog Asphodel,
Butterwort, Marsh Helleborine & sundews. Rare
orchids & sedges. Insect spp. inc. Large Heath & Small
Pearl-bordered Fritillary butterflies & Emperor Moth.
Directions: Sat nav: YO22 4US. NZ 945 002 (Jugger
Howe lay-by). Conservation area covers 2,750ha
within National Park off A171 S of Whitby, stretching
between Sneaton High Moor (Newton House
Plantation) & coast at Ravenscar.
Public transport: Bus - no.X93
between Scarborough & Whitby,
nearest stop at Flask Inn (approx
one mile N of Jugger Howe lay-by).
Arriva North East,
(T: 0344 800 4411).
Visiting: Open access. Parking
(inc. coaches) available at
Jugger Howe lay-by on A171.
Numerous footpaths inc.
Jugger Howe Nature Trail,
Lyke Wake Walk & Robin Hood's
Bay Road.
Contact: None.

4. MALHAM TARN

National Trust.
Habitats: Upland pasture, woodland, lake (highest in
England), limestone outcrops.
Birds: *All year:* Waterfowl inc, Great Crested Grebe,
regular gull spp., Peregrine, Barn Owl. *Spring/Summer:*
Oystercatcher, Lapwing, Redshank, Curlew, Redstart,
warblers, Twite. *Winter:* Wildfowl (inc. Goldeneye,
Pochard, Goosander), Woodcock, Water Rail, winter
thrushes, Redpoll, Siskin. Occasional: harriers, Osprey
on passage, Whooper Swan & Short-eared Owl (winter).
Other: Water Vole.
Directions: Sat nav: BD24 9PU. SD 894 658 (parking
S side of lake). BD24 9PT. SD 882 671 (parking N side
of lake/woodland. Five miles NE of Settle, two miles
NW of Malham.
Public transport: Bus - irregular & seasonal Skipton
to Malham.
Visiting: Open at all times, Various walks in the area,
graded easy to difficult, inc. tramper route & circular
walk (4.5 miles). No dogs in nature reserve. Nearest
facilities in Malham, inc. National Park Centre.
Malhan Cove one mile N of village for limestone
outcrop/Peregrine.
Contact: National Trust, T: 01729 830 416;
E: malhamtarn@nationaltrust.org.uk

5. NOSTERFIELD LNR

Lower Ure Conservation Trust.
Habitats: Wetland grassland & open water, magnesian
limestone grassland, gravel banks, hedgerows & scrub.
Birds: 150 spp. annually, 225+ spp. overall. *Spring/
autumn:* Up to 30 wader spp. annually, terns.
Summer: Breeding spp. inc. Redshank, Lapwing,
Avocet, Oystercatcher, Curlew, Ringed Plover,
Mediterranean Gull, Shoveler, Gadwall, Barn Owl,
Skylark, Lesser Whitethroat, Tree Sparrow, Linnet,
Reed Bunting. *Autumn:* Passage waders inc. regular
Pectoral Sandpiper.

Winter: Wildfowl (Wigeon, Teal, Greylag & rarer geese), waders (Golden Plover, Lapwing, Curlew) & Peregrine.
Other: Specialist grassland & wetland flora, inc. seven spp. orchid, Mudwort, Yellow Rattle, Golden Dock. Butterflies inc. White-letter Hairstreak, Brown Argus, Wall & large colony of Common Blue. Dragonflies inc. Emperor, Black-tailed skimmer, Red-veined Darter (has bred). 480+ spp. moths. Brown Hare & Water Shrew.
Directions: Sat nav: DL8 2QZ. SE 278 795. Six miles N of Ripon, between West Tanfield & Nosterfield E of A6108 (Ripon to Masham road) & approx four miles W of A1.
Public transport: Bus - no.159 (Mon-Sat) from Ripon to Masham, alight at West Tanfield (0.5 mile walk to reserve). Proctors Coaches (T: 01677 425 203).
Visiting: Open all year. Lower viewing area beyond car park allows viewing from cars only. Coaches, book in advance. Footpath (approx one mile) is wheelchair-friendly. Two disabled-friendly hides, interpretation panels (main hide).
Contact: Warden, E: simon.warwick@luct.org.uk; T: 01765 602 832; W: www.luct.org.uk

6. TIMBLE INGS

Yorkshire Water.
Habitats: Upland woodlands of pine, larch & spruce & nearby reservoirs (Fewston/Swinsty). SW corner of wood a good place to observe visible migration in autumn.
Birds: Bradford Ornithological Group spp. list stands at 134. Yorkshire Water habitat management makes site attractive to Long-eared & Tawny Owls, Nightjar & Tree Pipit. Buzzard breed & Red Kite regular but Goshawk numbers in decline. *Summer:* Breeding species inc. Redpoll, Siskin, Crossbill, Woodcock, Redstart & Grasshopper Warbler. Short-eared Owl hunt adjacent moorland. *Winter:* Fieldfare, Redwing, Brambling, occasional Waxwing & Hawfinch.
Other: Roe Deer, Badger, Brown Hare, shrew, vole & mouse spp. (all detected from owl pellets). Ponds attractive to amphibians & dragonflies, inc. Broad-bodied Chaser, Emperor & Black Darter.
Directions: Sat nav: LS21 2PP. SE 170 542 (parking opposite Anchor Farm). W of Harrogate, N of Otley, off A59 S of Blubberhouses, near Timble village.
Public transport: None.
Visiting: Open at all times, hard forest tracks. Toilets, cafes, pubs, coach parking nearby.
Contact: Recreation Officer, Yorkshire Water, E: Geoff.D.Lomas@yorkshirewater.co.uk

Yorkshire (South & West)

DESPITE BEING IN the heart of the industrial north, dominated by a large number of towns, the area still manages to offer birdwatchers a surprising number of interesting sites. There are a large number of water meadows & marshes (ings), many the result of the areas industrial past. Sites such as RSPB Fairburn Ings (next to the A1), Potteric Carr, RSPB Old Moor reserve & Bolton Ings all have a year-round birding interest.

1. BOLTON INGS (DEARNE VALLEY)

RSPB (Northern England).
Habitats: 43 ha, reedbed & scrub.
Birds: *All year:* Kingfisher, Grey Heron. *Spring/ summer:* Reed Bunting. breeding waders & warblers, Cuckoo, Garganey. Avocets & Spoonbills. *Autumn:* Passage waders inc.Greenshank, Green Sandpiper, Golden Plover. *Winter:* Wildfowl, inc. Goosander, Wigeon & Teal, Stonechat.
Other: Dragonflies inc. Banded Demoiselle, Brown Hare.
Directions: Sat nav: S73 0YF. SE 425 020. Park at RSPB Old Moor & walk east along Trans-Pennine Trail to Bolton Ings. See site 6.
Public transport: See site 6 (Old Moor).
Visiting: Open all year round. Dearne Way footpath & Trans-Pennine Trail open at all times, not suitable for wheelchair users. Dogs only on public footpaths. Cormorant View hide. More facilities at RSPB Old Moor.
Contact: RSPB - see site 6.

2. DENABY INGS

Yorkshire Wildlife Trust.
Habitats: Riverside meadows, hay meadows, open water, deciduous woodland, marsh, willows.
Birds: *All year:* common woodland birds, 3 spp. woodpecker, possible Willow Tit, Corn Bunting, Yellowhammer. *Spring/summer:* Waterfowl, Kingfisher, Barn & Tawny Owls, Sand Martin, Swallow, Whinchat, Grasshopper Warbler, Lesser Whitethroat, Whitethroat, other warblers *Passage:* waders, Common, Arctic & Black Terns, Redstart, Wheatear. *Winter:* Wildfowl (inc. Whooper Swan & Goosander), Jack Snipe & other waders, Grey Wagtail, Fieldfare, Redwing, Brambling, Siskin.
Other: Grass Snake, Bee, Pyramidal & Common Spotted Orchids.
Directions: Sat nav: S64 0JJ. SE 496 008. NE of Mexborough. Take A6023 from Mexborough, turn L down Pastures Road on outskirts of town. After one mile turn R into car park (shortly after crossing River Dearne). Climb flight of concrete steps to enter reserve.
Public transport: Train - Conisbrough or Mexborough, 30 mins to reserve.
Visiting: Open all year. Car park, interpretation panels, two hides/one viwingscreen, circular trail. Dogs on leads.
Contact: Yorkshire WT, T: 01904 659 570; E: info@ywt.org.uk

3. FAIRBURN INGS

RSPB (Northern England).

Habitats: Open water, wet grassland, marshand fen scrub, reedbed, reclaimed colliery spoil heaps.

Birds: *All year:* Kingfisher, Green Woodpecker, Tree Sparrow, Willow Tit, Bullfinch. *Spring:* Osprey, Little Gull, Wheatear, five spp. tern inc. annual Black Tern, Garganey, Little Ringed Plover. *Summer:* Nine spp. breeding warbler, Grey Heron, Gadwall, Little Ringed Plover. *Autumn:* Thousands of waders on passage inc Green Sandpiper, Little Ringed Plover & Black-tailed Godwit. *Winter:* Smew, Goldeneye, Goosander, Wigeon, Peregrine.

Other: Brown Hare, Harvest Mouse, Roe Deer, Leisler's & Daubenton's Bats, 28 spp. butterflies & 20 spp. dragonflies.

Directions: Sat nav: WF10 2BH. SE 451 277. 12 miles from Leeds, six miles from Pontefract, three miles from Castleford. Next to A1246 from Junc 42 of A1.

Public transport: Bus - no.493 from Pontefract to Fairburn (Mon-Sat). Arriva in Yorkshire. Train - Castleford, three miles.

Visiting: Open daily (not Dec 25/26). Car parking (inc. coaches) 9.30am-8pm Feb-Oct, 9.30am-4pm Nov-Jan - charge for non-members (after 30 mins), free for disabled badge holders. Visitor centre/shop open 9am-5pm Mar-Oct, 9am-4pm Nov-Feb. Hot/cold drinks & snacks available. Toilets inc. disabled & baby-changing facilities. Wildlife garden, pond-dipping & mini beast areas, duck feeding platform. Boardwalks leading to Pickup Pool, feeding station & Kingfisher viewpoint are wheelchair-friendly. Four hides/four shelters, two public trails (one accessible to wheelchairs). Mobility Scoter available - call to book. Dogs on leads.

Contact: RSPB, T: 01977 628 191; E: fairburnings@rspb.org.uk

4. GRENO WOODS

Sheffield & Rotherham Wildlife Trust.

Habitats: 170ha, ancient woodland, some heathland.

Birds: Inc. wider area - *All year:* Common woodland spp., Tawny Owl, Willow Tit, Crossbill. *Summer:* Woodcock, Nightjar, Cuckoo, warblers inc. Whitethroat & Willow Warbler, Tree Pipit.*Winter:* Winter thrushes, Stonechat, Redpoll.

Other: woodland plants inc. Bluebells & Cow Wheat.

Directions: Sat nav: S35 7DS. SK 325 949. Lies on N outskirts of Sheffield (adjacent to Wharncliffe & Wheata Woods - covering total area of 700ha). Head N from Shefield on A61 (Penistone Road) until it becomes Halifax Road, then turn L into Foxhill Road - continue on to Main Street & then on to Woodhead Road. After one mile, Forestry Commission car park is on L. Most of wood lies between Woodhead Road & A61.

Public transport: Bus - no.85 runs from Sheffield city centre to Grenoside village. No.86 run along the A61 with stops adjacent to reserve. Stagecoach.

Visiting: Open all times. Network of footpaths & bridleways - also three downhill mountain bike trails.

Contact: Sheffield & Rotherham Wildlife Trust, T: 0114 263 4335; E: mail@wildsheffield.com

5. HARDCASTLE CRAGS

National Trust.

Habitats: 160ha, unspoilt wooded valleys, ravines, streams, hay meadows & moorland edge.

Birds: *All year:* Sparrowhawk, Kestrel, Tawny, Barn & Little Owls, Green & Great Spotted Woodpeckers, Dipper, Grey Wagtail, Jay other woodland species. Goshawk in Crimsworth Dean. *Spring/summer:* Cuckoo, Redstart, Lesser Whitethroat, Garden Warbler, Blackcap, Wood Warbler, Chiffchaff, Spotted & Pied Flycatchers.

Other: Northern Hairy Wood Ant, Moss Carder Bee, Tree Bumblebee, Killarney Fern, Brittle Bladder Fern, Roe Deer, 8 spp. bat.

Directions: Sat nav: HX7 7AL. SD 988 291 (Midgehole car park). From Hebden Bridge follow National Trust signs to A6033 Keighley Road. Follow for 0.75 mile. Turn L at National Trust sign to car parks. Alternate pay-&-display car park at Clough Hole (HX7 7AZ. SD 969 298)) on Widdop Road, Heptonstall.

Public transport: Bus/train - to Hebden Bridge, then one mile walk to Midgehole. Sat/Sun & bank holidays bus (approx. May-Oct)- no.906 Widdop Reservoir-Hardcastle Crags-Hebden Bridge. TLC Travel (T: 0113 245 7676).

Visiting: Open all year. Two small car parks, NT car park charges - free for members & disabled badge holders. Cycle racks, several way-marked trails. Gibson Mill visitor centre has toilets, cafe, exhibitions & limited disabled parking (pre-book). Dogs under control.

Contact: National Trust, Hardcastle Crags, T: 01422 846 236; E: hardcastlecrags@nationaltrust.org.uk

6. INGBIRCHWORTH RESERVOIR

Yorkshire Water.
Habitats: Reservoir, small strip deciduous woodland.
Birds: *Spring/summer*: Whinchat, warblers, woodland birds, House Martin. *Spring/autumn passage*: Little Ringed Plover, Ringed Plover, Dotterel, other waders, Common Tern, Arctic Tern, Black Tern, Yellow Wagtail, Wheatear. *Winter*: Wildfowl, Golden Plover, waders, occasional rare gull such as Iceland or Glaucous, Grey Wagtail, Fieldfare, Redwing, Brambling, Redpoll.
Other: Woodland wildflowers, inc. Bluebells.
Directions: Sat nav: S36 7GS. SE 217 062. Leave M1 at Junc 37 & take A628 towards Manchester. After five miles turn R at roundabout onto A629 Huddersfield road. Drive 2.5 miles to Ingbirchworth. Turn L into Wellthorne Lane (signed to 'Inn'). Park on roadside just past The Fountain Inn, continue on foot to where road bears L (to cross the dam), go straight forward here onto track which follow N edge of reservoir. Can also walk across dam & onto a footpath through narrow strip of woodland at end of dam.
Public transport: Bus - no.24 Barnsley to Ingbirchworth (Mon-Sat). Stagecoach.
Visiting: Open all year. Car park, picnic tables. One of few reservoirs in area with public foot access.
Contact: Recreation Officer, Yorkshire Water, E: Geoff.D.Lomas@yorkshirewater.co.uk

7. OLD MOOR (DEARNE VALLEY)

RSPB (Northern England).
Habitats: Lakes & flood meadows, wader scrape & reedbeds.
Birds: *All year*: Kingfisher, Barn & Little Owl.s *Summer*: Breeding Bittern, Sand Martin waders, inc. Little Ringed Plover & drumming Snipe, migrant warblers & wildfowl. *Autumn*: passage waders. *Winter*: Large numbers of wildfowl, spectacular flocks of Lapwing & Golden Plover (up to 8,000 birds), Peregrine, Tree Sparrow (in garden feeding area).
Other: Water Vole, Brown Hare, Weasel, Pygmy Shrew, wildflowers inc. orchids & Adders Tongue Fern.
Directions: Sat nav: S73 0YF. SE 422 022. Old Moor is just off Manvers Way (A633). From M1, take Junc 36 & take A61. At next roundabout follow Old Moor signs for ca four miles. From A1M, take Junc 37 & follow A635 towards Barnsley, then follow RSOB OLd Moor signs.
Public transport: Bus - no.X20 to Old Moor reserve from Barnsley-Doncaster (not Sun). Stagecoach (T: 01709 515 151). Train - Wombwell & Swinton stations approx three miles from reserve.
Visiting: Open until 8pm Apr-Oct. Entrance charge, for non-members. Visitor centre open daily (not Dec 25/26) 9.30am-5pm . Cafe open 9.30am-3.00pm. Shop, accessible toilets, education & meeting rooms, mobility scooter for hire. Two trails with ten hides/viewing screens - suitable for wheelchair users. Guide dogs only.
Contact: RSPB, T: 01226 751 593; E: old.moor@rspb.org.uk

8. POTTERIC CARR

Yorkshire Wildlife Trust.
Habitats: Flood plain of River Torne, with reed fen, subsidence ponds, artificial pools, grassland, woodland.
Birds: 230 spp. 102 spp. have bred - waterfowl (inc. Shoveler, Gadwall, Pochard, Water Rail, Kingfisher, 3 spp.woodpecker, Lesser Whitethroat, Reed & Sedge Warblers, Willow Tit. *Passage/winter*: Bittern, Marsh Harrier, Black Tern, wildfowl & waders.
Other: 21 spp. dragonflies, 28 spp. butterflies inc. Purple Hairstreak & Dingy Skipper. Palmate & Great Crested Newt. Common Spotted & Bee Orchids.
Directions: Sat nav: DN4 8DB. SE 588 005. From M18, Junc 3 take A6182 (Doncaster) & at first roundabout turn R. Entrance & car park are on R after 50 yards.
Public transport: Bus - nos.72 & 73 from Doncaster Interchange, alight at B&Q on Woodfield Way. Cross White Rose Way, walk down Mallard Way. Cross car park to reserve entrance in Sedum House. First South Yorkshire. Train - Doncaster.
Visiting: Open daily (not Dec 24-27) 9am-5pm. Car park locked at 5pm but ask (before 5pm) if you would like to stay later. Visitor centre/cafe/shop free, non-members entrance fee to reserve. Groups of ten or more should book in advance. Cafe open daily (9am-4pm). Toilets at entrance reception, in cafe & outside. Around five miles of paths (3.2 miles accessible to wheelchairs, unassisted), 14 viewing hides (10 suitable for disabled). Guide dogs only.
Contact: Potteric Carr Nature Reserve, T: 01302 325 736; E: potteric.carr@ywt.org.uk

9. SPROTBOROUGH FLASH & DON GORGE

Yorkshire Wildlife Trust.
Habitats: Limestone gorge, limestone grassland on plateau, woodland, wetland & open water.
Birds: *Spring/autumn passage*: waders inc. Little Ringed Plover, Dunlin, Greenshank, Green Sandpiper, Yellow Wagtail. *Summer*: Hirundines, Whitethroat, Lesser Whitethroat, Garden Warbler, Blackcap, Chiffchaff, Willow Warbler, Cuckoo. *Winter/all year*: Wildfowl, Water Rail, Snipe, Little Owl, Tawny Owl, 3 spp. woodpecker, thrushes, Siskin.
Other: Brown Hare, Grass Snake, flora inc. Cowslip, common twayblade, bee orchid.
Directions: Sat nav: DN5 7NB. SE 537 015. Leave A1(M) at Junc 36 onto A630 towards Rotherham. After 0.5 mile, turn R at traffic lights to Sprotborough. After approx two miles road drops down into Don Gorge. Cross a bridge over river, then another over a canal, turn immediately L. Public car park on L next to toll house in Nursery Lane - two mins from reserve along towpath.
Public transport: Bus - no.219 Doncaster to Barnsley, alight Sprotbrough village (10 mins walk to reserve). Stagecoach Yorkshire. Train - Conisbrough (two miles).
Visiting: Open all year. Two hides along towpath, accessible to wheelchairs, interpretation panels, footpaths.
Contact: Yorkshire WT - see site 2.

South East England

Berkshire

DESPITE BEING CLOSE to London, & with the M4 running through its cenre, the county has a decent range of habitats. These include heathland & downland but it is the gravel pits that attract the widest range of bird species & where wintering Smew & Goosander can be regular visitors.

1. DINTON PASTURES

Wokingham Borough Council.
Habitats: 135ha, woodland, meadow & lakes on banks of River Loddon. Sandford Lake managed for wildfowl, Lavell's Lake (see site 3) best for waders & scrub species.
Birds: *All year:* Kingfisher, Water Rail, Barn Owl. *Spring/summer:* Hobby, Little Ringed Plover, Common Tern, Nightingale, common warblers. *Winter:* Bittern, wildfowl (inc. Goldeneye, Wigeon, Teal, Gadwall), thrushes. Waders inc. Green & Common Sandpipers, Snipe, Redshank.
Other: Water Vole, Harvest Mouse, Great Crested Newt, Loddon Pondweed & Loddon Lily. 18 spp. dragonflies inc. Emperor, Black-tailed Skimmer, Migrant Hawker, White-legged Damselfly & Banded Demoiselle.
Directions: Sat nav: RG10 0TH. SU 784 718. From Junc 10 of M4 head towards Reading, then follow sign to Winnersh on A329. Park is signposted off B3030 between Hurst & Winnersh.
Public transport: Bus - nos.127/128/129 between Reading & Wokingham stop near main entrance, Courtney Bus (T: 0118 973 3486). Train - Winnersh station is 15 min walk.
Visiting: Open all year, dawn-dusk. Car park charges apply 6am-10pm daily. Information centre, cafe open daily 8.30am-5pm (4pm in winter), toilets (suitable for wheelchairs). Various trails between one & three miles, one hide (overlooking Sandford Lake). Electric buggies for hire, walks leaflet. Dogs allowed.
Contact: Dinton Pastures Country Park,
T: 0118 974 6343; E: countryside@wokingham.gov.uk;
W: www.dinton-pastures.co.uk

2. HUNGERFORD MARSH

Town & Manor of Hungerford.
Habitats: An idyllic waterside site with chalk stream, water meadows, unimproved rough grazing & reedbed.
Birds: 120 spp. *All year:* Mute Swan, common wildfowl, Grey Heron, Little Grebe, Kingfisher, Reed Bunting, Bullfinch. *Spring/summer:* Reed & Grasshopper Warblers. *Winter:* Siskin & Water Rail.
Other: Water Vole, Otter & Grass Snake. Southern Marsh Orchid, Fen Bedstraw.
Directions: Sat nav: RG17 0JB. SU 333 687. On W side of Hungerford, beside Kennet & Avon Canal. From town centre, go along Church Street past town hall. Turn R under railway. Follow public footpath over swing bridge on canal near church. Reserve is separated from Freeman's Marsh by a line of willows & bushes.
Public transport: Train - Hungerford station 0.5 mile from reserve.
Visiting: Open all year. Car park, keep to footpath. Dogs on leads.
Contact: Clerk to T&M of H, T: 01488 686 555;
E: admin@townandmanor.co.uk;
W: www.hungerfordtownandmanor.co.uk

3. LAVELL'S LAKE

Wokingham Borough Council/Lavell's Wetland Trust.
Habitats: 10 ha, composed of gravel pits, two wader scrapes, reed beds, rough grassland, marshy area, sand martin banks, between River Loddon & Emm Brook. To N of Lavell's Lake, gravel pits are being restored to attract birds. The lake at Lea Farm is viewable walking N along the River Loddon from Lavell's Lake over small green bridge - on R & can be seen through a viewing screen & members only hide for members of Lavell's Wetland Trust - no access.

Birds: *All year:* Great Crested Grebe, Gadwall, Sparrowhawk, Kingfisher, Red Kite, Buzzard, Cetti's Warbler. *Summer:* Common Tern, Redshank, Lapwing, Hobby, warblers inc. Reed, Sedge, Whitethroat. *Passage:* Garganey, Little Ringed Plover, Common & Green Sandpiper & Greenshank. *Winter:* Water Rail, Bittern, Little Egret, Teal, Shoveler, Pochard, Goldeneye, occasional Smew & Goosander. Along River Loddon - Siskin, Lesser Redpoll, Fieldfare & Redwing.
Directions: Sat nav: RG10 0SU. SU 785 727. Parking on Sandford Lane off B3030 between Hurst & Winnersh, E of Reading or walk from Dinton Pastures, see site 1.
Public transport: See site 1.
Visiting: Open dawn-dusk. Car park open 9am-5pm, three hides, one with disabled access, Lea Farm hide open to LWT members only. Dogs on leads at all times.
Contact: Dinton Pastures Country Park - see site 1. W: www.lavells.org.uk/

4. MOOR GREEN LAKES

Lakes Group Moor Green/Blackwater Valley Countryside Partnership.
Habitats: 36ha, three lakes with gravel islands, beaches & scrapes. River Blackwater, grassland, surrounded by willow, ash, hazel & thorn hedgerows.
Birds: 200+ spp., 60 spp. regularly breeding. *Spring/summer:* Little Ringed Plover, Reed Warbler & Hobby. Whitethroat, Sedge Warbler, Common Sandpiper. Mandarin Duck, Common Tern & Barn Owl breed on site. Dunlin & Green Sandpiper on passage. *Winter:* Wigeon, Teal, Gadwall & of particular interest, a roost of Goosander on Grove Lake. Little Egret regular, Snipe, Lapwing & Green Sandpiper. Gull roost on adjacent Manor Farm workings inc. up to 1,000 Lesser Black-backed.
Other: 31 spp. butterflies & 15 spp. dragonflies.
Directions: Sat nav: RG40 3TF. SU 805 628 (free car park in Lower Sandhurst Road, Finchampstead (open 8am-dusk). Alternatively use Horseshoe Lakes free car park in Mill Lane, Sandhurst (Sat nav: GU47 8JW, SU 820 620). Lies ca one mile NW of Sandhurst - take A321 N from Sandhurst, from High Street turn L along Lower Church Road. At T-junction turn L for Mill Road car park or R for Lower Sandhurst Road car park.
Public transport: Train - nearest stations, Crowthorne & Sandhurst - both a one mile walk .
Visiting: No access to lakes, view from footpaths bordering eastern, southern & western sides - paths can be used by wheelchairs though surface not particularly suitable. Southern path forms part of Blackwater Valley long distance footpath. Two bird hides open to MGLG members, two public viewing screens. Feeding station viewable from bench on western path.
Contact: Moor Green Lakes Group, E: chairman@mglg.ork.uk; W: www.mglg.org.uk Blackwater Valley Countryside Partnership, T: 01252 331 353; E: blackwater.valley@hants.gov.uk; W: www.blackwatervalleycountryside.wordpress.com/

5. THEALE GRAVEL PITS

Theale Area Bird Conservation Group.
Habitats: Three complexes of various sized gravel pits spread out across Theale flood plain.
Birds: *Spring/summer:* Migrant warblers, breeding Nightingale & Common Tern, passage Arctic & Black Terns, large number of hirundines, resident Peregrine favours pylon area. *Autumn:* Dunlin, Common Sandpiper & other passage waders. Little Gull, Osprey, along with terns on passage. *Winter:* Large numbers of wildfowl, inc. Goldeneye & Goosander. Thousands of gulls on nearby Moatlands pit. Bittern sometimes recorded in Hosehill Lake LNR reedbed.
Other: Good variety of dragonflies & butterflies. Grass Vetchling worthy of note.
Directions: Sat nav: RG7 4GB. SU 646 699 (lay-by parking). Group of pits, S of Reading, situated between Juncs 11 & 12 of M4, immediately S of Theale town centre. From Theale town centre head S on Station Road/Hanger Road & park in lay-bys in Dean Copse Lane, by Fox & Hounds Pub - main pit & Hosehill Lake LNR.
Public transport: Train - Theale station, short walk to nearest pits.
Visiting: Open all times. Parking for a few vehicles in lay-bys near Fox & Hounds pub. Tern rafts, Sand Martin bank & wildflower meadow in Hosehill Lake LNR, with information boards/benches on mile-long circular walk.
Contact: TABCC Sec, Cathy McEwan T: 01189 415 792; E: tabcgsec@yahoo.com; https://tabcg.webs.com/thealesites.htm

6. WILDMOOR HEATH

Berks, Bucks & Oxon Wildlife Trust.
Habitats: 91 ha, wet & dry lowland heath, bog, mixed woodland & mature Scots pine plantation.
Birds: *Spring/summer:* 55 spp. inc. Hobby, Nightjar, Woodlark, Tree Pipit, Stonechat, Dartford Warbler, Reed Bunting.
Other: 20 spp. dragonflies, Silver-studded Blue butterfly, Slow Worm, Adder, Grass Snake, Common Lizard, Roe Deer. Bog plants inc. sundews.
Directions: Sat nav: RG45 7PW. SU 838 630. Between Bracknell & Sandhurst. From Sandhurst shopping area, take A321 NW towards Wokingham. Turn R at mini-roundabout on to Crowthorne Road. Continue for about one mile through one set of traffic lights. Car park is on R at bottom of hill.
Public transport: Bus - no.194 Bracknell-Camberley runs past reserve car park (Crowthorne Road/Sandhurst Road). Courtney Buses (T: 0118 973 3486). Train - Sandhurst station, one mile S of reserve.
Visiting: Open all year. Car park. No access to woodland N of Rackstraw Road at Broadmoor Bottom. Not suitable for wheelchairs due to slope of site & muddy, uneven terrain. Dogs on a lead.
Contact: BBOWT, T: 01628 829 574; E: info@bbowt.org.uk

Buckinghamshire

BETWEEN THE RIVER THAMES to the south &
the River Ouse to the north, the county offers
a good selection of woods, lakes & gravel pits.
The higher ground of the Chiltern escarpment
is an excellent place to watch Red Kites. Some
interesting species breed in the county including
Little Ringed Plover, Firecrest & Hawfinch.

1. BURNHAM BEECHES NNR

City of London Corporation.
Habitats: Ancient woodland, streams, pools,
heathland (Stoke Common), grassland, scrub.
Birds: *All year*: Mandarin (good population), 3 spp.
woodpecker, Sparrowhawk. *Spring/summer*: Cuckoo,
possible Turtle Dove. *Winter*: Siskin, Crossbill, regular
large flocks of Brambling. Possible Woodcock. Marsh &
Willow Tits, Red Kite & Buzzard.
Other: Ancient Beech & Oak pollards with associated
wildlife. Rich array of fungi.
Directions: Sat nav: SL2 3PS. SU 958 850. 2.5 miles
N of Slough & on W side of A355, running between
Junc 2 of M40 & Junc 6 of M4. Entry from A355 via
Beeches Road. Also smaller parking areas in Hawthorn
Lane & Pumpkin Hill to the S & Park Lane to the W.
Public transport: Bus - no.X74 Slough to Farnham
Common. First Berkshire & Thames Valley.
Train - Slough.

Visiting: Open all year (not Dec 25). Main Lord
Mayor's Drive open 8am-dusk. Coach parking. Visitor
centre, Beeches Cafe, public toilets & information
point open 10am-5pm. Network of wheelchair
accessible roads & paths, most start at Victory Cross.
Motorised buggy available for hire.
Contact: Burnham Beeches Office, Hawthorn Lane,
Farnham Common, SL2 3TE. T: 01753 647 358;
E: burnham.beeches@cityoflondon.gov.uk;
W: www.cityoflondon.gov.uk

2. CALVERT JUBILEE

Berks, Bucks & Oxon Wildlife Trust.
Habitats: Ex-clay pit, railway & landfill site. Now with
deep lake, marginal reedbed & scrub habitat.
Birds: *Summer*: Nesting Common Tern on rafts,
Kingfisher, Hobby, warblers & Cuckoo. *Passage
migrants*: Black Tern & fly-over waders. *Winter*:
Over-wintering wildfowl. Bittern, Water Rail & large
gull roost with occasional Glaucous & Iceland Gulls.
Rarer spp. regularly turn up.
Other: Rare butterflies, inc. Dingy & Grizzled
Skippers & Black Hairstreak. Bee & Common Spotted
Orchids.
Directions: Sat nav: OX27 0BQ. SP 681 246.
SW of Steeple Claydon, 6.5 miles E of Bicester.
Leave Steeple Claydon by West Street, continue to
crossroad, turn L towards Calvert. Small car park on L
(opposite entrance to Greatmoor Sailing Club).
Public transport: None.
Visiting: Small car park, two hides. Surfaced path to
bird hide, keep to network of paths. Guide dogs only.
Contact: BBOWT, T: 01442 826 774:
E: info@bbowt.org.uk

3. CHURCH WOOD

RSPB (Midlands Regional Office).
Habitats: 14ha, mixed woodland.
Birds: *All year*: Common woodland spp., inc. Green &
Great Spotted Woodpeckers, Nuthatch, Treecreeper.
Spring/summer: Red Kite, Buzzard, Swallow,
Blackcap, Garden Warbler. *Winter*: Winter thrushes,
Redpoll, Siskin.
Other: Wood Anenome, Wood Sorrel, Bluebell & other
woodland plants. Brimstone, Comma & White Admiral
butterflies. Good range of fungi spp.
Directions: Sat nav: SL2 3UY. SU 971 872. Reserve lies
three miles from Junc 2 of M40 in Hedgerley. Park in
village, walk down small track to R of village pond for
approx 200 yards. Reserve entrance is on L.
Public transport: Bus - no.583 (Mon-Sat) Slough to
Hedgerley. Redline (T: 01296 426 786). Alternatively:
bus - no.X74 Slough to Farnham Common (1.25 miles
from reserve). First Berkshire & Thames Valley.
Visiting: Open at all times. One marked trail
(1.25 miles) with some inclines, not suitable for
wheelchairs. Keep dogs on leads (Apr-Jun).
Contact: RSPB, T: 01865 351 163;
E: admin.otmoor@rspb.org.uk

4. COLLEGE LAKE

Berks, Bucks & Oxon Wildlife Trust.
Habitats: Deep lake in former chalk pit, shallow pools, chalk & rough grasslands, woodlands, scrub.
Birds: *Spring/summer*: Breeding Lapwing, Redshank & Little Ringed Plover. Sand Martin, Hobby, Common Tern, Skylark & Shelduck. *Winter*: Wildfowl (Wigeon, Shoveler, Teal, Gadwall), waders inc. Snipe, Peregrine. Scarcer birds turn up regularly.
Other: Chalk grassland flowers. Arable Weed Project inc. displays of cornfield flowers in Jun/Jul. Butterflies inc. Small Blue & Green Hairstreak. 16 spp. dragonflies. Brown Hare.
Directions: Sat nav: HP23 5QG. SP 935 139. Two miles N of Tring on B488, 0.25 mile N of canal bridge at Bulbourne turn L into gated entrance. Marked with brown tourist signs.
Public transport: Train - Tring, two mile walk mostly on canal towpath.
Visiting: Open daily, 9.30am-5pm (4pm in winter). Large car park, coach park. Visitor centre/shop, toilets inc. disabled. Cafe open daily (not 24-31 Dec) 9.30am-4pm Feb-Oct & 10am-3pm Nov-Jan. Interactive interpretation, 10 hides (some with wheelchair access). Network of wheelchair-friendly trails. Electric tramper available, phone to book.
Contact: BBOWT, T: 01442 826 774; E: collegelake@bbowt.org.uk

5. LITTLE MARLOW LAKES COUNTRY PARK

Lefarge Aggregates/private ownership.
Habitats: Gravel pit with sand spit (best viewed from west bank), lake, scrub.
Birds: *Spring*: Passage migrants inc. Whimbrel, Wheatear, Whinchat, Sand Martin, Garganey, Hobby. *Summer*: Reedbed warblers, Kingfisher, wildfowl. *Autumn*: Passage migrants. *Winter*: Wildfowl, possible Smew, Goldeneye, Water Rail, Yellow-legged Gull among large gull flocks, Lapwing, Snipe.
Directions: Sat nav: SL8 5PS. SU 884 877. NE of Marlow from Junc 4 of M40 tale A404 S to Marlow then turn L onto A4155 to Little Marlow. After ca 1.5 miles turn R into Coldmoorholme Lane - Spade Oak car park on R after pub. Use permissive path from Coldmoorholme Lane to Little Marlow village. Follow path over wooden bridge to N end of lake. Permissive path ends just past cottages where it joins a concrete road to sewage treatment works. Be careful at all times when walking round lake.
Public transport: Buses & trains to Bourne End (one mile walk to Coldmoorholme Lane, along riverside path).
Visiting: Open all year, permissive footpath. Do not enter gravel works & look out for heavy traffic when crossing site's entrance road.
Contact: Little Marlow Lakes Country Park, E: littlemarlowlakescountrypark@hotmail.co.uk

Hampshire

THE NEW FOREST dominates this huge county & holds many scarce breeding birds including Honey Buzzard, Goshawk, Firecrest, Hawfinch, Dartford Warbler & Nightjar, with Great Grey Shrike regular in winter. The marshes at Keyhaven & Pennington & elsewhere around the Solent are the best sites for migrants as well as for wintering wildfowl & waders. Blashford Lakes holds a good selection of waterbirds including wintering Bittern.

1. BLASHFORD LAKES

Hampshire & Isle of Wight Wildlife Trust/Wessex Water.
Habitats: Flooded gravel pits, areas of wet ancient woodland, also dry grassland & lichen heath.
Birds: *Spring/summer*: Breeding birds inc. Common Tern, Sand Martin (in artificial bank), Lapwing, Redshank, Oystercatcher, Little Ringed Plover. Kingfisher, Garden Warbler. *Autumn*: Waders on migration inc. Green & Common Sandpipers & reenshank, also Hobby, Black Tern & passerines. *Winter*: Up to 5,000 wintering wildfowl, inc. internationally important numbers of Gadwall. Grey Heron, Little Egret & Bittern. Large gull roost on Ibsley Water.
Other: 25 spp. dragonflies inc. Brown Hawker, Scarce Chaser, Large & Small Red-eyed damselflies. Roe Deer, Badger, Otter, Fox, reptiles inc. Adder & grass Snake.

Directions: Sat nav: BH24 3PJ. SU 151 083. From Ringwood take A338 for two miles towards Fordingbridge/Salisbury, pass Ivy Lane on R & take next R at Ellingham Cross, into Ellingham Drove. The main car park for hides is first L after 400 yards.
Public transport: Bus - no.X3 Bournemouth-Salisbury at Ellingham Cross, 500 yards W of main entrance. More Bus (T: 01202 338 420).
Visiting: Car parks (coaches/groups by arrangement). Education centre/toilets, six hides open daily (not Dec 25) 9am-4.30pm. Paths open outside these hours but no vehicle access. RADAR keys needed to open kissing gates for wheelchairs. Viewing screens, recent sightings board, webcams. No dogs.
Contact: Hampshire & Isle of Wight WT, T: 01425 472 760; E: Robert.Chapman@hiwwt.org.uk

2. FARLINGTON MARSHES

Hampshire & Isle of Wight Wildlife Trust.
Habitats: Coastal grazing marsh with pools & reedbeds. Views over saltmarshes/intertidal mudflats of Langstone Harbour.
Birds: *Summer*: Breeding waders & wildfowl (inc. Lapwing, Redshank & Shelduck) & Cetti's, Sedge & Reed Warblers, Bearded Tit. *Late summer*: Passage migrants (Yellow Wagtail, Whinchat, Wheatear etc) & returning waders, always a chance of rarities/less common spp. inc. Spotted Crake, Curlew Sandpiper, stints.

Autumn/winter: Waders & wildfowl, good numbers of Teal, Wigeon, Pintail, Marsh Harrier, Short-eared Owl regular visitors. Internationally-important numbers of Dark-bellied Brent Goose & Bar-tailed Godwit. Important high tide roost site, best viewed over high spring tides.
Other: Corky Fruited Waterdropwort, Slender Hares-ear, Southern Marsh & Early Marsh Orchids. Water Vole.
Directions: Sat nav: PO6 1RN. SU 685 045. N of Langstone Harbour. Main entrance off roundabout junction A2030/A27 - tale is small lane between the A27 westbound & A2030 Portsmouth road - height restriction barrier, three parking areas available.
Public transport: Bus - no.21 Portsmouth to Havant stops by Farlington Sainsbury's (north of A27), 20 min walk to reserve. Stagecoach South (T: 0345 121 0190). Train - Hilsea is 1.5 miles from reserve.
Visiting: Open all times. 2.5 mile circular walk around sea wall, plenty of benches - exposed to wing & sea spray. Information at entrance & shelter. Paths mostly level but main track along sea wall uneven in places, muddy when wet. Short slopes up to sea wall. Wheelchair access via RADAR gates. Dogs on leads at all times.
Contact: Hampshire & Isle of Wight Wildlife Trust, T: 07917 616 696; Christopher.Lycett@hiwwt.org.uk

3. FLEET POND LNR

Hart District Council Service/Fleet Pond Society.
Habitats: Largest freshwater lake in Hampshire - marsh, reedbed, heathland, wet & dry woodland.
Birds: 180 spp. *Spring/autumn:* Migrant waders inc. Little Ringed Plover, Dunlin, Greenshank. Little Gull, Lesser Spotted Woodpecker, occasional Kittiwake, terns, Woodlark, Skylark, occasional Ring Ouzel, Firecrest, Pied Flycatcher. *Summer:* Hobby, Common Tern, Tree Pipit, occasional Red Kite & Osprey.
Winter: Bittern, wildfowl inc. occasional Smew, Snipe, occasional Jack Snipe, Siskin, Redpoll.
Other: Dragonflies in wet areas of marshes/heathland (21 spp.), 26 spp. butterflies, 400+ plant spp.
Directions: Sat nav: GU51 2RR. SU 823 553. Located in Fleet, W of Farnborough. Main site car park (free) is off Cove Road B3013/A327 (follow brown signs).
Public transport: Train - Fleet lies just to NW of site.
Visiting: Open all year. Additional parking in Wellington Avenue, Chestnut Grove, Kenilworth Road & Westover Road (take A3013 S from train station (0.25 mile), turn L into Avondale Road - roads are on L off this road. some time restrictions/charges may apply). Some surfaced paths, boardwalks in wet areas.
Contact: Hart District Council, T: 01252 623 443; E: countryside@hart.gov.uk; W: www.hart.gov.uk/fleet-pond W: www.fleetpond.org.uk/

4. LOWER TEST MARSHES

Hampshire & Isle of Wight Wildlife Trust.
Habitats: Saltmarsh, brackish grassland, wet meadows, reedbed, scrapes, meres, estuary.
Birds: *Summer/breeding:* Kingfisher, Oystercatcher, Reed Warbler, Cetti's Warbler, Sedge Warbler, Reed Bunting. *Passage:* Osprey, Marsh Harrier, Wood Sandpiper, Garganey. *Winter:* wildfowl inc. Wigeon, Teal, Mallard, Shelduck. Green Sandpiper, Common Sandpiper, Oystercatcher, Redshank, Curlew, Black-tailed Godwit, Lapwing. Peregrine, Water Pipit.
Other: Good variety of common butterflies. Dragonflies inc. Scarce Chaser, Emperor & Migrant Hawker. Early Marsh, Green-winged, Southern Marsh Orchids & Green-flowered Helleborine.
Directions: Sat nav: SO40 3BR. SU 365 145. Area bounded by M27, M271 & A35 W of Southampton. Limited on-road parking near Salmon Leap pub, Testwood Lane, Totton (two access points to reserve via lane to L of pub).
Public transport: Bus & train - Totton within easy walking distance.
Visiting: Open at all times. Hide (open daily 9am-4pm), two screens, also accessible on foot from Compton Road (500m from parking area). Boardwalk over wetter areas. Disabled access limited. Another viewpoint at Old Redbridges, an unsurfaced lay-by off A36. Dogs allowed only on Test Way footpath. NOT accessible at high tide.
Contact: Hampshire & Isle of Wight Wildlife Trust, E: Clare.Bishop@hiwwt.org.uk

NATURE RESERVES - SOUTH EAST ENGLAND

5. MARTIN DOWN NNR

Natural England (Wessex Team)/Hampshire County Council.
Habitats: 350ha, unimproved chalk downland & scrub.
Birds: *All year:* Yellowhammer, Skylark. *Spring/ summer:* Grey Partridge, Turtle Dove, Nightingale (all now scarce), Cuckoo, plus warblers inc. Lesser Whitethroat. *Winter:* Occasional Merlin, Hen Harrier.
Other: Species-rich chalk downland with variety of orchids, plus Pasqueflower & Milkwort. 20+ spp. butterflies.
Directions: Sat nav: SP5 5RH. SU 036 200 (main car park). Fourteen miles SW of Salisbury, 0.6 mile W of Martin village. N part of site is crossed by the A354. Main car park is on A354 & another at end of Sillens Lane, a minor road from Martin village.
Public transport: Bus - no.20 (Mon-Fri) Salisbury to Blandford. Damory (T: 01202 338 420).
Visiting: Open access, but organised groups of 10+ should book in advance. Two car parks, interpretative boards. Main car park height barrier (7ft 6 ins), coaches by prior arrangement. Hard flat track from A354 car park suitable for wheelchairs.
Contact: Hampshire County Council, T: 01590 674 656; E: centralcountrysidesites@hants.gov.uk

6. SWANWICK LAKES NATURE RESERVE

Hampshire & Isle of Wight Wildlife Trust.
Habitats: Mixed woodland, flower-rich meadows & deep lakes.
Birds: Good variety of birds inc. Little Grebe, Gadwall, Buzzard, Kingfisher, Great Spotted & Green Woodpeckers, Nuthatch, Treecreeper, finches & tits.
Other: Common butterflies, with occasional Silver-washed Fritillary & Purple Emperor, common dragonflies & other insects inc. mining bees. Great Crested Newts. Common Spotted Orchid. Rich variety of fungi. Roe Deer.
Directions: Sat nav: SO31 7AY. SU 507 099. SE from Southampton. About two miles from Bursledon & seven miles from Fareham. From Junc 8 of M27, follow signs to A3024 Southampton & Hamble & then A27 to Park Gate. At lights by The Navigator pub turn onto Swanwick Lane. Cross motorway then L onto Sopwith Way. Turn R at mini roundabout by security gates. From Junc 9 follow signs for Southampton A27 up to Park Gate. Take road to Botley. At Elm Tree pub turn L onto Swanwick Lane. After about a mile, turn R onto Sopwith Way. Turn R at mini roundabout by security gates.
Public transport: Bus - nos X4, X5 from Southampton stop on A27, at bottom of Swanwick Lane. First (T: 0345 646 0707). Train - about 30 mins walk from Swanwick. From station turn R at end of access road then continue to Elm Tree Pub. Turn L onto Swanwick Lane then continue as above.
Visiting: Car park closed at dusk. Toilets available when education centre open. Network of surfaced (suitable for wheelchairs) & unsurfaced paths, three waymarked trails,benches, viewpoints. Groups by arrangement. Dogs may need to be on lead if schools visiting.
Contact: Hampshire & Isle of Wight Wildlife Trust, T: 01489 570 240; swanwickLakes@hiwwt.org.uk

7. TESTWOOD LAKES NATURE RESERVE

Southern Water/
Hampshire & Isle of Wight Wildlife Trust.
Habitats: Flooded gravel pits, scrapes, wet & dry grasslands, woodland & hedgerows.
Birds: *Spring:* Shelduck, Little Ringed Plover, Lapwing, Sand Martin, Willow Warbler. *Summer:* Swift, Swallow, Blackcap, Whitethroat. *Autumn:* Wheatear, Yellow Wagtail, Goldfinch. *Winter:* Wildfowl (inc. Tufted Duck, Wigeon, Pochard, Teal, Gadwall, Goosander), Common & Green Sandpipers, Meadow Pipit, Redwing, Fieldfare, Siskin, Hawfinch.
Other: Variety of butterflies & dragonflies inc. Emperor, Scarce Chaser, Migrant Hawker & Golden-ringed.
Directions: Sat nav: SO40 3YD. SU 347 155. Take M271 West Junc 2 towards Totton. L at first roundabout, then L onto A36. L at next roundabout onto Brunel Rd. Entrance on L after 0.25 mile.
Public transport: Bus - nos.12 / X7 (not Sun) from Southampton stop at Testwood Crescent (0.5 mile from reserve) - Bluestar (T: 01202 338421) / Salisbury Reds. Train - Totton is 1.5 miles from reserve.
Visiting: Car parks open 8am-5pm (4pm winter) - height restriction. Two hides (open 10am-4pm daily), two screens. Surfaced paths around lakes & to hides relatively flat - RADAR key (available at centre) needed for wheelchair users to get through gates. Testwood Lakes Centre open 9am-4pm Mon-Fri & 1pm-4pm Sun (summer), 12pm-3pm (winter) - weekday access may not be possible if school groups in attendance. Disabled toilet in Education Centre, mobility vehicle available (book in advance). No dogs in conservation & education areas.
Contact: Hampshire & Isle of Wight Wildlife Trust, T: 02380 667 929; E: TestwoodLakes@hiwwt.org.uk

8. TITCHFIELD HAVEN NNR

Hampshire County Council.
Habitats: 150ha, in Lower Meon valley. Shoreline, reedbeds, freshwater scrapes, wet grazing meadows.
Birds: 200+ spp. *Spring/summer:* Waders (inc. Avocet & Black-tailed Godwit), wildfowl, Common Tern, breeding Cetti's Warbler, Water Rail. *Autumn/winter:* Bittern, Kingfisher, Bearded Tit, Brent Geese, Wigeon, Teal, Shoveler & Snipe. Occasional rarities at any time.
Other: Six spp. nationally rare plant, Roe Deer, Badger & Pipistrelle Bat. Water Voles released in 2013. 19 spp. dragonflies & 30+ spp. butterflies.
Directions: Sat nav: PO14 3JT. SU 532 022. Located on Cliff Road, Hill Head in Fareham. Reach from A27 & B3334 W of Fareham. Car park adjacent to Hill Head Sailing Club (free for blue badge holders).
Public transport: Bus - no.21 (not Sun) Stubbington to Fareham stops in Solent Road, 200 yards from reserve. First Bus.
Visiting: Free entry to visitor centre, charge for reserve. Open daily 9.30am-5pm Apr-Oct, 9.30am-4pm (Nov-Mar, not Dec 25/26). Centre has information desk, toilets, cafe, shop. Seven hides (wheelchair access). Guided walks. Public footpath follows derelict canal along W of reserve & road skirts S edge. Guide dogs only.
Contact: Titchfield Haven, T: 01329 662 145; E: titchfield.enquiries@hants.gov.uk

Kent

A GREAT COUNTY for birders. The Dungeness area offers excellent birding with an RSPB reserve & a bird observatory ensuring that it is well watched. Seawatching from the shingle spit here will pick up divers, seaduck, shearwaters, skuas & terns as they move through the Channel. There is another observatory at Sandwich Bay, marshes all along the north coast (where a wide selection of birds of prey winter on the Isle of Sheppy), & reedbeds at Stodmarsh.

1. BOUGH BEECH RESERVOIR

Kent Wildlife Trust.
Habitats: Reserve occupies northern end of reservoir & adjacent woodland & farmland.
Birds: 60 spp. breed annually in/around reserve, with Tufted Duck, Mandarin & Great Crested Grebe notable amongst waterfowl. Little Ringed Plover breed most years. *Autumn:* Good for waders inc. Green & Common Sandpipers & Greenshank. Osprey most years. Many rarities have been recorded. *Winter:* wildfowl numbers much higher than summer & inc. Goldeneye & Goosander.
Other: Great Crested Newt, Common Toad, dragonflies (Black-tailed Skimmer, Ruddy Darter, Emperor, Southern & Migrant Hawkers, Red-eyed damselfly), Common Lizard, Roesel's Bush Cricket, Long-winged Conehead, Dormouse, Water Shrew, White Admiral butterfly, Glow-worm, bats (Pipistrelle, Daubenton, Noctule, Brown Long-eared).
Directions: Sat nav: TN14 6LD. TQ 496 489. Lying SW of Sevenoaks, Bough Beech is situated 3.5 miles S of Ide Hill, signposted off B2042.
Public transport: Train - Penshurst (The Causeway is 2.5 miles to NW).

Visiting: Roadside parking along The Causeway. Circular nature trail - paths uneven & can be muddy. Hide overlooks wader scrape, wheelchair accessible. Dogs on lead at all times.
Contact: Kent WT, T: 01622 662 012;
E: info@kentwildlife.org.uk

2. CLIFFE POOLS

RSPB (South East Region Office).
Habitats: A mix of saline lagoons, freshwater pools, grassland, saltmarsh & scrub.
Birds: *Spring/autumn passage:* Good variety of spp. *Summer:* Breeding spp. inc. Lapwing, Redshank, Avocet, Ringed Plover, Shelduck. Hobby, Mediterranean Gull, Cuckoo, Turtle Dove, Nightingale. *Winter:* Massed flocks of waders inc. Black-tailed Godwit & Dunlin in thousands, wide variety of wildfowl. Hen & Marsh Harriers, Merlin.
Other: Good range of insects (rare bees inc. Shrill & Brown-banded Carder Bees). Butterflies, inc. Marbled White, Common Blue, Essex Skipper & Clouded Yellow, grasshoppers & bush crickets, inc. Roesel's.
Directions: Sat nav: ME3 7SX. TQ 722 757. From coastbound A2, take A289 near Strood. From A289 follow signs for Wainscott & Cliffe onto B2000. At T-junction turn L to Cliffe. At crossroads, turn L to Higham. Before entering Cliffe, take 2nd L after Cliffe sign. Turn L at next T-junction & L again into Salt Road. Car park is on L just past a sharp right-hand bend.
Public transport: Bus - no.133 (Mon-Sat) from Chatham, Rochester & Strood stops in Cliffe (1.5 miles from reserve). Arriva in Kent & Surrey.
Visiting: Car park (free) open daily 9am-5pm (not xmas period). Group bookings welcome, monthly guided walks available. Six viewing points. Public rights of way encircle & bisect reserve, pushchair friendly. Dogs only on public footpaths.
Contact: RSPB, T: 01634 222 480;
E: northkentmarshes@rspb.org.uk

3. DUNGENESS BIRD OBSERVATORY

Dungeness Bird Observatory Trust.
Habitats: Shingle promontory with scrub & gravel pits.
Birds: *Summer:* Breeding spp. inc. Raven, Wheatear & Black Redstart. *Passage:* Important migration site, regular overshoots inc. Bee-eater, Hoopoe, Purple Heron & Red-rumped Swallow. Excellent seawatching when weather conditions suitable. Power station outfall, 'The Patch' good for terns & gulls, inc. Mediterranean, Caspian & Yellow-legged.
Other: Long Pits are excellent for dragonflies, inc. Small Red-eyed damselfly. Moth trapping throughout year.
Directions: Sat nav: TN29 9NA. TR 085 173. Three miles SE of Lydd. Turn S off main Dungeness Road, past Pilot Inn - continue to end of road, past two lighthouses.
Public transport: Bus - see site 3 - alight at Pilot Inn, 1.75 miles from Observatory.
Visiting: Observatory open throughout year. Wardens on site between Mar & Nov. Accommodation for up to nine people (reduced charges for Friends). Apply in writing to the warden or by phone. No wheelchair access. Bring own sleeping bag/sheets & toiletries. Shared facilities inc. a fully-equipped kitchen. Coach parking available at mini-railway station.
Contact: Dungeness Bird Observatory, 11 RNSSS Cottages, Dungeness, Romney Marsh, Kent TN29 9NA.
T: 01797 321 309; E: dungenessobs@vfast.co.uk;
W: www.dungenessbirdobs.org.uk

4. DUNGENESS NNR

RSPB (South East Region Office).
Habitats: Shingle, 90 flooded gravel pits, sallow scrub, newly-extended reedbed on Denge Marsh, wet grassland.
Birds: *All year:* Bittern, Marsh Harrier, Bearded Tit, Cetti's Warbler. *Spring:* Garganey, Little Ringed Plover among a wide variety of waders, Wheatear, Yellow Wagtail, Lesser Whitethroat, Black Redstart. *Autumn:* Migrant waders & passerines, inc. large flocks of swallows & martins. *Winter:* Smew, Goldeneye, Black-necked & Slavonian Grebes, Wigeon, Goosander, Bewick's Swan, Marsh & Hen Harriers, other raptors.
Other: Jersey Cudweed, Nottingham Catchfly, endemic leafhopper.
Directions: Sat nav: TN29 9PN. TR 062 197. One mile out of Lydd on Dungeness Road, turn R for main site. Visitor centre & car park are one mile along entrance track. Entrance to Hanson ARC site & car park is opposite main reserve entrance on L of Dungeness Road.
Public transport: Bus - no.11 (not Sun) from Ashford via Lydd stops at reserve entrance on request. Stagecoach.
Visiting: Open daily (not Dec 25/26) 9am-9pm/sunset when earlier. Coach parking available. Visitor centre open 10am-5pm (4pm Nov-Feb). Parties 12+ by prior arrangement. Entry fee for non-RSPB members. Visitor centre, fully equipped classroom/meeting room, toilets (inc. disabled access), shop, light refreshments. Six hides (wheelchair accessible), viewing screen, two nature trails. Assistance dogs only. Hide & viewing screen at Hanson ARC site.
Contact: RSPB, T: 01797 320 588;
E: dungeness@rspb.org.uk

5. ELMLEY MARSHES NNR

Private.
Habitats: 1335ha estate - coastal grazing marsh, ditches & pools alongside Swale Estuary with extensive intertidal mudflats & saltmarsh.
Birds: *Spring/summer:* Breeding waders - Redshank, Lapwing, Avocet plus passage waders. Hobby, , Yellow Wagtail. *Autumn:* Passage waders. *Winter:* Spectacular numbers of wildfowl, especially Wigeon & White-fronted Goose. Waders. Hunting raptors - Peregrine, Merlin, Hen Harrier & Short-eared Owl.
Other: Water Vole.
Directions: Sat nav: ME12 3RW. TQ 937 680. From Junc 5 of M2, follow A249 towards Sheerness. Reserve signposted from exit for Iwade & Ridham Dock, immediately before Sheppey bridge. At roundabout, take second exit onto old road bridge. On Isle of Sheppey, after 1.25 miles, turn R following reserve sign. Follow rough track for approx two miles to car park at Kingshill Farm. do not leave car on entrance track.
Public transport: Train - Swale nearest station, Sittingbourne-Sheerness line - three miles to reserve.
Visiting: Open daily (not Tues or Dec 25/26) 9am-5pm. Honesty box in car park for parking fee. Groups by appointment. Toilets in car park. Four hides, nearest one mile from car park. Disabled access to Wellmarsh hide, Blue Badge holders may drive to hide. Swale viewing screen 200 yrds from car park. Paths pushchair friendly. Guide dogs only.
Contact: T: 07930 847 520;
E: info@elmleynaturereserve.co.uk;
W: www.elmleynaturereserve.co.uk

6. NORTHWARD HILL

RSPB (South East Region Office).
Habitats: Ancient & scrub woodland overlooking grazing marsh.
Birds: *Spring/summer:* Wood holds UK's largest heronry, with c150 pairs of Grey Heron & c50 pairs of Little Egret. Breeding Nightingale (ca 20 pairs), Turtle Dove, scrub warblers & woodpeckers. Marshes - breeding Lapwing, Redshank, Avocet, Marsh Harrier, Shoveler, Pochard. *Winter:* Wigeon, Teal, Shoveler. Passage waders, inc. Black-tailed Godwit, raptors, Corn Bunting. Long-eared Owl.
Other: Good variety of dragonflies over marsh, White-letter Hairstreak butterfly in woods.
Directions: Sat nav: ME3 8DS. TQ 768 765. Four miles NE of Rochester. Leave M2 at Junc 1 & join A228, signposted Grain. Turn off A228 for High Halstow then L in village into Cooling Road - reserve signposted ca one mile on R.
Public transport: Difficult, contact reserve for more info.
Visiting: Open all times. Car park (dawn-dusk), toilets. Trails in public area of wood joining Saxon Shoreway link to grazing marsh. Three trails, from 0.7 to 2.3 miles - often steep, not suitable for wheelchairs. Four viewpoints with benches. Dogs only allowed on Saxon Shoreway.
Contact: RSPB, T: 01634 222 480;
E: northkentmarshes@rspb.org.uk

NATURE RESERVES - SOUTH EAST ENGLAND

7. OARE MARSHES LNR

Kent Wildlife Trust.
Habitats: Grazing marsh, freshwater dykes, open water scrapes, reedbed, mudflats/Swale Sea Channel.
Birds: *All year*: Waders & wildfowl, Little Egret, Marsh Harrier, Water Rail, Barn & Little Owls. *Spring/ summer*: Avocet, Garganey, Green, Wood & Curlew Sandpipers, Little Stint, Black-tailed Godwit, Little Tern. *Winter*: Brent Goose, Red-breasted Merganser, Hen Harrier, Merlin, Peregrine, Short-eared Owl, Bittern, Stonechat. Divers, grebes & sea ducks on Swale. Good record for attracting rarities.
Other: Dragonflies, Common Seal on sandbank.
Directions: Sat nav: ME13 0QA. TR 013 647 (car park). Off Church Road, Oare, two miles N of Faversham. From A2 follow signs to Oare & Harty Ferry.
Public transport: Bus - no.3 (not Sun) Sittingbourne-Canterbury stops in Oare, one mile from reserve. Stagecoach in East Kent. Train - Faversham (three miles).
Visiting: Open all times. Car park opposite Watch House near seawall, restricted turning space (not suitable for coaches). Disabled-only car park 300 yards from East Flood hide. Three hides. Roadside viewpoint of East Hide accessible to wheelchair users. Those with pneumatic tyres can reach seawall path & hide. Access along marked paths only. Dogs on leads.
Contact: Kent WT, T: 01622 662 012;
E: info@kentwildlife.org.uk

8. SANDWICH BAY BIRD OBSERVATORY

Sandwich Bay Bird Observatory Trust.
Habitats: Coastal, dune land, farmland, marsh, two small scrapes.
Birds: *All year*: Breeding residents inc. Oystercatcher, Grey Partridge, Stonechat, Stock Dove, Little Owl, Corn Bunting. *Spring/autumn passage*: Good variety of migrants & waders. Annual Golden Oriole. Firecrest & Yellow-browed Warbler in The Elms. *Summer*: Little Ringed Plover. *Winter*: Waders, Short-eared & Long-eared Owl.
Other: Sand dune plants inc. Lady's Bedstraw & Sand Sedge. Small Heath butterfly, Red-veined Darter.
Directions: Sat nav: CT13 9PF. TR 355 575. 2.5 miles from Sandwich, five miles from Deal. A256 to Sandwich from Dover or Ramsgate. From Sandwich follow signs to Golf Courses, continue on into Sandwich Bay Estate, turn R after 0.25 mile. There is small fee at Tollgate for non-members visiting Obs.
Public transport: Train - Sandwich two miles from Observatory.
Visiting: Aim to open daily 10am-6pm (summer) 10am-1pm/4pm on Sat, (winter), disabled access. Field Study Centre - toilets, refreshments, hostel-type accommodation & self-contained flat.
Contact: Sandwich Bay Bird Obs, Guildford Road, Sandwich, CT13 9PF; T: 01304 617 341;
E: sbbotmail@gmail.com; W: www.sbbot.org.uk

9. STODMARSH NNR

Natural England (Kent, S.London & E.Sussex Team).
Habitats: Internationally-important mix of open water, reedbed (largest in SE England), wet meadows, dry meadows, woodland.
Birds: *Spring/summer*: Breeding Bittern, Garganey, Marsh Harrier, Bearded Tit, Cetti's, Reed, Sedge & Willow Warblers, Nightingale. Migrant Black Tern, Hobby, Osprey, Little Egret. *Autumn*: Large roosts of Swallows, martins & Starlings. *Winter*: Wildfowl, Hen Harrier, Bittern.
Other: Nationally rare plants & invertebrates, inc. Shining Ram's Horn Snail. Water Vole, Marsh Frog.
Directions: Sat nav: CT3 4BB. TR 220 609 (Stodmarsh village entrance). Lies alongside River Stour & A28, five miles NE of Canterbury. Car park in Stodmarsh - along turn off between Red Lion pub & church.
Public transport: Bus - nos.8/8A/8X Canterbury to Margate, alight at Upstreet for Grove Ferry entrance. Stagecoach.
Visiting: Open all times. Fully accessible toilets in Stodmarsh car park entrance. Five hides (one fully accessible), one viewpoint, easy access nature trail, footpaths & information panels. Car park (pay-&-display), picnic area & toilets adjoining Grove Ferry entrance with easily accessible path, viewing mound & two wheelchair-accessible hides. Keep to paths. No dogs.
Contact: Natural England, T: 07767 321 053;
E: Stephen.Etherington@naturalengland.org.uk

10. TUDELEY WOODS & PEMBURY HEATH

RSPB (South East Region Office).
Habitats: Ancient, semi-natural mixed woodland, heathland.
Birds: *All year*: Common woodland species, 3 spp. woodpeckers, Marsh Tit. *Spring/summer*: Turtle Dove, Spotted Flycatcher, common warblers, inc. Garden. Nightjar & Tree Pipit on heath. *Winter*: Woodcock, winter thrushes & finches, Crossbill.
Other: Butterflies, inc. White Admiral & Silver-washed Fritillary. Golden-ringed Dragonfly, 1000+ spp. fungi. Bluebells, orchids & other woodland plants. Dormouse.
Directions: Sat nav: TN11 0PT. TQ 617 433. 0.5 mile SW Tonbridge. Take A21 from Tonbridge towards Tunbridge Wells. Take L turn (signposted to Chapel) into Half Moon Lane - also known as Dislinbgbury Road - (immediately before petrol station). Parking area 0.3 mile on L. Pembury Heath can be accessed from here, footpath to S of the road links to trail.
Public transport: None.
Visiting: Open all times. Car park can be opened for groups by arrangement, limited parking outside gate. Three trails of one, 1.5 & three miles. Dogs allowed on public footpaths/bridleways & some parts of reserve - contact for info.
Contact: RSPB, T: 01892 752 430.

London (Greater)

THE LONDON NATURAL HISTORY SOCIETY, publishers of the London Bird report, base their recording area on a 20-mile radius from St Paul's Cathedral (which overlaps with some of the surrounding counties). Despite being a sprawling city, it offers a number of green spaces and purpose-built reservoirs, all attractive to the capital's birds and the occasional oddity that turns up from time to time.

1. BEDFONT LAKES COUNTRY PARK

London Borough of Hounslow.
Habitats: Country Park inc. a private nature reserve - 73ha of lakes, reedbed, wildflower meadows, scrub, wet woodland.
Birds: 155 spp. *Summer:* Common Tern, Willow, Garden, Reed & Sedge Warblers, Whitethroat, Lesser Whitethroat, hirundines, Hobby, Blackcap, Chiffchaff, Skylark. *Passage:* Wheatear, Wood Warbler, Spotted Flycatcher, Ring Ouzel, Redstart, Yellow Wagtail. *Winter:* Water Rail, Bittern, Smew & other wildfowl, Meadow Pipit.
Other: 350 plant spp. inc. Bee & Pyramidal Orchids. Nathusius Pipistrelle Bat, butterflies & dragonflies (inc. Emperor).
Directions: Sat nav: TW14 8QA. TQ 076 724 (Clockhouse Lane). From M25 take Junc 13 (A30) towards central London. Continue through Crooked Billet traffic light complex, past Ashford Hospital & take B3003 (Clockhouse Lane) from Clockhouse roundabout.
Public transport: Bus - no.H26 Feltham to Hatton Cross & no.116 from Hounslow to Ashford Hospital. Transport for London. Train - Ashford (Surrey) station one mile.
Visiting: Nature reserve - access by BLCP membership or annual fee only. Country park - open daily (not Dec 25) 8am-4.30pm. Toilets, information centre, several hides, nature trail, free parking, up-to-date information. Disabled friendly. Dogs on leads.
Contact: Bedfont Lakes Country Park LNR; Managed by Lampton Greenspace 360, T: 020 8583 2000; Friends of BLCP: E: info@bedfontlakes.co.uk; W: www.bedfontlakes.co.uk

2. BRENT RESERVOIR (WELSH HARP)

Canal & River Trust.
Habitats: Reservoir surrounded by marshland, woodland, unimproved grassland & playing fields.
Birds: 250+ spp. *Spring/summer:* Breeding Great Crested Grebe, Gadwall, Shoveler, Pochard, Common Tern, woodland species & up to eight spp. warbler. Long history of rare birds inc. London's first Great Egret in 1997 & UK's first Iberian Chiffchaff in 1972. *Winter:* Good variety of wildfowl & gull spp.
Other: 28 spp. butterflies, inc. Marbled White & Ringlet, 15 spp. dragonflies. A notable site for bats.
Directions: Sat nav: NW9 8SE. TQ 208 870 (Birchen Grove). NW london close to M1/junc 1 - take A406 (N Circular Rd) towards Neasden, then 2nd sliproad on L onto A4088 (brown sign to reservoir), continue to next brown sign, turn R into Birchen Grove continue to car park.

Public transport: Train - Hendon station (Thameslink) & Neasdon (Underground) at opposite ends of the reservoir.
Visiting: Open access at all times. Park in Birchen Grove to access Welsh Harp Open Space nature reserve. Raised viewing platform & permanently open public hide overlooks northern marsh. Circular walk.
Contact: Welsh Harp Conservation Group, E: via website; W: https://brentres.wordpress.com/ (see website for other access arrangements)

3. DAGENHAM CHASE LNR

London Borough of Barking & Dagenham.
Habitats: Shallow wetlands, reedbeds, horse-grazed pasture, scrub & wetland.
Birds: 190 spp. *Summer:* Breeding Reed Warbler, Lapwing, Water Rail, Lesser Whitethroat, Little Ringed Plover, Kingfisher, Reed Bunting. *Spring/ autumn passage:* Yellow Wagtail, Wheatear, Ruff, Wood Sandpiper, Sand Martin, Ring Ouzel, Black Redstart & Hobby regular. *Winter:* Good numbers of Teal, Shoveler, Snipe, Redwing & Fieldfare.
Other: 140 plant spp., the nationally rare black poplar tree. Wasp Spider, butterflies & dragonflies.
Directions: Sat nav: RM7 0SS. TQ 509 860 (Millenium Centre). Lies in Dagenham Corridor S of A124 between A1112 & A125, an area of green belt between London Boroughs of Barking, Dagenham & Havering.
Public transport: Bus - no.174 from Romford or Dagenham, five mins walk. Transport for London. Train - Dagenham East (District Line), 15 mins walk.
Visiting: Open all times, not suitable for wheelchairs. Eastbrookend & Beam Valley Country Parks border site - surfaced footpaths suitable for wheelchairs. Millennium Centre (T: 0208 595 4155) in Eastbrookend CP, toilets, car parking, Timberland Trail walk.
Contact: LBB&D, T: 0208 227 2332; E: parksandcountryside@lbbd.gov.uk

4. LONDON WETLAND CENTRE

The Wildfowl & Wetlands Trust.
Habitats: Main lake, reedbeds, wader scrape, open water lakes, wet woodland, grazing marsh.
Birds: *All year:* Cetti's Warbler. *Summer:* Important numbers of wetland breeding spp. inc. grebes, swans, variety of duck (inc. Pochard), Lapwing, Little Ringed Plover, Redshank, warblers, Reed Bunting. Artifical nesting bank for Sand Martins & rafts for nesting terns. Peregrines which nest on Charing Cross Hospital sighted regularly. *Winter:* Nationally important numbers of waterfowl, inc. Gadwall & Shoveler. Bittern, Jack Snipe, Water Pipit.
Other: Water Voles, Slow Worm, Grass Snake, Common Lizard. Seven spp. bat, 22 spp. dragonflies & 25 spp. butterflies. Notable plants inc. Snake's Head Fritillaries, Cowslip, Pyramidal & Bee Orchids.
Directions: Sat nav: SW13 9WT. TQ 226 768. Less than one mile N of South Circular Road (A205), take A306 N, signposted into Queen Elizabeth's Walk, Barnes. In London Zone 2/3, one mile from Hammersmith.

Public transport: Bus - no.485 (not Sun/bank hol) comes into centre. Others from Hammersmith nos.33 & 209; from Richmond no.33. Train: Barnes. Tube: Hammersmith. Transport for London.
Visiting: Coaches by arrangement. Open 9.30am-5.30pm Mar-Oct, 9.30am-4.30pm Nov-Feb (not Dec 25), last admission one hour before closing. Admission charge for non-WWT members. Visitor centre, discovery centre & children's adventure area, restaurant (hot/ cold food), cinema, shop, observatory building, six hides (all wheelchair accessible), sustainable gardens, interactive pond zone, three interpretative buildings, nature trails. Events. Assistance dogs only.
Contact: London Wetland Centre, T: 020 8409 4400; E: info.london@wwt.org.uk

5. SYDENHAM HILL WOOD

London Wildlife Trust.
Habitats: New & ancient woodland, remnants of Victorian gardens, meadow & small pond.
Birds: *All year*: 3 spp. woodpecker, Tawny Owl, Kestrel, Sparrowhawk, Goldcrest, Nuthatch, Treecreeper, Stock Dove. *Summer*: Blackcap, Chiffchaff, Willow Warbler. *Winter*: Fieldfare, Redwing.

Other: Five spp. bat, inc. Noctule & Brown Long-eared. Bluebell, Wood Anemone, Dog Violet & Primrose. Oak & Hornbeam. Brown Argus, Comma, Speckled Wood, Painted Lady & Orange-tip butterflies.
Directions: Sat nav: SE26 6RU. TQ 342 7252. Between Forest Hill & Crystal Palace (SE London), just to S off South Circular Road (A205) to Upper Sydenham. Entrances at Crescent Wood Road & Cox's Walk.
Public transport: Bus - nos. 356, 363 stop along Sydenham Hill, 176, 185, P4, P13 stop near Cox's Walk entrance. Train stations - Forest Hill (from London Bridge) or Sydenham Hill (from Victoria). Transport for London.
Visiting: Open all times. Nature trail, information boards. Some steep slopes - wheelchair access difficult. Dogs on lead.
Contact: London WT, T: 020 3897 6151; E: rdowse@wildlondon.org.uk

Surrey

LONDON'S URBAN SPRAWL has continued to spread into much of the north of the county, but reservoirs & the sewage farm at Beddington still offer opportunities for birders. To the west, the heathlands at Thursley Common & around Frensham are good for finding the specialities - Hobby, Nightjar, Woodlark & Dartford Warbler.

1. CHOBHAM COMMON NNR

Surrey Wildlife Trust.
Habitats: Largest NNR in south-east England (575ha). Lowland wet & dry heath, with pools, mixed broadleaf & pine woodlands.
Birds: 115+ spp. inc. Hobby, Nightjar, Woodlark & Dartford Warbler. Also Cuckoo, Lesser Spotted Woodpecker, Skylark, Stonechat, Linnet & Yellowhammer.
Other: 350+ spp. flowering plants, 25 spp. mammal, 29 spp. butterflies inc. Silver-studded Blue & 22 spp. dragonflies, Raft Spider.
Directions: Sat nav: KT16 0ED. SU 973 648 (Staple Hill car park). From Junc 3 of M3 head N on A322 & A30 in direction of Sunningdale. From Broomhall turn R into Chobham Road (B383) then L at roundabout (B386) & R at next roundabout over M3 - R into Staple Hill Road. Other car parks in area.

Public transport: Buses - Woking to Chobham. No.73, Falcon Buses (T: 01932 787 752). No.37A (Mon-Fri, limited). Stagecoach. Both stop in Bowling Green Road, S of Common. Services to Sunningdale from Ascot, Windsor, Camberley & Staines. Train - Sunningdale, 0.5 mile from NW corner of Common. **Visiting:** Open at all times. Six car parks with information boards (parking charges apply), three self-guided trails. Site leaflet available from rangers.
Contact: Surrey WT, T: 01483 795 440; E: info@surreywt.org.uk

NATURE RESERVES - SOUTH EAST ENGLAND

2. FARNHAM HEATH

RSPB (South East Region Office).
Habitats: Heathland & pine woodland.
Birds: *Spring/Summer*: Woodcock, Nightjar, Woodlark, Tree Pipit, Dartford Warbler, woodland birds, inc. Stock Dove, Green & Great Spotted Woodpeckers, Blackcap. *Winter*: Crossbills in pine woods, winter finches & thrushes, inc. Brambling around feeders.
Other: 150+ spp. fungi. Bats in summer. Sand Lizard, plus variety of butterflies inc. Grayling.
Directions: Sat nav: GU10 2DL. SU 859 433. Take B3001 SE from Farnham. Take R hand fork, signposted Tilford, immediately past level crossing. Keep to that road. Just outside Tilford village look for sign to Rural Life Centre. Entrance is on R after 0.5 mile.
Public transport: Bus - no.19 Farnham to Hindhead (not Sun) stops in Millbridge village, outside entrance to Pierrepont House. Reserve is a mile away, along Reeds Road (follow signs to Rural Life Centre). Stagecoach in Hants & Surrey. Train - Farnham.
Visiting: Open all times. Large grass car park, shared with adjacent Rural Life Centre (open 9.30am weekdays, 10.30am weekends - some parking lay-bys on adjacent roads outside of these hours). Three way-marked trails - good for walking, pushchair friendly. Rural Life Centre open Wed-Sun 11am-4pm (Apr-Sep) & Wed, Thurs & Sun (Oct-Mar). Cafe, toilets (inc. disabled), picnic area. Group bookings accepted, guided walks available.
Contact: RSPB, T: 01252 795 632;
E: farnham.heath@rspb.org.uk

3. FRENSHAM COMMON & PONDS

Waverley Borough Council/National Trust.
Habitats: 400ha, dry & humid heath, woodland, two large ponds, reedbeds.
Birds: *Summer*: Common Tern, Hobby, Nightjar, Dartford Warbler, Woodlark, Stonechat, Spotted Flycatcher, Sedge & Reed Warblers, Reed Bunting. *Winter*: Wildfowl (inc. occasional Smew), Bittern, Great Grey Shrike.
Other: Tiger Beetle, Purple Hairstreak & Silver-studded Blue butterflies, Sand Lizard, Smooth Snake.
Directions: Common lies on either side of A287 between Farnham & Hindhead. Sat nav: GU10 2QD. SU 844 405 (Great Pond, WBC). GU10 3BT. SU 856 418 (Little Pond, NT).
Public transport: Bus - no.19 Farnham to Hindhead (not Sun) stops at Frensham Pond Lane. Stagecoach in Hants & Surrey. Train - Farnham.
Visiting: Open all times. Keep to paths, many are smooth & fairly level. Dogs on leads during breeding season. *Great Pond*: car park open 8am-9pm, free during week, charges 9.30am-4pm at weekends/bank holidays (Apr-Sep). NT members free. *Little Pond*: Pay-&-display, NT members free. Cafe & toilets open 10am-5pm.
Contact: WBC - Rangers Office, T: 01483 523 394 or 01252 792 416 (weekend in summer months);
E: parks&countryside@waverley.gov.uk
National Trust, T: 01428 681 050;
E: frensham@nationaltrust.org.uk

4. LIGHTWATER COUNTRY PARK

Surrey Heath Borough Council.
Habitats: Heathland, woodland, ponds & meadows.
Birds: *All year*: 3 spp. woodpecker, Goldcrest, Coot, Moorhen, Grey Heron & Kingfisher. *Summer*: Nightjar, Willow Warbler, Chiffchaff, Blackcap, Whitethroat. *Winter*: Fieldfare, Redwing, Siskin.
Other: Ox-eye Daisy, Knapweed & Common Spotted Orchid in meadow, heathers & gorse species on heath. Wood ant nests in woodlands. Variety of dragonflies & butterflies.
Directions: Sat nav: GU18 5TS. SU 920 621. From Junc 3 of M3, take A322 & follow brown Country Park signs. From Guildford Road in Lightwater, turn into The Avenue - entrance to park is at end of road.
Public transport: Bus - nos.34 & 35, Camberley to Woking, stop in Lightwater. Arriva in Kent & Surrey. Train - Bagshot two miles from Lightwater.
Visiting: Open all year, dawn-dusk. Car park, toilets, waymarked trails, leaflets available. Cafe & information point open daily 10am-4pm.
Contact: Surrey Heath BC, T: 01276 707 100;
E: leisure.services@surreyheath.gov.uk

5. THURSLEY NNR

Natural England (Thames Team).
Habitats: Wet & dry heathland, woodland, peat bog.
Birds: *Summer*: Hobby, Lapwing, Curlew, Snipe, Nightjar, Woodlark, Spotted Flycatcher, Stonechat, Redstart, Crossbill. *Passage*: waders inc. Redshank, Greenshank, Wood & Common Sandpipers. *Winter*: Hen & Marsh Harriers, Great Grey Shrike.
Other: Large populations of Silver-studded Blue, Grayling & Purple Emperor butterflies can be seen, alongside 26 spp. dragonflies. Sandier sites on reserve provide habitat for many spp. of solitary bees & wasps & tiger beetles. Damp areas support carnivorous sundews & large population (1,000's) of Early Marsh Orchid. All six native reptiles.
Directions: Sat nav: GU8 6LW. SU 898 417 (The Moat car park). From Guildford, take A3 SW to B3001 (Elstead/Churt road). Moat car park, S of Elstead village. Alternative parking on recreation ground in Thursley.
Public transport: Bus - no.46 (not Sun) Guildford/Godalming to Farnham stops in Elstead. Stagecoach.
Visiting: Open access. Boardwalk in wetter areas along the Heath Trail (2.25 miles in length). Parties must obtain prior permission.
Contact: Natural England, T: 01428 685 675;
E: james.giles@naturalengland.org.uk

Sussex

THE COUNTY, USUALLY referred to as 'East Sussex' & 'West Sussex, is dominated by the chalk hills of the South Downs. Coastal sites from Chichester Harbour in the west to Rye Harbour in the east guarantee a good day's birdwatching, with an interesting mix of wildfowl, waders, raptors, terns & Bittern, depending on the season. Selsey Bill (west) is good for migrants & a good spot to seawatch from where there is a noticeable skua passage in the spring & Beachy Head (east) also attracts spring and autumn migrants. Ashdown Forest offers a fine mix of woodland & heathland birds while RSPB Pulborough Brooks holds important numbers of wintering wildfowl, with a chance of Bewick's Swans.

West

1. ADUR ESTUARY

RSPB (South East Region Office).
Habitats: Mudflats & saltmarsh.
Birds: *All year:* Oystercatcher. *Spring/autumn:* Little Egret, Turnstone, Ringed Plover, Dunlin, Redshank, *Summer:* Common & Sandwich terns. *Winter:* Good range of wildfowl, waders & gulls, Kingfisher.
Directions: Sat nav: BN43 5EN. TQ 215 049. On W side of Shoreham-on-Sea: view from Coronation Green, situated near town centre or footbridge linking High Street & Riverside Road.
Public transport: Bus & Train - services to Shoreham-by-Sea town centre - within easy walking distance from here.
Visiting: No direct access to reserve areas, but good views from riverside paths between footbridge in Shoreham town centre & A259 road bridge. Free public car park at Council's recreational field on N side of A259 (after road bridge) or pay-&-display on S side of A259 on Lower Beach Road (S side of footbridge).
Contact: RSPB, T: 01798 875 851;
E: pulborough.brooks@rspb.org.uk

2. ARUNDEL WETLAND CENTRE

Wildfowl & Wetland Trust.
Habitats: 26ha, lakes, wader scrapes, reedbed.
Birds: *All year:* 3 spp. woodpecker, Kingfisher. *Summer:* Breeding Redshank, Lapwing, Oystercatcher, Common Tern, Sedge, Reed & Cetti's Warblers, Peregrine, Hobby. *Winter:* Teal, Wigeon, Reed Bunting, Water Rail, Cetti's Warbler & occasionally Bewick's Swan.
Other: Bee Orchid, Water Shrew, Palmate & Smooth Newts, Grass Snake, 6 spp. bats.
Directions: Sat nav: BN18 9PB. TQ 020 081. Centre on Mill Road clearly signed from Arundel, just N of A27.
Public transport: Bus - no.85 Chichester to Arundel (Mon-Fri). Compass Travel (T: 01903 690 025). No.9 Littlehampton to Arundel. Stagecoach. Train - Arundel, 20 min walk.
Visiting: Open daily (not Dec 25) 9.30am-5.30pm (4.30pm winter), last admissions 30 mins before closing. Admission charges for non-WWT members. Visitor centre, cafe, shop, hides, picnic area, seasonal nature trails. Corporate hire facilities. Electric boat safaris. Manual wheelchairs available. Approx 1.5 miles of level footpaths, suitable for wheelchairs. Guide dogs only.
Contact: Arundel Wetland Centre, T: 01903 883 355; E: info.arundel@wwt.org.uk

3. CHICHESTER HARBOUR

Chichester Harbour Conservancy.
Habitats: Deep saltwater channels, mud banks, sand dunes & shingle.
Birds: Internationally-important for birds, with an estimated 55,000 birds residing or passing through each year. *Spring/summer:* Little, Sandwich & Common Terns breed. Dartford Warbler breeds at Sandy Point NR. *Autumn/winter:* Waders inc. Lapwing, Golden Plover, Curlew, Whimbrel, Black & Bar-tailed Godwits, Oystercatcher, Turnstone, Snipe, Dunlin & Sanderling. Up to 10,000 Brent Geese, Red-breasted Merganser & common wildfowl species. Kingfisher, Short-eared owl, Hen Harrier, Skylark.

West Sussex   East Sussex

Other: Common Seal, Water Vole, Stoat, Marsh Samphire, Sea Purslane, Sea Lavender & Sea Aster.
Directions: West of Chichester, with various viewing points along 47 miles of coastline to Hayling Island. East Head/West Wittering good for birding - from A27 S of Chichester, follow brown signs for West Wittering Beach. Sandy Point NR in SE corner of Hayling Island can only be visited on guided walks.
Public transport: Various Stagecoach services in area.
Visiting: Five paths suitable for wheelchairs: Cobnor Point/ Itchenor/ Prinsted/ North Common, Northney/ Sandy Point, Hayling Island. Wheelchair-accessible viewing platform & toilet at Itchenor. RADAR-key toilet at Dell Quay.
Contact: Harbour Office (inc Friends of Chichester Hbr), Itchenor, PO20 7AW. T: 01243 512 301;
E: info@conservancy.co.uk; W: www.conservancy.co.uk
E: info@friendsch.org; W: www.friendsch.org

4. KINGLEY VALE NNR

Natural England (Solent & Downs Team).
Habitats: Greatest yew forest in W.Europe (30,000+ yew trees). Chalk grassland, mixed oak/ash woodland & scrub. Chalk heath. Part of South Downs National Park.
Birds: All year: Common woodland spp. inc. Green Woodpecker, Treecreeper, Nuthatch, Goldcrest, Firecrest, Bullfinch. Woodcock, Buzzard, Red Kite, Barn & Tawny Owls, Hawfinch, Raven. Spring/summer: Nightingale, Grasshopper Warbler, Whitethroat, Lesser Whitethroat, Blackcap. Autumn: Osprey, Hen Harrier & Hobby on passage. Winter: Redwing, Fieldfare, other thrushes (attracted to Yew berries).
Other: Ancient Yew trees, Yellow Meadow Ant, 39 spp. butterflies inc. Brown Argus & Chalkhill Blue, 11 spp. orchid, Brown Hare, Dormouse, Fallow & Roe Deer, bats.
Directions: Sat nav: PO18 9BE. SU 825 087 (West Stoke car park). Approx five miles NW of Chichester town centre. N from Chichester on A286 to Mid Lavant, then turn L by church on to Downs Road, follow to West Stoke. Turn R at junction after church to West Stoke car park - 0.6 mile from reserve entrance).
Public transport: Train - Chichester (three miles)
Visiting: Via footpath from car park, bridleway access via Woodend. No disabled access. Nature trail & an unmanned information centre, leaflets & nature trail guides. Dogs on lead.
Contact: Natural England, T: 0300 060 6000;
E: enquiries@naturalengland.org.uk
South Downs National Park Authority, T: 01730 814 810;
E: info@southdowns.gov.uk

5. PAGHAM HARBOUR

West Sussex County Council/RSPB.
Habitats: Mudflats, intertidal saltmarsh, shingle beaches, lagoons, grassland & farmland.
Birds: All year: Little Egret. Spring: Passage migrants (warblers, hirundines, Wheatear). Summer: Breeding Little & Common Terns. Autumn: Passage waders inc. Curlew Sandpiper, Ruff & Little Stint, wildfowl, migrants, inc. Pied & Spotted Flycatchers. Winter: 20,000 wildfowl & waders inc. Brent Goose, Slavonian Grebe.

Other: Common & Grey Seals (winter). Wide variety of grasses, butterflies & dragonflies (inc. Emperor, Broad-bodied Chaser & Hairy Dragonfly).
Directions: Sat nav: PO20 7NE. SZ 856 966. Five miles S of Chichester on B2145 towards Selsey. After 0.5 mile turn R at first roundabout still following Selsey. Look for entrance just after leaving Sidlesham after speed limit increases to 50mph.
Public transport: Bus - no.51 (Chichester-Selsey) stops by visitor centre. Stagecoach. Train - Chichester.
Visiting: Sidlesham Ferry & Church Norton car parks open all times. Groups & coach parties must book in advance. Visitor centre, with hot drinks/light snacks, toilets (inc. disabled) open daily (not Dec 25/26), 10am-4pm. Two hides, several viewpoints, three trails. Dogs on leads.
Contact: RSPB, T: 01243 641 508;
E: pagham.harbour@rspb.org.uk

7. PULBOROUGH BROOKS

RSPB (South East Region Office).
Habitats: Lowland wet grassland (wet meadows/ ditches). Restored heathland, hedgerows, scrub & woodland.
Birds: Spring/summer: Breeding waders & songbirds (inc. Lapwing & Nightingale), Hobby, Nightjar, Woodlark, Lesser-spotted Woodpecker, Barn Owl. Autumn: Passage waders, Redstart, Whinchat, Yellow Wagtail, incoming wildfowl spp. Winter: Thousands of wildfowl & waders, Bewick's Swan. Peregrine, Hen Harrier, Merlin & Short-eared Owl hunt regularly.
Other: Good variety of butterflies & dragonflies (inc. Emperor, Four-spotted Chaser & Downy Emerald).
Directions: Sat nav: RH20 2EL. TQ 058 164. Part of South Downs National Park, signposted on A283 between Pulborough (via A29) & Storrington (via A24). Two miles SE of Pulborough.
Public transport: Train - Pulborough (two miles) with connecting bus no.100 (Burgess Hill to Horsham, not Sun) - request stop, ask driver to stop outside reserve entrance. Compass Travel (T: 01903 690 025).
Visiting: Two trails, four hides, two viewpoints open dawn-dusk (not Dec 25). Large car park inc. coach area, cycle stands. Admission fee for nature trails (RSPB members free). Visitor centre open daily (not Dec 25/26) 9.30am-5pm (inc. shop, cafe until 4.30pm), displays, toilets. Play & picnic areas. Electric buggy available for hire - book in advance, only suitable for wetland trail. Assistance dogs only on wetland trail, access on lead to parts of wooded heathland trail/public footpaths.
Contact: RSPB - see site 1.

8. WARNHAM LNR

Horsham District Council.
Habitats: 37ha inc. 7ha millpond, reedbeds, marsh, meadow & woodland (deciduous & coniferous).
Birds: 170 spp. Summer: Mandarin Duck, Common Tern, Hobby, Kingfisher, woodpeckers, Marsh Tit, Goldcrest, hirundines, warblers. Passage: Waders, terns, pipits & hirundines. Winter: Wildfowl, Cormorant, Little Grebe, gulls, Water Rail, Brambling, Siskin, Redpoll, thrushes.

Other: Extensive invertebrate interest, inc. 35 spp. butterfly & 25 spp. dragonfly. 32 spp. mammals inc. Harvest Mouse & Water Shrew. 450+ spp. plants, inc. Broad-leaved Helleborine & Common Spotted Orchid.
Directions: Sat nav: RH12 2RA. TQ 167 323. 1.5 mile NW of Horsham town centre on B2237, just off A24 'Robin Hood' roundabout.
Public transport: Bus - nos.51 & 62 (not Sun) from Horsham town centre stop close to reserve. Metrobus (T: 01293 449 191). Train - Horsham (one mile - along Hurst Road, with R turn onto Warnham Road).
Visiting: Open all year (not Dec 25/26) 10am-6pm Mar-Oct, 10am-5pm Nov-Feb. Large car park. Admission charge to reserve/annual permit available. Visitor centre & cafe (free entry -10am-4pm summer/ 3pm winter). Toilets (inc. disabled), four hides, millpond nature trail, bird feeding station, wader scrapes, boardwalks, benches & hardstanding paths, reserve leaflets. Good wheelchair access over most of reserve. No dogs or cycling.
Contact: Horsham DC, T: 01403 215 256; E: parks@horsham.gov.uk
Friends of WLNR, T 01403 756 238; W: www.warnhamnaturereservefriends.org.uk

East

9. LULLINGTON HEATH NNR

Natural England (Kent, S.London & E. Sussex Team).
Habitats: Grazed chalk downland/heath, scrub/gorse.
Birds: *Summer:* Breeding Nightingale, Turtle Dove, Cuckoo, Garden Warbler, Yellowhammer.
Passage: migrants inc. Wheatear, Redstart, Ring Ouzel.
Winter: Woodcock, Brambling (adjacent forest).
Other: Bell Heather, Ling, gorse on chalk heath, orchids.
Directions: Sat nav: BN26 5QJ. TQ 562 013 (Jevington). Five miles NW of Eastbourne, between Jevington & Litlington, on N edge of Friston Forest. Turn off A259 at Friston and head to Jevington - park here. Walk past church (on South Downs Way), after ca 0.5 mile, once out of trees, continue straight (SDW goes off to R) on for 0.25 mile to reserve. Alternative parking around Friston Forest, inc. Seven Sisters CP visitor centre on A259.
Public transport: Bus - nos.12/12X Brighton to Eastbourne stop at Friston/Seven Sisters CP. Brighton & Hove Buses (T: 01273 886 200).
Visiting: Access on foot via footpaths & bridleways (some steep). Nearest toilets/refreshments at pubs in Jevington, Litlington or Seven Sisters CP, 1.25 miles to S.
Contact: Natural England, T: 01323 423 962.

10. OLD LODGE RESERVE

Sussex Wildlife Trust.
Habitats: 74ha, heath, pine & deciduous woodlands.
Birds: *All year:* Stonechat, possible Dartford Warbler (found in wider forest area). *Spring/summer:* Breeding Nightjar, Woodcock, Woodlark, Redstart, Tree Pipit. *Autumn/winter:* Raven, Crossbill, Redpoll, Siskin.
Other: Good for dragonflies inc. Black Darter, Golden-ringed & Small Red Damselfly. Silver-studded Blue butterfly. 250 spp. fungi inc Nail Fungus.

Directions: Sat nav: TN22 3JD. TQ 469 306. A Local Nature Reserve within much larger Ashdown Forest on W side of B2026 between Maresfield & Hartfield, about 0.75 mile N of junction with B2188 at Kings Standing.
Public transport: None.
Visiting: Open all year, well-marked nature trail leading from car park - steep paths. Dogs must be kept on leads Jan-Sep & when livestock present.
Contact: Sussex WT - see site 9.

11. RYE HARBOUR

Sussex Wildlife Trust/Environment Agency/ East Sussex County Council/Rother District Council - main partners of management agreement. [Inc. Castle Water (88ha) owned by Sussex Wildlife Trust.]
Habitats: 465ha, sea, sand, shingle, saline lagoons, saltmarsh, coastal grazing marsh, ditches, freshwater gravel pits & reedbeds.
Birds: 280 spp., 70 spp. have bred. *Spring:* Passage waders, especially roosting Whimbrel. *Summer:* Turtle Dove, breeding terns (three spp), waders (seven spp. inc. Avocet), gulls (six spp. inc Mediterranean), Garganey, Shoveler, Cetti's Warbler, Bearded Tit, Wheatear. *Winter:* Wildfowl & waders, inc. nationally important numbers of Shoveler & Sanderling. Smew, Water Rail, Bittern, Barn & Short-eared Owls.
Other: Good shingle flora inc. endangered Least Lettuce & Stinging Hawksbeard. Marsh Mallow & Sea-heath & specialist insects inc. Saltmarsh Bee & Star-wort Moth. Dragonflies inc. Red-veined Darter & Scarce Emerald Damselfly.
Directions: Sat nav: TN31 7TX. TQ 942 189. Main access (large car park) is 1.5 miles SE Rye, off A259 along Harbour Road (to the end) - signposted Rye Harbour. Access also from Winchelsea (SW of site).
Public transport: Bus - no.313 Rye (train station) to Rye Harbour. Stagecoach in Hastings. Train - Rye & Winchelsea.
Visiting: Open all times - public footpaths & two trails: short trail (2.5 miles) & long trail (5.5 miles). Car park with information kiosk in Rye Harbour village, local facilities inc. shop, pubs, toilets & disabled facilities near car park. New Discovery Centre (due for completion in early 2020). Site is flat with some wheelchair access to four hides on eastern side, although there are stiles where stock is grazing. One hide & viewpoint on Castle Water side. Organised groups should book in advance.
Contact: Sussex WT, T: 07884 494 982; E; RHNRoffice@sussexwt.org.uk; W: sussexwildlifetrust.org.uk/visit/rye-harbour
Friends of Rye Harbour, W: www.rhnrfriends.co.uk

South West England

Cornwall

FOR THE SEAWATCHING enthusiast an autumn visit to a Cornish headland, such as St Ives or Porthgwarra, is a must with a good chance of Cory's, Great & Sooty Shearwaters, skuas, terns & gulls or even something much rarer. Spring and, particularly, autumn brings many migrants passing through the county & birds (including rarities) can turn up anywhere - migrant hotspots near Land's End include Cot & Nanquidno Valleys. Choughs have recolonized the Lizard and Cirl Buntings are beginning to spread as the result of a re-introduction programme.

1. CROWDY RESERVOIR

South West Lakes Trust.
Habitats: Reservoir, bog, moorland, forestry.
Birds: *Spring*: Passage migrants, inc. Wheatear, Whimbrel, Ruff. *Summer*: Black-headed Gull, Grasshopper, Reed & Sedge Warblers, returning waders. *Autumn*: Waders, raptors possible inc. Peregrine, Goshawk, Merlin. *Winter*: Wildfowl, inc. Goosander & possible Smew. Golden Plover, Woodcock, Fieldfare, Redwing. Starling murmuration (nearby Rough Tor).
Other: Mire floral communities. Marsh Fritillary.
Directions: Sat nav. PL32 9XJ. SX 138 833. Follow signs from A39 at Camelford to Davidstow Airfield & pick up signs to reservoir. Park in main car park or continue to edge of forestry plantation & park in pull-in spot near cattle grid - track leads to hide via stiles from here.
Public transport: Buses - to Camelford (2.25 miles).
Visiting: Open all year. Hide (N side). Access along reservoir banks (unsuitable for wheelchairs).
Contact: South West Lakes Trust, T: 01566 771 930; E: info@swlakestrust.org.uk; W: www.swlakestrust.org.uk

2. HAYLE ESTUARY

RSPB (South West England Office).
Habitats: Intertidal mudflats, saltmarsh, lagoon & islands (access to Ryan's Field, Lelant Water, Carnsew Pool, Copperhouse Pool).
Birds: *Spring/summer*: Migrant waders, breeding Shelduck. *Autumn*: Rare waders, often from North America, terns, gulls (inc. Mediterranean). *Winter*: Large numbers of wildfowl & waders. Top UK site for Ring-billed Gull, but not annual. Other gull spp., Kingfisher, Great Northern Diver.
Directions: Sat nav: TR27 6JF. SW 551 364. Follow signs to Hayle from A30. Take B3301 through Hayle past Tempest factory, turn L into Chenalls Road signposted St Erth & Hayle Estuary NR, turn R after 200 yeards into Ryans Field car park. Other parking in Hayle & Lelant.
Public transport: Bus - services to Hayle. Train - Hayle (limited stops) & St Erth (one mile).

Visiting: Open all times. Ryan's Field: no coaches. Eric Grace Memorial Hide (information board) overlooks Ryan's Field but birds here only at high tide. Not suitable for wheelchair users. Circular walk around Ryan's Field. Public footpath around Carnsew Pool. Dogs on leads restricted to public footpaths.
Contact: RSPB, T: 01736 360 624; E: hayle.estuary@rspb.org.uk

3. HELMAN TOR NATURE RESERVE

Cornwall Wildlife Trust.
Habitats: 217ha, inc. wetland, grassland, heath & scrub.
Birds: Curlew, Sparrowhawk, Nightjar, Tree Pipit, Lesser Whitethroat, Willow Tit.
Other: Butterflies (inc. Marsh & Small Pearl-bordered Fritillaries, Silver-studded Blue). Royal Fern, sundews & other bog plants.
Directions: Sat nav: PL30 5DF. SX 062 615 (Tor car park). Large wetland complex spreading from slopes of Helman Tor inc. Breney Common & Red Moor Memorial Reserve. 2.5 miles S of Bodmin. From A30/A391 (Innis Downs) roundabout south of Bodmin, turn N to Lanivet & take first R under A30 bridge. For Breney Common entrance, turn R at Reperry Cross, then L fork to Trebell Green & on towards Gurtla. Entrance track is on L in Gurtla, after Methodist church, opposite The Barn (SX 053 610).
Public transport: None.
Visiting: Open all times, keep to paths. Small car park at Helman Tor, Wilderness trail from here can be very muddy after heavy rain - boardwalk sections only suitable surface for wheelchairs (can be slippery when wet).
Contact: Cornwall WT, T: 01872 273 939; E: info@cornwallwildlifetrust.org.uk

NATURE RESERVES - SOUTH WEST ENGLAND

4. MARAZION MARSH

RSPB (South West England Office).
Habitats: Wet reedbed, willow carr.
Birds: 250+ spp. *Spring/summer:* Breeding Reed, Sedge & Cet ti's Warblers, herons, swans. *Autumn:* Large roost of Swallows & martins in reedbeds, migrant warblers (inc. regular Aquatic - difficult to see) & Water Rail. *Winter:* Wildfowl, Snipe, occasional Bittern, impressive pre-roost flocks of Starlings up to New Year attract Buzzard & Sparrowhawk.
Other: 22 spp. dragonflies, 500 spp. vascular plants, inc. Lawn Camomile & Yellow Flag.
Directions: Sat nav: TR17 0AA. SW 510 312. Reserve is one mile E of Penzance, 500 yards W of Marazion. Entrance off seafront road near Marazion.
Public transport: Bus - nos. A2 & U4 from Penzance bus station to Marazion. Alight Godolphin Place (opp. St Michael's Mount car park). First Group.
Visiting: Open all times, not suitable for wheelchair users. Park in car parks within walking distance. No coaches. Viewing bay on seafront pavement overlooks pools & reedbeds of sanctuary area. Dogs on leads. Nearest toilets in Marazion & seafront car park.
Contact: RSPB, 01736 360 624;
E: marazion.marsh@rspb.org.uk

5. NARE HEAD

National Trust.
Habitats: Headland, open sea.
Birds: *Spring/summer:* Razorbill, Guillemot, Shag, Sandwich, Common & Arctic Terns, possible Whimbrel, Fulmar, occasional Chough. *Passage:* Migrants. *Winter:* Great Northern, Black & Red-throated Divers, Slavonian, Black-necked & Red-necked Grebes, Common & Velvet Scoter.
Directions: Sat nav: TR2 5PQ. SW 919 378 (Nare Head car park). Parking also in Carne. Part of NT's Roseland estate. Approx ten miles SE of Truro. From A390 head S on A307 to two miles S of Tregony just past garage. Follow signs to Veryan then L signposted to Carne. Go straight over at crossroad, following Carne & Pendower. Turn L on a bend following NT signs for Nare Head. Bearing R, cross over a cattle grid to car park (Nare Head is about four miles from garage).
Public transport: None.
Visiting: Open daily. Car Park. Unstable cliff edges approach with care.
Contact: National Trust, T: 01872 580 553;
E: roseland@nationaltrust.org.uk

6. STITHIANS RESERVOIR

South West Lakes Trust.
Habitats: Open water, marshland, meadows, wet woodland, heathland.
Birds: *Passage:* Good for waders inc. Common, Green & Wood Sandpipers. Osprey, Black Tern, Garganey. *Winter:* County's best open water site for wildfowl. Winter gull flocks inc. Mediterranean. Reservoir has good track record for *rarities:* inc. Pied-billed Grebe, Pectoral, White-rumped & Semipalmated Sandpipers, Lesser Yellowlegs, Wilson's Phalarope, Caspian Tern & Black Kite.

Directions: Sat nav: TR16 6NW. SS 709 369. Signposted from B3297 S of Redruth.
Public transport: None.
Visiting: Good viewing from causeway. Hide near main centre (opposite Golden Lion Inn), open to all. Two other hides for members of CBWPS. Toilets, cafe (9am-4pm). Footpath around reservoir.
Contact: Stithians Activity Centre, T: 01209 860 301; South West Lakes Trust - see site 1.

7. TAMAR ESTUARY

Cornwall Wildlife Trust.
Habitats: 110ha, tidal mudflats, some saltmarsh.
Birds: *Spring/summer:* Breeding Shelduck. *Winter:* Waders - inc. large number of Avocet. Black-tailed Godwit, Redshank, Dunlin, Curlew, Whimbrel, Spotted Redshank, Green Sandpiper, Golden Plover, Snipe, Kingfisher.
Directions: Sat nav: PL12 6LJ. SX 431 614 (Landulph). PL12 6NX. SX 436 626 (Cargreen). N of Saltash. From Plymouth head W on A38, after Saltash turn R on to A388. Access parking at Cargreen & Landulph from minor roads off A388.
Public transport: None.
Visiting: Open all times. Footpath from Cargreen to Landulph. Also access to two hides (from China Fleet Club car park, Saltash PL12 6LJ. SX428 604). Follow path alongside golf course (keep off course). Combination number for hide locks available at club reception. Two hides on foreshore, first (0.25 mile from car park) overlooks estuary, second (0.5 mile) has views across Kingsmill Lake.
Contact: Cornwall WT - see site 3.

8. TAMAR LAKES

South West Lakes Trust.
Habitats: Two freshwater lakes, swamp, scrub & grassland (on Cornwall-Devon border).
Birds: *All year:* Great Crested Grebe, Black-headed Gull, Kingfisher, Willow Tit, Reed Bunting. *Spring:* Black Tern. *Summer:* Breeding Sedge, Reed & Willow Warblers & House Martin. *Winter:* Moderate numbers of wildfowl, inc. Wigeon & Teal & gulls.
Other: Badger, Roe Deer, Otter, Southern Marsh Orchid, Wood White butterfly, Grass Snake.
Directions: Sat nav: EX22 7RW. SS 288 116 (Upper). EX22 7LB. SS 194 107 (Lower). Site lies E of A39, N of Bude. Follow brown tourist signs from Holsworthy or Kilkhampton.
Public transport: None.
Visiting: Open all year. Pay-&-display car parks. Sailing & other watersports means Upper Lake is limited for birding, nature reserve located on Lower Lake - limited wheelchair access. Hides at both lakes. Cafe (10am-4pm) at Upper Lake. Toilets at Upper Lake open all year & at Lower Lake open summer only. Trail leaflet available from cafe.
Contact: Upper Tamar Lakes Activity Centre, T: 01288 321 712; South West Lakes Trust - see site 1.

Devon

THE COUNTY HAS a wide variety of habitats including the marshes of the Exe estuary, near Exeter (wildfowl & waders), the pebblebed heathlands (Dartford Warbler) in the east, the moorlands of Exmoor, that spread into west Somerset, & Dartmoor (where Red-backed Shrikes are attempting to re-establish themselves). The south coast holds localised but increasing pockets of Cirl Buntings. The island of Lundy in the Bristol Channel regularly turns up rarities.

1. AYLESBEARE COMMON

RSPB (South West England Office).
Habitats: Heathland, wood fringes, streams & ponds.
Birds: *All year*: Buzzard, Dartford Warbler, Yellowhammer. *Spring/summer*: Hobby, Nightjar, Tree Pipit, Stonechat. *Winter*: Possible Hen Harrier.
Other: Good variety of dragonflies (inc Southern Damselfly) & butterflies.
Directions: Sat nav: EX5 2JS. SY 057 897. Five miles E of Junc 30 of M5 at Exeter, 0.5 mile past Halfway Inn on B3052. Turn R to Hawkerland, car park is on L. Reserve is on opposite side of main road.
Public transport: Bus - nos.9 & 9A Exeter to Seaton/Honiton request stop at Joneys Cross (reserve entrance). Stagecoach South West.
Visiting: Open all year. Car park, two trails, picnic area, group bookings, guided walks & special events. One track suitable for wheelchairs & pushchairs, disabled access via metalled track to private farm. Dogs on lead.
Contact: RSPB, T: 01395 233 655;
E: aylesbeare.common@rspb.org.uk

2. BERRY HEAD NNR

Torbay Coast & Countryside Trust.
Habitats: Limestone cliffs (200ft), grassland, quarry.
Birds: *All year*: Cirl Bunting (in flocks in winter), Peregrine (hunting in quarry area), Fulmar. *Spring/summer*: Up to 1,200 nesting Guillemots on cliffs below Southern Fort. *Passage*: Well known as a migrant watchpoint.
Other: Limestone flora inc. eight spp. orchid, Small Hare's-ear. Harbour Porpoise, Common Dolphin, Greater & Lesser Horseshoe Bats (walks arranged), Bloody Nose Beetle & variety of butterflies.
Directions: Sat nav: TQ5 9AP. SX 940 561 (Berry Head car park). Signposted from Brixham on minor roads from A3022 & A379. Located at end of Gillard Road, past Landscove Holiday Village.
Public transport: Bus - no.17 from Brixham to Victoria Road (0.5 mile walk to Berry Head: some steep sections). Stagecoach South West.
Visiting: Open all year. Pay-&-display car park. Guardhouse visitor centre open easter-Oct 10am-4pm Tues-Sun/1pm-4pm Mon & Oct-easter 10am-4pm Sat/Sun only. CCTV images of nesting seabirds, cafe & toilets. Wheelchair-friendly 300 yards path from car park to visitor centre & cafe. Two mobility vehicles for hire (pre-book). Bird hide overlooking cliffs.
Contact: Berry Head NNR, T: 01803 882 619;
E: noel@countryside-trust.org.uk,
W: www.countryside-trust.org.uk/berryhead

3. BOVEY HEATHFIELD

Devon Wildlife Trust.
Habitats: 24ha, mix of wet/dry lowland heath - surrounded by secondary woodland. Numerous ponds.
Birds: Breeding Nightjar, Tree Pipit, Stonechat & Dartford Warbler, Skylark, Linnet & Yellowhammer.
Other: Heathers, wet & dry heathland plants, 60+ endangered insect spp., Grayling & Green Hairstreak butterflies, Slow Worm, Adder & Grass Snake.
Directions: Sat nav: TQ12 6TU. SX 823 763. On outskirts of Bovey Tracey on SE edge of Dartmoor. From A382 Bovey Tracey head S turning L into Heathfield Industrial estate (Battle Road), then L into Cavalier Road & L into Dragoon Close – reserve is along a gravel path.
Public transport: Bus - 'South West Falcon' service Exeter to Plymouth, stops at Drumbridges Roundabout (on A38), a 20 mins walk to reserve. Stagecoach South West.
Visiting: Open all year. No coach access. Several routes around site - keep to paths (rough, not suitable for wheelchairs). Circular way-marked path & viewpoint. Keep dogs under control.
Contact: Devon WT, T: 01392 279 244;
E: contactus@devonwildlife trust.org

4. BOWLING GREEN & GOOSEMOOR

RSPB (South West England Office).
Habitats: Coastal grassland, open water/marsh.
Birds: *Spring:* Shelduck, passage waders inc. Ringed Plover, Little Stint, Ruff & sandpipers, Whimbrel, passage Garganey & Yellow Wagtail. *Summer:* Gull/tern roosts, high tide wader roosts contain many passage birds. *Autumn:* Wildfowl, Peregrine, wader roosts. *Winter:* Large numbers of Wigeon, Shoveler, Teal, Black-tailed Godwit, Curlew, Golden Plover. Avocet & Brent Geese.
Other: Hairy Dragonfly, Wasp Spider.
Directions: Sat nav: EX3 0EN. SX 683 825 (Holman Way car park). On E side of River Exe, four miles SE of Exeter in Bowling Green Road, Topsham.
Public transport: Bus - no.57 Exeter to Topsham, alight at Elm Grove Road (0.6 mile from reserve). Also stops at Darts Farm Shopping Village (inc. RSPB shop). Stagecoach. Train - Exeter to Exmouth stops at Topsham (one mile from reserve).
Visiting: Open all times. Park at Holman Way or The Quay public car parks in Topsham, not in lane by reserve. Lookout Hide located on Bowling Green Road - short walk from parking areas (Blue Badge bay outside). Nearest RADAR toilets at The Quay car park. Wheelchair accessible hide/viewing platform. RSPB shop at Darts Farm (EX3 0QH, T: 01392 879 438), one mile from reserve, east of Topsham across River Clyst - weekly guided walks from here.
Contact: RSPB, T: 01392 833 311;
E: exe.estuary@rspb.org.uk

5. BURRATOR RESERVOIR

South West Lakes Trust.
Habitats: Pine forests, wooded streams, open moorland scrub.
Birds: *All year:* 3 spp. woodpecker, Buzzard, Kestrel, Sparrowhawk, Barn Owl, Tree Sparrow. *Winter:* Goosander, Dipper, Grey Wagtail, Green Sandpiper, Brambling, Crossbill, Siskin, Redpoll.
Other: Marsh Fritillary butterfly, dragonflies, esp. in arboretum, bats, Otter.
Directions: Sat nav: PL20 6PE. SX 552 685 (Discovery Centre). On S side of Dartmoor, 10 miles NE of Plymouth, off A386 (Tavistock road). At Yelverton take B3212 towards Princetown. Turn R at Burrator Inn (Dousland) & follow signs to reservoir.
Public transport: Bus - no.1 Plymouth/Tavistock to Yelverton - Stagecoach South West - then no.56 (limited) Yelverton to Dousland (1.5 miles from reservoir/not Sun). Target Travel (T: 01752 242 000).
Visiting: Open all year. Car park around reservoir (inc. Quarry car park, Norsworthy Bridge car park & Arboretum car park (free/donations welcome). Visitor centre (opening times/days vary depending on time of year), toilets (inc disabled). Snack & ice-cream vans during summer. Main circular route, though suitable for disabled access, is used by cars & cyclists. One mile wildlife trail in Arboretum suitable for wheelchairs.
Contact: Burrator Discovery Centre,
T: 01822 855 700; E: heritage@swlakestrust.org.uk;
W: www.swlakestrust.org.uk

6. DAWLISH WARREN NNR

Teignbridge District Council.
Habitats: High tide roost site for wildfowl & waders of Exe estuary on mudflats & shore. Dunes, dune grassland, woodland, scrub, ponds.
Birds: Excellent variety of birds all year, esp. on migration. *Summer:* Particularly good for terns. *Winter:* Waders & wildfowl in large numbers. Also good for divers & Slavonian Grebe offshore.
Directions: Sat nav: EX7 0NF. SX 983 788. On S side of Exe estuary mouth. Turn off A379 just N of Dawlish (signposted to Dawlish Warren). At mini-roundabout, just after Welcome Inn, turn R. Pass under tunnel (by train station) then turn L (away from amusements) & park at far end of car park & walk through gates.
Public transport: Bus - no.22 Torquay/Paignton to DW. Stagecoach South West. Train - Dawlish Warren.
Visiting: Open public access, but avoid mudflats & beach beyond groyne nine around high tide (roosting birds). Pay-&-display car park. Visitor centre open Apr-Aug 2pm-5pm/Sat-Sun, 2pm-4pm/Wed-Fri (closed Mon-Tues) Sep-Mar 1pm-4pm/Sat-Sun (may be closed if in use by groups or wardens out on site). Toilets at entrance tunnel & in resort area. Hide one mile NE of visitor centre, open at all times - best around high tide. No dogs on beach or dunes between ninth groyne at any time (inc. hide).
Contact: Teignbridge District Council, T: 01626 215 751;
E: greenspaces@teignbridge.gov.uk;
W: www.dawlishwarren.co.uk (DW Recording Group)

7. EAST DARTMOOR WOODS & HEATHS NNR

Natural England (Devon, Cornwall & Isles of Scilly Team).
Habitats: Three connected sites (Yarner Wood, Trendlebere Down & Bovey Valley Woodlands), 365 ha of upland oakwood, heathland, bogs & streams.
Birds: *All year:* Raven, Buzzard, Sparrowhawk, Goshawk, 3 spp. woodpecker, Dipper, Grey Wagtail & Dartford Warbler (Trendlebere Down). *Spring/summer:* Cuckoo, Tree Pipit, Skylark, Pied Flycatcher, Redstart, Stonechat, Whitethroat, Wood Warbler, Linnet. Nightjar on heaths. *Autumn/winter:* Good variety of birds feeding at Yarner Wood hide, inc. Siskin, Redpoll. Hen Harrier (Trendlebere Down).
Other: Good for butterflies inc. fritilleries & Grayling.
Directions: Sat nav: TQ13 9LJ. SX 785 788 (Yarner Wood). NNR is two miles from Bovey Tracey on road to Becky Falls & Manaton. Road continues across Trendlebere Down - three roadside car parks & adjacent paths.
Public transport: None.
Visiting: Yarner Wood car park open 7.30am-7.30pm/dusk if earlier - outside these hours, access on foot from Trendlebere Down. Information/interpretation display & self-guided trails available in Yarner Wood car park & hide with feeding station (Nov-Mar). Dogs under close control.
Contact: Natural England, Yarner Wood,
T: 01626 832 330.

NATURE RESERVES - SOUTH WEST ENGLAND

8. EXMINSTER & POWDERHAM MARSHES

RSPB (South West England Office).
Habitats: Coastal grazing marsh with freshwater ditches & pools, reeds, scrub-covered canal banks, winter stubbles/crops managed for farmland birds.
Birds: *Spring:* Lapwing, Redshank & wildfowl breed, Cetti's Warbler on canal banks. *Summer:* Gull roosts, passage waders, hirundines, Hobby. *Autumn/Winter:* Peregrine, Short-eared Owl, finch flocks (inc. Cirl Bunting. *Winter:* Hundreds of Brent Geese & Wigeon, smaller numbers of common ducks, Water Rail, Short-eared Owl, winter thrushes.
Other: 23 spp. dragonflies inc. Hairy & Scarce Chaser.
Directions: Sat nav: EX6 8DZ. SX 954 872. Five miles S of Exeter on W bank of River Exe, on outskirts of Exminster. At S end of village take Station Road exit off A379 from Swans Nest roundabout. Go past Swans Nest Inn, over railway bridge - lane to car park immediately on R (signposted). Powderham Marsh is accessed from car park behind Swan's Nest Inn.
Public transport: Bus - no.2 Exeter to Newton Abbot, Swan's Nest roundabout stop is 400 yards from reserve car park - walk down Station Road (past Swans Nest Inn). Stagecoach South West.
Visiting: Open all times (except permissive path at Powderham). Information in RSPB car park (Exminster), marked footpaths across reserve , viewing screen - 2.5 mile circular walk takes 90 mins. No dogs at Powderham Marshes, one mile trail, viewing platform. Refreshments & toilets at Swans Nest Inn & Turf pub.
Contact: RSPB - see site 4.

9. LABRADOR BAY

RSPB (South West England Office).
Habitats: Reserve covers 1.25 miles of coastline. Part of a working farm grazed by cattle in summer, sheep in winter with coastal cliff top, woodland, scrub, arable & semi-improved grassland.
Birds: Purchased to help secure future of Cirl Buntings that can be seen all year round - breeding pairs in spring/summer & in flocks during autumn/winter when they feed on stubbles with other farmland birds inc. Skylark, Chaffinch & Yellowhammer. Peregrine & Buzzard also regular.
Other: Offshore - Dolphins, Basking Shark.
Directions: Sat nav: TQ1 4TP. SX 931 705. The bay lies 2.7 miles S of Teignmouth on the A379 coast road between Shaldon & Maidencombe.
Public transport: Train - Teignmouth is two miles away, then use SW Coast Path (no bus services).
Visiting: Open at all times. Pay-&-display car park, nearest toilets one mile (Maidencombe, summer only). Several walks around the site, longest inc. three miles of South West Coast Path.
Contact: RSPB - see site 4.

10. LUNDY

Owned by National Trust/managed by Landmark Trust.
Habitats: Island (3.5 miles long, 0.5 miles wide), 12 miles N of Hartland Point in Bristol Channel. Farmed area in S, moorland to N & Marine Protected Area.
Birds: 140 spp. annually. *Breeding:* Seabird colonies, inc. Manx Shearwater (5,500 prs) & Puffin (400 prs) - both recovering after rat eradication. Fulmar, Shag, Razorbill,Guillemot, Kittiwake. Gannet (offshore), Storm Petrel (possibly breeds, occassionally offshore). *Spring/autumn passage:* Regular common migrants pass through during both periods, always with a chance of scarce or rare spp. Sometimes large 'falls' of birds occur.
Other: Endemic Lundy Cabbage & Bronze Lundy Cabbage Flea Beetle.
Directions: Sat nav: EX39 2EY (Bideford Office). TQ7 2QP (Ilfracombe Office). Parking in both towns.
Public transport: None.
Visiting: Lundy's own ferry/supply ship MV Oldenburg sails at least three times pw from either Bideford or Ilfracombe (crossing takes ca. two hours each way). *Day trips.* Boat runs from Apr-Sep, onshore time limited to four/six hours depending on sailing. *Residential trips* (accommodation available). Boat runs from Apr-Oct & helicopter from late-Jan to Mar & Nov to early Jan (Fri/Mon only). Contact/see website for sailing/flight dates, times, costs & for accommodation options. Crossings may be cancelled during bad weather.
Contact: Booking Office - T: 01271 863 636; E: info@lundyisland.co.uk; W: www.landmarktrust.org.uk/Lundyisland Lundy Field Society, E: secretary@lundy.org.uk; W: www.lundy.org.uk

11. SLAPTON LEY NNR

Field Studies Council/Natural England.
Habitats: Freshwater lake, reedbeds, marsh & woodland.
Birds: *All year:* Cirl Bunting, Cetti's Warbler. Most south-westerly population of Great Crested Grebe. *Spring/summer:* Migrant warblers. Good seawatching in favourable conditions in spring & autumn, migrants on passage. Large gathering of Swallows in autumn roosts. *Winter:* Divers & grebes on sea, Bittern at Higher Ley. Diving ducks & grebes on Lower Ley.
Other: UK's only site for Strapwort. Otter, Dormouse.
Directions: Sat nav: TQ7 2QP. SX 825 448 (Field Centre). Largest freshwater lake in SW England, lying S of Dartmouth on south coast, is separated from Start Bay by a shingle bank which carries A379.
Public transport: Bus - no.3 from Plymouth/ Kingsbridge to Dartmouth stops at Slapton (outside field centre - limited on Sun)). Stagecoach South West.
Visiting: Pay-&-display car parks off A379 at Torcross & Slapton Sands. Higher Ley is closed to public, but can be viewed from public footpath. Hides overlooking Torcross & Stokely Bay areas of lagoon & surrounding backdrops. Field Centre offers variety of residential courses.
Contact: Slapton Ley Field Centre, T: 01548 580 466; E: enquiries.sl@field-studies-council.org; W: www.slnnr.org.uk

170

Dorset

THE COUNTY HOLDS INTERNATIONALLY important habitats & the Isle of Portland is a migration hot-spot - making this one of England's top birding counties. The heathlands hold Dartford Warbler, Woodlark & Nightjar, Poole Harbour attracts internationally important numbers of wintering waders & wildfowl. Two RSPB reserves in Weymouth (Lodmoor & Radipole) are probably the best urban birding sites in the country & the Portland Bird Observatory is the place to be at migration time. An Osprey re-introduction programme in Poole Harbour is in its early stages.

Public transport: None to reserve. Train - nearest station is Wareham (four miles).
Visiting: Trails open all times. Pay-&-display car park open 8.30am-6pm Nov-Mar/ 10pm Apr-Oct (free for RSPB members). Coaches & escorted parties by prior arrangement. Shop open daily (not Dec 25/26) 9.30am-5pm/cafe 9.30am-4.30pm (opposite car park), small Welcome Hut (9am-4.30pm) & toilets in car park/cafe. Seven signposted trails, limited wheelchair access on trails. Two hides, one viewpoint & two viewing screens. Dogs on leads/no dogs on new Hyde Heath extension, take dog waste away.
Contact: RSPB, T: 01929 553 360; E: arne@rspb.org.uk

1. ARNE

RSPB (South West England Office).
Habitats: Lowland heath, woodland, reedbed & saltmarsh, extensive mudflats of Poole Harbour.
Birds: *All year*: Little Egret, Spoonbill, Marsh Harrier (breed in harbour), Barn Owl, Dartford Warbler, Stonechat. *Summer*: Sandwich & Common Terns, Hobby, Nightjar, hirundines, warblers. *Passage*: Osprey, Spotted Redshank, Whimbrel, Greenshank. *Winter*: 30,000 waders/wildfowl use Poole Harbour, many seen from Arne inc. grebes, divers, Brent Goose, Black-tailed Godwit, Avocet, plus occasional Eider, Scaup & Long-tailed Duck. Hen Harrier, winter thrushes & finches. A five-year Osprey re-introduction programmed started in Poole Harbour in 2017.
Other: Sika Deer, all six spp. UK reptile, 32 spp. butterflies inc. Silver-studded Blue, 23 spp. dragonflies, 850 spp. moths & 500 spp. flowering plants.
Directions: Sat nav: BH20 5BJ. SY 971 876. Head S from Wareham over causeway, turn off L at Stoborough to Ridge continue to Arne.

2. BROWNSEA ISLAND NATURE RESERVE

Dorset Wildlife Trust/National Trust.
Habitats: 101ha, saline lagoon, reedbed, lakes, coniferous & mixed woodland.
Birds: *All year*: Spoonbill, Little Egret, Golden Pheasant. *Summer*: Common & Sandwich Terns, Little Grebe, Mediterranean Gull. *Autumn*: Curlew Sandpiper, Little Stint & rarities often turn up on DWT Lagoon. *Winter*: Avocet, Black-tailed Godwit, Spotted Redshank & other waders, Water Rail, gulls & wildfowl.
Other: Red Squirrel (up to 250 on island), Water Vole, Bechstein's Bat. Good variety of butterflies & dragonflies.
Directions: Sat nav: BH15 1HJ. SZ 010 902 (Poole Quay). Brownsea Island Ferries (T: 01929 462 383): half hourly crossings from Poole Quay/Sandbanks Quay (BH13 7QN. SZ 037 870 by Studland chain-ferry). Greenslade Pleasure Boats (T: 01202 669 955): half hourly crossings from Poole Quay. Boat charges apply in addition to landing fee.
Public transport: Poole - bus & train stations are short walk from Poole Quay/boats (mainly down pedestrian shopping area to the Old Town).

Visiting: Island open late-Mar to end-Oct, 10am-5pm. Landing fee (free for NT members). Free admission to nature reserve for DWT members (show card to NT staff) but landing fee must be paid if visiting rest of island. Toilets, information centre, cafe, gift shop, five hides, nature trail. Assistance dogs only.
Contact: Dorset WT, T: 01202 709 445;
E: info@dorsetwildlifetrust.org.uk
National Trust, T: 01202 707 744;
E: brownseaisland@nationaltrust.org.uk

3. DURLSTON NNR & COUNTRY PARK

Dorset County Council.
Habitats: 113ha, sea cliffs, woodland, grassland, hedges, cliff, meadows & downland.
Birds: *All year:* Peregrine, Kestrel, Raven, woodland species. *Spring/autumn passage:* migrants (esp. important site for visible migration in autumn). *Summer:* Cliff-nesting seabird colonies inc. Fulmar, Guillemot, Razorbill & Shag, good variety of scrub & woodland breeding spp. Can be good for seabird passage - esp. Apr/May & Aug/Nov.
Other: 34 spp. butterflies inc. Lulworth Skipper, 800 spp. moths & 500+ spp. flowering plants, inc. nine spp. orchid. Bottlenose Dolphin.
Directions: Sat nav: BH19 2JL. SZ 032 773. Lighthouse Road, Swanage, one mile S of town centre (signposted).
Public transport: Bus - Durlston Explorer 5 runs between end-May to end-Sep (half-hourly from pick-up points in Swanage running approx. 10am-5pm).
Visiting: Open dawn-dusk. Pay-&-display parking. Durlston Castle: visitor centre open daily (not Dec 25/26) 10am-5pm Apr-Oct, 10am-4pm Nov-Mar. Cafe (in Castle) open daily (not Dec 25/26) 9.30am-5pm & Fri/Sat evenings Apr-mid Oct. Toilets, exhibitions, art displays & shop. Dolphin watchpoint hide, waymarked trails. Walks & events.
Contact: Durlston CP, T: 01929 424 443;
E: info@durlston.co.uk; W: www.durlston.co.uk

4. GARSTON WOOD

RSPB (South West England Office).
Habitats: Actively-managed ancient woodland inc. large area of coppiced hazel & maple. Oak woodland, scrub & mixed plantation, glades, rides & dead wood.
Birds: Turtle Dove & Nightingale formally bred. *All year/summer:* Common woodland birds & migrant warblers inc. Blackcap, Willow & Garden Warbler, Spotted Flycatcher. Raptors inc. Buzzard, Sparrowhawk & (occasional) Goshawk. *Winter:* Winter thrushes.
Other: Bluebells & spring flowers. Butterflies, inc. Silver-washed Fritillary & elusive White Admiral. Adders can be seen on rides. Variety of fungi. Fallow Deer.
Directions: Sat nav: SP5 5PA. SU 003 194. SW from Salisbury. From A354 take turn to Sixpenny Handley then take Bowerchalke road (Dean Lane). Proceed for approximately 1.5 miles on single-track road (with passing places). Garston Wood car park on L.
Public transport: Bus - no.20 (Mon-Fri) Blandford to Salisbury alight at Sixpenny Handley (Roebuck Inn). Damory (T: 01202 338 420). 1.5 mile walk to reserve along Dean Lane.

Visiting: Open all times. Car park, reserve leaflet, picnic area, group bookings/guided walks available, No defined trails but plenty of rides/tracks & suggested routes. Accessible to pushchairs but terrain is best in dry conditions. Dogs on leads.
Contact: RSPB - see site 1.

5. LODMOOR NATURE RESERVE

RSPB (South West England Office).
Habitats: Marsh, shallow pools, large reedbed & scrub, remnant saltmarsh.
Birds: *All year:* Little Egret, Marsh Harrier (breeding), Kingfisher, Cetti's Warbler, Bearded Tit. *Spring/summer:* Common Tern colony, warblers (inc. Reed, Sedge, Lesser Whitethroat, occassionally Grasshopper), Hobby. *Passage:* Waders (inc. Black-tailed Godwit, Green & Wood Sandpipers) - other migrants & rarities regularly turn up. *Winter:* Wildfowl, waders, Bittern.
Directions: Sat nav: DT3 6HS. SY 688 809. NE of Weymouth, one mile from town centre adjacent to A3155 (Preston Road).
Public transport: Bus - frequest local service to Overcombe Corner, Lodmoor Country Park from Weymouth seafront. Train - Weymouth, bus or easy walk along seafront to reserve (one mile).
Visiting: Open all times. Pay-&-display car parks nearby, street parking on N side (Southdown Ave). One viewing shelter, trails mostly accessible to wheelchairs.
Contact: RSPB, T: 01305 778 313;
E: weymouth.reserves@rspb.org.uk

6. MOORS VALLEY COUNRTY PARK & FOREST

East Dorset Council/Forestry Commission.
Habitats: Lakes, ponds, river, scrub, deciduous woodland, coniferous forest, meadow, heathland.
Birds: *All year:* Buzzard, Lapwing, Woodcock, Little Owl, Grey Wagtail, Kingfisher, Dartford Warbler, Crossbill, usual woodland species. *Spring/summer:* Cuckoo, Nightjar, Sand Martin, Tree Pipit, Whitethroat. Occasional Woodlark, Sedge Warbler. *Passage:* Whimbrel, Common Sandpiper, waders. *Winter:* Teal, Pochard, Gadwall, Snipe, Redpoll. Occasional Brambling, Goosander.
Other: 20+ spp. dragonflies. Good number butterflies & other invertebrates. Roe Deer, Badger, reptiles.
Directions: Sat nav: BH24 2ET. SU108 047 - on Horton Road, Ashley Heath. Two miles W of Ringwood, signposted from Ashley Heath roundabout (junction of A31 & A338) between Ringwood & St Leonards.
Public transport: Bus - no.38 Ringwood to Ferndown stops at Lions Lane, at Castleman Trailway, near main entrance. Morebus (T: 01202 338 240).
Visiting: Pay-&-display car park, accessible parking spaces, coach parking. Open daily (not Dec 25) 8am-5pm Sep-Mar, (6pm Apr-May & 7pm Jun-Aug). Visitor centre open 9am-4.30pm, toilets, restuarant, gift shop. Way-marked trails, many wheelchair friendly.
Contact: Moors Valley Country Park, T: 01425 470 721,
W: rangers@moors-valley.co.uk; W: www.moors-valley.co.uk;
Forestry England, T: 0300 067 4600

NATURE RESERVES - SOUTH WEST ENGLAND

7. MORDEN BOG NNR (WAREHAM FOREST)

Natural England (Wessex Team).
Habitats: NNR - mainly lowland heath (dry & wet heath, bog & valley mire), large decoy pond with surrounding area consisting of coniferous forest & lowland heath.
Birds: *All year:* Buzzard, Dartford Warbler, Meadow Pipit, Stonechat, Siskin, Lesser Spotted Woodpecker (by Sherford Bridge - best in spring). *Spring/summer:* Hobby, Nightjar, Woodlark, Tree Pipit, Redstart. *Winter:* Great Grey Shrike (almost annual).
Other: Butterflies, inc. Silver-studded Blue, dragonflies, & all six British reptile spp.
Directions: Sat nav: BH20 7ES. SY 919 926 (parking area). N of Wareham, part of a wider Wareham Forest site. From Wareham take A351 to Sandford then turn L onto B3075 towards Morden. Drive through forest until reaching layby (on R) at Sherford Bridge. Park & cross road through metal gate.
Public transport: Can access forest from Wareham train station follow blue signs (bus stop here as well).
Visiting: Open at all times, many footpaths.
Contact: Natural England (main enquiries), T: 0300 060 3900; E: enquiries@naturalengland.org.uk

8. PORTLAND BIRD OBSERVATORY

Portland Bird Observatory.
Habitats: Portland - cliffs, scrub, quarries, open fields. Migration watchpoint, seawatching.
Birds: 355+ spp. on Portland. *All year:* Little Owl. *Spring/autumn:* Most of regular common & scarce migrants recorded annually, national rarities frequently turn up. Good selection of offshore passage inc. divers, Common Scoter, shearwaters (inc. Balearic), skuas (inc. Pomarine & occasional Long-tailed), terns (inc. Arctic & Black). *Summer:* Breeding Razorbill, Guillemot, Fulmar, Shag, Little Tern (Ferrybridge). Puffin (occasionally at the Bill).
Winter: Purple Sandpiper, Short-eared Owl, Black Redstart, Mediterranean Gull (large numbers at Ferrybridge), divers, grebes, Red-breasted Merganser (Portland Harbour).
Directions: Sat nav: DT5 2JT. SY 681 690. Six miles S of Weymouth, Observatory on road to Portland Bill.
Public transport: Bus - no.1 Weymouth to The Bill. First Wessex, Dorset & Somerset.
Visiting: Open at all times. Parking only for Portland Bird Obs members. Self-catering accommodation available - take own towels, sheets, sleeping bags. Information, toilets, natural history bookshop. Large pay-&-display car park & toilets at The Bill.
Contact: Martin Cade (Warden PBO), T: 01305 820 553; E: obs@btinternet.com; W: http://portlandbirdobs.blogspot.co.uk/

9. RADIPOLE LAKE

RSPB (South West England Office).
Habitats: Lake, reedbeds.
Birds: Excellent for rare/scarce gulls, regular rarities. *All year:* Marsh Harrier, Bearded Tit, Cetti's Warbler. *Spring/summer/autumn:* Hirundines, Reed & Sedge warblers, passage waders & other migrants. Garganey regular in spring. *Winter:* Bittern, wildfowl, Water Rail, pre-roost gatherings of gulls & Pied Wagtail.
Directions: Sat nav: DT4 7TZ. SY 675 795. In Radipole Park Drive, Weymouth (signposted with brown signs). Enter footpaths from Swannery car park.
Public transport: Train - station 400 yards from reserve, serving London & Bristol.
Visiting: Public footpaths open all times. Public pay-&-display car park. Discovery Centre open daily (not 24-26 Dec) 9.30am-5pm (4pm Nov-Jan). Centre has small cafe & disabled toilets. Network of wheelchair friendly paths, two viewing trails, one viewing shelter, viewpoints. Dogs on leads.
Contact: RSPB - see site 5.

Somerset

HABITAT RESTORATION ON the old peat workings of the Somerset Levels has changed the area dramatically. Breeding Bitterns & Common Cranes (from a successful re-introduction programme) have been boosted by this work and a variety of herons & egrets are colonising the area. In winter the Levels hold large numbers of wildfowl & are worth a visit to witness a spectacular Starling murmuration. Coastal sites attract wintering waders & wildfowl.

1. BREAN DOWN

National Trust.
Habitats: Extension of Mendips hard limestone, featuring calcareous grassland, scrub & steep cliffs.
Birds: *All year:* Peregrine, Raven. *Summer:* Blackcap, Garden Warbler, Whitethroat, Stonechat. *Passage:* Gannet, divers, shearwaters, waders, skuas, gulls & passerines. *Winter:* Shelduck, Curlew, Dunlin on mudflats.
Other: Chalkhill Blue, Marbled White & other butterflies. Three rare plants - White Rock Rose, Somerset Hair Grass, Dwarf Sedge.
Directions: Sat nav: TA8 2RS. ST 296 586. 300ft high promontory jutting into Bristol Channel, five miles N of Burnham-on-Sea. From junc 22 of M5, head for Weston-super-Mare on A38/A370. Turn off at Lympsham & head for Brean. In Brean head N to car park at bottom of Brean Down.

Public transport: Bus - no.20 Burnham-on-Sea to Weston-super-Mare, alight at Brean - 1.75 miles to reserve). First Bristol, Bath & the West.
Visiting: Open all year. Pay-&-display car park opens with shop & cafe (9am-5pm), NT members free. Toilet (inc. disabled) at bottom of Brean Down. Steep slope not recommended for wheelchair users. Dogs on lead.
Contact: National Trust, T: 01278 751 874;
E: breandown@nationaltrust.org.uk

2. BRIDGWATER BAY NNR

Natural England (Wessex Team).
Habitats: 2,560ha, Parrett River estuary, intertidal mudflats, saltmarsh.
Birds: 200 spp. *All year:* Curlew, Oystercatcher, Avocet. Shelduck (Europe's second largest moulting ground with up to 2,000 birds in Jul). *Spring/autumn:* Passage migrants, inc. occasional vagrants. Waders inc. internationally important numbers of Whimbrel & Black-tailed Godwit. *Winter:* Raptors inc. Peregrine, harriers & Short-eared Owl. Waders & wildfowl inc. nationally important numbers of Wigeon.
Other: Saltmarsh flora. Rare invertebrates inc. Great Silver Water Beetle, Aquatic Snail & Hairy Dragonfly.
Directions: Sat nav: TA5 2PL. ST 257 408. 3.25 miles N of Bridgwater & extends to Burnham-on-Sea. Take Junc 23 or 24 off M5. Turn N off A39 at Cannington & take minor roads to car park at Steart.
Public transport: None.
Visiting: Car park, interpretive panels, leaflet dispenser at Steart - follow footpath approx 0.5 mile to tower hide & three other hides at mouth of River Parrett. Hides open daily (not Dec 25). Permits needed for Steart Island (by boat only). Dogs on leads. Disabled access to hides by arrangement, other areas accessible.
Contact: Natural England, T: 01458 860 120;
E: somersetavonandwiltshire@naturalengland.org.uk

3. CATCOTT NATURE RESERVES

Somerset Wildlife Trust.
Habitats: Wet meadows with winter flooding & summer grazing.
Birds: *All year:* Little Egret, Kingfisher, Cetti's Warbler, Reed Bunting. *Spring:* Nationally important numbers of roosting Whimbrels, plus passage Greenshank, Ruff & Black-tailed Godwits. *Summer:* Breeding Lapwing, Snipe, Redshank, Yellow Wagtail, warblers. Nightingale (Catcott Heath). *Winter:* Wildfowl, Peregrine & other raptors. Siskin & Redpoll.
Other: Otter, Roe Deer, Great Crested Newt, rare dragonflies, threatened Saw Sedge.
Directions: Sat nav: TA7 8NQ. ST 400 414. Catcott Lows - approx one mile N of Catcott (off A39 from Junc 23 of M5). Access to Catcott Heath on foot, east-south-east from ST 399 405 along drove ca.0.5 mile to reserve entrance in a wooded area on R.

Public transport: Bus - no.75 (not Sun) Wells to Bridgwater stops in Catcott - 1.5 mile to reserve. First Buses Somerset.
Visiting: Open all times. Car park. Four hides (disabled access to hide by car park), information board..
Contact: Somerset WT, T: 01823 652 400;
E: enquires@somersetwildlife.org

4. CHEW VALLEY LAKE

Avon Wildlife Trust/Bristol Water Plc.
Habitats: Largest artificial lake in SW England with important reedbed.
Birds: 270+ spp. - often attracts rarities. *Summer:* Breeding Great Crested & Little Grebes, Gadwall, Tufted Duck, Shoveler, Pochard, Reed Warbler. Hobby hunt in late summer. When mud exposed can attract waders inc. Dunlin, Ringed Plover & Green Sandpiper. *Winter & passage:* Wildfowl inc. important numbers of Shoveler, Gadwall, Teal & Tufted Duck. Large numbers of Goosander, Great Crested Grebe & Cormorant. Bewick's Swan, Goldeneye, Smew. Large winter gull roost (up to 50,000+), mostly Black-headed, Common & Mediterranean.
Other: Ruddy Darter & Migrant Hawker dragonflies.
Directions: Sat nav: BS40 6HN. (Avon WT reserve at Herriotts Bridge). Nine miles S of Bristol. Take B3114 south from Chew Stoke, bear L for West Harptree & head NE on A368. View reserve from causeway at Herriotts Bridge where there is car parking.
Public transport: None.
Visiting: Permit (fee) required to enter reservoir enclosure & to use access road, paths & five hides - available to members of recognized ornithological/naturalist societies - contact Bristol Water. Roadside viewing at Herons Green Bay (parking for coaches) & Harriotts Bridge. Public trails/hide (Hollow Brook, E shore: Grebe Trail (0.75 mile), hard surface for wheelchairs, dogs on leads. Unsurfaced Bittern Trail (one mile) leads to hide - can be muddy. No dogs.
Contact: Avon WT, T: 0117 917 7270;
E: hello@avonwildlifetrust.org.uk;
Bristol Water, Woodford Lodge, Chew Stoke, BS18 8SH.
T: 01275 332 339.

NATURE RESERVES - SOUTH WEST ENGLAND

5. DUNKERY & HORNER WOOD NNR

National Trust.
Habitats: 1,600ha, ancient oak woodland, moorland, part of 4,850ha NT Holnicote Estate in Exmoor National Park.
Birds: *All year*: Dipper, Grey Wagtail, woodpeckers, Buzzard, Sparrowhawk. *Spring/summer*: Redstart, Stonechat, Whinchat, Tree Pipit, Pied Flycatcher, Wood Warbler. Dartford Warbler possible.
Other: Holnicote estate holds 15 of UK's bat spp. Silver-washed & Heath Fritillary butterflies. Red Deer.
Directions: Sat nav: TA24 8HY. SS 898 309 (Horner). 4.5 miles W of Minehead. Take A39 W to minor road 0.5 mile E of Porlock signposted to Horner. Park in village.
Public transport: Bus - no.10 between Minehead to Porlock. Operated by various companies - First Buses of Somerset, Atwest & W Ridler & Sons.
Visiting: Open all year. Pay-&-display car parks at Bossington (SS 920 469) & Horner (SS 920 469), inc. toilets. Free small car parks at Allerford, Selworthy (overflow only), Selworthy Beacon, Webbers Post, 150 miles of footpaths. Webber's Post circular walk suitable for wheelchairs. Rugged terrain to reach Dunkery Beacon.
Contact: National Trust, T: 01643 862 452; E: holnicote@nationaltrust.org.uk

6. GREYLAKE

RSPB (South West England Office).
Habitats: Wet grassland, formerly arable farmland.
Birds: *Spring/summer*: Kingfisher, Grey Heron, Little Egret & breeding Garganey, Snipe, Lapwing, Redshank, Skylark, Meadow Pipit, Yellow Wagtail. *Autumn*: Green Sandpiper, waders on passage. *Winter*: Waders & wildfowl (inc. Lapwing, Golden Plover, Shoveler, Pintail, Teal & Wigeon). Peregrine, Merlin, Hen Harrier. Cranes re-introduced in area sometimes seen.
Other: Roe Deer, Water Vole, Stoat, Otter, dragonflies inc. Four-spotted Chaser.
Directions: Sat nav: TA7 9PB. ST 399 346. Off A361 Taunton to Glastonbury road, midway Othery & Greinton.
Public transport: Bus - no.29 (not Sun) Taunton to Glastonbury stops in Greinton (by phone box) or Othery (by London Inn) - driver may stop at reserve on request otherwise two mile walk along A361 - NOT ADVISABLE (fast road, no path). First Buses of Somerset.
Visiting: Open all year, dawn-dusk. Two circular trails interpretive signs, two hides, one viewing platform, easy-access trail suitable for wheelchairs. Assistance dogs only, on leads.
Contact: RSPB, T: 01458 252 805; E: greylake@rspb.org.uk

7. HAM WALL

RSPB (South West England Office).
Habitats: 265ha, wetland, inc. SW's largest reedbed.
Birds: *All year*: Bittern, Great & Little Egret, Cetti's Warbler, Water Rail, Barn Owl. *Spring/summer*: Migrant warblers, hirundines, Hobby, Whimbrel, sandpipers. Possible rare herons. *Autumn*: Migrant thrushes, Redpoll, Siskin, Kingfisher, Bearded Tit. *Winter*: Wildfowl, million-plus Starling roost, Peregrine, Merlin, Short-eared Owl. Cranes re-introduced in area sometimes seen.

Other: Otter, Roe Deer, Water Vole, dragonflies, butterflies.
Directions: Sat nav: BA6 9SX. ST 449 397. W of Glastonbury. From A39 turn N in Ashcott & follow road onto moor (towards Meare). After three miles pass Church Farm Horticultural building. Shortly after, at metal bridge, reserve is opposite side of road to Shapwick Heath NNR (also has car park) .
Public transport: Bus - no.75 (not Sun) Wells to Bridgewater stops in Ashcott - two miles to reserve. First Buses Somerset. No.688 (Mon-Fri) Glastonbury to Meare - 1.5 miles to reserve. Libra Travel (T: 01373 812 255).
Visiting: Open all year. Car park open 5am-6.30pm (Oct-Jan), 5am-8pm (Feb-Mar), 5am-10pm (Apr-Sep), parking charge for non-RSPB members. Alternative car park operated by Natural England available outside of Ham Wall opening times. Coach parking - check with reserve. Welcome Building with drink machine/light snacks open weekends 10am-4pm, weekdays when volunteers available. Toilets. Five viewing screens, two raised hides, four trails. Wheelchair users can access viewing areas from main track (use RADAR key/can be borrowed from Welcome Building when open). Assistance dogs welcome on all parts of reserve. Other dogs (short lead) on main path & public footplath (Ham Wall loop) only - take waste away.
Contact: RSPB, T: 01458 860 494; E: ham.wall@rspb.org.uk

8. SHAPWICK MOOR

Hawk & Owl Trust.
Habitats: 54ha, wet grassland - grazing pasture, hay meadows with rough grass edges, fen, open ditches, pollard willows & hedges.
Birds: *All year*: Buzzard, Kestrel, Sparrowhawk, Kingfisher, Lapwing, Grey Heron, Mute Swan. *Spring/summer*: Hobby, Barn Owl, Whimbrel & other waders on passage. Skylark, Cetti's Warbler, Bullfinch, Reed Bunting & Yellowhammer. *Autumn/winter*: Finch flocks, Snipe, Shoveler, Gadwall, Stonechat, Brambling. Peregrine & harriers may fly over.
Other: Roe Deer, Brown Hare, Stoat, Badger, Otter & Water Vole.
Directions: Sat nav: TA7 9NW. ST 417 398. From Junc 23 of M5 take A39 towards Glastonbury, after six miles turn N signposted Shapwick, on to minor road, straight over cross-roads & through Shapwick village, turn L at T-junction following signs for 'Avalon Marshes Centre'. Reserve is about half way between Shapwick village & AM Centre.
Public transport: Bus - no.75 (not Sun) Wells to Bridgewater stops in Shapwick - one mile to reserve, two mile to AM Centre. First Buses Somerset.
Visiting: Open all year (not Dec 25). Car park. Access only along public footpaths & permissive path. Dogs on leads only. Information panels, two hides. Toilets at AM Centre (BA6 9TT, ST 425 414).
Contact: Hawk & Owl Trust, T: 01328 850 590; E: enquiries@hawkandowl.org; W: www.hawkandowl.org

9. SWELL WOOD

RSPB (South West England Office).
Habitats: Semi-natural ancient oak woodland & views across wet grassland from woodland trails. Part of Somerset Levels & Moors.
Birds: Largest heronry in SW England - up to 100 pairs of Grey Heron & small number of Little Egret. *All year:* common woodland spp. inc. Treecreeper, Green & Great Spotted Woodpeckers, Nuthatch. *Spring/summer:* Breeding Buzzard, Bullfinch, Spotted Flycatcher, Song Thrush, warblers inc. Chiffchaff, Blackcap & Garden Warbler. *[On escorted walks]:* Curlew, Snipe, Sedge Warbler, Yellow Wagtail, Skylark, Nightingale.
Other: Roe Deer, Dormouse, woodland flora inc. Bluebells, Wood Anemone, Lesser Celandine. Dragonflies & butterflies.

Directions: Sat nav: TA3 6PX. ST 360 238. Reserve lies 11 mile E of Taunton. From A378 (Taunton) to Langport road, take minor road one mile E of Fivehead (signposted to car park).
Public transport: Bus - no.54 (not Sun) from Taunton stops on A378 at Swell where reserve can be accessed via stile onto Scarp Trail. First Buses of Somerset.
Visiting: Swell Wood car park & heronry hide open all year (dawn-dusk), disabled parking area. Coach parking in lay-by across main road. Heronry hide & part of woodland trail are wheelchair accessible. Scarp Trail (only path accessible to dogs) links to public footpaths.
Contact: RSPB, T: 01458 252 805;
E: swell.wood@rspb.org.uk

Wiltshire

THE CHALK DOWNLANDS of Marlborough Downs & the extensive Salisbury Plain are internationally threatened habitats & make up most of the county. The latter is used extensively by the Army & has limited public access so the birds, including breeding Quail & Stone Curlew, are subject to less disturbance than the former. The re-introduction of Great Bustards is being undertaken on the Plain. The Wildlife Trust manage nearly 40 reserves across the county.

Visiting: Open at all times. Car park, most paths firm & flat but subject to severe flooding in winter. Dogs on short leads at all times. Toilets, refreshments & information available at Gateway Centre next to A419.
Contact: Cotswold Water Park Trust,
T: 01793 752 413; E: info@waterpark.org;
W: www.waterpark.org

1. CLEVELAND LAKES

Cotswold Water Park Trust.
Habitats: Lakes with islands, scrapes, lagoons, reedbed, marsh, ditches, loafing areas. [Part of CWP, covering 40 sq. miles/150 lakes, across Wilts, Gloucs & W Oxfordshire]
Birds: *Summer:* Breeding ducks, Great Crested Grebe, Hobby, Sand Martin, Reed Bunting, Little Egret, Grey Heron. *Winter:* Large numbers wildfowl spp., plus Bittern, Water Rail, Stonechat. These & passage waders also viewable from "Twitchers' Gate" on lane to N of Lake 74 (SU 065 946).
Other: Otter, Water Vole, several spp. of dragonflies & butterflies.
Directions: Sat nav: SN6 6QW. SU 059 933 (Waterhay Car Park). Lakes 68A/B & 74 of Cotswold Water Park. From A419 Cirencester to Swindon road, take B4696 towards Cotswold Water Park West (passing GAteway Centre). After 1.5 miles turn L on to Fridays Ham Lane. Follow road to Ashton Keynes village & turn L to Cricklade/Leigh road. Waterhay Car Park is on L next to River Thames. Take bridleway north to kissing gate on R. Permissive path follows southern edge of Lake 68A/B before turning N towards hide.
Public transport: Bus - no.51 between Swindon, Cheltenham, Cirencester stops at Gateway Centre. Stagecoach West.

NATURE RESERVES - SOUTH WEST ENGLAND

2. LANGFORD LAKES

Wiltshire Wildlife Trust.
Habitats: Four former gravel pits, with islands &
reed fringes. 12ha, open water, wet woodland, scrub,
chalk river.
Birds: 150+ spp. *Summer:* Breeding Coot, Moorhen,
Tufted Duck, Pochard, Gadwall, Little & Great
Crested Grebe. Kingfisher, Common Sandpiper, Grey
Wagtail, warblers (eight spp.). *Passage:* Sand Martin,
Green Sandpiper & other waders, Black Tern. *Winter:*
Common wildfowl - Wigeon, Shoveler, Teal, Water
Rail, Little Egret, occassionally Bittern.
Other: Otter, Water Vole, Water Shrew. Spawning
Salmon & Trout in river.
Directions: Sat nav: SP3 4NH. SU 037 370. Nr
Steeple Langford, S of A36, approx eight miles W of
Salisbury. In centre of village, turn S into Duck Street,
signposted Hanging Langford. Langford Lakes is first L
just after small bridge.
Public transport: Bus - no.265 (not Sun) Salisbury to
Bath stops in Steeple Langford (0.3 mile from reserve).
First West of England.
Visiting: Main gates open during day. Advance notice
required for coaches. Visitor centre, cafe, toilets,
education centre. Trails & five hides, accessible to
wheelchairs. Cycle racks (reserve 250 yards from
Wiltshire Cycleway between Great Wishford &
Hanging Langford). No dogs.
Contact: Wiltshire WT, T: 01380 725 670;
E: info@wiltshirewildlife.org

3. RAVENSROOST WOOD & MEADOWS

Wiltshire Wildlife Trust.
Habitats: Woodland, both coppice & high oak forest,
& ponds. Surrounding meadows rich in wildflowers.
Birds: *Summer:* Woodland birds inc. Blackcap,
Chiffchaff, Willow & Garden Warbler. *Winter:* mixed
flocks of tits, Nuthatch, & Treecreeper move noisily
through wood & Woodcock (wet, muddy areas).
Other: Butterflies inc. Silver-washed Fritillary &
White Admiral. Good display of spring flowers inc.
Bluebells, Wood Anemone, Wood Sorrel, Sanicle,
violets & Primrose. Common spotted, early purple &
greater butterfly orchids, hemp agrimony & betony.
Directions: Sat nav: SN16 9RN. SU 024 876 & SU 020 876
(parking - Ravensroost Wood, Meadows & Avis Meadows).
NW of Swindon. Take B4696 Ashton Keynes road N from
Wootton Bassett. After two miles take second turn L
to Minety. Go straight on when main road turns R. Go
straight over next crossroads - car park is 0.25 mile on R.
Sat nav: SN16 9RH. SU 031 892 & SU 032 895 (parking
- Distillery & Warbler Meadows). One mile S of Minety.
In Minety turn S off B4040, after ca.0.3 mile turn R
(to Brinkworth). Hill Ground part of reserve is first
field on R (parking in gateways). Rest of reserve
is about 0.25 mile down lane to double gateway
entrance to reserve R.
Public transport: None.
Visiting: Sites connected - open at all times.
Contact: Wiltshire WT - see site 2.

4. SAVERNAKE FOREST

Savernake Estate.
Habitats: Ancient woodland, with one of largest
collections of veteran trees in Britain. Four mile
Beech avenue - longest in UK.
Birds: *All year:* Sparrowhawk, Buzzard, Red Kite,
Woodcock, owls, 3 spp. woodpecker, Marsh & Willow
Tits, Jay, other woodland birds. *Spring/summer:*
Garden Warbler, Blackcap, Willow Warbler, Chiffchaff,
Wood Warbler, Redstart, occasional Nightingale,
Tree Pipit, Spotted Flycatcher. *Winter:* Finch flocks
possibly inc. Siskin, Redpoll, Brambling & Hawfinch.
Other: Rare lichens & fungi, all main deer spp.,
Badger, Fox. Ancient trees.
Directions: Sat nav: SN8 3HN. SU 210 683 (entrance
to Grand Avenue). From Marlborough, A4 Hungerford
road runs along N side of forest. Two pillars mark
Forest Hill entrance on A4, 1.5 mile E of A346/A4
junction. The 'Grand Avenue' leads straight through
middle of woodland to join minor road from Stibb.
Public transport: None.
Visiting: Privately owned - no vehicular rights of way
or public footpaths but open all year to public. Car
park, picnic site at NW end by A346. Visitors can drive
along main avenues, but all roads closed on one day
a year - usually first working day of week. Only enter
fenced-off areas if there is a footpath.
Contact: Savernake Estate Office, T: 01672 512 161;
E: savernakeestate1@gmail.com ;
W: www.savernakeestate.co.uk

5. SWILLBROOK LAKES

Lower Mill Estate.
Habitats: Gravel pits with shallow pools, rough grassland
& scrub around edges. [Part of CWP, covering 40 sq.
miles/150 lakes, across Wilts, Gloucs & W Oxfordshire]
Birds: *Summer:* Breeding Nightingale, Garden, Reed
& Sedge Warblers, Blackcap, Cetti's Warbler, Sand &
House Martins, Swallow. One of best sites for Hobby
& Nightingale in Cotswold WP. *Winter:* Wildfowl inc.
Gadwall, Pochard, Smew, Goosander, Goldeneye.
Other: 13 spp. dragonflies inc. Downy Emerald &, in
recent years, Lesser Emperor.
Directions: Sat nav: SN16 9GA. SU 016 931. NW
of Swindon. Lakes 46/48 of Cotswold Water Park.
From A419 Swindon to Cirencester road, turn L onto
Cotswold Water Park Spine Road. Cross B4696 South
Cerney/Ashton Keynes road, take next L, Minety
Lane, after about 1.5 miles. Park in gateway either
side of road, after about 0.5 mile. Swillbrook Lakes
nature reserve & information board on E side of road.
Public transport: See site 1.
Visiting: Open all times. Adjacent to Clattinger Farm,
Wiltshire Wildlife Trust reserve. Footpath along N &
E sides of lakes. Toilets, refreshments & information
available at Gateway Centre next to A419.
Contact: Cotswold Water Park Trust - see site 1.

Scottish Borders

Borders

THIS AREA IS OFTEN overlooked as birders head north on the A1 but there are many good sites to make a stopover (or a visit) worthwhile. St Abb's Head holds a large summer seabird colony, while migrants move past in spring & autumn. Goosander is present all year, joined in the winter by Whooper Swan, geese & other wildfowl.

1. BEMERSYDE MOSS

Scottish Wildlife Trust.
Habitats: Long narrow strip of marsh, willow scrub, open water.
Birds: *Summer:* Breeding spp. inc. Black-necked Grebe, Lapwing, Curlew, Spotted Flycatcher, Tree Sparrow, Yellowhammer, Reed Bunting, Grasshopper Warbler & up to 15,000 pairs of Black-headed Gulls. *Winter:* wildfowl inc. large numbers of Wigeon & Greylag Goose.
Other: Otter, Water Vole.
Directions: Sat nav: TD6 9DS. NT 614 340. Located eight miles E of Melrose. Head S on A68 to St Boswells, then take B6404 across the Tweed into minor road to Maidenhall. At T-junction turn R & reserve is 0.5 mile ahead (lay-by on sharp bend).
Public transport: None.
Visiting: Open at all times. Limited parking in lay-by on southern edge of loch. Boardwalk leads to wheelchair-friendly bird hide.
Contact: Scottish WT, T: 0131 312 7765;
E: enquiries@scottishwildlifetrust.org.uk

2. DUNS CASTLE NATURE RESERVE

Private.
Habitats: Two man-made lochs (Heron Pool (Hen Poo) & Mill Dam), woodland.
Birds: *All year:* woodland spp. inc. Green & Great Spotted Woodpeckers, Goldcrest. *Summer:* Redstart, Pied Flycatcher & warblers. *Winter:* wildfowl.
Other: Red Squirrel, Roe Deer, occasional Otter. Woodland rich in wild flowers.
Directions: Sat nav: TD11 3NW. NT 778 550. Duns lies W of Berwick-upon-Tweed. From town centre head N on Castle Street & North Castle Street. Alternatively drive N on A6112 for one mile & turn L on B6365 to car park on northern edge of reserve.
Public transport: Bus - no.60 Galashiels to Tweedmouth stops at Duns. Borders Buses (T: 01896 754 350).
Visiting: Grounds open all year. Network of well-marked paths, some suitable for wheelchairs.
Contact: Duns Castle,
T: 01361 883 211;
info@dunscastle.co.uk;
W: www.dunscastle.co.uk

3. ETTRICK MARSHES

Habitats: 125ha, floodplain mosaic of woodland, wetland, grassland, open water.
Birds: 80 spp. *All year:* Goosander, Kingfisher, Buzzard, Crossbill, Dipper, occasional Goshawk. *Summer:* Redstart, Sedge Warbler, Sand Martin & occasional Osprey.
Other: Red Squirrel, Otter. Moths & plants at northern edge of range.
Directions: Sat nav: TD7 5HU. NT 294 167 (by Honey Cottage caravan park). Sited in Ettrick Valley, off B7009, approx 16 miles SW of Selkirk.
Public transport: None.
Visiting: Open all times. Two car parks, network of footpaths & board walk (best access from main car park by Honey Cottage - other car park at Tima Water end of site). Can flood quickly after heavy rain.

4. GUNKNOWE LOCH & PARK

Scottish Borders Council.
Habitats: River, loch, parkland, scrub, woodland.
Birds: *All year:* Goosander, Great Spotted & Green Woodpeckers, Redpoll, possible Marsh Tit. *Spring/summer:* Grey Wagtail, Kingfisher, Sand Martin, Blackcap, Sedge & Grasshopper Warblers. *Passage:* Yellow Wagtail, Whinchat, Wheatear. *Winter:* Wigeon, Tufted Duck, Pochard, Goldeneye, thrushes, Brambling.
Directions: Sat nav: TD1 3SZ. NT 517 345. In Tweedbank, two miles from Galashiels on A6091. Park at Gunknowe Loch (Tweedbank Road, off roundabout on A6091).
Public transport: Bus - no.X62 Melrose to Galashiels stops in Tweedbank. Borders Buses (T: 01896 754 350).
Visiting: Open all year. Car park, Various surfaced paths suitable for wheelchairs.
Contact: Ranger Service,
T: 01835 825 070;
W: www.scotborders.gov.uk

NATURE RESERVES - SCOTTISH BORDERS

5. ST ABBS HEAD

National Trust for Scotland.
Habitats: Cliffs, coastal grasslands, freshwater loch.
Birds: *Apr-Aug:* Seabird colonies with large number of Guillemot & Kittiwake, also Shag, Razorbill, Fulmar. *Apr-May & Sep-Oct:* Good seawatching.
Other: Common Rock-rose, Purple Milk-vetch, Spring Sandwort. Northern Brown Argus butterfly.
Directions: Sat nav: TD14 5QF. NT 913 674 for car park/bus stop. Lies five miles N of Eyemouth. Follow A1107 from A1 then take B6438 to St Abbs.
Public transport: Bus - no.235 from Berwick-upon-Tweed. Borders Buses (T: 01896 754 350). Train - Berwick-upon-Tweed.
Visiting: Open all year. Car park (free for members, coach parking arrangements - contact Old Smiddy Coffee Shop (T: 07773 347 209). Nature Centre open daily (usually unmanned) 10am-5pm easter-Oct, public toilets (inc. disabled). All-ability path to viewpoint at Starney Bay. Dogs welcome, keep under control - ensure waste is taken to bins in car park.
Contact: NTS, T: 01890 771 443;
E: st.abbs@nts.org.uk

Dumfries & Galloway

BARNACLE GEESE WINTER on The Solway in nationally important numbers, WWT Caerlaverock & RSPB Mersehead are the best sites to see them. Ospreys & Red Kites are colonising & there is a chance of a Golden Eagle over upland areas or Hen Harrier on moorland. The Mull of Galloway has fine seabird cliffs, while the Ken/Dee Marshes have wintering Whooper Swan, Greenland White-fronted & Pink-footed Geese, & resident Willow Tit.

6. CAERLAVEROCK WETLAND CENTRE

The Wildfowl & Wetlands Trust.
Habitats: Saltmarsh, grassland, wetland.
Birds: *Summer:* Osprey, Barn Owl, Skylark, Tree Sparrow, migrant warblers. *Winter:* Wildfowl esp. Barnacle (up to 40,000) & Pink-footed Geese, Whooper Swan.
Other: Natterjack Toad, Badger, Tadpole Shrimp, bats. Northern Marsh, Common Spotted & Twayblade Orchids.
Directions: Sat nav: DG1 4UF. NY 051 656. Overlooks the Solway. From St Michael's church in Dumfries take B725 towards Bankend, following tourist signs. Also signposted from A75 W of Annan.
Public transport: Bus - no.6A (not Sun) from Dumfries stops one mile from reserve. Stagecoach West Scotland.
Visiting: Open daily (not Dec 25), 10am-5pm. Parking for coaches. Charge for non-WWT members. Visitor centre & Cathan coffee shop (10.30am-4.30pm), gift shop. Binocular hire. Live CCTV pictures inc Ospreys. 20 Hides, four towers, heated observatory & sheltered picnic area. Self-catering farmhouse accommodation. Summer meadow walk May-Aug, wild swan feeds Oct-Apr. Assistance dogs only.
Contact: WWT Caerlaverock, T: 01387 770 200;
E: info.caerlaverock@wwt.org.uk
W: wwt.org.uk/caerlaverock

7. CROOK OF BALDOON

RSPB (South & West Scotland).
Habitats: Saltmarsh, wet grassland.
Birds: *Summer:* Osprey (possible), Lapwing, Redshank, Skylark, Wheatear, Linnet. *Winter:* Pink-footed & Barnacle Geese, Shelduck, Whooper Swan, Golden Plover, Curlew, Lapwing, Hen Harrier, Peregrine, Merlin, Twite.
Other: Thrift, Sea-lavender.
Directions: Sat Nav: xxx xx NX 442 530. Four miles S of Wigtown. From Wigtown, head S along A714. Go through Bladnoch, then take minor road to L (at Penkiln Sawmill sign) - follow this road down to Crook of Baldoon car park (ignoring left hand turns).
Public transport: None.
Visiting: Open at all times. Car park, viewing point & picnic tables. Not suitable for disabled access. Dogs under close control.
Contact: RSPB, T: 01988 402 130;
E: crookofbaldoon@rspb.org.uk

8. GLENTROOL

Forestry & Land Scotland.
Habitats: Part of Galloway Forest Park. Loch, waterfalls, conifer & oak woodlands, moorland.
Birds: *All year:* Common woodland spp., Peregrine, Hen Harrier, Siskin, Crossbill. *Summer:* Redstart, Pied Flycatcher, Wood Warbler.
Other: Red Squirrel, Roe Deer.
Directions: Sat nav: DG8 6SX. NX 371 786. Eight miles NW of Newton Stewart. Leave A714 at Bargrennan to Glentrool - visitor centre signposted from unclassifield road that passes N from village.
Public transport: None.
Visiting: Open all times. Car parking (charge), visitor centre with toilets & cafe - open 10.30am-5pm easter to end-Aug. Various trails of between 1.75 miles & 5.75 miles. Single track road (with passing places) continues past visitor centre along N side of Loch Trool to two other parking areas.
Contact: Forestry & Land Scotland, T: 0131 370 5900.
E: enquiries.south@forestryandland.gov.scot

9. KEN-DEE MARSHES

RSPB (South & West Scotland).
Habitats: Open water, marsh, grassland, woodland.
Birds: *All year:* Mallard, Grey Heron, Buzzard, Nuthatch, Willow Tit. *Spring/summer:* Lapwing & Oystercatcher nest in fields. Pied Flycatcher, Redstart, Tree Pipit, Sedge Warbler. *Winter:* Greenland White-fronted & Greylag Geese, raptors (Hen Harrier, Peregrine, Merlin, Red Kite).
Other: Red Squirrel, Roe Deer, Otter.
Directions: Sat nav: DG7 2LY. NX 699 684. Six miles NW of Castle Douglas. On minor road off A762 (N of Laurieston) or off B795 (at Glenlochar), parking at Mains of Duchrae.
Public transport: None.

Visiting: Open dawn/dusk. Car park at entrance to Mains of Duchrae farm. Two hides (one wheelchair-accessible, limited parking for elderly/disabled next to first hide), viewing platform, three miles of trails. Dogs under close control. Part of Galloway Kite Trail.
Contact: RSPB, T: 01988 402 130;
E: wood.cree@rspb.org.uk;

10. MERSEHEAD

RSPB (South & West Scotland).
Habitats: Wet grassland, arable farmland, saltmarsh, inter-tidal mudflats.
Birds: *Summer:* Breeding birds inc. Lapwing, Redshank, Skylark. *Winter:* Whooper Swan, 9,500 Barnacle Geese, 4,000 Teal, 2,000 Wigeon, 1,000 Pintail, waders (inc. Dunlin, Knot, Oystercatcher), Hen Harrier.
Other: Natterjack Toad, Otter.
Directions: Sat nav: DG2 8AH. NX 928 566. From Dumfries take A710 S for about 16 miles. Reserve is signposted from New Abbey & then on L just before Caulkerbush village. Single track road with passing places runs for one mile to car park, adjacent to visitor centre. From Castle Douglas, take A745, then A711 to Dalbeattie. Follow signs from Dalbeattie before joining A710.
Public transport: Bus - no.372 Dalbeattie to Dumfries. Bus stop at Caulkerbush (Southwick), ca one mile from visitor centre. Houstons Coaches (T: 01576 203 874).
Visiting: Dawn-dusk daily (not Dec 25). Car park (members free). Visitor centre open 10am-4pm, occassionally unmanned - viewing room, toilets, refreshments (when manned). Wheelchair-friendly hides/trails, open all times, Blue Badge parking spaces within 400 yards of hides & next to visitor centre.
Contact: RSPB, T: 01387 780 579;
E: mersehead@rspb.org.uk

11. MULL OF GALLOWAY

RSPB (Scotland).
Habitats: Sea cliffs, coastal heath.
Birds: *All year:* Peregrine. *Spring/summer:* Fulmar, Shag, Guillemot, Razorbill, Black Guillemot, Puffin, Kittiwake, Raven, Wheatear, Rock Pipit, Twite. Gannet (feeding offshore). *Early Autumn:* Departing Manx Shearwaters gathering offshore.
Other: Harbour Porpoise, dolphins, Grey Seal.
Directions: Sat nav: DG9 9HP. NX 156 305. Most southerly tip of Scotland - follow brown signs for five miles from village of Drummore, S of Stranraer.
Public transport: None.
Visiting: Open all times. Blue Badge parking by centre. Visitor centre open easter-Oct, toilets, nature trail, CCTV on cliffs. Small shop in Gallie Craig cafe (not RSPB). Steep stairway to foghorn viewing platform overlooking seabird colonies. Trail uneven.
Contact: RSPB, T: 01988 402 130 or 01776 840 539 easter to end-Oct); E: mullofgalloway@rspb.org.uk

12. WIGTOWN BAY LNR

Dumfries & Galloway Council.
Habitats: 2,845ha, largest LNR in Britain - estuary with extensive saltmarsh/merse, mudflats & a freshwater wetland at Wigtown Harbour.
Birds: *Summer:* Breeding Osprey, Peregrine, waders & duck. *Winter:* Internationally important for Pink-footed Goose, nationally important for Curlew, Whooper Swan & Pintail, with major gull roost & other migratory coastal birds. Small Twite flock.
Other: Fish inc. Smelt & Shad. Lax-flowered Sea-lavender, Sea Aster.
Directions: Sat nav: DG8 9ED. NX 438 548. Between Wigtown & Creetown, S of Newton Stewart. The A75 runs along E side, with A714 S to Wigtown & B7004 providing views of LNR.
Public transport: Bus - no.415 from Newton Stewart to Wigtown. Stagecoach West Scotland.
Visiting: Open all times. Main access points: roadside lay-bys on A75 near Creetown, parking at Martyr's Stake (on B7004 just out of Wigtown) & Wigtown Harbour - suitable for coaches. Visitor Centre - open Mon-Sat 10am-5pm (later some days), Sun 2pm-5pm - located in Wigtown County Building has coach parking plus full disabled access, inc. lift & toilets. CCTV of Ospreys breeding in Galloway during summer & wetland birds in winter. Hide at Wigtown Harbour overlooking River Bladnoch, saltmarsh & fresh water wetland has disabled access from harbour car park. Another hide at Martyr's Stake car park.
Contact: D&G Council, T: 0303 333 3000;
E: contact@dumgal.gov.uk

13. WOOD OF CREE

RSPB (Scotland).
Habitats: Deciduous oak woodland, riverside meadow, streams, moorland.
Birds: *All year:* Sparrowhawk, Buzzard, Woodcock, Barn & Tawny Owls, Great Spotted Woodpecker, Willow Tit. Black Grouse on moorland. *Summer:* Redstart, Tree Pipit, Pied Flycatcher, Wood & Grasshopper Warblers, Dipper, Grey Wagtail, Common Sandpiper. *Autumn/ winter:* Whooper Swan, Goldeneye.
Other: Otter, Roe Deer, Red Squirrel, eight spp. bats inc. Leisler's. Bluebells & woodland flowers in spring.
Directions: Sat nav: DG8 6SW. NX 381 708. Travel N along minor road from Newton Stewart through Old Minnigaff. Turn L past Monigaff church, continue three miles along minor road until reaching Wood of Cree car park (go past Barclye car park on way - at NX 386 694).
Public transport: None.
Visiting: Open all times. Main car park at Wood of Cree. Keep to trails - 1.25 waymarked woodland trail can be extended to 3.5 mile walk inc. scrubland trail - steep, rough & uneven in parts. Another car park at Barclye Wood - one mile before Wood of Cree. Dogs under control, esp. during breeding season.
Contact: RSPB - see site 9.

Central Scotland

Argyll

ISLANDS TAKE THE BIRDING honours for this area - Coll, Tiree, Islay & Mull all have excellent birding. Islay is renowned for its wintering wildfowl, which includes huge numbers of Barnacle & White-fronted Geese. Choughs, raptors & Corncrakes are other island specialities although the latter has a better chance of being seen at RSPB reserve on Coll. Mull is home to the highest breeding densities of Golden & White-tailed Eagles in Britain.

1. COLL RESERVE

RSPB (South & West Scotland).
Habitats: Sand dunes, beaches, machair grassland, moorland, farmland.
Birds: *Spring:* Great Northern Diver offshore. Corncrake arrive in late Apr. Displaying waders, inc. Redshank, Lapwing, Snipe. *Summer:* Auks offshore, plus Gannet, shearwaters & terns. *Autumn:* Barnacle & Greenland White-fronted Geese arrive, thrushes on passage. Waders inc. Purple Sandpiper. *Winter:* Long-tailed Duck, divers offshore. Hunting Hen Harrier & Merlin. Twite.
Other: Good for ceteceans & Basking Shark. Otter, 300+ spp. machair wildflowers inc. rare orchids, Great Yellow Bumblebee.
Directions: Sat nav: PA78 6TB, NM 167 563. By ferry from Oban to Coll. Take B8070 W from Arinagour for five miles. Turn R at Arileod. Continue for about one mile. Park at end of road. Reception point at Totronald.
Public transport: Ferry from Oban - Caledonian MacBrayne (T: 08705 650 000; W: www.calmac.co.uk)
Visiting: Open all year. Two car parks, info bothy at Totronald, guided walks in summer. Corncrake viewing bench. Natural site with unimproved paths not suitable for wheelchairs. Avoid walking through fields & crops.
Contact: RSPB, T: 01879 230 301.

2. LOCH GRUINART, ISLAY

RSPB (South & West Scotland).
Habitats: Lowland wet grassland, sea loch, farmland, moorland.
Birds: *All year:* Birds of prey, esp. Hen Harrier & Peregrine, Chough feed in nearby fields. *Spring/summer:* displaying Snipe, Lapwing, Curlew & Redshank. Corncrake. *Sep-Nov:* Passage migrants & arriving wildfowl. *Oct-Apr:* Large numbers of Barnacle & White-fronted Geese, other wildfowl & waders.
Other: Otter, Red & Roe Deer. Marsh Fritillary butterfly.
Directions: Sat nav: PA44 7PP. NR 275 672. On N coast of Islay, seven miles NW of Bridgend. Signposted from A847 Bridgend to Bruichladdich road, three miles from turn-off.
Public transport: Ferry from Kennacraig - Caledonian MacBrayne (T: 08705 650 000; W: www.calmac.co.uk)
Visiting: Open all times. Car parking at centre & start of trails, coaches at visitor centre only. Visitor centre open daily 10am-5pm (not xmas/new year), manned Apr-Oct. Toilets (inc. disabled), two hides, two trails, viewpoints. Weekly guided walks Apr-Oct, group bookings accepted. Disabled access to south hide, viewing area. No dogs in hides & under close control on trails.
Contact: RSPB, T: 01496 850 505:
E: loch.gruinart@rspb.org.uk

3. MACHRIHANISH SEABIRD/WILDLIFE OBSERVATORY

Eddie Maguire (sponsored by SNH).
Habitats: Marine, rocky shore, upland habitats.
Birds: *Summer:* Golden Eagle, Peregrine, Storm Petrel, Twite. *Autumn:* Passage seabirds & waders. On-shore gales/squalls often produce inshore movements of Leach's Petrel & other scarce seabirds, inc. Balearic Shearwater, Sabine's Gull, Grey Phalarope. *Winter:* Great Northern Diver, Purple Sandpiper, Turnstone, occasional Glaucous & Iceland Gulls.
Other: Grey & Common seals, Bottlenose Dolphin, Otter, Wild Goat.
Directions: Sat nav: PA28 6PZ. NR 608 209. SW Kintyre, Argyll. Six miles W of Campbeltown on A83, then B843 to Macrihanish. Signposted from village.
Public transport: Bus - from Campbeltown. West Coast Motors (T: 01586 552 319).
Visiting: Open daily Apr-Oct. Parking for three cars. Coach parking. Seawatching hide, toilets in nearby village. Wheelchair access. Dogs welcome.
Contact: Eddie Maguire, Warden, T: 07895 952 640; E: msbowarden@gmail.com;
W: www.machrihanishbirdobservatory.org.uk/

4. MULL (WHITE-TAILED) EAGLE WATCH

RSPB (South & West Scotland)/Forestry & Land Scotland/ SNH/MICT/Police Scotland/Craignure Golf Club.
Habitats: Large sea loch with tidal mudflats at its head (Loch Beg).
Birds: *All year:* Apart from White-tailed Eagles, other raptors in area inc. Golden Eagle, Hen Harrier & Buzzard. Waders on muddy areas. *Winter/early spring:* (on loch) three spp. diver, Slavonian Grebe, Eider, Red-breasted Merganser.
Other: Otter sightings are common here.
Directions: Sat nav: PA65 6BA. Tours are hosted from Craignure Golf Club on outskirts of Craignure (one mile from ferry terminal). Further details of when/ where to meet are given when booking made.
Public transport: Ferry from Oban - Caledonian MacBrayne (T: 08705 650 000; W: www.calmac.co.uk).
Visiting: Tours for observing nesting White-tailed Eagles - ranger led trips run daily (not Sat) 11am & 2pm (Apr-Sep) - booking required, charges apply.
Contact: Booking through Visit Scotland Information Centre at Craignure, T: 01680 812 556; W: www.mulleaglewatch.com

Ayrshire

THE BEST KNOWN site is the island of Ailsa Craig, which boasts a huge gannetry & plenty of other breeding seabirds. The shore at Barassie & Troon sees a large build-up of passage waders in spring & autumn & seawatching here in the autumn can be rewarding whilst white-winged gulls often turn up in winter. Martnaham Loch is good for wildfowl & a range of common species & Turnberry Point for seawatching, plus Twite. The river valleys and inland woodlands offer other good birding opportunities.

5. AILSA CRAIG

Private.
Habitats: Volcanic plug (350ft high) provides nest sites for seabirds.
Birds: *Summer:* Hosts third largest gannetry in UK (up to 36,000 pairs of Gannets). Other breeding seabirds inc. Guillemot, Razorbill, Puffin, Black Guillemot, Kittiwake. Twite.
Other: Slow Worm.
Directions: Sat nav: KA26 9AJ. NX 181 981 (Girvan Hbr). Island is nine miles offshore. Girvan, nearest town on mainland.
Public transport: None.
Visiting: No formal arrangements - accessible only by boat during summer:

Ailsa Craig Trips/MFV Glorious (T: 01465 713 219 or 07773 794 358; E: mccrindlem@aol.com)

JAG Charters Ltd (T: 01465 713 174; E: info@seafishingchartersscotland.com)

6. CULZEAN CASTLE COUNTRY PARK

National Trust for Scotland.
Habitats: 260ha estate - shoreline, parkland, woodland, gardens, streams, ponds.
Birds: *All year:* Good numbers of common woodland species inc. Jay, Great Spotted Woodpecker & thrushes. *Spring/summer:* Arriving migrants, esp. Blackcap, Chiffchaff & Willow Warbler. Nesting Raven & Gannet on cliffs, Gannet & terns offshore. *Autumn/ winter:* Wildfowl on pond inc. Little Grebe, Tufted Duck, Goldeneye. Crossbill, regular flocks of winter thrushes. Offshore divers & Eider.
Other: Roe Deer, Otter, Water Vole, several spp. of bat. Shoreline SSSI rich in rock pool life.
Directions: Sat nav: KA19 8LE. NS 234 103. 12 miles SW of Ayr off A719.
Public transport: Bus - no.60 (Ayr to Girvan) stops at site entrance. One mile walk downhill to castle. Stagecoach West Scotland.
Visiting: Open 9am-5pm. Entrance fee to country park (members free). Three car parks, cafe/ shops open daily (not Dec 25/26, Jan 1), children's playground, picnic areas, many footpaths & estate tracks, ranging from unsurfaced woodland paths to metalled roads. Access leaflet available.
Contact: NTS Culzean, T: 01655 884 455; E: culzean@nts.org.uk

Clyde

THE TWO RSPB RESERVES of Lochwinnoch & Baron's Haugh offer a good selection of commoner species throughout the year, with breeding Whinchat at the latter. The Scottish Wildlife Trust's Falls of Clyde reserve has a good selection of woodland birds, with Dippers & Kingfishers along the river. Cloch Point can be good for passing seabirds in late summer/early autumn.

7. BARON'S HAUGH

RSPB (South & West Scotland).
Habitats: Marshland, flooded areas, woodland, parkland, meadows, scrub, river.
Birds: *Summer:* Breeding Gadwall, Common Sandpiper, Kingfisher, Sand Martin, Whinchat, warblers (inc. Garden & Grasshopper). *Autumn:* Excellent for waders (22 spp.). *Winter:* Whooper Swan, Pochard, Wigeon, Sparrowhawk.
Directions: Sat nav: ML1 2PZ. NS 756 553. On SW edge of Motherwell. From M74/Junc 6 take road to Motherwell. Bear R at next traffic lights signposted to Wishaw. Turn R at third mini-roundabout & follow road to junction, turn L then immediately R to enter reserve.
Public transport: Buses - various from Motherwell stop in Airbles estate (0.5 mile from reserve). Train - Airbles ca.15 mins walk.
Visiting: Open all year. Car park, info boards, four hides (two with steps), four trails. Most paths are wide & surfaced, except longer circuit (steeper slopes, soft surfaces & gates).
Contact: RSPB, T: 0141 331 0993; E: baronshaugh@rspb.org.uk

8. FALLS OF CLYDE

Scottish Wildlife Trust.
Habitats: Reserve stretches along both sides of an ancient gorge, with waterfalls, meadow, wet woodland.
Birds: 100+ spp. *Summer:* Goosander, Kingfisher, Dipper, Jay, Spotted Flycatcher, Grey Wagtail
Other: Badger, Otter, bats & wildflowers.
Directions: Sat nav: ML11 9DB. NS 881 423 (visitor centre). Reserve covers both sides of Clyde Gorge from New Lanark to Bonnington Weir, approx one mile S of Lanark. From Glasgow travel S on M74 until Junc 7, then along A72, following signs for New Lanark.
Public transport: Bus - no.135 Lanark to New Lanark. Stuarts Coaches (T: 01555 773 533). Train - Lanark.
Visiting: Open daily. From New Lanark car park, walk into village, through iron gates & down steps to R of New Lanark Visitor Centre, follow road to Falls of Clyde Visitor Centre (open daily 10am-4pm, admission charge for non-SWT members, wheelchair friendly inc. toilet facilities). Woodland trails & range of guided walks (inc. self-guided) & badger watches. Reserve terrain unsuitable for wheelchairs.
Contact: Falls of Clyde Visitor Centre, T: 01555 665 262; E: fallsofclyde@scottishwildlifetrust.co.uk

9. LOCHWINNOCH

RSPB (Scotland).
Habitats: Shallow lochs, marsh, mixed woodland.
Birds: *Summer:* Breeding Great Crested Grebe, Water Rail, Sedge & Grasshopper Warblers, Reed Bunting. *Passage:* Occasional migrants inc. Whimbrel, Greenshank. *Winter:* Wildfowl (inc. Whooper Swan, Wigeon, Goosander, Goldeneye). Hen Harrier, Kingfisher.
Other: Roe Deer, small mammals, possible Otter, butterflies, moths & dragonflies.
Directions: Sat nav: PA12 4JF. NS 358 580. 18 miles SW of Glasgow, adjacent to A760 Largs Road, off A737 (Irvine Road). Leave M8 at Junc 28A.
Public transport: Bus - nos X34/X36 Glasgow to Irvine/Ardrossan, alight Roadhead roundabout, 0.5 mile from reserve. Stagecoach West Scotland. Bus - no.4 (not Sun) Johnstone to Lochwinnoch (Key Coaches T: 01505 358 589) & no.307 (Sun) McGills. Train - Lochwinnoch.
Visiting: Open all times (charge for non-RSPB members). Visitor centre open daily (not Dec 25/26, Jan 1/2) 9.30am-5pm, refreshments, shop, toilets. Three trails, two hides & toilets - all have disabled access.
Contact: RSPB, T: 01505 842 663; E: lochwinnoch@rspb.org.uk

Fife

THE COUNTY'S COASTLINE has a number of interesting sites: Fife Ness is good for seawatching & autumn migrants; the Eden Estuary holds good numbers of wildfowl & waders throughout the year but especially in winter, & wintering flocks of seaduck off Ruddons Point (Largo Bay) often hold a few Surf Scoters among the more numerous Common & Velvet Scoters. Tentsmuir offers an unusual mix of woodland (scarce in the county) & coastal habitats.

10. EDEN ESTUARY LNR

Fife Coast & Countryside Trust.
Habitats: 891ha, mainly intertidal mud & sandflats with saltmarsh, river, reed, sand dunes, wetland.
Birds: *Winter/passage:* Significant numbers of waders & wildfowl. Outer estuary - seaduck inc. scoters, Eider, Long-tailed Duck, Red-breasted Merganser & Gannet, terns, skuas. Mudflats - godwits, plovers, sandpipers, Redshank, Shelduck. River - Kingfisher, Common Sandpiper, Goosander. Surrounding area attracts Short & Long-eared Owls, Peregrine, Merlin, Marsh Harrier & White-tailed Eagle. Osprey regular visitor.
Other: Northern Marsh Orchid, dune grasses & herbs. Common & Grey Seals, Bottlenose Dolphin, Harbour Porpoise, Brown Hare, Stoat & Ootter. Butterflies inc. Grayling, Small pearl-bordered & Dark Green Fritillaries.
Directions: Sat nav: KY16 0UG. NO 450 192 (Eden Estuary Centre). Centre is off main street in Guardbridge, two miles from St Andrews on A91, & from Leuchars via Tentsmuir Forest off A919 (four miles). Use Outhead at St Andrews, off West Sands beach, to access Balgove Bay.
Public transport: Bus - regular services from Cupar, Dundee & St Andrews. Train - Leuchars (1.5 miles).
Visiting: Eden Estuary Centre, Guardbridge open daily, not Dec 25/26/31, Jan 1) 9am-5pm (4pm Nov-Mar) - (access code for centre from local ranger). Evans Hide at Balgove Bay: NO 482 181, parking at Pilmuir Links golf course car park. Viewing platform & picnic area at Outhead.
Contact: Ranald Strachan, Ranger, T: 07985 707 593; E: Ranald.Strachan@fifecountryside.co.uk

11. ISLE OF MAY NNR

Scottish Natural Heritage.
Habitats: Island, sea cliffs, rocky shoreline.
Birds: *Spring/autumn:* Weather-related migrations inc. rarities each year. *Summer:* Breeding Shag, Eider, Fulmar, Kittiwake, other gulls, terns, auks (inc. 45,000+ pairs of Puffin),
Directions: KY10 3RR. NT 655 995 (island). Small island lying five miles E of Anstruther in Firth of Forth.
Public transport: Bus - regular services to Anstruther & North Berwick harbours.
Visiting: Ferries (Apr-Sep). Trips take 4-5 hours, inc. time to explore island. From Anstruther (5 miles): Anstruther Pleasure Cruises (T: 07957 585200, E: info@isleofmayferry.com) & Osprey of Anstruther (T: 07473 631 671, E info@isleofmayboattrips.co.uk). From North Berwick (13 miles) - check with Scottish Seabird Centre (T: 01620 890 202).
If staying at Observatory delays getting on/off island are possible due to weather. Keep to paths, no dogs, no camping/fires. Permission required to carry out scientific work or filming.
Contact: Obs accomodation Bookings Sec: Mark Newell. T: 07909 707 971; E: bookings@isleofmaybirdobs.org; W: www.isleofmaybirdobs.org
Other enquiries: Reserve Manager, T: 01738 458 800; E: nnr@nature.scot;
W: www.nature.scot/enjoying-outdoors/scotlands-national-nature-reserves/isle-may-national-nature-reserve

Forth

THE RSPB RESERVE at Inversnaid is good for Black Grouse, Twite, Redstart, Wood Warbler & Pied Flycatcher. A Red Kite feeding station at Argaty provides visitors with close-up views. Cambus Pools attract passage waders & winter wildfowl, while high tide at Kinneil produces good numbers of waders in spring & autumn.

12. CAMBUS POOLS

Scottish Wildlife Trust.
Habitats: Wet grassland, reedbeds & two salty pools.
Birds: *Spring/autumn:* Used extensively by migrants. Wildfowl inc. Mute & Whooper Swans, Goldeneye, Teal, Shelduck, waders inc. Black-tailed Godwit, Oystercatcher, Greenshank. Kingfisher regularly seen. Gadwall have bred, Small birds inc. Yellowhammer & Reed Bunting.
Other: Brown Hare, Stoat, Short-tailed vole, 115 spp. of vascular plants. Harbour Porpoise seen in Forth.
Directions: Sat nav: FK10 2PG. NS 846 937. From Stirling, take A907 east towards Alloa. From roundabout drive 0.6 mile to where B9096 leads off to Tullibody. Take minor road (Station Road) R to small village of Cambus.
Public transport: None.
Visiting: Open all year. Cross River Devon by bridge at NS 853 940 & walk down stream on R bank past bonded warehouses. Best viewing around high tide. Bench on S side of western pool. Dogs under control.
Contact: Scottish WT, T: 0131 312 7765;
E: enquiries@scottishwildlifetrust.org.uk

Lothian

MORE THAN 250 SPECIES have been recorded at Aberlady Bay, where thousands of geese gather in winter. The Seabird Centre at North Berwick is worth a visit & a boat can be taken out from here to the gannetry at Bass Rock. The Lammermuir Hills hold a range of upland species including Red Grouse, Whinchat & Ring Ouzel.

13. ABERLADY BAY LNR

East Lothian Council.
Habitats: Tidal mudflats, saltmarsh, freshwater marsh, dune grassland, scrub, open sea.
Birds: *Summer:* Breeding spp. inc. Shelduck, Eider, Reed Bunting & up to eight spp. of warbler. *Passage:* waders inc. Green, Wood & Curlew Sandpipers, Little Stint, Greenshank, Whimbrel, Black-tailed Godwit. *Winter:* Divers (esp. Red-throated), Red-necked & Slavonian Grebes & geese (in autumn 30,000+ Pinkfeet roost & feed before moving on), sea-duck, waders.
Directions: Sat nav: EH32 0QB. NT 471 804. From Edinburgh take A198 E to Aberlady. Reserve car park is on A198 just to E of Aberlady village.

Public transport: Bus - nos.124/X24 Edinburgh to N Berwick pass reserve (ask to be dropped nearby). East Coast Buses.
Visiting: Open all times. Small (free) car park & toilets. Notice board with recent sightings at end of footbridge. Stay on footpaths to avoid disturbance. Disabled access from reserve car park. No dogs. The Scottish Ornithologists' Club (SOC) HQ, Waterston House, is located W of Aberlady village, open daily (not Dec 25/26, Jan 1) 10am-4pm inc. shop, library, gallery, hot/cold drinks. T: 01875 871 330.
Contact: Countryside Rangers, T: 01620 827 279;
E: ranger@eastlothian.gov.uk

14. BASS ROCK/SCOTTISH SEABIRD CENTRE

Private.
Habitats: Sea cliffs.
Birds: The spectacular cliffs hold a massive Gannet colony (up to 150,000 birds, largest in world). Puffin, Guillemot, Razorbill, Kittiwake, Shag, Common Tern, Fulmar.
Directions: NT 602 873. Island NE of North Berwick. Scottish Seabird Centre is located in North Berwick Harbour (Sat nav: EH39 4SS. NT554 856).
Public transport: None.
Visiting: Bass Rock is private - contact Seabird Centre/check website for details of exclusive Bass Rock landing trips (inc. three hours on island). Terms & conditions apply to bookings. Sailings/landings are subject to weather conditions. No facilities on island. Seabird Centre - entrance fee: open Jan 11am-4pm; Feb/Mar & Sep/Oct 10am-5pm; Apr-Aug 10am-6pm; Nov-Dec (not Dec 25) 10am-4pm. Aquaria, telescope deck & toilets. Free to visit cafe & shop.
Contact: The Scottish Seabird Centre,
T: 01620 890 202; E: info@seabird.org;
boat trips: E: boats@sebird.org; W: www.seabird.org

15. BAWSINCH RESERVE & DUDDINGSTON LOCH

Scottish Wildlife Trust.
Habitats: Edinburgh's only natural freshwater loch. Reedbed, marsh, ponds, mixed woodland, flower meadow & scrub. Bawsinch reserve developed from former industrial wasteland.
Birds: *Summer:* Heronry, breeding swans, geese, ducks, grebes & Water Rail. Kingfisher. Migrants inc. Spotted Flycatcher, hirundines, warblers, inc. occasional Grasshopper Warbler. *Winter:* Bittern, wildfowl, gulls.
Other: Fox, Water Vole & Otter. Dragonflies, four spp. of amphibian.
Directions: Sat nav: EH15 3PY. NT 282 726. Two miles from centre of Edinburgh, below Arthur's Seat. Use car park just W of Duddingston Village on Duddingston Low Road.
Public transport: Bus - no.42 Edinburgh to Portabello, alight Duddingston Village (by Holyrood School). Lothian Buses (T: 0131 555 6363).
Visiting: Open access to north shore of loch. Southern shore (& hide) by prior arrangement with SWT.
Contact: Scottish WT - see site 12.

Eastern Scotland

Angus & Dundee

THE ANGUS GLENS hold a typical range of upland species, including Ring Ouzel, grouse, chats & Golden Eagle. Black-necked Grebe breeds at RSPB Loch of Kinnordy & Ospreys regularly fish here. Montrose Basin is a flagship Scottish Wildlife Trust reserve, with a good selection of wildfowl ever present & waders on passage.

1. LOCH OF LINTRATHEN

Scottish Water/Scottish Wildlife Trust.
Habitats: Oligotrophic-mesotrophic loch. Surrounded by mainly coniferous woodland in foothills of Braes of Angus.
Birds: *Summer:* Grey Heron, Great Crested Grebe & other water birds. Osprey occasionally. *Winter:* Internationally-important numbers of Icelandic Greylag Geese (up to 3,000), Pink-footed Goose, Goosander, Whooper Swan, Wigeon, Teal, other wildfowl. Birds feed on surrounding farmland during day.
Other: Red Squirrel, Otter, Pipistrelle Bat.
Directions: Sat nav: DD8 5JH. NO 278 550. Located next to Bridgend of Lintrathen, seven miles W of Kirriemuir. Take B951 & choose circular route on unclassified roads round loch.
Public transport: None.
Visiting: Roadside parking at NO 276 557 off a minor road W of loch, forest track leads to hide. Second hide (wheelchair accessible) on E side of loch. Hides open all times. Rest of reserve is private, but good views possible from unclassified roads. Viewpoint can accommodate five cars.
Contact: Scottish WT, T: 0131 312 7765;
E: enquiries@scottishwildlifetrust.org.uk

2. MONTROSE BASIN LNR

Scottish Wildlife Trust/Angus Council.
Habitats: Estuary, saltmarsh, reedbeds, farmland.
Birds: *Summer:* Breeding Common & Arctic terns, gulls, Shelduck, Goldeneye, Eider (up to 2,000), Grey Partridge in surrounding fields. Nationally important moulting site for Mute Swan (approx 300 birds). *Winter:* Wildfowl & waders (Curlew peak numbers in Aug, Dunlin in Feb). Internationally important for Pink-footed Goose, Knot & Redshank.
Directions: Sat nav: DD10 9TA. NO 700 564. SWT Wildlife Centre on A92, one mile S of Montrose. Main car park for western end at Old Mill, Mains of Dun (DD10 9LQ. NO 668 591).
Public transport: Bus - no.30 Arbroath to Montrose, request stop outside Visitor Centre. Stagecoach East Scotland. Train - Montrose (1.5 miles).
Visiting: Admission fee (non-members) to visitor centre open, daily 10.30am-5pm mid-Feb to Oct & 10.30am-4pm, Fri-Mon, Nov to mid-Feb (not Dec 25/26 & Jan 1/2). Shop, fair-trade drinks/snacks, toilets, disabled access to centre. Rest so reserve open at all time inc. two hides on western half of reserve.
Contact: Montrose Basin Wildlife Centre,
T: 01674 676 336;
E: montrosebasin@scottishwildlifetrust.org.uk

Moray & Nairn

TWO RIVERS, THE SPEY & the Findhorn, flow into the Moray Firth - the bays they flow into attract passage waders, terns, Ospreys, seabirds & wildfowl. More than half of the area is over 250m. Lochindorb is the best area of moorland to explore, with breeding grouse, raptors, divers & waders. Extensive woodlands hold Crested Tit (conifer) & Tree Pipit & Redstart (birch).

3. CULBIN SANDS

RSPB (East Scotland).
Habitats: Saltmarsh, sandflats, dunes.
Birds: *Spring:* Terns, esp. Sandwich, passage waders. *Summer:* Breeding Eider, Ringed Plover, Oystercatcher. Osprey on passage. *Winter:* Common Scoter, Long-tailed Duck, Red-breasted Merganser, Knot, Bar-tailed Godwit. Raptors inc. Peregrine, Merlin & Hen Harrier attracted by wader flocks. Roosting geese, Snow Bunting.
Other: Dolphins, Grey & Common Seals in Firth. Otters sometimes seen.
Directions: Sat nav: IV12 5BX. NH 900 576. Approx 1.5 miles NE of Nairn, overlooking Moray Firth. Use East Beach car park, signed off A96. Follow road through Maggot Road caravan park (car park at end of road).Track along dunes & saltmarsh - from far end of car park take 0.5 mile 'all abilities footpath' to reach reserve.

185

Public transport: Bus - from Inverness to Nairn - stops in Nairn, one mile W of site. No.10. Stagecoach North Scotland. No.11. Stagecoach Highlands. Train - Nairn, 1.5 miles W of reserve.

Visiting: Open all times. Car park with bike racks, seasonal toilets (inc. disabled, RADAR key).

Contact: RSPB, T: 01463 715 000; E: nsro@rspb.org.uk

4. SPEY BAY

Scottish Wildlife Trust.

Habitats: Shingle, rivermouth, coastal habitats.

Birds: *Summer:* Osprey, waders, wildfowl, terns. *Winter:* Seaduck & divers offshore, esp. Long-tailed Duck, Common & Velvet Scoters, Red-throated Diver.

Other: Dolphins offshore. Otter, dragonflies.

Directions: Eight miles NE of Elgin. Sat nav: IV32 7NW. NJ 334 656 (Kingston - west side) - from Elgin take A96 & B9015 to Kingston. Sat nav: IV32 7PJ. NJ 347 654 (Tugnet - east side) - from Elgin take A96 & B9014 to Spey Bay, Scottish Dolphin Centre located here by car park, T: 01343 820 339; W: https://dolphincentre.whales.org/

Public transport: Bus - no.224 Elgin to Garmouth/Kingston (west side). Moray Council (T: 01343 562 534).

Visiting: Reserve open at all times.

Contact: Scottish WT - see site 1.

NE Scotland

TROUP HEAD HOLDS Scotland's only mainland gannetry &, together with Fowlsheugh, has a good variety of other seabirds. The RSPB's Loch of Strathbeg sees the arrival in autumn of huge numbers of Pink-footed Geese. The Ythan Estuary is good for breeding terns, Eider, & passage & wintering waders. Inland, Deeside holds most of the typical highland species.

5. FORVIE NNR

Scottish Natural Heritage.

Habitats: 1,000ha, estuary, dunes, coastal heath.

Birds: *Spring/summer:* Breeding Eider & terns, migrant waders & seabirds offshore. *Autumn:* Pink-footed Goose, migrant seabirds, waders & passerines inc. occasional scarce/rare spp. *Winter:* Waders & wildfowl, inc. Whooper Swan, Long-tailed Duck, Golden Plover.

Other: Occasional ceteceans offshore, esp. summer.

Directions: 12 miles N of Aberdeen, inc. Ythan Estuary. Access inc. Sat nav: AB41 8RU. NK 034 289 (Forvie Visitor Centre) - three miles NE of Newburgh at Collieston. Waterside car park (AB41 6AB, NK 003 270) one mile N of Newburgh. Waulkmill hide (AB41 8RL. NK 004 287) - turn L off A975 opp. Collieston junction.

Public transport: Bus - no.63 Aberdeen to Peterhead (via Cruden Bay) stops in Newburgh & at Collieston crossroads. Stagecoach North Scotland.

Visiting: Open all times, ternery closed Apr to end-Aug. Coach parking at Forvie Visitor Centre: open daily Apr-Oct, toilets, interpretive display. Hide, waymarked trails - short trail & hide wheelchair-accessible.

Contact: SNH Reserve Manager, T: 01358 751 330; E: nnr@nature.scot; W: www.nature.scot/

6. FOWLSHEUGH

RSPB (East Scotland).

Habitats: Sea cliffs.

Birds: Peregrine regular throughout year. *Summer:* Spectacular 130,000 strong seabird colony, mainly Kittiwake & Guillemot with Razorbill, Fulmar, Puffin. Gannet, Eider & skuas offshore, *Autumn:* Red-throated Diver on sea, terns on passage.

Other: Grey & Common Seals, Bottlenose Dolphin. White-beaked Dolphin & Minke Whale occasional (summer).

Directions: Sat nav: AB39 2TP. NO 879 808. Reserve is three miles S of Stonehaven. From A92 take minor road signposted Crawton. Car park just before end of road.

Public transport: Bus - no. 747 request stop on A92 Crawton turn-off (Stonehaven to Johnshaven). Stagecoach North East. One mile to reserve entrance.

Visiting: Open at all times, not suitable for wheelchairs. Car park 200 yards from reserve. Viewing shelter at end of footpath (one mile). Toilets in Stonehaven. Dogs under close control.

Contact: RSPB, T: 01346 532 017; E: strathbeg@rspb.org.uk

7. HADDO COUNTRY PARK

Aberdeenshire Council.

Habitats: Parkland, woodland, wetland, loch, ponds.

Birds: *All year:* Goosander, Grey Heron, Cormorant, Buzzard, Sparrowhawk, Grey Partridge, Great Spotted Woodpecker, Tawny Owl, Grey Wagtail. *Spring/summer:* Osprey, Lapwing, Sedge Warbler, Blackcap, Chiffchaff. *Winter:* Canada & Greylag Geese, Teal, Wigeon, Goldeneye, Brambling.

Other: Red Squirrel, Otter, Pipistrelle & Daubenton's Bats. Meadow Brown, Ringlet & Common Blue butterflies.

Directions: Sat nav: AB41 7EQ. NJ 875 345. From Ellon (off A90) follow signs for Metlick & B9005. Once out of Ellon, cross Ythan bridge & contine straight on (signposted Haddo House).

Public transport: None.

Visiting: Grounds open daily dawn-dusk. Car park (free/donation welcomed) - if busy, do not park on road verges, coach parking, display boards, over 3.2 miles of surfaced paths, toilets (inc. disabled), hides with wheelchair access. Visitor centre (10am-4pm), tearoom (10am-4.30pm) & shop connected to Haddo House.

Contact: Haddo House & Country Park, T: 01651 851 041; E: haddo@visithaddo.com; www.visithaddo.com

8. LOCH OF STRATHBEG

RSPB (East Scotland).

Habitats: 894ha, inc. Britain's largest dune loch, with surrounding marshes, reedbeds, grasslands.

Birds: *All year:* Tree Sparrow. *Spring/autumn:* Spoonbill, Avocet, Marsh Harrier, Garganey, Little Gull, regular Pectoral Sandpiper. Osprey (almost daily), Common Crane (annual). *Summer:* Common Tern, Water Rail, Corn Bunting. *Winter:* Pink-footed (up to 20% of world population) & Barnacle Geese, Whooper Swan, large numbers of duck. Snow Goose & Smew annual. Raptors inc. Hen & Marsh Harriers. Great Northern Diver offshore.

Other: Otter, Badger, Stoat, Roe Deer. Early Purple, Butterfly & Northern Marsh Orchids, Dark Green Fritillary butterfly.
Directions: Sat nav: AB43 8QN. NK 055 577. Near Crimond on A90, nine miles S of Fraserburgh. Reserve signposted from village - at T-junction at end of road turn L, after ca.0.3 mile turn R at reserve entrance.
Public transport: Bus - no.69 Fraserburgh to Peterhead stops in Crimond, one mile from centre. Stagecoach North Scotland.
Visiting: Open all times (not Dec 25/26). Visitor Centre open daily (not Dec 25/26) 9am-5pm. observation room, toilets, coffee machine. Wildlife garden, indoor children's area. Tower Pool hide offers panoramic views, open dawn-dusk (0.5 mile from centre). Willow hide (200 yards from centre), Fen & Bay hides (500 yards from airfield car park - footpath from centre to airfield hides open easter-end Jul). Beach & dune walks accissible from Rattray or St Combs.
Contact: RSPB - see site 6.

9. TROUP HEAD

RSPB (East Scotland).
Habitats: Sea cliffs, farmland.
Birds: Spectacular seabird colony, inc. Scotland's largest mainland Gannet colony (2000+ pairs). Fulmar, Kittiwake, Guillemot, Razorbill, Puffin. Bonxies may linger in summer. Migrants occur during spring/autumn.
Other: Impressive common flower assemblage in spring. Ceteceans possible offshore in summer inc. Minke Whale. Brown Hare.
Directions: Sat nav: AB45 3JJ. NJ 822 665. Troup Head is between Pennan & Gardenstown on B9031, E along coast from Macduff. It is signposted off B9031 - look for small RSPB signs (& sign for Northfield Farm). At farm go through farmyard & onto a rough track to car park.
Public transport: None.
Visiting: Open at all times, not suitable for wheelchairs. Parking for small number of cars, but not coaches.
Contact: RSPB - see site 6.

Perth & Kinross

LOCH LEVEN NNR (including the RSPB's Vane Farm) is the region's best known reserve & holds 1000+ breeding duck & large numbers of wintering geese, ducks & swans. Ospreys fish there too but the well-known watchpoint of Loch of the Lowes offers views of birds on the nest. Woodland species & moorland species are well represented including Woodcock, Redstart, Wood Warbler, Red & Black Grouse (the latter can be elusive).

10. LOCH LEVEN (VANE FARM)

RSPB (East Scotland).
Habitats: Wet grassland & flooded areas by Loch Leven. Arable farmland, native woodland, moorland. Part of Loch Leven NNR.
Birds: *Spring/summer:* Breeding & passage waders (inc. Lapwing, Redshank, Snipe, Curlew), hirundines, Great Crested Grebe, Osprey. Farmland birds (inc. Skylark & Yellowhammer), Tree Pipit. *Autumn:* Migrating waders on exposed mud. *Winter:* Major fuelling stop for Pink-footed Geese (around 20,000 in late autmn). Whooper Swan (6% of Scotland's wintering population), Bewick's Swan, White-tailed Eagle, finch & tit flocks.
Other: 237 spp. butterflies & moths, 25 spp. mammal inc. Pipstrelle Bat & Roe Deer.
Directions: Sat nav: KY13 9LX. NT 160 990. Halfway between Perth & Edinburgh, seven miles from Cowdenbeath, signposted two miles E Junc 5 of M90 follow signs for B9097 towards Glenrothes. Drive for approx two miles, car park on R (signposted).
Public transport: Bus - from Edinburgh, Perth & nearby towns to Kinross. Can walk Loch Leven Heritage Trail from here to reserve (ca. four miles).
Visiting: Trails & hides open all times. Free car parking, coach parking available. Visitor centre open daily (not Dec 25/26, Jan 1/2) 10am-5pm. Entry fee to reserve, RSPB members free. Disabled access to shop, toilets, cafe (open 10am-4pm) & observation room with telescopes overlooking Loch Leven & reserve. Binocular hire. 1.25 mile Hill Trail through woodland/moorland. Wetland Trail has three hides. Eight-mile cycle path around loch. Other than assistance dogs, dogs not permitted in visitor centre (but can use courtyard) or on Wetland Trail. Permitted on Loch Leven Heritage Trail & Sleeping Giant Path (both accessed from centre).
Contact: RSPB, T: 01577 862 355;
E: lochleven@rspb.org.uk

11. LOCH OF THE LOWES

Scottish Wildlife Trust.
Habitats: Freshwater loch fringed by areas of fen, reedbeds, semi-natural woodland.
Birds: Breeding Ospreys (Apr-end Aug) nest 200 yards from hide. Wildfowl & woodland birds.
Other: Red Squirrel, Beaver.
Directions: Sat nav: PH8 0HH. NO 041 435. Sixteen miles N of Perth, two miles NE of Dunkeld, just off A923 Dunkeld to Blairgowrie road (signposted from A9).
Public transport: Bus - no.23 Perth to Dunkeld, two miles via Fungarth Path. Stagecoach. Train - Dunkeld, three miles via Fungarth Path.
Visiting: Entrance fee for non-members. Visitor Centre open daily (not Dec 25/26, Jan 1/2) 10.30am-5pm Mar-Oct & Fri to Sun 10.30am-4pm Nov-Feb. Light refreshments, exhibition, shop & toilets. Observation hide open daily during daylight hours, Crannog hide accessible during visitor centre opening hours. Full access for wheelchairs. No dogs in centre/hides, keep under control on reserve.
Contact: Loch of the Lowes Visitor Centre, T: 01350 727 337; E: lochofthelowes@scottishwildlifetrust.org.uk

Highlands & Islands

Highlands

HABITATS, UNIQUE IN BRITAIN, hold a range of scarce species: Dotterel, Ptarmigan & Snow Buntings on the high tops, Crested Tit, the endemic Scottish Crossbill & Capercaillie in the Caledonian pine forests. The boggy Flow Country of Caithness & Sutherland attracts breeding Red & Black-throated Divers, Common Scoter, Greenshank. Handa Island holds important numbers of seabirds.

1. BEINN EIGHE & LOCH MAREE ISLANDS NNR

Scottish Natural Heritage.
Habitats: Caledonian forest, moorland, mountain tops, freshwater loch shore.
Birds: *All year:* Golden & White-tailed Eagles, Scottish Crossbill, Ptarmigan, Red Grouse, Siskin. *Summer:* Black-throated Diver, Redwing, Snow Bunting. Golden Plover.
Other: Wide range of dragonflies inc. Northern Emerald, Golden-ringed & Common Hawker. Red Deer, Pine Marten, Mountain Hare.
Directions: Sat nav: NH 019 630. IV22 2PD. Complex mountain massif. Visitor centre two miles NW of village of Kinlochewe, Wester Ross, 50 miles from Inverness & 20 miles from Gairloch on A832.
Public transport: Bus - very limited, Inverness to Kinlochewe.
Visiting: Open all times. Visitor centre open 10am-5pm Mar-Oct (T: 01445 760 258). Toilets. Two woodland trails from visitor centre. From shore of Loch Maree (continue N on A832 to Coille na Glas-Leitir) - self-guides woodland walk & mountain trail - leaflets from visitor centre.
Contact: SNH, T: 01463 701 660;
E: nnr@nature.scot; W: www.nature.scot/

2. CORRIMONY

RSPB (North Scotland).
Habitats: 1,531ha, Caledonian forest, moorland, blanket bog.
Birds: *Spring/summer:* Red-throated Diver, Goosander. Greenshank, Black (30+ displaying males) & Red Grouse, Tree Pipit, Whinchat, Crested Tit, Scottish Crossbill, occasional Golden Eagle & Osprey. *Autumn/Winter:* Whooper Swan, Pink-footed Goose, Woodcock.
Other: Red Deer, Pine Marten, many orchids in Jul.
Directions: Sat nav: IV63 6TW (Corrimony village). NH 384 303 (car park). Lies 22 miles SW of Inverness between Cannich & Glen Urquhart, off A 831. Park in Corrimony Cairns car park.
Public transport: Bus - no.17 (not Sun) from Inverness to Cannich stops 1.5 miles from reserve (request stop). Stagecoach Highlands.
Visiting: Open all times. Waymarked trail (8.5 miles) passes through farm, suitable for wheelchairs but unimproved paths may not be suitable. Leave gates as you find them.
Contact: RSPB, T: 01463 715 000;
E: nsro@rspb.org.uk

NATURE RESERVES - HIGHLANDS & ISLANDS

3. FORSINARD FLOWS

RSPB (North Scotland).
Habitats: Blanket bog, upland hill farm.
Birds: *All year:* Red Grouse, Golden Eagle, Raven & Buzzard. *May-Jul:* Join a guided walk for best chance of Red-throated Diver, Golden Plover, Greenshank, Dunlin, Hen Harrier, Merlin, Short-eared Owl, Dipper.
Other: Red Deer, Otter, Water Vole, Azure Hawker dragonfly, Emperor Moth, bog plants inc. sundews.
Directions: Sat nav: KW11 6UE. NC 891 425.
30 miles SW of Thurso on A897. From S turn off A9 at Helmsdale (24 miles) or from N coast road turn off A836, two miles E of Melvich (14 miles).
Public transport: Train - between Inverness & Thurso stop at Forsinard.
Visiting: Open all times. Contact reserve office during breeding season (mid-Apr/end-Jul) & during deerstalking season (Jul-Feb 15) for advice. Visitor centre situated in Forsinard station open daily 9am-5pm, Apr-Oct. Wheelchair access to centre & toilet. Two self-guided trails open all year. Boardwalk access to viewpoint on Dubh Lochan Trail (one mile walk). Forsinain Trail starts at roadside car park four mile N of Forsinard (four mile walk). Stay on trails. Guided walks. Dogs under control at all times.
Contact: RSPB, T: 01641 571 225;
E: forsinard@rspb.org.uk

4. HANDA

Scourie Estate/Scottish Wildlife Trust.
Habitats: Island - sea cliffs, blanket bog & heath, small sandy beaches, coastal grassland.
Birds: *Spring/summer:* 100,000 seabirds: largest Guillemot & Razorbill colony in Britain. Nationally important for Kittiwake, Arctic & Great Skuas. Puffin, Shag, Fulmar, Common & Arctic Terns.
Directions: Sat nav: IV27 4SS. NC 164 488 (Tarbet). Island accessible by boat from Tarbet, near Scourie - follow A835/A894 N from Ullapool for 40 miles. Turn L down single track road, continue another three miles to Tarbet.
Public transport: Post bus (hail & ride) - no.806 (Mon-Fri) Lairg to Durness via Scourie. No transport between Scourie & Tarbet (three miles). The Far North Bus (T: 07782 110 007). Train - Inverness to Lairg connects with service.
Visiting: Open Apr-Aug, no Sun sailings (& subject to weather). Ferry runs 9.30am-16.45pm (last boat to island at 2pm) - part of ferry ticket price goes to SWT. Visitors given introductory talk & leaflet with map on arrival. Three mile circular path, visitor shelter, compost toilet. Not suitable for disabled due to uneven terrain. No dogs.
Contact: Handa Ranger (Apr-Aug), T: 07920 468 572;
E: handaranger@scottishwildlifetrust.org.uk;
Ferry operator: Roger Tebay, T: 07780 967 800;
E: info@handa-ferry.com

5. INSH MARSHES

RSPB (North Scotland).
Habitats: 1,000+ha, marsh, woodland, river, open water.
Birds: *Spring/summer:* Waders (Lapwing, Curlew, Redshank, Snipe), wildfowl (inc. Goldeneye & Wigeon), Osprey, Wood Warbler, Redstart, Tree Pipit. *Winter:* Hen Harrier, Whooper Swan, Greylag Goose, Teal, Wigeon, other wildfowl.
Other: Roe Deer. Black Darter dragonfly & Northern Brown Argus butterfly along Invertromie trail. Five spp. orchid in Tromie Meadow.
Directions: Sat nav: PH21 1NTS. NN 775 998. In Spey Valley. From A9 take exit to Kingussie. Follow B970 S from village & then beyond Ruthven Barracks. Entrance to reserve is 0.6 mile further on.
Public transport: Bus - no.32 Newtownmore to Carrbridge stops at Kingussie. Stagecoach Highlands. Train - Kingussie. Both one mile.
Visiting: Open all times. Car park, coach parking. Disabled access to unmanned information viewpoint. Two hides, three trails.
Contact: RSPB, T: 01540 661 518; E: insh@rspb.org.uk

6. ISLE OF RUM NNR

Scottish Natural Heritage.
Habitats: Island - wild & rugged dominated by mountains. Blanket bog, grassland, woodland, wet & dry heath, scree & rocky slopes.
Birds: *Breeding:* Golden & White-tailed Eagles, Merlin, Hen Harrier, Peregrine, Golden Plover, Twite. Red-throated Diver, 70,000 pairs Manx Shearwater. & small number of other seabirds inc. Guillemot, Razorbill, Fulmar, Kittiwake.
Other: Red Deer, Wild Goat. 2,000+ spp invertebrates inc. 11spp. dragonfly, 19 spp. butterfly.
Directions: Sat nav: PH41 4RA. NM674 969 (Mallaig).
Public transport: Ferry from Mallaig to Rum - Caledonian MacBrayne, T: 08705 650 000;
W: www.calmac.co.uk). No cars permitted on island - parking for ferry passangers in Mallaig.
Visiting: SNH owns & manages most of island. Isle of Rum Community Trust owns some property & land in & around village at Kinloch. Access all times. Visitor centre on lower shore road near old pier, open daily in summer. Toilets at village campsite (10 mins from ferry terminal). Otter hide one mile through woods to S of main pier.
Contact: SNH, T: 0131 314 4181; E: nnr@nature.scot;
W: www.nature.scot/

7. LOCH GARTEN & ABERNETHY FOREST

RSPB (North Scotland).
Habitats: Caledonian pine forest.
Birds: *Spring/summer:* Ospreys nesting from Apr-Aug, Crested Tit, Redstart, Spotted Flycatcher, Tree Pipit, Scottish Crossbill. Possible views of lekking Capercaillie from Osprey Centre (Apr/mid-May). On loch - Wigeon, Goldeneye & Common Sandpiper. *Autumn/winter:* Greylag & Pink-footed Geese roost on loch, Whooper Swan, various duck spp.Wider Cairngorm area: Golden Eagle, Black & Red Grouse, Ptarmigan, Dotterel.

Other: Red Squirrel, Roe Deer, Otter. Fungi.
Directions: Sat nav: PH25 3HA. NH 978 183. 2.5 miles from Boat of Garten, eight miles from Aviemore. Off B970, follow 'RSPB Ospreys' road signs (Apr-Aug only).
Public transport: Bus - nearest stop is on B970, no.34 Aviemore to Grantown on Spey (ask for Raebreck junction) - from here dedicated footpath leads to Osprey Centre (1.6 miles). Stagecoach Highland.
Visiting: Osprey Centre (overlooking Osprey nest) open daily 10am-6pm (Apr to first sunday Sep). Entrance fee, RSPB members free. Optics & CCTV live pictures, shop & light refreshments (closes 5pm), toilets. Disabled access. Guide dogs only. On reserve: three way-marked trails open all year. Dogs on leads.
Contact: RSPB, T: 01479 821 409 (Reserve)
T: 01479 831 476 (Osprey Centre);
E: abernethy@rspb.co.uk

8. UDALE BAY

RSPB (Scotland).
Habitats: Mudflat, saltmarsh, wet grassland.
Birds: *Spring/summer:* 10,000 Pink-footed Goose on passage, other wildfowl, Oystercatcher, Redshank, waders. Possible Osprey. *Autumn/winter:* Large flocks of wildfowl (inc. 10,000 Wigeon & Scaup), geese, waders inc. Oystercatcher, Knot, Bar-tailed Godwit & Dunlin. Peregrine.
Directions: Sat nav: IV7 8LU. NH 712 651. On Black Isle, one mile W of Jemimaville on the B9163.
Public transport: None.
Visiting: Open all year. Limited parking: Main hide Highland Council lay-by (wheelchair accessible hide). Kirkmichael Viewing Screen. Ivy Cottage - Highland Council car park Newhall Point - Highland Council car park.
Contact: RSPB - see site 2.

Orkney

BREEDING SEABIRDS, MOORLAND specialities and passage migrants make the islands an attractive destination. Hen Harriers breed here in good numbers, other scarce breeders include Whimbrel, Great & Arctic Skuas & Red-throated Diver. For seabirds, Marwick Head (mainland) & North Hill (Papa Westray) are worth a visit. North Ronaldsay Bird Observatory is a good base to stay to look for rare migrants.

9. HOBBISTER

RSPB (East Scotland).
Habitats: Moorland, bog, fen, saltmarsh, sandflats, sea cliffs, scrub.
Birds: *Summer:* Breeding Red-throated Diver, Eider, Red-breasted Merganser, Black Guillemot, Merlin, Hen Harrier, Short-eared Owl, Red Grouse, Twite. *Autumn/winter:* Waulkmill Bay for wildfowl & waders, sea ducks, divers, auks & grebes (inc. Great Northern, Red & Black-throated Divers, Slavonian Grebe, Long-tailed Duck).
Other: Otter, Grey & Common Seals.

Directions: Sat nav: KW17 2RA. HY 395 069 (car park) or HY 382 068 (Waukmill Bay) - are main access points. Overlooking Scarpa Flow 3.2 miles W of Kirkwall on A964.
Public transport: Bus - no.2 Kirkwell to Houton Ferry along A964 passes reserve. Stagecoach (T: 01856 870 555).
Visiting: Open access between A964 & sea. Two car parks - circular walk from RSPB car park along cliff top & Scapa Flow. A council-maintained footpath to Waulkmill Bay. Dogs on leads.
Contact: RSPB, T: 01856 850 176;
E: orkney@rspb.org.uk

10. HOY

RSPB (East Scotland).
Habitats: 3,920ha covering entire NW of Hoy: sea cliffs, moorland.
Birds: *All year:* Hen Harrier. *Summer:* Red-throated Diver, White-tailed Eagle, Fulmar, Puffin, Guillemot, Razorbill, Kittiwake, Black Guillemot, Arctic & Great Skuas, Stonechat. *Autumn/winter:* Finches & thrushes, Great Northern Diver, Long-tailed Duck, Merlin.
Other: Primroses & Arctic alpine flowers. Old Man of Hoy landmark.
Directions: Sat nav: KW16 3NJ. HY 222 034. Hoy reached from mainland by Houton car ferry or Stromness passanger ferry to Moaness, 1.5 miles to N part of reserve. From Lyness ferry turn R (signposted 'Hoy') onto B9047 & take first L after 8.5 miles (signposted Dwarfie Stone) toward Rackwick. Car parks at Dwarfie Stone & Rackwick beach.
Public transport: Bus (limited) - Hoy Community Bus service, T: 01856 701 356 (office), 07833 777 760 (driver).
Visiting: Access all times. Local car parks (not RSPB). Three trails - five miles return (to Old Man of Hoy) - from Rackwick); 2.5 miles Old Post Road (crosses moorland); & 0.6 mile return path to Dwarfie Stone). Rough terrain not suitable for wheelchairs. Dogs under control at all times.
Contact: RSPB - see site 9.

11. MARWICK HEAD

RSPB (East Scotland).
Habitats: Orkney's largest cliffside seabird colony: rocky bay, sandstone cliffs. The Choin low-tide lagoon good for waders & ducks.
Birds: *May-Jul:* up to 25,000 seabirds. Large numbers of Kittiwake & auks, inc. Puffin, also Fulmar, skuas, Rock Dove, Raven, Rock Pipit, Short-eared owl.
Other: Cetaceans possibility from Marwick with Harbour Porpoise & Minke Whale occasionally seen. Beach path for Great Yellow Bumblebee in Aug.
Directions: Sat nav: KW17 2NB. HY 229 240 (Marwick car park). Lies four miles N of Skara Brae (neolithic village) on W coast of mainland Orkney, NW of Dounby. Path N from Marwick Bay, or from council car park at Cumlaquoy at HY 232 251 (best for Kitchener Memorial).
Public transport: Bus - no.8S (Mon, Thurs, Sat - limited) stops at Marwick. Stagecoach (T: 01856 870 555).
Visiting: Open all year. Info board in Marwick car park. Cliff top path. Rough terrain not suitable for wheelchairs.
Contact: RSPB - see site 9.

NATURE RESERVES - HIGHLANDS & ISLANDS

12. NORTH HILL, PAPA WESTRAY

RSPB (East Scotland).
Habitats: Sea cliffs, maritime heath.
Birds: *Summer*: Close views of Puffin, Guillemot, Razorbill & Kittiwake. Black Guillemot nest under flagstones around reserve's coastline. One of UK's largest colonies of Arctic Tern. Arctic & Great Skuas. Breeding Lapwing, Redshank & Snipe in grazed areas. *Winter*: Gannet, Fulmar, Eider & winter thrushes.
Other: One of best areas (Fowl Craig) to see Scottish Primrose (*primula scotica*) - two flowering periods that just overlap (May to Aug). Whales on migration in autumn, inc. Killer Whale. Grey & Common seals.
Directions: Sat nav: KW17 2BU. HY 495 538. From pier or airfield travel N along main road. From shop/ hostel, take road N to junction at Holland Farm & turn R onto main road. Continue past Rose Cottage to reserve entrance.
Public transport: Ferry - Kirkwall to Papa Westray (car ferry, Tues & Fri). Pierowall (Westray) to Papa Westray passanger ferry (daily). Orkney Ferries (T: 01856 872 044). Flights - daily (end-Feb-Oct) from Kirkwall to North Ronaldsay. Loganair (T: 01856 872 494 or 01856 873 457).
Visiting: Access all times. Limited parking. Two trails (Coastal - 3.5 miles, around N peninsula of Papa Westray) & Fowl Craig (1.5 miles loop for nesting seabirds). Also additional short walk (200 yards each way) to North Hill hide. Not suitable for wheelchairs. Trail guide & info available in hide.
Contact: RSPB - see site 9.

13. NORTH RONALDSAY BIRD OBSERVATORY

North Ronaldsay Bird Observatory.
Habitats: Crofting island with a number of eutrophic & oligotrophic wetlands. Sandy bays & rocky shores.
Birds: *Spring/autumn*: Prime migration site inc. many rarities & sub-rarities. Walled gardens concentrate passerines. *Summer*: breeding seabirds, wildfowl & waders. *Winter*: Waders & wildfowl inc. Whooper Swan.
Directions: Sat nav: KW17 2BE. HY 748 524. Observatory in SW of island, at Twingness.
Public transport: Ferry - Kirkwall to North Ronaldsay (car ferry, Tues & Fri May-Sep, Fri only Oct-Apr). Flights - daily (end-Feb-Oct) from Kirkwall to North Ronaldsay. Loganair (T: 01856 872 494 or 01856 873 457).
Visiting: Open all year (not xmas). Guest house & hostel accommodation, fully licenced restaurant, cafe.
Contact: North Ronaldsay Bird Observatory, T: 01857 633 200; E: enquiries@nrbo.org.uk; W: www.nrbo.co.uk

Outer Hebrides

THESE ATTRACTIVE ISLANDS are the stronghold of the Corncrake in Britain... they should be heard easily enough but can be much harder to see! May sees a strong passage of Long-tailed & Pomarine Skuas past RSPB Balranald. Black Guillemot, Hen Harrier, Short-eared Owl, Twite & passage waders all provide added interest.

14. BALRANALD

RSPB (North Scotland).
Habitats: Freshwater loch, machair, coast, crofts.
Birds: *Spring*: Skuas & divers at sea, waders inc. Purple Sandpiper, Turnstone, Dunlin. *Summer*: Corncrake, Lapwing, Oystercatcher, Dunlin, Ringed Plover, Redshank, Snipe, terns, Corn Bunting. *Autumn*: Hen Harrier, Peregrine, Greylag Goose. *Passage*: Barnacle Goose, Pomarine & Long-tailed Skuas. *Winter*: Whooper Swan, Greylag Goose, Wigeon, Teal, Shoveler, Merlin, Twite, Snow Bunting. Golden & White-tailed Eagles more regular.
Other: Blanket bog & machair plants reach their peak in Jul. Look for rare Great Yellow Bumblebee on wildflowers. Otters on freshwater lochs.
Directions: Sat nav: HS6 5DL. NF 706 707. On W coast of North Uist, three miles N of Bayhead. Follow A865 N from Clachan towards Sollas. Take L turn for Hogha Gearraigh township & another L for signposted visitor centre prior to reaching Hogha Gearraigh.
Public transport: Bus - runs across Outer Hebrides - Grenitote Travel (T: 01876 560 244) - contact on morning of travel to ensure bus will stop at Balranald. Ferry from Mallaig to Lochboisdale - Caledonian MacBrayne (T: 08705 650 000; W: www.calmac.co.uk).
Visiting: Open all times. Visitor centre open all year. Toilets (inc. disabled), group bookings welcome. Marked circular nature trail (three miles), not suitable for wheelchairs. Dogs on leads.
Contact: RSPB, T: 01876 560 422; E: jamie.boyle@rspb.org.uk

15. LOCH DRUIDIBEG NNR

Stòras Uibhist (community ownership)/RSPB (Scotland).
Habitats: 1,677ha, coast, freshwater lochs, marshes, machair, moorland.
Birds: *Spring/autumn*: Migrant waders & wildfowl. *Summer*: Breeding waders, Corncrake, Black-throated Diver, Greylag Goose, wildfowl, terns & raptors. *Winter*: Waders, wildfowl, raptors inc. Golden Eagle & Hen Harrier.
Directions: Sat nav: HS8 5RS. NF 789 382. Lies just N of Kildonan on South Uist. Turn off A865 in Stillgarry at B890 road for Loch Sgioport. Track is 1.5 miles further on - park at side of road.
Public transport: Bus - no.W17 (not Sun) Benbecula to Lochboisdale stops at Stillgarry (for NNR). DA Travel (T: 01878 700 357 or 01878 700 599). Ferry from Mallaig to Lochboisdale - Caledonian MacBrayne (T: 08705 650 000; W: www.calmac.co.uk).
Visiting: Open all year. View E part of reserve from public roads but parking & turning areas for coaches is limited. Several tracks & one walk covering a range of habitats - most not suitable for wheelchairs. Stout footwear essential. Guided walks.
Contact: RSPB, T: 01870 610 318; E: lochdruidibeg@rspb.org.uk

Shetland

WITH ITS LARGE seabird colonies, a summer visit to Britain's most northerly islands will always be a fantastic experience. Apart from the huge numbers of the common species, Arctic and Great Skuas breed here - particularly around Hermaness (Unst) - and an evening visit to the small island of Mousa is a great way to catch up with the largely nocturnal Storm Petrel. The islands, in particular Fair Isle, always attract a large number of common, scarce and rare migrants annually in the spring and autumn. Many UK 'firsts' have been recorded here.

16. FAIR ISLE BIRD OBSERVATORY

Fair Isle Bird Observatory.
Habitats: Heather moor & lowland pasture/crofting land, sea cliffs.
Birds: *Summer:* Large seabird colonies (Gannet, Shag, Arctic & Great Skuas, Kittiwake, Arctic Tern, auks). *Spring (Apr to early-Jun) & Autumn (late-Aug to Nov):* Many common, scarce & rare migrants annually.
Other: Northern Marsh, Heath Spotted & Frog Orchid, Lesser Twayblade, Small Adders Tongue, Oyster Plant. Killer & Minke Whales, White-backed, White-sided & Risso's Dolphins. Endemic Field Mouse.
Directions: SE of Shetland/NW of Orkney - midway between them, access from Shetland.
Public transport: Regular UK flights to Sumburgh, Shetland or ferry from Aberdeen to Lerwick.
To Fair Isle: by air - Airtask services from Tingwell (nr Lerwick) - contact for details, T: 01595 840 246. By sea - Good Shepherd ferry (12 passangers) from Grutness, Shetland on Tues, Thurs, Sat (May-Sep) - contact for details (T: 01595 760 363).
Visiting: NOTE: Due to the fire that destroyed the Observatory in March 2019 accommodation will not be available for the forseeable future, check out the Obs website for alternative options. If the landline is unavailable use e-mail to make contact. Public toilets at airstrip & Stackhoull Stores (shop).
Contact: Fair Isle Bird Obs, T: 01595 760 258; E: fibo@btconnect.com; W: www.fairislebirdobs.co.uk

17. FETLAR

RSPB (East Scotland).
Habitats: Serpentine heath, rough hill land, upland mire.
Birds: *Summer:* Breeding Red-throated Diver, Eider, Shag, Manx Shearwater, Storm Petrel, Whimbrel, Dunlin, Golden Plover, Arctic & Great Skuas. Red-necked Phalarope on Loch of Funzie, viewed from road or hide overlooking Mires of Funzie. *Autumn to Spring:* Whooper Swan, Goldeneye, Long-tailed Duck, Great Northern Diver, passage migrants.
Other: Heath spotted orchid & autumn gentian. Otters common, Grey & Common seals breed.
Directions: ZE2 9DJ HU 655 900. Small island lying E of Yell. Take car ferry from Gutcher on Yell to Hamarsness, then drive 6 miles E to small car park W of Loch of Funzie. Ferry times & booking , T: 01595 745 804.
Public transport: None.

Visiting: Open at all Times. Car park, 500 yards from reserve. Hide open Apr-Oct (0.3 mile from car park). Loch of Funzie can be observed from road. Toilets & payphone at ferry terminal. Shop & cafe on island.
Contact: RSPB, T: 01950 460 800; E: shetland@rspb.org.uk

18. HERMANESS

Scottish Natural Heritage.
Habitats: Sea cliffs, moorland/grassland, blanket bog.
Birds: *Summer:* 100,000 seabirds. Fulmar, Shag, Gannet, Guillemot, Razorbill, Puffin, Kittiwake. Arctic & Great Skuas, Dunlin, Golden Plover, Snipe.
Other: Spring Squill. Grey Seal.
Directions: Sat nav: ZE2 9EQ. HP 612 149. On northern island of Unst (from Lerwick via Yell & Unst ferries). On Unst, head N on A968 through Baltasound, turn on to B9086 just before Haroldswick signposted Burrafirth & Hermaness. Continue to fork in road, go straight to reserve car park.
Public transport: None to reserve (bus - Lerwick to Baltasound but overnight stay needed).
Visiting: Access all times. Walk to cliffs starts in car park (notice board/leaflets). Gravel path N to Winnaswarta Dale then boardwalk takes you across reserve to western cliffs - keep to boardwalk to avoid damaging vegetation (moderate walk). Can explore coast from cliffs (strenuous walk), N tip overlooks Muckle Flugga (UK's most northerly lighthouse).
Contact: SNH Reserve Manager, T: 01595 693 345; E: nnr@nature.scot; W: www.nature.scot/

19. NOSS NNR

Scottish Natural Heritage.
Habitats: Dune & coastal grassland, moorland, heath, blanket bog, sea cliffs.
Birds: *Spring/summer:* Breeding Fulmar, Shag, Gannet, Arctic Tern, Kittiwake, Herring & Great Black-backed Gulls, Great & Arctic Skuas, Guillemot, Razorbill, Puffin, Black Guillemot, Eider, Lapwing, Dunlin, Snipe, Wheatear, Twite plus migrants.
Other: Grey & Common seals, Otter, Harbour Porpoise, Killer Whales (annual).
Directions: Sat nav: ZE2 9ES. HU 525 408 (Bressay parking for Noss). Take car ferry to Bressay from Lerwick & follow signs for Noss (3.2 miles). At end of road walk to shore (600 yards) where inflatable ferry (passenger only) to island will collect you. If red flag is flying, island is closed due to sea conditions.
Public transport: None.
Visiting: Car park on Bressay side. Access to island, subject to weather, by small inflatable 10am to 5pm, May to end-Aug (not Mon or Thurs). Daily update on crossings by 9am - Noss Ferry Line: 0800 107 7818. Visitor centre, toilets (open during sailing times). Steep rough track down to ferry. Walk around island ca. three hours. No dogs on ferry.
Contact: SNH Reserve Manager, see site 18.

Wales

Breconshire, Montgomeryshire, Radnorshire

Eastern

THE COUNTY OF POWYS, formed from these three counties, is a largely upland rural area of mountains, bogs, coniferous forest plantations and typical Welsh woodlands (home to Pied flycatcher, Wood Warbler & Redstart). Birds of prey are well represented - Hen Harrier, Merlin, Red Kite & Peregrine are all well established, while Cors Dyfi is a successful breeding site for Osprey.

1. BRECHFA POOL

Freshwater Habitats Trust.
Habitats: Marshy grassland, large shallow lake (900ft asl).
Birds: *Summer:* Common wildfowl, gulls. *Winter:* Wildfowl inc. Teal, Gadwall, Tufted Duck, Shoveler, Wigeon, Little Grebe, Lapwing, Dunlin, Redshank.
Other: Rich in flors inc. Rare Pillwort around pond margins, Crowfoot, Penny Royal & Orange Foxtail. Dragonflies.
Directions: Sat nav: LD3 0NL. SO 118 377. Travelling NE from Brecon to Llyswen. 1.5 miles SW of Llyswen look for lane off A470 to Upper Brechfa. Continue past Upper Brechfa, pool is on R after cattle grid.
Public transport: None.
Visiting: Open dawn-dusk. Road runs around three-sides of the pool, giving good access.
Contact: Freshwater Habitats Trust T: 01865 595 505 (Oxford office); E: info@freshwaterhabitats.org.uk

2. CORS DYFI NATURE RESERVE

Montgomeryshire Wildlife Trust.
Habitats: Bog, wet woodland & scrub.
Birds: *Spring/summer:* Osprey (first bred 2011), Snipe, Nightjar, Grasshopper, Sedge & Reed Warblers, Stonechat, Reed Bunting.
Other: Common Lizard, Four-spotted Chaser dragonfly.
Directions: Sat nav: SY20 8PZ. SN 704 984. Lies 3.5 miles SW of Machynlleth on A487 Abersytwyth road. Approx 2.5 miles S of Derwenlas, turn R after caravan park.
Public transport: Bus - X28 Cambrian Coastliner, Machynlleth to Aberystwyth will save @ Osprey Project (not Sun). Lloyds Coaches (T: 01654 702 100).
Visiting: Open 10am-5.30pm Apr-Aug & weekends Oct-Mar. Programme of special events in winter. Car park (no large coaches), visitor centre, toilets (inc. disabled), small cafe, hides, 360 degree observatory. Extensive boardwalks, site wheelchair-accessible apart from elevated hide. Assistance dogs only.
NOTE - closed until new visitor centre opens in 2020.
Contact: Montgomeryshire WT, T: 01938 555 654; E: info@montwt.co.uk
Osprey Project (Mar-Aug) T: 01654 781 414; E: enquiries@dyfiospreyproject.com; W: www.dyfiospreyproject.com/

3. ELAN VALLEY

Elan Valley Trust/Welsh Water.
Habitats: 18,000ha, moorland, bog, woodland, river & reservoir.
Birds: 180 spp. *All year:* Red Kite, Buzzard, Sparrowhawk, Peregrine, Tawney & Barn Owls, Raven, Green Woodpecker, Dipper, Grey Wagtail & Marsh Tit. Common woodland spp. *Spring/summer:* Cuckoo, Pied & Spotted Flycatchers, Wood Warbler, Redstart, Tree Pipit. Upland birds inc. Curlew, Golden Plover & Dunlin. *Autumn/winter:* Short-eared Owl, Ring Ouzel (autumn), Fieldfare, Redwing.
Other: Internationally important oak woodlands. 3,000+ spp. of flora & fauna recorded.
Directions: Sat nav: LD6 5HP. SN 928 646. Three miles SW of Rhayader (A470), take B4518 - don't cross iron bridge, drive over cattle grid to visitor centre.
Public transport: None.
Visiting: Mostly open access. Pay-&-display car park with Blue Badge spaces. Coaches, contact in advance for access advice. Visitor centre, cafe, shop & toilets open daily (not Dec 25) 9am-5pm. Nature trails. Dogs, keep under close control.
Contact: Visitor Centre, T: 01597 810 880; E: elanrangers@dwrcymru.com; W: www.elanvalley.org.uk

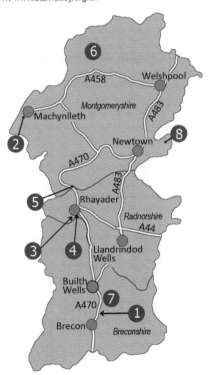

4. GIGRIN FARM

Private.
Habitats: 80ha, upland sheep farm rising to 1,200ft asl.
Birds: Daily feeds attract Red Kite, numbers can
vary from a few dozen to 100's when weather is bad.
Other species inc. Buzzard, Raven, Jackdaw, Carrion
Crow. Other feeding stations attract small birds
inc. Brambling, Yellowhammer & Siskin. A wetland
area attracts wild ducks, Grey Heron & wagtails.
Directions: Sat nav: LD6 5BL. SN 978 676. Farm lies
0.5 mile south of Rhayader, Powys off A470.
Public transport: Bus - X47 (not Sun) Llandrindod
Wells to Aberystwyth stops at Rhayader. Celtic Travel
(T: 01686 412 231).
Visiting: Gigrin has been an official Red Kite feeding
station for Wales since early 1990's, helping young
birds survive in winter. By attracting large numbers
of birdwatchers it relieves pressure on nest sites in
summer. Open for kite feeding sessions 1pm-5pm
Sat-Thurs (closed Tues/Wed) & daily during school
holidays - 27th Dec to end-Nov (closed 1-26 Dec).
Feeding times: 2pm (winter) & 3pm (summer). No
booking required. Admission charge. Red Kite Shop,
five hides (three with disabled access), plus specialist
photography hides (fee applies). Dogs on leads.
1.5 mile trail offers views of Elan Valley & Cambrian
Hills - rough terrain.
Contact: Chris Powell, Gigrin Farm, South Street,
Rhayader, Powys LD6 5BL. T: 01597 810 243;
E: chris@gigrin.co.uk; W: www.gigrin.co.uk

5. GILFACH FARM RESERVE

Radnorshire Wildlife Trust.
Habitats: 165ha, working organic hill farm, grassland,
moorlannd, river, oak woods, meadows.
Birds: 73 spp., 55 breed regularly, inc. Barn Owl,
Common Sandpiper, Stock Dove, Grey Wagtail, Dipper,
Pied & Spotted Flycatchers, Redstart, Tree Pipit,
Wheatear, Whinchat, Stonechat, Wood Warbler,
Marsh & Willow Tits, Raven, Linnet, Yellowhammer,
Siskin, Redpoll. Other spp. inc. Goosander, Curlew,
Merlin, Red Kite, Goshawk, Sparrowhawk, Peregrine,
Kingfisher, Reed Bunting.
Other: Green Hairstreak, Wall Brown & Ringlet
butterflies, Mountain Pansy, Bloody-nosed Beetle.
Welsh Clearwing Moth - first record for Radnorshire.
Directions: Sat nav: LD6 5LF. SN 965 716 (Old
Farmyard). Gilfach is just off A470, three miles N of
Rhayader (signposted for St Harmon). Follow brown
reserve signs. Parking just off A470 (Pont Marteg) just
after cattle grid.
Public transport: Bus - X47 (not Sun) Llandrindod
Wells to Aberystwyth passes entrance. Celtic Travel
(T: 01686 412 231).
Visiting: Open daily. Small car park at Old Farmyard
with some visitor facilities. Disabled access to centre,
toilets & purpose-built trail. Several waymarked trails.
Wye Valley Walk & Gwastedyn Church Trail pass through
reserve. Dogs on leads.
Contact: Radnorshire WT, T: 01597 823 298;
E: info@rwtwales.org

6. LAKE VYRNWY

Severn Trent/RSPB (Wales HQ).
Habitats: Heather moorland, woodland, meadows,
rocky streams & large reservoir.
Birds: All year: Buzzard, Red & Black Grouse, Raven.
Spring/summer: Hen Harrier, Peregrine, Hobby, Common
Sandpiper, Curlew, Cuckoo, Whinchat, Dipper, Kingfisher,
Ring Ouzel, Pied Flycatcher, Wood Warbler, Redstart.
Other: Otter, polecat, brown hare. Golden-ringed
dragonfly.
Directions: Sat nav: SY10 0LZ. SJ 016 192. WSW of
Oswestry. Nearest village is Llanfyllin on A490. Take
B4393 to Llanwddyn & at dam, turn L & L again.
Public transport: None.
Visiting: Open at all times. Visitor centre open (not
Dec 24/27, Jan 1) 10.30am-5pm Apr-Oct, 4pm Nov-
Mar), toilets, shop, cafe (nearby), six waymarked
trails, three hides (one with wheelchair access).
Contact: RSPB, T: 01691 870 278;
E: vyrnwy@rspb.org.uk

7. PWLL-Y-WRACH

Wildlife Trust of South & West Wales
Habitats: 17.5ha, ancient woodland, river &
spectacular Witches Pool waterfall.
Birds: All year: Dipper, Kingfisher, common woodland
spp. inc. Great Spotted Woodpecker, Mistle & Song
Thrushes, Nuthatch. Spring/summer: Chiffchaff,
Wood Warbler, Pied Flycatcher.
Other: Otter, Dormouse, bats, Common Lizard. Early
Purple & Birds' Nest Orchids.
Directions: Sat nav: LD3 0DU. SO 165 326. From
Talgarth (on A479) town centre cross over River Enig,
then L turn Bell Street. After 50 yards L (opp. Bell
Hotel) follow minor road one mile, reserve is on R.
Public transport: Bus - T14 (not Sun) Hereford to
Cardiff stops at Talgarth. Stagecoach South Wales.
Visiting: Open all year. Information panel in car park.
Keep to footpaths. Level, wheelchair-friendly path
runs halfway into site - elsewhere paths can be
muddy & there are steps. Dogs under close control.
Contact: WT of South & West Wales, T: 01874 625 708;
E: info@welshwildlife.org

8. ROUNDTON HILL NNR

Montgomeryshire Wildlife Trust.
Habitats: Ancient hillfort - grassland, woodland,
streamside wet flushes, scree, rock outcrops.
Birds: All year: Buzzard, Red Kite, Raven, 3 spp.
woodpecker, Tawny Owl, Linnet. Spring/summer:
Wheatear, Redstart, Whitethroat.
Directions: Sat nav: SY15 6EL. SO 293 946. SE of
Montgomery. Follow brown duck signs from Churchstoke
on A489, taking minor road towards Old Churchstoke.
After one mile turn R at phone box, then first R.
Public transport: Bus - no.81 (not Sun) Newtown to
Montgomery/Welshpool stops at Old Churchstoke,
0.3 mile from reserve. Tanat Valley (T: 01691 780 212).
Visiting: Open all times. Car park. Trails - rough in
places, not suitable for wheelchairs. Dogs on leads.
Contact: Montgomeryshire WT - see site 2.

Anglesey, Caernarfonshire, Denbighshire, Flintshire, Merioneth

Northern

ANGLESEY HOLDS MANY of the areas highlights including a seabird colony (with Choughs) at South Stack, terns at Cemlyn Bay & waders at Malltraeth. On the mainland, the RSPB's man-made Conwy reserve has good selection of wildfowl & waders, with rarities often turning up. Bardsey Island is a migrant hotspot & the Mawddach Valley area has the typical Welsh woodland species.

1. BARDSEY BIRD OBSERVATORY

Bardsey Bird Observatory.
Habitats: 180ha island, sea-bird cliffs viewable from boat only. Farm & scrubland, spruce plantation, willow copses & gorse-covered hillside.
Birds: All year: Chough, Peregrine. Spring/summer: Night walks to see Manx Shearwaters (20,000 pairs). Other seabirds, migrant warblers, chats, thrushes. Autumn: Common migrants, many rarities (have inc. Eye-browed Thrush, Lanceolated Warbler, American Robin, Yellowthroat, Summer Tanager).
Other: Autumn Ladies' Tresses. Grey Seal. Moths.
Directions: 15 miles SW of Pwllheli. 30 min boat crossing from Porth Meudwy, near Aberdaron - sat nav: LL53 8DA. SH163 255. From Aberdaron (Spar on your L) go over first bridge & turn sharp R, signposted Whistling Sands. Follow road uphill & for another 0.5 mile, take first L, signposted Uwchmynydd. After 400 yards take first L signposted Tir Glyn campsite. After 0.5 mile look out for Cwrt Farm on R. Porth Meudwy car park 75 yards further on L.
Bardsey Ferries, Colin Evans T: 07971 769 895 (sailings subject to weather).
Public transport: Bus - no.17 (not Sun) Pwllheli to Aberdaron 1.6 miles to boat (one mile along coast path). Berwyn (T: 01286 660 315).
Visiting: Private island, open Mar-Nov. Day trips allow 3 to 4 hours on island. Public toilets available for day visitors. Three hides, one on small bay, two seawatching. Gift shop, payphone. No dogs.
Staying at Obs: Hostel-style accommodation available (Sat-Sat, end-Mar to end-Oct): two singles, two doubles, two four bed dorms).
Bookings - Alicia Normand, T: 01626 773 908; E: stay@bbfo.org.uk
Contact: Steven Stansfield (Warden), T: 07855 264 151; E: warden@bbfo.org.uk; W: www.bbfo.org.uk

2. CEMLYN

North Wales Wildlife Trust.
Habitats: Brackish lagoon, shingle ridge, salt marsh, mixed scrub.
Birds: Spring: Wheatear, Whitethroat, Sedge Warbler, Manx Shearwater, Black-tailed Godwit, Whimbrel, Dunlin, Knot, passage migrants. Summer: Breeding Arctic, Common & Sandwich Terns, Black-headed Gull, Oystercatcher, Ringed Plover. Autumn: Golden Plover, Lapwing, Curlew, Manx Shearwater, Gannet, Kittiwake, Guillemot, passage migrants. Winter: Wildfowl inc. Shoveler, Shelduck, Red-breasted Merganser. Little & Great Crested Grebes, Purple Sandpiper, Turnstone.
Other: 20 spp. butterflies. Sea Kale, Yellow Horned Poppy, Sea Purslane, Sea Beet, Glasswort. Grey Seal, Harbour Porpoise, Bottlenose Dolphin.
Directions: Sat Nav: LL67 0DX. SH 336 931. Cemlyn on N coast of Anglesey, signposted from Tregele on A5025 between Valley & Amlwch. 'Beach' (east) car park, follow road taking sharp R at first fork. 'Bryn Aber' car park (west/closest to warden's viewpoint - SH 329 935), continue L, taking R turns at next two forks.
Public transport: Bus - no.61 (not Sun) Amlwch to Holyhead stops at Tregele (1.5 miles to reserve). Goodsir (T: 01407 764 340) & Lewis Y Llan (T: 01407 832 181).
Visiting: Open all year. In summer walk on seaward side of shingle ridge to minimise disturbance. Dogs on leads.
Contact: North Wales WT, T: 01248 351 541; E: info@northwaleswildlifetrust.org.uk

3. CONNAH'S QUAY POWER STATION RESERVE

EON/Deeside Naturalists Society.
Habitats: Saltmarsh, mudflats, grassland scrub, open water, wetland meadow.
Birds: Summer: Small roosts of non-breeding estuarine birds. Winter: High water roosts of waders & wildfowl inc. Black-tailed Godwit, Oystercatcher, Redshank, Spotted Redshank, Curlew, Lapwing, Teal, Pintail & Wigeon.
Other: 17 spp. butterflies.

Directions: Sat nav: CH6 5TE. SJ 271 713. Travel W to end of M56 which then becomes A494. Follow signposts for Flint. Take first slip road to L joining large roundabout & turn R onto A548. Continue straight on this road (there are several roundabouts) After crossing the River Dee take first slip road & turn R at first roundabout & then straight on at second roundabout. Follow signs for power station: reserve entrance is on L at next roundabout. If approaching from W follow A548, exiting on slip road for Connah's Quay. Turn L at roundabout & follow power station signs.
Public transport: Bus - 10A (no.10 on Sun, longer walk) Chester to Connah's Quay (Swan Inn). Arriva in Wales.
Visiting: Entry for DNS members only but group bookings possible in advance from DNS. Public welcome on open days - see website for details. Field studies centre, five hides. Wheelchair access.
Contact: Secretary, Deeside Naturalists' Society E: secretary@deenats.org.uk

4. CONWY

RSPB (North Wales).
Habitats: Lagoons, islands, reedbed, scrub, estuary.
Birds: *Spring:* Passage waders, hirundines & wagtails. *Summer:* Lapwing, waterbirds & warblers. *Autumn:* Black-tailed Godwit & other passage waders. *Winter:* Kingfisher, Goldeneye, Water Rail, Red-breasted Merganser, wildfowl, huge Starling roost.
Other: Common butterflies through summer, esp. Common Blue. Great display of Cowslips in Mar, Bee Orchids in summer. Otters seen early mornings.
Directions: Sat nav: LL31 9XZ. SH 797 773. On E bank of Conwy Estuary. Exit 18 (Conwy & Deganwy) of A55, reserve on S side of roundabout (signposted).
Public transport: Bus - no.27 Conwy to Colwyn Bay & no.24 Colwyn Bay to Llandudno Junction both stop at Tesco, Llandudno Junction (five mins walk from reserve). Arriva in Wales. Train - Llandudno Junction, 0.5 mile from reserve.
Visiting: Car park open daily (not Dec 25) 9am-5pm. Coach parking. Visitor centre (9.30am-5pm), shop, toilets inc. disabled, cafe (10am-4.30/ 4pm Nov-Mar). Three trails firm/level, though a little rough in places & wet in winter. Four hides (accessible to wheelchairs) with adjacent viewing screens.
Contact: RSPB, T: 01492 584 091; for events T: 01492 581 025; E: conwy@rspb.org.uk

5. LLYN CEFNI

Welsh Water.
Habitats: Large area of open water, reedy bays, coniferous woodland, scrub, carr.
Birds: *All year:* Common wildfowl, Little Grebe, Buzzard, Stonechat, Treecreeper, Song Thrush. *Summer:* Kingfisher, Sedge & Grasshopper Warblers, Whitethroat, Tawny Owl. *Winter:* Wildfowl inc. Whooper Swan, Goldeneye, Redwing, Crossbill, Redpoll, Siskin.
Other: Northern Marsh Orchid, Rustyback Fern, Needle Spikerush. Banded Demoiselle, Migrant Hawker, Golden-ringed Dragonfly, Emerald Damselfly. Ringlet, Gatekeeper, Clouded Yellow & Wall Brown butterflies. Bloody-nose Beetle.

Directions: Sat nav: LL77 7RQ. SH 451 782 (Rhosmeirch car park). Reservoir located two miles NW of Llangefni, in central Anglesey. NE section of reservoir managed as nature reserve - entrance just N of Rhosmeirch. Follow B5111 from village.
Public transport: Bus - nos.4/4A/X4 Bangor to Holyhead alight Langefni (1.5 miles to reservoir see visiting). Arriva in Wales.
Visiting: Open all times. Two picnic sites, coach parking at Rhosmeirch car park. Good footpath (wheelchair accessible) for most of site, bridges over streams. Walkers can reach reservoir from Dingle nature reserve, Llangefni, on boardwalks & cycle route (one mile). Dogs allowed except in sanctuary area.
Contact: none.

6. MAWDDACH VALLEY

RSPB (North Wales).
Habitats: Oak woodland, bracken & heathland at Coed Garth Gell. Willow & alder scrub & raised bog at Arthog Bog.
Birds: 1: Coed Garth Gell. *All year:* Buzzard, Peregrine, Sparrowhawk, Lesser Spotted Woodpecker, Grey Wagtail, Dipper, Raven, Hawfinch. *Summer:* Cuckoo, Pied & Spotted Flycatchers, Wood Warbler, Redstart, Tree Pipit. 2: Arthog Bog. *All year:* Buzzard, Sparrowhawk, Peregrine, Raven. *Summer:* migrants inc. Tree Pipit, Grasshopper Warbler, Cuckoo. *Winter:* Redpoll, Siskin. Red-breasted Merganser & Little Egret on nearby estuary.
Other: Coed Garth Gell has Tunbridge Filmy & Beech Ferns. Butterflies. Golden-ringed dragonfly regular.
Directions: 1: Coed Garth Gell sat nav: LL40 2TT. SH 683 192 (on A496 between Taicynhaeaf & Bontddu), N side of Mawddach Estuary, (park in laybys/parking spaces). 2: Arthog Bog (LL39 1BQ. SH 630 138) off Dolgellau-to-Tywyn road (A493) west of Arthog. Park at Morfa Mawddach station.
Public transport: 1: Bus - no.T3 Dolgellau to Barmouth alight Taicynhaeaf (0.5 mile to reserve). 2: Bus - no.28 Dolgellau to Twywn, alight Arthog (0.25 mile from reserve). Lloyds Coaches (T: 01654 702 100).
Visiting: Trails on both sites, open all times. Dogs on leads. Information boards.
Contact: RSPB, T: 01654 700 222; E: mawddach@rspb.org.uk

7. SOUTH STACK CLIFFS

RSPB (North Wales).
Habitats: Sea cliffs, maritime grassland, maritime & lowland heath.
Birds: *Spring/summer/autumn:* Peregrine, Chough, Shag, Fulmar, Puffin, Guillemot, Razorbill, Skylark, Rock Pipit, Stonechat, Linnet, migrant warblers & passage seabirds.
Other: Spathulate Fleawort, endemic to South Stack, Adder, lizards, Harbour Porpoise.
Directions: Sat nav: LL65 1YH. SH 211 818 (visitor centre), SH 206 820 (Ellin's Tower info centre). Follow A55 to W end in Holyhead, proceed straight on at roundabout, continue straight on through traffic lights. After another 0.5 mile turn L & follow brown tourist signs for RSPB South Stack.
Public transport: None.

NATURE RESERVES - WALES

Visiting: RSPB car park (free), Blue Badge parking. Visitor centre, cafe, shop open daily 10am-5pm (not Dec 25). Ellin's Tower Seabird Centre has windows overlooking main auk colony, open daily 10am-5pm, easter to Sep - access via staircase. Reserve covered by extensive network of paths, some accessible to wheelchairs. 'Access for all' track to viewing area overlooking the lighthouse.
Contact: RSPB, T: 01407 762 100; E: south.stack@rspb.org.uk

8. SPINNIES ABEROGWEN

North Wales Wildlife Trust.
Habitats: Series of lagoons, woodland, scrub, grassland, reed swamp, shingle beach & mudflats.
Birds: *Spring/summer:* Little Grebe, Red-breasted Merganser, Sandwich Tern, large number of Mute Swan, Blackcap & Sedge Warbler. *Autumn/winter:* Large numbers of wintering wildfowl & waders inc. Redshank, Greenshank, Wigeon & Teal. Kingfisher Sep-Mar.
Other: Broad-leaved Helleborine, Dog's Mercury, Bluebells. Common butterflies.
Directions: Sat nav: LL57 3YH. SH 613 720. E of Bangor - from Bangor (A5) follow Tal-y-Bont road, at roundabout near Penrhyn Castle entrance take first exit & stay on this road for ca. one mile - reserve is signposted on L Minor road leads to car park where reserve entrance is signposted. Can also be approached from A55 (junc 12).
Public transport: Bus - no.5/5X Bangor to Llandudno stops near to minor road to reserve. Arriva Buses.
Visiting: Open all year. Drop-off point at main entrance. Two hides, signposted from car park, main hide is wheelchair accessible with views of Traeth Lafan sands & Spinnies lagoon. Keep to paths, good throughout. Dogs on leads.
Contact: North Wales WT - see site 2.

9. TRAETH LAFAN LNR

Gwynedd Council.
Habitats: 2,500ha, intertidal sands & mudflats, (adjacent to Spinnies (Site 8), Morfa Aber NNR & Morfa Madryn NNR) .
Birds: *Summer:* Breeding Lapwing (Morfa Madryn). *Autumn:* nationally important for moulting Great Crested Grebe & Red-breasted Merganser. *Winter:* Goldeneye, waders inc. Greenshank, internationally important for Oystercatcher & Curlew, regionally significance for Black & Red-throated & Great Northern Divers, Black-necked & Slavonian Grebes.
Directions: NE of Bangor, stretching six miles to Llanfairfechan. 1: Spinnies - see site 8. 2: Morfa Aber (LL33 0LB. SH 647 731) follow brown signs from junc 13 of A55. 3: Access to Morfa Madryn is on foot one mile W from Llanfairfechan promenade (LL33 0DA. SH 678 754).
Public transport: Bus - no.5/5X Bangor to Llandudno. 1: see site 8. 2: stops at Abergwyngregyn. 3: stops at Llanfairfachan. Arriva Buses. Train: Llanfairfachan.
Visiting: Open access, Wales Coastal Path. 1: Car park, hides 200 yards away at Spinnies. 2: Car park, hide. 3: Car & coach park, toilets, cafe, hides. All sites are wheelchair accessible.
Contact: Gwynedd Council, T: 01766 771 000.

Glamorgan, Gower, Gwent

Southern

THE GOWER COASTLINE has breeding seabirds, Peregrines & thousands of Manx Shearwaters offshore. Cardiff Bay is good for passage & wintering waders & the Newport Wetlands Reserve/ Gwent Levels has good numbers of wintering wildfowl & waders. Kenfig Pools have a history of turning up rarities.

1. CWM CLYDACH

RSPB (Wales HQ).
Habitats: Oak & beech woodland on steep slopes along banks of fast-flowing Lower Clydach River.
Birds: *All year:* Red Kite, Sparrowhawk, Buzzard, Raven, Green Woodpecker, Dipper & Grey Wagtail. *Summer:* Spotted Flycatcher, Garden Warbler, Wood Warbler, Cuckoo. *Winter:* Woodcock, Siskin, Redpoll.
Other: Fungi, Wood Sorrel, Silver-washed Fritillary & Speckled Wood butterflies.
Directions: Sat nav: SA6 5SU. SN 684 026. N of Swansea. Three miles N of Junc 45 of M4, through village of Clydach on B4291, follow signs for Craig-cefn-Parc. Car park is close to New Inn pub.
Public transport: Bus - no.214 & X6C (not Sun) Graig Felen to Craig Cefn Parc stops at reserve entrance. South Wales Transport (T: 01792 799 575).
Visiting: Open all times. Car park (no coaches). Two trails link to network of public footpaths - not suitable for wheelchairs. Dogs on leads.
Contact: RSPB, T: 029 2035 3000; E: cwm.clydach@rspb.org.uk

2. CWM COLHUW

The Wildlife Trust of South & West Wales.
Habitats: Unimproved calcareous grassland, woodland, scrub & Jurassic blue lias cliff. Iron Age promontory fort on site overlooking Bristol Channel.
Birds: *All year:* Peregrine. *Summer:* Cliff-nesting House Martin colony, Fulmar, Whitethroat, Grasshopper Warbler, Linnet, Yellowhammer. *Autumn:* Large passerine passage. Seawatching vantage point, occasional passing Chough.
Other: Wild Cabbage. Butterflies inc. Small Blue.
Directions: Sat nav: CF61 1YX. SS 956 674. SE of Bridgend. From Bridgend take B4265 S to Llanwit Major (0.6 mile SW of village). Follow beach road from village to car park.
Public transport: Bus - no.303 from Bridgend to Barry, alight Llantwit Major & no.321 (not Sun) from Talbot Green to Llantwit Major. Then walk towards beach. New Adventure Travel (T: 02920 442 040). Train - Llantwit Major.
Visiting: Open all year. Includes part of Wales Coast Path. Access from stile at head of valley (SS 968 678) or by steps from car park - unsuitable for wheelchairs. Information boards. Toilets.
Contact: WT of S&W Wales, T: 01656 724 100; E: info@welshwildlife.org

3. KENFIG NNR

Bridgend County Borough Council.
Habitats: 526ha, sand dune system, freshwater lake with reeds, numerous wet dune slacks, sandy coastline with some rocky outcrops.
Birds: *Summer*: Warblers inc. Cetti's, Sedge, Reed, Grasshopper & Willow Warbler, Blackcap & Whitethroat. *Winter*: Wildfowl, Water Rail, Bittern, grebes.
Other: 16 spp. orchid (inc. Fen), Hairy Dragonfly, Red-veined & Ruddy Darters, Small Blue, Dark Green Fritillary, Grayling & Brown Argus butterflies.
Directions: Sat nav: CF33 4PT. SS 802 811. Seven miles W of Bridgend. From Junc 37 of M4, take A4229 towards Porthcawl, then R at roundabout on B4283 to North Cornelly, signposted from here.
Public transport: Bus - no.63 Bridgend to Porthcawl stops at North Cornelly (1.5 miles). First South & West Wales.
Visiting: Open all times. Car park - coach parking available. Toilets (9am-5pm), hides, signposted paths. Unsurfaced sandy paths, not suitable for wheelchairs. Flooding possible in winter/spring.
Contact: Kenfig NNR, T: 01656 815 070.

4. LAVERNOCK POINT

The Wildlife Trust of South & West Wales.
Habitats: Sea, coastal calcareous grassland & scrub.
Birds: *Summer*: Chiffchaff, Whitethroat, Lesser Whitethroat, Bullfinch. Important site for migration - Autumn: large flocks of Swallow, thrushes & finches.
Other: Butterflies, wild flowers.
Directions: Sat nav: CF64 5XQ. ST 181 681. Five miles S of Cardiff. Access is from B4267 via Fort Road, signposted Lavernock Point. Limited parking by gate or in public car park at end of Fort Road.
Public Transport: Bus - no.94 Cardiff to Barry stops near turn to Fort Road. Cardiff Bus (T: 02920 666 444).
Visiting: Info boards. Access via a stile, not suitable for wheelchairs.
Contact: WT of S&W Wales - see site 2.

5. MAGOR MARSH

Gwent Wildlife Trust.
Habitats: 36ha, sedge fen, reedswamp, willow carr, damp hay meadows & open water.
Birds: *All year*: Little Egret, Little Grebe, Reed Bunting, Cetti's Warbler & Water Rail. *Spring*: Reed, Sedge & Grasshopper Warblers, occasional Garganey & Green Sandpiper on passage, Hobby. *Winter*: Teal, Peregrine, Jack Snipe, Snipe, occasional Shoveler, Gadwall & Bittern.
Directions: Sat nav: NP26 3DN. ST 428 866. Reserve lies to S of Magor. Leave M4 at Junc 23, turning R onto B4245. Follow signs for Redwick in Magor village. Take first L after railway bridge. Reserve entrance is 0.5 mile further on R (car park by Derek Upton Centre).

Public transport: Bus - no.X74 Newport to Chepstow stops in Magor (Renwick Road - 0.5 mile to reserve). Newport Bus (T: 01633 670 563).
Visiting: Open at all times. Car park, hide (wheelchair access), footpaths, boardwalks - keep to paths. No dogs.
Contact: Gwent WT, T: 01600 740 600; E: info@gwentwildlife.org

6. NEWPORT WETLANDS NNR

Natural Resources Wales/ RSPB (Wales HQ)/ Newport City Council.
Habitats: 438 ha, wet meadows, saline lagoons, reedbed, scrub & mudflats on Severn estuary.
Birds: *Spring/summer*: Breeding waders inc. Lapwing & Oystercatcher. Bearded Tit, Cetti's Warbler, Cuckoo & regular migrants on passage. *Autumn*: Large numbers of migrating wildfowl & waders - regulars inc. Curlew, Dunlin, Ringed Plover. Shoveler. *Winter*: Large Starling roost (up to 50,000 birds). Bittern, nationally important numbers of Black-tailed Godwit, Shoveler & Dunlin.
Other: Badger, Wood Mouse, Otter. Great Crested Newt. Orchids in spring, 16 spp. dragonflies, 23 spp. butterflies & ca.200 spp. moths.
Directions: Sat nav: NP18 2BZ. ST 334 834. SW of Newport. From Junc 24 or 28 of M4, take A48 to Spytty Retail Park roundabout, exit on to A4810 Queensway Meadows. At first roundabout take 3rd exit onto Meadow Road - follow brown tourist signs to reserve. Close to Uskmouth Power Station.
Public transport: Bus - no.63 (limited, not Sat/Sun) from Newport city centre to reserve. Newport Bus (T: 01633 670 563).
Visiting: Car park (charge - members free) & visitor Centre open daily (not Dec 25) 9am-5pm. Cafe (10am-4pm), shop, toilets (inc. disabled). Four trails, hide & viewing screens - wheelchair accessible. Dogs only on perimeter footpath.
Contact: Newport Wetlands Reserve (NRW), RSPB Visitor Centre, T: 01633 636 363; E: newport-wetlands@rspb.org.uk

NATURE RESERVES - WALES

7. OXWICH NNR

Natural Resources Wales (Swansea Office).
Habitats: Freshwater marsh, saltmarsh, foreshore, dunes, woodlands.
Birds: *Summer:* Breeding Reed, Sedge & Cetti's Warblers, Treecreeper, Nuthatch, woodpeckers. *Winter:* Wildfowl.
Directions: Sat nav: SA3 1LS. SS 501 865. From Swansea take A4118 Gower road towards Killay, Parkmill & continue through Nicholaston to Oxwich village.
Public transport: Bus - no.117 (not Sun) Killay to Scurlage, alight Oxwich. New Adventure Travel (T: 02920 442 040).
Visiting: Most of NNR open all times, groups can visit some restricted areas by arrangement. No permit required for access to foreshore, dunes, woodlands & facilities. Private car park (charge) & toilets (Apr-Oct). Marsh boardwalk & lookout.
Contact: NRW, T: 0300 065 3000;
E: enquiries@naturalresourceswales.gov.uk

8. PARC SLIP NATURE PARK

The Wildlife Trust of South & West Wales.
Habitats: Restored opencast mining site, wader scrape, lagoons, grassland, woodland.
Birds: *Summer:* Breeding Tufted Duck, Lapwing, Kingfisher, Green Woodpecker. Skylark. Migrant waders (inc. Little Ringed Plover). *Winter:* Wildfowl, Snipe, Water Rail, Bittern.
Other: 20 spp. dragonflies, inc. Emperor & Scarce Blue-tailed Damselfly. Great Crested Newt, Harvest Mouse, reptiles. Seven spp. orchid inc. Twayblade & Broad-leaved Helleborine.
Directions: Sat nav: CF32 0EH. SS 880 840. 0.6 mile W of Aberkenfig. From Junc 36 of M4 take A4063 towards Maesteg, then B4281 (signposted Aberkenfig & Pyle) & follow brown signs to visitor centre in Fountain Road.
Public transport: Bus - no.63 Bridgend to Porthcawl stops at Fountain Inn, bottom of Fountain Road. Firstbus South & West Wales. Tondu.
Visiting: Open dawn-dusk. Free car park off Fountain Road, space for coach. Visitor centre/coffee shop open daily (not mon/xmas period) 10am-4pm. Five hides, regular events. Good access for wheelchairs.
Contact: WT of S&W Wales - see site 2.

9. TAF FECHAN

The Wildlife Trust of South & West Wales.
Habitats: Ancient broadleaved woodland, calcareous grasslands, river gorge & cliffs.
Birds: Pied Flycatcher (summer), Tawny Owl, Dipper, Kingfisher, Grey Wagtail, Peregrine, Woodcock.
Other: Otter, migrating Salmon.
Directions: Sat nav: CF48 2HH. SO 033 084, SO 037 076 & SO 045 097 (main entrances). Two miles N of Merthyr Tydfil centre. Several entrances along Taff Trail & footpath from Cyfarthfa Park.
Public Transport: Bus - nos.25 (not Sun) Merthyr Tydfil to Tefechan. Stagecoach. Train - Merthyr Tydfil.
Visiting: Open all year. Information boards. Not accessible to wheelchairs due to steep terrain & steps.
Contact: WT of S&W Wales - see site 2.

Carmarthenshire, Gower, Pembrokeshire

Western

SUMMER BOAT TRIPS running to the seabird islands of Ramsay & Skomer (daily) & Skokholm (no day trips/residential only) get you close to the huge Welsh seabird colonies, a must-do outing. In spring & summer, the steep wooded valleys through the area are good for Red Kite, Redstart, Pied Flycatcher & Wood Warbler. The National Wetland Centre (Llanelli) & the Welsh Wildlife Centre (Cardigan) are good for wintering wildfowl & waders.

1. CASTLE WOODS

The Wildlife Trust of South & West Wales.
Habitats: 25ha, old mixed deciduous woodlands overlooking River Tywi, castle.
Birds: Buzzard, Sparrowhawk, 3 spp. woodpecker, Raven. *Summer:* Pied & Spotted Flycatchers, Redstart, Wood Warbler. *Winter:* Teal, Wigeon, Goosander, Shoveler, Tufted Duck, Pochard.
Other: Fallow Deer, Badger, butterflies inc. Silver-washed Fritillary.
Directions: Sat nav: SA19 6RP. SN 623 223. 1.25 miles W of Llandeilo town centre, adjacent to Dinefwr Park (National Trust). Take footpath from Tywi Bridge (Pen Lan Park), Llandeilo or park next to fire station off A40 & walk down Dinefwr Park Drive.
Public transport: Bus - nos.X13 & 103 (not Sun) from Swansea/Ammerford to Llandeilo. First Bus. No.280 (not Sun) from Carmarthen to Llandovery. Morris Travel (T: 01267 235 090). Train - Llandeilo.
Visiting: Open all year - Footpaths, mostly too steep for wheelchairs, hide.
Contact: WT of S&W Wales, T: 01656 724 100;
E: info@welshwildlife.org

2. CORS CARON NNR

Natural Resources Wales (Mid Wales Area).
Habitats: Raised bog, river, fen, wet grassland, willow woodland, reedbed.
Birds: *All Year:* Red Kite. *Summer:* Lapwing, Redshank, Curlew, Hobby, Grasshopper Warbler, Whinchat, Redpoll, Reed Bunting. *Winter:* Teal, Wigeon, Whooper Swan, Hen Harrier.
Other: Small Red Damselfy amongst abundant dragonflies. Otter. Adder & Common Lizard.
Directions: Sat nav: SY25 6JF. SN 692 625. Two miles N of Tregaron, Ceredigion, NE of Lampeter. Car park on B4343 (signposted). Also car parking in layby just N of Maesllyn Farm.
Public transport: Bus - nos.585 & 588 (not Sun) Lampeter to Aberystwyth stop in Tregaron. Brodyr James T: 0800 084 3596), Lloyds Coaches (T: 01654 702 100) & Mid Wales Travel (T: 01970 828 288).

Visiting: Open access from car park on B4343, space for coaches, toilets & picnic area. Cors Caron walk - boardwalk, accessible, dogs on lead. Riverside Walk, shut at times due to flooding/management requirements - circular walk, no dogs. Old Railway Walk, dogs under control. Hide on boardwalk & hide on Old Railway Walk 1.5 miles from car park. Footpath through reserve part of Ystwyth Trail.
Contact: NRW, T: 0300 065 3000;
E: enquiries@naturalresourceswales.gov.uk

3. DYFI NNR

Natural Resources Wales (Mid Wales Area).
Habitats: 2,000ha, sandflats, mudflats, saltmarsh, creeks, dunes, raised bog, grazing marsh.
Birds: *Summer:* Breeding wildfowl & waders (inc. Teal, Shoveler, Red-beasted Merganser, Lapwing, Curlew, Redshank). *Winter:* Greenland White-fronted Goose, wildfowl, waders & raptors (inc. Hen Harrier).
Directions: Sat nav: SY24 5JZ. SN 608 940. (Ynyslas visitor centre). Extensive reserve midway between Machynlleth & Aberystwyth & seaward side of A487, inc. part of Dyfi estuary, Ynyslas dunes & Borth Bog.
Public transport: Bus - no.512 (not Sun) Aberystwyth to Borth & Ynyslas. Mid Wales Travel (T: 01970 828 288).
Visiting: Ynyslas dunes/estuary - two waymarked trails. Cors Fochno - one circular boardwalk trail (no dogs). Good views over bog & Aberleri marshes from W bank of Afon Leri. Public footpaths off A493 E of Aberdyfi & off B4353 (S of river), minor road from B4353 at Ynyslas to dunes & parking area. NRW visitor centre/shop/toilets at Ynyslas open 9am-5pm, easter to end-Sep). Public hide overlooking marshes beside footpath at SN 611 911.
Contact: NRW, T: 01970 872 901 (easter/end Sep) or 0300 065 3000 (Oct-easter).
E: ynyslas@cyfoethnaturiolcymru.gov.uk

4. GWENFFRWD-DINAS

RSPB (Wales HQ).
Habitats: Hillside oak woods, streams & bracken slopes. Spectacular upland scenery.
Birds: *All year:* Red Kite, Buzzard, Peregrine, Raven, Goosander, Dipper, Grey Wagtail, Marsh Tit & 3 spp. woodpecker. *Summer:* Common Sandpiper, Cuckoo, Pied & Spotted Flycatcher, Wood Warbler, Redstart, Tree Pipit.
Other: Golden-ringed Dragonfly, Purple Hairstreak, Silver-washed Fritillary, Wilson's Filmy Fern.
Directions: Sat nav: SA20 0PG. SN 788 471. N of Llandovery. From A483 take B road signposted to Llyn Brianne Reservoir & then follow signs to reserve, which lies between Cynghordy & Llanwrda.
Public transport: None.
Visiting: Public nature trail at Dinas open dawn-dusk. Car park & information board at start of trail, coach parking can be arranged. Nature trail inc. a boardwalk. Other parts of trail are rugged. Toilets at Llyn Brianne reservoir car park (one mile N).
Contact: RSPB, T: 02920 353 000 ;
E: gwenffrwd.dinas@rspb.org.uk

5. LLANELLI WETLAND CENTRE

The Wildfowl & Wetlands Trust.
Habitats: Inter-tidal mudflats, reedbeds, pools, marsh, waterfowl collection.
Birds: *Winter:* Up to 50,000 waterbirds, inc. Pintail, Wigeon, Teal. Little Egret, Curlew, Oystercatcher, Redshank. Short-eared & Barn Owls, Peregrine.
Other: Bee & Southern Marsh Orchids, Yellow Bartisa. Dragonflies, Water Vole, Otter.
Directions: Sat nav: SA14 9SH. SS 532 985. Overlooks Burry Inlet near Llanelli on B4304. Leave M4 at Junc 48. Signposted from A484, E of Llanelli.
Public transport: Bus - Llanelli 'Dial a Ride' service operates between Llanelli bus station, railway station & the centre - book with Carmarthenshire County Council T: 01267 228 326 or call centre: T: on T: 0845 634 0661 Mon-Fri 9.30am-12pm up to the day before travel (bookings for Sat & Mon must be made by Fri before).
Visiting: Free car/coach parking. Open daily (not Dec 24/25) 9.30am-5pm grounds open until 6pm in summer). Entrance fee, members free. Visitor centre fully accessible with toilets, hides, restaurant, shop, education facilities. Mobility scooters/wheelchairs free to hire. Centre has level access & hard-surfaced paths.
Contact: WWT Llanelli Wetland Centre, T: 01554 741 087; E: info.llanelli@wwt.org.uk

6. RAMSEY ISLAND

RSPB (Wales HQ).
Habitats: Acid grassland, maritime heath, seacliffs.
Birds: *All year:* Peregrine, Raven, Chough. *Spring/ summer:* Cliff-nesting auks (Guillemot, Razorbill), Kittiwake, Fulmar, Shag, Stonechat, Wheatear, Skylark, Linnet, Little Owl. *Passage:* migrants.
Other: Largest Grey Seal colony in south-west Britain, Red Deer, Harbour Porpoise.
Directions: Sat nav: SA62 6PY. SM 721 249 (mainland). One mile offshore from lifeboat station at St Justinians, two miles west of St Davids, Pembrokeshire.

Public transport: Bus - no.T11 (not Sun) from Haverfordwest to St Davids (Richards Bros, T: 01239 613 756) & then no.403 Celtic Coaster St David's to St Justinians, May-Sep (Sarah Bell, T: 07828 940 955). Train - Haverfordwest. **Visiting:** Coach & car parking at St Justinians (ask boat company for advice/options). Island open daily 10am-4pm, weather permitting, Apr 1st/easter if earlier) to Oct. RSPB landing fee for non-members, in addition to boat fare. Small RSPB visitor centre/shop selling snacks & hot/cold drinks. Compost toilets - five minute walk uphill from harbour. 3.5 mile circular trail (or two shorter walks) - rugged in parts. Introduction from resident wardens. Guided walks available. No wheelchair access. Boat - sails from lifeboat station at 10am & 12pm, returns at 4pm. To book: Thousand Island Expeditions, T: 01437 721 721; E: sales@thousandislands.co.uk **Contact:** RSPB, T: 07836 535 733; E: ramsey.island@rspb.org.uk

7. SKOKHOLM NNR
The Wildlife Trust of South & West Wales.
Habitats: Cliffs, bays & inlets.
Birds: *Spring:* Manx Shearwaters arrive at end of Mar (50,000 pairs). *Summer:* Internationally important colonies of Razorbill, Puffin, Guillemot, Storm Petrel, Lesser Black-backed Gull. *Passage:* Migrants inc. rare species.
Other: Grey Seal, Harbour Porpoise, occasional Common, Bottlenose & Risso's Dolphins, nationally rare moths.
Directions: Sat nav: SA62 3BJ. SM 760 089 (Marloes/Martin's Haven parking). 15 miles SW of Haverfordwest. Take B4327, turn-off for Marloes, continue two miles past village to embarkation point at Martin's Haven (National Trust car park, fee payable).
Public transport: None.
Visiting: No day visitors, residential stays available Apr-Sep (bookings open in autumn for following season). Has Bird Observatory status & welcomes visting ringers. Self-catering accommodation for up to 20 people, small shop selling basic foodstuffs. Boat fare paid directly to boatman in cash.
Contact: Main Office & Island Bookings (Mon-Fri 9am-5pm), T: 01656 724 100; E: islands@welshwildlife.org

8. SKOMER
The Wildlife Trust of South & West Wales.
Habitats: Maritime cliff, freshwater ponds.
Birds: *Summer:* World's largest Manx Shearwater colony (300,000+ pairs). Puffin, Guillemot, Razorbill, Kittiwake (until end-Aug), Fulmar, Short-eared Owl, Chough, Peregrine, Buzzard, migrants (inc. rarities).
Directions: See site 7.
Public transport: None.
Visiting: Island open Apr-Sep (easter if earlier). Information centre, toilets, two hides, booklets, guides, nature trails. Take water/food. Not suitable for infirm (87 steep landing steps/rough ground). Day visitors: (not Mon, except bank holidays/max 250 tickets per day, on first come first served basis). Island landing fee (members free), payable at Lockley Lodge.

Boats leave 10am, 11am & 12pm - returning 3pm. Boat fare paid on boat. T: 01646 636 800 to see if boats running. No dogs. Overnight visitors: Boat sails at 9am - booking essential (bookings open in autumn for following season)/length of stay conditions apply. **Contact:** Main Office & Island Bookings - see site 7.

9. WELSH WILDLIFE CENTRE/TEIFI MARSH NR
The Wildlife Trust of South & West Wales.
Habitats: Wetlands, marsh, swamp, reedbed, open water, creek (tidal), river, saltmarsh, woodland.
Birds: *Summer:* Breeding Kingfisher, gulls, Sand Martin, Great Spotted Woodpecker, Redstart, Cetti's Warbler. *Winter:* Wildfowl inc. Teal, Wigeon & Mallard. Water Rail, Curlew, Snipe, Lapwing & Peregrine. Occasional Bittern & Red Kite.
Other: Otter, Water Shrew, Sika & Red Deer, good variety dragonflies.
Directions: Sat nav: SA43 2TB. SN 188 451. Visitor centre 1.25 miles from Cilgerran, two miles SE of Cardigan. River Teifi is N boundary. Signposted from A478 Cardigan to Fishguard road.
Public transport: Bus - nos.430 (not Sun) Cardigan to Narberth, alight at Cilgerran, then walk to centre. Richards Bros (T: 01239 613 756).
Visiting: Open all year. Free parking for members, charge for non-members. Visitor centre/cafe/shop open 10am-5pm Easter-Oct, 4pm Nov-Mar (not xmas week), network of four nature trails & seven hides. Binoculars for hire. Disabled access to visitor centre, paths, four hides. Dogs on leads.
Contact: Welsh Wildlife Centre, T: 01239 621 600; E: wwc@welshwildlife.org

10. YNYS-HIR
RSPB (Wales HQ).
Habitats: Estuary, freshwater pools, woodland & wet grassland.
Birds: *All year:* Red Kite, Buzzard, Little Egret, Lapwing, Teal. *Spring/summer:* Redstart, Pied Flycatcher, nine spp. warbler inc. Grasshopper & Wood. *Winter:* Greenland White-fronted & Barnacle Geese, Wigeon, Hen Harrier.
Other: 16 spp. dragonflies inc. Small Red Damselfly & Golden-ringed Dragonfly. Butterflies inc. Dark Green Fritillary, Brimstone & Speckled Wood. Otter (rarely seen), Brown hare.
Directions: Sat nav: SY20 8TA. SN 681 960. Car park is one mile from Eglwys-fach village, off A487, six miles SW of Machynlleth.
Public transport: Bus - no.X28 Machynlleth to Aberystwyth, alight Eglwys-fach. Lloyds Coaches (T. 01654 702 100). Train - Machynlleth.
Visiting: Open daily (dawn-dusk). Coaches welcome, call for parking info. Visitor centre open daily (not xmas period) 9am-5pm Apr-Oct, 10am-4pm Nov-Mar. Drinks/light refreshments, toilets. Entrance fee for reserve, members free. Three trails, five hides, two viewpoints, some wheelchair accesss. No dogs.
Contact: RSPB, T: 01654 700 222; E: ynyshir@rspb.org.uk

INDEX TO RESERVES

INDEX TO RESERVES

INDEX TO RESERVES

Neil Gartshore

The colourful Waxwing *Bombycilla garrulus* is always a pleasure to see during the winter when they can often turn up in large numbers if the conditions are right.

DIRECTORY OF WILDLIFE LECTURERS, PHOTOGRAPHERS & ARTISTS

WILDLIFE LECTURERS & PHOTOGRAPHERS

THIS DIRECTORY LISTS a number of individuals who offer lectures covering a wide variety of wildlife related subjects. In addition, a number of them also offer a range of photographic products/services.

Each listing indicates whether the individual offer lectures (L) and/or photographic product/services (P) followed by a short biography.

Under *'Lectures'* there is an indication of the talks that are available but bear in mind that this is probably not the full list of what may be available.
• Fee: this will inevitably vary due to the travel distances involved but will give an idea of what is charged.
• Distance: how far lecturers are willing to travel/any restrictions are noted here.
• Time: when lecturers are available/any restrictions are noted here.

If any of the listings offer photographic products/services they are described under *'Photography'*.

If you are an organiser of a group looking to book a speaker for your meetings or would like further information about the photographic products/services offered please contact the individuals directly via the details at the end of their listing - please mention *'The Birdwatcher's Yearbook'* when making an enquiry.

Wildlife Lecturers & Photographers Listings

Do you offer talks and / or photographic products & services?
Would you like a listing in this directory? (A charge applies)
Contact us for details (see page 6)

ALIBONE, Mike L
Northamptonshire-based birder, Optics Editor for Birdwatch magazine, producing equipment reviews and providing buying advice for readers while writing other ad hoc features. Also qualified ecologist and experienced logistician, having undertaken numerous birding trips to the four corners of the Western Palearctic, with Israel as a speciality destination, as well as to Africa, south-east Asia and USA.

Lectures: Birding Israel - north to south, migration and conservation; Birding Northamptonshire - key sites and population dynamics; Birding Optics - how they work, brand overviews and what to look for when buying.

Fee: Standard £85 (negotiable for small groups) plus travel, charged at 15p per mile.
Distance: Any considered. **Time:** Flexible.

Contact: T: 07950 707 697;
E: alibone.mike@gmail.com;
W: www.northantsbirds.com; twitter: @bonxie

ALMOND, Jim L, P
A very active birder, bird photographer and experienced lecturer with additional interest in Butterflies/Odonata.

Lectures: See website for full descriptive details and titles, inc. Wild Peregrines; Birding in Shropshire/ Venus Pool; Scilly Pelagics; North Norfolk; New England; Vancouver; Bird & Nature Photography; Bird identification; other wildlife inc. butterflies & dragonflies. All talks are digitally presented in an entertaining style with audio-visual finale. All levels of interest catered for.

Fee: £95 for standard lecture and fuel at 30p per mile.
Distance: Any. **Time:** Any.

Photography: All UK birds, special interest in wild Peregrines. See website for main interests, gallery and portfolio. **Products & services:** Images for publication, lectures and workshops / individual tuition available. Vast library of images. Available for commissions, lectures / tours. Competitive terms for larger projects.

Contact: 5 Coolock Close, St Peters Park, Shrewsbury, SY3 9QD; T: 07940 678 719;
E: shropshirebirder@gmail.com;
W: www.shropshirebirder.co.uk

WILDLIFE LECTURERS & PHOTOGRAPHERS

BELL, Graham L, P

A professional ornithologist, cruise lecturer worldwide (covering all seven continents), photographer, author, former British Birds Rarities Committee member.

Lectures: Arctic; Antarctic; Siberia; Australia; Iceland; Seychelles; UK - identification, behaviour, seabirds, garden birds, entertaining bird sound imitations, birds in myth & fact, bird names, taking better photos, etc.

Fee: £20 donation to BirdLife International plus travel and B&B (if required). **Distance:** Any. **Time:** Any.

Photography: Birds, animals, flowers, landscapes, all seven continents from Arctic to Antarctic. **Products & services:** Original slides for sale, £2.00 ea.; Photographic lecture available - Taking Better Photos.

Contact: Ros View, South Yearle, Wooler, Northumberland NE71 6RB; T: 01668 281 310; E: seabirdsdgb@hotmail.com

BOWDEN, Paul L

Birdwatcher and nature photographer (4K-Video and DSLR photos of birds and other wildlife) for 30+ years (serious amateur). Founder member and current Chairman of Glamorgan Wildlife Photographic Club. Member of local and national organisations (Glamorgan Birds, RSPB and WWT). Provide own HD Projector, HD Laptop, amplifier and speakers.

Lectures: Birds of Europe (Austria, Belarus, Bulgaria, Estonia, Finland, Germany, Greece (Lesvos), Hungary, Italy, Portugal & Madeira, Spain & Balearic and Canary Islands, Sweden & UK) and further destinations: Egypt; Libya; Morocco; Oman; Armenia; Azerbaijan; Georgia; India; Hong Kong; Japan; Australia; Panama; Costa Rica; Brazil; USA (nine States: AZ, CA, FL, HI, IL, MO, OR, TX, WA) & Canada. Also Butterflies and Dragonflies from UK, Europe and Overseas. Presentations in HD Video Movie and/or Powerpoint formats.

Fee: £65 plus reasonable travelling expenses (with overnight accommodation for longer trips). **Distance:** Any. **Time:** Any by arrangement.

Contact: 4 Patmore Close, Gwaelod-y-Garth, Cardiff, CF15 9SU; T: 029 2081 3044 or 07771 664 819; E: bowden_pe@hotmail.com

BUCKINGHAM, John L, P

Long-standing and popular lecturer, worldwide bird and wildlife photographer, tour leader.

Lectures: 60+ titles covering birds, wildlife, botany, ecology and habitats in UK, Europe, Africa, Australia, Indian sub-continent, North-South and Central America. Includes favourites such as How Birds Work; The Natural History of Birds; Wonders of Bird Migration.

Fee: £100 plus expenses. **Distance:** Any. **Time:** Any.

Photography: Huge range of birds, botany and wildlife from UK, Europe, Africa, Americas, Australia, Asia and worldwide. **Products & services:** Digital images available for publication and purchase plus original slides for lectures and personal use.

Contact: 10 Courtlands, Kingsdown Road, Kingsdown, Walmer, CT14 8BW; T: 01304 364 231; E: john.birdtalk@btinternet.com

CLEAVE, Andrew MBE L

Wildlife photographer, author, lecturer and tour leader.

Lectures: More than 30 talks (incl. Canadian Rockies; New Zealand seabirds and endemics; Varangerfjord birds and wildlife; India; Southern Sweden; Belarus; Bermuda; Mediterranean birds and wildlife; Isles of Scilly; Lundy; Shetland; Ancient Woodlands; Dormice; Coastal Birds: Life Between the Tides. Full list available.

Fee: £75 plus petrol. **Distance:** Approx. 70 miles without accommodation. **Time:** Afternoons and evenings, not school holidays.

Contact: 31 Petersfield Close, Chineham, Basingstoke, Hampshire RG24 8WP; T: 01256 320 050 & 07785 767 263; E: andrew@bramleyfrith.co.uk; W: http://andrewcleave.co.uk/

COLLINS, Chris L

Wildwings tour leader, Neotropical Bird Club council member & treasurer, experienced lecturer and wildlife photographer.

Lectures: Birds of the Russian Far East/In search of the Spoon-billed Sandpiper; Arctic Russia: Realm of the Ice Bear; Birds of Guyana; Unknown Antarctica: Birds of the Ross Sea and New Zealand Subantarctic Islands; Around the World in 80 minutes; Amazing Birds; Pacific Odyssey: New Zealand to Japan.

Fee: £105 + travel expenses. **Distance:** Four hours from Surrey/London or overnight accommodation. **Time:** Any by prior agreement.

Contact: 9 Pound Close, Long Ditton, Surbiton, Surrey KT6 5JW; T: 020 8398 1742; E: chris@birdsandwildlife.com; W: www.birdsandwildlife.com/lectures

207

WILDLIFE LECTURERS & PHOTOGRAPHERS

COUZENS, Dominic [L]

Full-time birdwatcher, tour leader (UK /overseas), writer and lecturer.

Lectures: The Secret Lives of Garden Birds; Birding a Local Patch; Mammal Watching in Britain; Encounters with Remarkable Birds; Have Wings Will Travel (the marvel of bird migration).

Fee: £100 plus travel. **Distance:** London/south. **Time:** Any.

Contact: 61 Felton Road, Poole, Dorset BH14 0QR; T: 07721 918 174; E: dominic.couzens@btinternet.com; W: www.birdwords.co.uk

DAVIES, Alan & MILLER, Ruth [L]

Alan and Ruth both worked for the RSPB before giving up their jobs to travel the world birding for a whole year in 2008. They now run their own birdwatching tour company called BirdwatchingTrips based in North Wales, offering relaxed, small-group birdwatching tours in the UK, Europe and further afield.

Lectures: A wide range of illustrated talks including: The Biggest Twitch, around the world in 4,000 birds - the entertaining warts-and-all story of their big birding year; Birding in the Land of the Midnight Sun: Finland and Norway; Quetzals and More: Costa Rica; A Spoonful of Thailand; Birdwatching in North Wales- more than just sheep! Southern Africa – Birding below the Equator: a fast-paced tour of South Africa, Namibia, Botswana, Zambia and Uganda, packed with colourful birds, wonderful mammals, stunning scenery – and a few hair-raising adventures; Norfolk, where birding began. We are continuously adding to our range of talks.

Fee: £0 free of charge. We do ask for our fuel costs to be covered. **Distance:** Any considered, but overnight accommodation may be required. **Time:** Very flexible all year apart from Mar-Jun and Sep/Oct when we are away guiding. Please e-mail to check availability.
Contact: 12 Ormeside Court, 19 Church Walks, Llandudno, LL30 2HG; T: 01492 872 407; E: info@birdwatchingtrips.co.uk; W: www.birdwatchingtrips.co.uk

EYRE, John [L]

Author, photographer, ornithological consultant.

Lectures: Many talks covering birding around the world (Europe, Africa, Asia, Australasia and the Americas), plus special Hampshire subjects. Examples include: New Zealand - Seabird Feast, Land Bird Famine; California Birds - Sea, Sage and Spotted Owls; Birds of Wallacea - Where Continents Collide; Family Quest - In search of all the worlds' bird families; Gilbert White's Birds; The Secret Lives of Heathland Birds; The Hampshire Bird Atlas. Several others, so please call/ e-mail to discuss options.

Fee: £90 plus travel. **Distance:** Negotiable. **Time:** Any.

Contact: 3 Dunmow Hill, Fleet, Hampshire GU51 3AN; T: 01252 677 850; E: John.Eyre@ntlworld.com

FORGHAM, Jonathan [L]

Primary school teacher for 30 years, now running science enhancement company and professional bird guide. Has given over 100 illustrated talks to bird groups in last three years in south east of England and occasionally, further afield. Visited most of Europe and parts of Asia and Australia, too. Life-long birder and all round naturalist, recording all aspects of nature within the parish of Little Hadham, East Hertfordshire. References available, all excellent. See website for recent bookings.

Lectures: The Birds of the North Norfolk Coastal Footpath; The Birds of The Camargue; The Birds of The Algarve and Baixa Alentejo; The Birds of southern Sri Lanka; The Bird Reserves of Kent; The Whole Natural History of an East Hertfordshire Parish; The Walk to Hel (a 50-mile walk around Gdansk Bay, Poland); Moths of Hertfordshire. (Will provide own laptop, cables, and projector).

Fee: £100 in total for 150 mile round trip. £125 in total for in excess of 150 mile round trip. In excess of 200 mile round trip, fee negotiable. **Distance:** Live in Herts so easy access to motorways, no restrictions under around 200 mile round trip. **Time:** Available evenings, daytime too (if early booking).

Contact: 6 Chapel Lane, Little Hadham, Ware, Herts SG11 2AA; T: 01279 776 112 (eves) or 07805 571 551 (day/texts); E: jforgham@hotmail.com; W: http://littlehadhambirding.blogspot.co.uk

GALLOP, Brian [L]

Speaker, photographer.

Lectures: 35 talks covering UK, Africa, India, Galapagos, South America and Europe (all natural history subjects). Made-to-measure talks available on request. 24hr emergency service.

Fee: £50 plus travel expenses. **Distance:** Any, but overnight accommodation if over 100 mls. **Time:** Any.

Contact: 13 Orchard Drive, Tonbridge, Kent TN10 4LT; T: 01732 361 892; E: brian_gallop@hotmail.co.uk

GALVIN, Chris L, P
A birding photographer with passion for wildlife for more than 30 years.

Lectures: Northwest Year; Around the World in 80 Birds; Bee-eaters & Kingfishers: an intro to the Birds of Goa; Birding by Camera; Birding on the Doorstep; Just Add Water; Kenya – More than just Birds.

Fee: £90 to £150 depending on distance travelled. **Distance:** 150 miles radius from home. **Time:** Any.

Photography: Birds. **Products & services:** Images for publication, prints, mounted prints, commissions considered.

Contact: 17 Henley Rd, Allerton, Liverpool, Merseyside L18 2DN; T: 0151 729 0123 or 07802 428 385; E: chris@chrisgalvinphoto.com; W: www.chrisgalvin.co.uk

GARNER, Jackie L
Professional wildlife artist, author & illustrator of *The Wildlife Artist's Handbook*. Tour leader for Aigas Field Centre and Art Safari Holidays.

Lectures: Birds/Nature in Art; Focus on the Falklands; Wildlife of Ancient Egypt; Lifting the Lid on Lundy; Brief Encounters (the art of field sketching).

Fee: £140 + expenses for almost all groups, though negotiable for venues over 100 miles away. **Distance:** Any. **Time:** Any.

Contact: The Old Cider House Studio, Humphries End, Randwick, Stroud, Glos GL6 6EW; T: 01453 847 420 or 07800 804 847; E: artist@jackiegarner.co.uk; W: www.jackiegarner.co.uk

GARTSHORE, Neil L
Editor/publisher of *'The Birdwatcher's Yearbook'* and author of *'Best Birdwatching Sites in Dorset'*. Spent 23-years working in the nature conservation field with The National Trust; The Percy FitzPatrick Institute of African Ornithology/Cape Town, South Africa; RSPB. Now a freelance bird surveyor, natural history book seller, tour guide, writer and lecturer.

Lectures: Dorset's Best Birdwatching Sites; Poole Harbour and its Birds; Japan - birding in the land of the rising sun; Birding in Spain - marshes, mountain and migration; Lesvos - Jewel in the Aegean; Wildlife Wanderings in South Africa; A Sub-Antarctic Experience - the Prince Edward Islands; The Farne Islands - Northumberland's seabird city. Ask for a list/further details.

Fee: Variable, depending on distance travelled. **Distance:** Any considered. **Time:** Flexible - sometimes available at short notice.

Contact: Moor Edge, 2 Bere Road, Wareham, Dorset BH20 4DD; T: 01929 552 560 or 07986 434 375; E: birding@callunabooks.co.uk; W: www.callunabooks.co.uk

GINNAW, Simon L
Birder & naturalist since childhood, worked with the RSPB, as a Country Park Ranger, and Forestry Commission Woodland Officer in South-east England. Freelance bird surveyor, tour leader & guide, tutor, writer, & lecturer.

Lectures: Kent's Wild Year; A Woodland Year; Birds Beyond The Boughs - Secret Lives Of Our Woodland Birds; Secret Lives Of Our Coastal Birds; Hungary: Birding the heart of Europe; A Year on my Local Patch; Wildlife Tales From The Riverbank; Exploring Britain's Mammals. Ask for a list/details.

Fee: Variable, depending on distance travelled. Distance: Any considered. **Time:** Evenings preferred, but flexible - sometimes available at short notice.

Contact: Exploring The Wild, 32 Amsbury Road, Coxheath, Kent ME17 4DP; T: 07783 354 337; E: info@simonginnaw.com; W: www.simonginnaw.com

GLENN, Neil L
Author of *Best Birdwatching Sites in Norfolk* and *Best Birdwatching Sites in Yorkshire*; regular contributor to *Bird Watching* magazine; bird tour leader for Avian Adventures. UK Rep for South Texas Nature and also a Patron for Birding For All.

Lectures: Wildlife of the Lower Rio Grande Valley, Texas; Birding the Arctic Circle; Moroccan Spice: from The Sahara to the Atlas Mountains; Warbler Wonderland: Spring Migration in Ohio and Michigan; A Year in the Life of a Bird Tour Guide; more to follow!

Fee: Negotiable. **Distance:** Any. **Time:** Any.

Contact: 13 Gladstone Avenue, Gotham, Nottingham NG11 0HN; T: 07771 934 738; E: n.glenn@ntlworld.com

WILDLIFE LECTURERS & PHOTOGRAPHERS

GROVE, Ashley L, P

Professional photographer, wildlife watcher and tour leader, with a specialism in birds. A list of available lectures is below. References on request if required. Recommended speaker by the RSPB, BTO and Royal Horticultural Society.

Lectures: Shetland to Scilly, Birds of the British Isles; Jewels of the Gambia, Kingfishers, Bee-eaters & Rollers; Great British Birds; Lammergeiers of the Spanish Pyrenees; Trinidad & Tobago, Home of the Hummingbird; Wonderful Winter Wildlife, Vibrant Sri Lanka, Blue Magpies, Blue Whales & Blue skies; Crane Spotting..., around Swedens Lake Hornborga; A Beginners Guide to Birdwatching. More talks under construction.

Fee: £80 plus 25p per mile expenses (may be negotiable if you're able to recommend a nearby group to speak to on an adjacent evening). **Distance:** Any within reason. **Time:** Any.

Photography (and Birdwatching Tours) - Ashley's company, 'Experience Nature',run very reasonably priced holidays for wildlife photographers and birdwatchers. Trips to The Gambia, Spain, Sweden, Sri Lanka, Scotland and Trinidad & Tobago are run regularly, plus other foreign and UK destinations. Visit Ashley's website for more information on the tours and for a selection of images gathered on these trips.

Contact: 16 Lint Meadow, Wythall, Worcestershire B47 5PH; T: 07704 189 835;
E: experiencenaturetours@gmail.com;
W: www.experiencenature.co.uk

LINGARD, David L, P

Photographer, retired from RAF, now UK delegate to LIPU (BirdLife in Italy).

Lectures: Choice of talks on birding but primarily on Birdwatching in Italy and the work of LIPU.

Fee: Donation to LIPU, plus petrol costs. **Distance:** Any. **Time:** Any.

Photography: Birds and views of places visited around the world. **Products & services:** 35mm transparencies (last Century) but now, exclusively digital images.

Contact: Fernwood, Doddington Road, Whisby, Lincs LN6 9BX; T: 01522 689 030; E: mail@lipu-uk.org;
W: www.lipu-uk.org

LOVELL, Stephen L

All round naturalist with interests in all aspects of natural history. RSPB and RHS listed speaker and cruise ship speaker for Peel Talent. Guest speaker for the British Wildlife Watching Club in Scotland. Photographer and Adult Education Tutor. Now running Greenspaces which specialises in small group daytrips, short breaks and holidays in the UK. Also organises workshops covering a variety of topics - see website for further details.

Lectures: Available on a wide range of European destinations including Lesvos, Majorca, Menorca, Extremadura. A wide range of talks on various areas of Britain with many covering Scotland. Other talks available on a wide variety of destinations around the world including Costa Rica, Trinidad and Tobago, Cuba, Nepal, Sri Lanka, India, New Zealand, Australia, Tanzania, St Lucia, Borneo, Iceland and whale watching in Mexico. I have a wide variety of talks covering garden related topics such as Encouraging Wildlife into the Garden. There is also a talk on The Miracle of Migration. More talks are constantly being added.

Fee: £70 to £90 + travel (negotiable according to distance travelled). **Distance:** Any considered. **Time:** Any.

Contact: 6 Abingdon Close, Doddington Park, Lincoln, LN6 3UH; T: 01522 689 456 or 07957 618 684;
E: stephenlovell58@btinternet.com;
W: www.stevelovellgreenspaces.co.uk

LOWEN, James L, P

Multi-award-winning author of 11 nature and travel books making wildlife accessible to the non-specialist... 52 European wildlife weekends: a year of short breaks for nature lovers / 52 wildlife weekends: a year of British wildlife-watching breaks / A summer of British wildlife: 100 great days out watching wildlife / Year round Walks, Norfolk / Antarctic Wildlife / Pantanal Wildlife / The Butterfly Pavilion / Birds of France / Birds of Spain / Spotlight: Hedgehogs / Spotlight: Badgers. Columnist in Bird Watching and The Countryman magazines, and regular feature- and travel-writer for BBC Wildlife and The Telegraph among other publications. Professional photographer represented by FLPA and Alamy. His Bird Fair lectures routinely pack marquees each year, including in the Author's Forum!

Lectures: Many talks, e.g. Antarctic wildlife; Pantanal wildlife; Europe's best wildlife weekends; The Butterfly Pavilion; Gaucho birding in Argentina; Japan - the world's best winter birding?; Seeing t best of Britain's summer wildlife; Britain's top wildlife weekends; Butterfly Britain; Britain's dragonflies; Britain's amazing orchids; Wildlife photography made easy; Why moths are magic.

Fee: £80 plus 25p per mile plus £10 per hour travel time over two hours total. **Limits:** Negotiable, overnight accommodation may be needed. **Time:** Any.

WILDLIFE LECTURERS & PHOTOGRAPHERS

Photography: All wildlife, from UK, Argentina, Brazil, Antarctica, Japan, various European countries. **Products & services:** digital images, prints, lectures, commissioned photography.

Contact: Norwich, Norfolk. T: 07523 000 490; E: lowen.james@gmail.com; W: http://jameslowen.com; W: www.pbase.com/james_lowen; Twitter: @JLowenWildlife; Instagram: @JLowenWildlife

MAYER, Edward [L]

Founder of Swift Conservation advice service, formerly Head of Gallery Management at the Tate Gallery.

Lectures: Swifts, Their Lives and Conservation. Also Biodiversity Awareness and Techniques for the Built Environment - talks and training sessions for enthusiasts, ornithologists, architects, developers, planners, biodiversity and facilities staff. Talks from 30 minutes to two hours, training from one hour to one day.

Fee: From £95, depending on type and length of talk, or collection/donation, plus travel expenses. **Distance:** UK/Europe. **Time:** Any.

Contact: 28 Yale Court, Honeybourne Road, London NW6 1JG; T: 020 7794 2098; E: mail@swift-conservation.org; W: www.swift-conservation.org

MILES, John [L]

Former warden for RSPB, tour guide [Nature Scotland], consultant, journalist and author of...
Best Birdwatching Sites: The Solway; Best Birdwatching Sites: Yorkshire [co-author]; *Hadrian's Birds; Exploring Lakeland Wildlife; Pharoah's Birds; Hadrian's Wildlife* and a series of children's books [ten titles, growing every year with Chickbooks].

Lectures: The Solway - the whole of Cumbria and Dumfries & Galloway; Hadrian's Wildlife - History of birds back to Roman times + many present day locations to visit; Death on the Nile - looks at the history of birds from Ancient Egypt to present time birds while cruising the Nile; Mull: Not just Eagles! - year round look at this island; Go Birding - follows John around Britain in search of articles in 'Go Birding' in Bird Watching magazine; British Bee-eaters - Will they ever BEE Every Year!; Caithness - the forgotten part of Scotland!; Islay - Not just Geese!; Yorkshire - Not just a White Rose!

Fee: Prices on request. **Distance:** Anywhere in UK. **Time:** Evenings best.

Contact: Jockey Shield, Castle Carrock, Carlisle, Cumbria CA4 9NF; T: 01228 670 205; E: john@chickbooks.co.uk; W: chickbooks.co.uk

CHICK **BOOKS**

OFFORD, Keith [L]

Raptor specialist. Coordinator of North-east Wales Raptor Study group. Photographer, lecturer, course & workshop tutor, tour leader, conservationist.

Lectures: 16 talks covering raptors (biology and identification), bird flight, British uplands, gardens, migration, woodland wildlife, Texas, Spain, Sri Lanka, Estonia, Morocco, Iceland, Costa Rica, Namibia, Kruger National Park, Western Cape.

Fee: £100 (pro-rota to travel distance per mile after 100 miles) plus travel costs. **Distance:** Any. **Time:** Sept to Apr.

Contact: Yew Tree Farmhouse, Craignant, Selattyn, Nr Oswestry, Shropshire SY10 7NP; T: 01691 718 740; E: keith@keithofford.co.uk; W: www.keithofford.co.uk

READ, Mike [L, P]

Photographer (wildlife/landscapes), tour leader, writer.

Lectures: 12 talks featuring British and foreign subjects (list available on receipt of sae or see website).

Fee: £70 plus travel. **Distance:** 80 miles from Ringwood. **Time:** Available Sept to Mar.

Photography: Birds, mammals, plants, landscapes, and some insects. UK, France, USA, New Zealand, Falkland Isalnds plus many more. Behaviour, action, portraits, artistic pictures available for publication. More than 100,000 images in stock. **Products & services:** Extensive stock photo library. Canvas and giclee prints, greetings cards, books.

Contact: Claremont, Redwood Close, Ringwood, Hampshire BH24 1PR; T: 01425 475 008; E: mike@mikeread.co.uk; W: www.mikeread.co.uk

REDMAN, Nigel [L]

Author, editor and tour leader.

Lectures: Mostly birds, inc. Ethiopia; Somaliland; Eritrea; Kenya; Morocco; Russia (and former Soviet Union); the Caucasus; Antarctica; Arctic (North-west Passage/Svalbard); New Zealand; Mexico.

Fee: Negotiable. **Distance:** Any (but overnight accommodation may be required). **Time:** Any.

Contact: Hollyhocks, Edgefield Road, Briston, Norfolk NR24 2HX; T: 01263 862 866 or 07734 886 515; E: nigelredman28@hotmail.com

WILDLIFE LECTURERS & PHOTOGRAPHERS

ROTHERHAM, Prof Ian [L]

Former local authority ecologist, environmental campaigner, researcher, lecturer, writer and broadcaster.

Lectures: Numerous illustrated talks on all aspects of conservation inc.: Rewilding Nature; Rewilding Your Garden; Rewilding the River Don; Wild Deer of the Peak District; the Lost Fens; Yorkshire's Forgotten Fenlands; Shadow Woods - a search for lost landscapes; Wild woods and woodland heritage; Wildlife and history of moors, heaths and bogs; Urban Wildlife; Gardening for Wildlife; Alien and invasive species; Wild Peak District; Eco-history; Wilding Nature ; Wilder Visions - re-constructing nature for the 21st century; Eco-fusion - our hybrid future; Loving the aliens?; Understanding the ancient woods; Sherwood Forest - wildlife, history & heritage; Sherwood Forest's Ancient Trees; Wildlife & Heritage - Yorkshire's Viking Coast.

Fee: £85, plus petrol 50p per mile. **Distance:** Prepared to travel if expenses are covered. **Time:** Any by arrangement.

Contact: 42 School Lane, Norton, Sheffield, S8 8BL; T: 07751 089 499; E: i.d.rotherham@shu.ac.uk; W: www.ukeconet.org; Blog: http://ianswalkonthewildside.wordpress.com/

SIMPSON, Rick and Elis [L]

Joint founders of the wader conservation charity Wader Quest. Birders, fundraisers and conservationists. Rick: speaker, artist, writer (Confessions of a Bird Guide (2013); Eury the Spoon-billed Sandpiper (for children 6-11, 2016); An Inspiration of Waders (2018). Elis: team photographer.

Lectures: Wader Quest (stories and facts about waders and their conservation); Confessions of a Bird Guide (guiding in Brazil); many other titles, mainly concerned with the waders of the world... full list on application.

Fee: £110 flat fee. **Distance:** Any considered. **Time:** Any, often available at short notice.

Contact: 20 Windsor Avenue, Newport Pagnell, Bucks, MK16 8HA. T: 07484 186 443; E: rick@rick-simpson.com; W: www.waderquest.net

SCOTT, Ann [L]

Retired. Formerly Senior Wildlife Adviser for RSPB, lecturer and teacher of ornithology.

Lectures: Various talks on UK & abroad. Latest talk: The Kenyan Coastal Forest and Area – Key Migration Hotspots. Featuring Mida Creek, Lake Jilore , Dakatcha and Arabuko-Sokoke Forest, all wildlife rich areas. Mentions Bob Scott Memorial Appeal and our work/involvement out there.

Learn more at: http://www.whytsbirds.org or from www.justgiving.com/ann-scott1/

Fee: £80 plus expenses (negotiable). **Distance:** Normally 2 hours drive from Huntingdon but willing to discuss. **Time:** Available mid-Mar to mid-Nov.

Contact: 17 Springfield Close, Buckden, Huntingdon, Cambs PE19 5UR; T: 01480 811 848; E: abscott@buckdencambs.co.uk

Since the 2014 purchase of 219 acres of Kenyan Coastal Forest in the Dakacha area, with funds from the Bob Scott Memorial Appeal (BSMA) A Rocha, who watch over and maintain the Kirosa Scott Reserve, have themselves raised money to purchase more forest. Together with BSMA we have now secured around 1,000 acres. This is important for many Inter African, African, Eastern European, Asian, and Endemic species e.g. the Oriental Cuckoo overwinters in the Coastal Forest having travelled from Central China to do so.

Now the BSMA is also helping nine villages, who have formed themselves into the "Tujipange Community Based Organisation (TCBO), to replant forest in the Gedi area spreading north and including Lake Jilore. This lake is a wonderful area which holds many species of water birds at certain times of the year. With help from that group over 6,700 trees have been planted in the last two years and we have lost just 14 despite the lack of rainfall at times! These trees are mainly indigenous plants and their presence has already seen the return, into the area, of many of the once abundant local species that had been missing for a number of years.

We CAN achieve success if we work with the people and that it what BSMA is increasingly doing whilst trying to ensure the continued expansion of owned Dakacha forest by A Rocha.

WILDLIFE LECTURERS & PHOTOGRAPHERS

SUMMERFIELD, Saffron [L]

Lifelong Birdwatcher and Professional Musician/ Composer and Sound Recordist. Artist in Residence at Rye Harbour Nature Reserve in 2008. Birdsong project for Norfolk Wildlife Trust Cley Calling 2019.

Lecture: WHEN BIRDS SING
Just why does a small bird (Marsh Warbler) 'collect' up to 250 other bird songs and calls on its migratory path from Africa to Northern Europe? What is happening inside a bird's brain when it sings.

How many composers have been inspired by listening to bird song? Mozart kept a pet starling and taught him to sing some of his melodies.

Birdsong and the Human Condition. Why does the Dawn Chorus have such an emotional and calming effect on some Humans?

This fascinating, entertaining and extensively researched talk is digitally presented with many of her own field recordings, photos and sonograms; all levels of interest catered for.

Fee: £100 inclusive. **Distance:** East Anglia/East Midlands. **Time:** Any.

Contact: 15 Pond Gate, Redhouse Park, Bucks MK14 5FB. T: 07941 932 543;
E: saffronsummerfield@icloud.com; W: see videos and sound recordings at www.motherearthmusic.co.uk

TODD, Ralph [L]

Lecturer & photographer, former tour leader and course tutor.

Lectures: On the Trail of the Crane – parts 1 and 2; Polar Odyssey; Return of the Osprey; Natural Wonders and Wildlife of Iceland; Birds and People - Travels Through Time; Where Yeehaa meets Ole; Birds in the Land of Disney; Antarctic Adventure; Springtime in Lesvos.

Fee: £75 plus expenses. **Distance:** Any. **Time:** Any - also short notice.

Contact: 9 Horsham Road, Bexleyheath, Kent DA6 7HU; T: 01322 528 335; E: rbtodd@btinternet.com

van GROUW, Katrina [L]

Katrina van Grouw, author of *The Unfeathered Bird and Unnatural Selection*, inhabits that no-man's land slap bang between art and science. She holds degrees in fine art and natural history illustration, and is a former curator of ornithological collections at a major national museum. She's a self-taught scientist with a passion for evolutionary biology and its history. After a long and varied career on both sides of the art/science divide she now devotes her time exclusively to her books.

Katrina offers two talks about her books:
From Art to Zoology: A story of evolution. An entertaining and inspiring talk on the making of The Unfeathered Bird and the transition from fine artist to science author.

Unnatural Selection: Evolution at the Hand of Man. About Darwin, evolution, and why domesticated animals deserve a second look.

"Katrina is a dazzling speaker. Her talk will enthral anyone interested in birds."

"One of the most interesting and entertaining talks we had heard for a long time. This talk is really not to be missed!"

Fee: £90 local; £100-£150 non-local. **Distance:** Any. **Time:** Flexible - sometimes available at short notice.

Contact: 36 Northern Road, Aylesbury, Bucks HP19 9QY; T: 01296 398 571 & 07503 038 687;
E: katrinavangrouw@aol.co.uk;
W: www.unfeatheredbird.com

WHITE, Mick LRPS [L, P]

Professional wildlife photographer and Lecturer

Lectures: I offer a selection of talks covering a range of wildlife subjects and destinations, along with some practical guidance on taking wildlife Images both in the UK and Abroad.

A full list can be found on my web site at mickwhitephotography.com which is updated regularly.

Photography: I also offer a range of photographic workshops for small groups and individuals covering a wide range of wildlife subjects, full details of which can be found on my web site along with booking information.

Fee: Lectures: £70 + Travel @ 40p per mile + any accommodation costs incurred. Workshops: max group size 6 is £65pp or Individual tuition is £135 per day. **Distance:** Any. **Time:** Anytime.

Contact: 230 The Glade, Shirley, Croydon, Surrey CR0 7UG T: 07765 131 588; E: mickwhite870@gmail.com;
W: www.mickwhitephotography.com

BTO SPEAKERS

THIS DIRECTORY HAS been compiled to help Bird Clubs and similar organisations in finding speakers from the BTO for indoor meetings. Each entry consists of an individual speaker, a list of talks/lectures available, details of fees and expenses required and travel distance limitations. If you are interested in any of the speakers, please contact Ieuan Evans (ieuan.evans@bto.org). Alternatively, contact the BTO on 01842 750 050.

Austin, Dr Graham (Snr Res Ecol, Wetland & Marine Research)
Subjects: Wetland Bird Survey. Fee: £40. Distance: Travel by agreement.

Baillie, Dr Stephen (Science Director Modelling & Demography)
Subjects: BirdTrack; Population Monitoring. Fee: £40. Distance: Travel by agreement.

Balmer, Dawn (Head of Surveys)
Subjects: Bird Atlas 2007-11; House Martins; BTO Surveys. Fees: £40. Distance: 100 mile radius of Thetford, further by agreement.

Barimore, Carl (Nest Records Organiser)
Subjects: Nest Records Scheme. Fee: £40. Distance: By agreement.

Blackburn, Jez (Licensing & Sales Manager)
Subjects: Bird Moult (suitable for ringers); Ringing for Conservation; Sule Skerry Seabirds. Fee: £40 (£70 for private talks). Distance: East Anglia.

Boersch-Supan, Dr Philipp (Ecological Statistician)
Subjects: Southern Ocean Seabirds (penguins, albatrosses); Maths & Models in Ecology & Conservation. Fee: Negotiable. Distance: Negotiable.

Boothby, Claire (Garden Birdwatch Development Officer)
Subjects: Garden Birds and Wildlife. Fee: £40. Distance: By agreement.

Border, Dr Jennifer (Spatial Ecologist)
Subjects: Population Limitation in Whinchats; The Effect of Planned Housing on Bats. Fee: £40. Distance: Negotiable.

Calbrade, Neil (Wetland Bird Survey National Organiser)
Subjects: BTO/JNCC/RSPB Wetland Bird Survey (WeBS). Fee: £40. Distance: By agreement.

Conway, Greg (Research Ecologist, Land-use Research)
Subjects: Nightjar Ecology & population change; Nightjar Migration & Tracking Studies; Woodlark Ecology & Population Change; Dartford Warbler Ecology & Population Change; Ecology & Origins of Wintering Warblers in the UK; Firecrests Population Change & Studies in Thetford Forest. Fee: £40. Distance: 100 mile radius of Thetford.

Dadam, Dr Daria (Reseach Ecologist, Demography)
Subjects: Bird Disease; Marsh Tits; House Sparrow Ecology & Decline. Fees: £40. Distance: By agreement.

Darvill, Ben (Development & Engagement Manager, Scotland)
Subjects: Upland Birds; Ecology, Conservation and How You Can Help; Cuckoos and Other Long-distance Migrants; Birding With Your Eyes Shut; Fascinating Facts About Our Feathered Friends Found Through Technology, Tags and Tracks. Fee: Negotiable. Distance: Negotiable.

Evans, Ieuan (Director, Engagement))
Subjects: Unravelling the Mysteries of Bird Migration. Fee: Negotiable. Distance: Negotiable.

Franks, Samantha (Research Ecologist, Population Ecology)
Subjects: Bird Migration; North American Waders; Alaska; Wildlife of British Columbia and the Pacific Northwest. Fee: Negotiable. Distance: Negotiable.

Frost, Dr Teresa (Wetland Bird Survey National Organiser)
Subjects: BTO/JNCC/RSPB Wetland Bird Survey (WeBS). Fee: £40. Distance: By agreement.

Gillings, Dr Simon (Head of Population Ecology & Modelling)
Subjects: Atlas 2007-11. Fee: £40. Distance: Negotiable.

Hanmer, Dr Hugh (Terrestrial Res Ecol & Project Owl Coordinator)
Subjects: Urban Birds; Owls; Project Owls. Fee: £40. Distance: By agreement.

Harris, Sarah (Breeding Bird Survey National Organiser)
Subjects: BTO/JNCC/RSPB Breeding Birds Survey; Arctic Skua Tagging Research. Fee: £40. Distance: By agreement.

Henderson, Dr Ian (Snr Res Ecol, International Research)
Subjects: Arable Farming and Birds; Nightjars. Goshawk. Whinchat. Fee: £40. Distance: By agreement.

Jones, Kelvin (BTO Cymru Development Officer)
Subjects: Work of the BTO, other subjects via discussion e.g. Hawfinch and Twite in North Wales; Ringing in Aras Turkey. Fee: £40. Distance: By agreement.

McAvoy, Stephen (BirdTrack Support Officer)
Subjects: Mapping Migration with BirdTrack. Fee: £40. Distance: By agreement.

Moran, Nick (Training Manager)
Subjects: Better Birding; Birding With Your Eyes Shut; Nocmig - Sound-recording Birds at Night; What BirdTrack Can Do For You; Work of the BTO (incl surveys/schemes, tagging); Birds and Birding in Arabia (non-BTO). Fee: £40. Distance: By agreement.

Musgrove, Dr Andy (Head of Monitoring)
Subjects: Ornithology: How Can Birdwatchers Contribute to Recording Other Wildlife. Fee: £40. Distance: By agreement.

Noble, Dr David (Principal Ecologist, Monitoring)
Subjects: Developing Bird Indicators; Population Trends. Fee: £40. Distance: By agreement.

Pearce-Higgins, Dr James (Director, Science)
Subjects: Birds and Climate Change; Upland Birds; A Year in the Life of a Golden Plover; Where Have All Our Curlews Gone? Fee: £40. Distance: By agreement.

214

BTO SPEAKERS

Risely, Kate (Garden BirdWatch Organiser)
Subjects: Garden Birds and Wildlife. **Fee:** £40.
Distance: Prefer no overhight stay.

Robinson, Dr Rob (Principle Ecologist, Modelling & Demography)
Subjects: Farming & Birds; Conservation Value of
Ringing. **Fee:** £40. **Distance:** By agreement.

Ross-Smith, Dr Viola (Science Communications Manager)
Subjects: Gulls; Seabirds; Tracking Studies (General).
Fee: £40. **Distance:** By agreement.

Siriwardena, Dr Gavin (Head of Terrestrial Ecology)
Subjects: Farmland Bird Research - Causes of Decline &
Potential Solutions; Agri-Environment Schemes; Birds &
Ecosystem Sevices. **Fee:** £40. **Distance:** Negotiable.

Standiffe, Paul (Media Manager)
Subjects: Atlas 2007-11; Homes to Let – Nestboxes;
Birds, Birders and the Work of the BTO; Tracking
African Migrants. **Fee:** £40. **Distance:** Negotiable.

Toms, Mike (Head of Communications)
Subjects: Are Gardens Good for Birds or Birdwatchers?;
Owls and Man - a Cultural History; **Fee:** Negotiable.
Distance: Negotiable.

Wernham, Dr Chris (Senior Research Ecologist, BTO Scotland)
Subjects: The Work of BTO Scotland; Breeding Bird
Survey in Scotland; BirdTrack in Scotland; Working
for Scotland's Waders. **Fee:** £40. **Distance:** Travel
Scotland and NE England.

Woodward, Ian (Research Officer)
Subjects: House Martins; Heronries Census; London
Birds; **Fee:** £40. **Distance:** Negotiable.

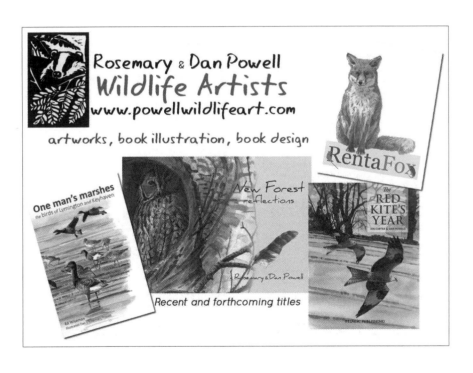

WILDLIFE ART

There are many talented wildlife artists based in the UK. This section lists a selection of art galleries that regularly display wildlife art and the websites of a number of individual artists. Check them out to see if there is anything you like.

Organisation

SOCIETY OF WILDLIFE ARTISTS (founded 1964)
Registered charity that seeks to generate an appreciation of the natural world through all forms of fine artinspired by wildlife. The Natural Eye exhibition held annually in Oct/Nov at the Mall Galleries, London. Through bursary schemes, the Society has been able to help young artists with awards of up to £750 towards travel, education or the cost of materials.

Contact: The Federation of British Artists, 17 Carlton House Terrace, London SW1Y 5BD.
T: 020 7930 6844;
E: info@mallgalleries.com;
W: www.swla.co.uk

Galleries

BIRDSCAPES GALLERY
Manor Farm Barns, Glandford, Holt, Norfolk NR25 7JP; T: 01263 741 742; E: art@birdscapes.co.uk; W: www.birdscapesgallery.co.uk

Opening times: All year, daily 11am to 5pm, but may close for part of the day before a new exhibition.

DAVID SHEPHERD WILDLIFE FOUNDATION
7 Kings Road, Shalford, Guildford, Surrey GU4 8JU.
T: 01483 272 323; E: dswf@davidshepherd.org;
W: www.davidshepherd.org

Opening times: Mon - Fri, 9am to 5pm.

CHENG KIM LOKE GALLERY, SLIMBRIDGE
Wildfowl & Wetland Trust, Slimbridge, Gloucestershire GL2 7BT; T: 01453 891 900;
E: info.slimbridge@wwt.org.uk; W: www.wwt.org.uk
Opening times: All year, daily except Dec 25, 9.30am to 5.30pm/last admission at 4.30pm [5pm/4pm winter]. Admission charge for non-WWT members.

GORDALE (host of EXHIBITION OF WILDLIFE ART)
Gordale Garden and Home Centre, Chester High Road, Burton, South Wirral, Cheshire CH64 8TF;
T: 0151 336 2116; E: admin@gordale.co.uk;
W: www.gordale.co.uk & www.ewa-uk.com

Opening times: Stages an annual Exhibition of Wildlife Art in late July. Daily 9.30am to 6pm (11am-5pm Sunday). Free admission.

HOUSE OF BRUAR (includes WILDLIFE ART GALLERY)
By Blair Atholl, Perthshire PH18 5TW;
T: 0345 136 0111; E: mailorder@houseofbruar.com;
W: www.houseofbruar.com/gallery/

Opening times: All year, daily except Dec 25 & Jan 1. 9.30am to 6pm. Free admission.

MALL GALLERIES
The Mall, London SW1; T: 0207 930 6844;
E: info@mallgalleries.com;
W: www.mallgalleries.org.uk

Opening times: Stages British Wildlife Photography Awards and the Society of Wildlife Artists' annual exhibition around Sep/Oct/Nov (10am to 5pm). Admission charge.

NATURE IN ART
Wallsworth Hall, Main A38, Twigworth, Gloucester GL2 9PA; T: 01452 731 422 (admin); E: via website; W: www.natureinart.org.uk

Opening times: Closed Mondays (exc. Bank Holidays) and Dec 24 to 26 otherwise open daily 10am to 5pm. Admission charge.

PINKFOOT GALLERY
High Street, Cley-next-the-Sea, Norfolk NR25 7RB;
T: 01263 740 947; E: info@pinkfootgallery.co.uk;
W: www.pinkfootgallery.co.uk

Opening times: All year, daily (exc xmas) 10.00am to 5.00pm (Mon to Sat), 11am to 4pm (Sun). Free admission.

WATERSTON HOUSE
Donald Watson Gallery, The SOC, Waterston House, Aberlady, East Lothian EH32 0PY; T: 01875 871 330; E: exhibitions@the-soc.org.uk; W: www.the-soc.org.uk

Opening times: All year, daily 10.00am to 4.00pm. Free entry.

THE WILDLIFE ART GALLERY
Online Art Gallery. E: wildlifeartgallery@btinternet.com;
W: www.wildlifeartgallery.com

Artists

AKROYD, Carry
E: carry@carryakroyd.co.uk; W: www.carryakroyd.co.uk

ALLEN, Richard
T: 01206 826 753; E: richardallenart@btinternet.com;
W: www.richardallenillustrator.com

ANGUS, Max
T: 07766 277 915; E: info@maxangus.co.uk;
W: www.maxangus.co.uk

ARTINGSTALL, Nigel
T: 01204 412 531; E: the-artist@ntlworld.com;
W: www.nigelartingstall.com

BARTLETT, Paul
T: 01382 698 346; E: pauljbartlett@hotmail.com;
W: www.naturalselectiongallery.co.uk

BENNETT, David
E: via website; W: www.davidbennettwildlifeart.com

WILDLIFE ART

BOWLES, Ian
T: 01732 810 637; E: via website;
W: www.ianbowleswildlifeartist.co.uk

BROCKIE, Keith
T: 01887 830 609; E: kbrockie@btinternet.com;
W: www.keithbrockie.co.uk

COOK, Robert
T: 07905 394 099; E: info@robcookart.com;
W: www.robcookart.com

COX, Jackie
T: 07780 877 300; E: jcox953@btinternet.com;
W: www.sindencox-art.co.uk/jackie.html

DALY, David
E: via website; W: www.davedalyartist.com

DAVIS, John
T: 01243 512 351; E: johndavis.wildlife@tiscali.co.uk;
W: www.johndavisartist.co.uk

DAY, Nick
T: 07763 109 020; E: birdmanday@yahoo.com;
W: www.nick-day-wildlife-artist.co.uk

DEMAIN, Michael
E: via website; W: www.michaeldemainwildlifeart.co.uk

DERRY, Nick
E: via website; W: https://nickderry.webs.com/

EDWARDS, Brin
T: 01787 211 162; E: studio@brin-edwards.com;
W: www.brin-edwards.com

FINNEY, David
E: via website; W: www.davidfinney.co.uk

FOKER, John
E: jffoker@googlemail.com; W: www.bearparkartists.co.uk

FORKNER, Andrew
T: 01993 776 322; E: andrew.forkner@gmail.com;
W: www.andrewforkner.co.uk

FULLER, Robert
T: 01759 368 355; E: mail@robertefuller.com;
W: www.robertefuller.com

GALE, John
E: johngaleartist@outlook.com;
W: www.galleryofbirds.co.uk

GARNER, Jackie
T: 01453 847 420; E: artist@jackiegarner.co.uk;
W: www.jackiegarner.co.uk

GREENHALF, Robert
E: via website; W: www.robertgreenhalf.co.uk

GRIFFITHS, Ian
T: 07971 678 464; E: mail@artbygriff.com;
W: www.artbygriff.com

HASLEN, Andrew
E: wildlifeartgallery@btinternet.com;
W: http://andrewhaslen.com/

HESELDEN, Russ
T: 01953 850 145; E: heselden860@btinternet.com;
W: www.russheselden.co.uk

HEWITT, Angela
T: 01983 296 110; E: angela.hewitt@btclick.com;
W: www.angelahewittdesigns.co.uk

HODGES, Gary
T: 01273 047 897; E: gary@garyhodges-wildlife-art.com;
W: www.garyhodges-wildlife-art.com

HOWEY, Paul
E: via website; W: www.paulhowey.co.uk

HUNT, Alan
E: via website; W: www.alanmhunt.com

INGRAM, Alison
T: 01403 263 179; E: alison@alisoningram.co.uk;
W: www.alisoningram.co.uk

JOHNSON, Richard
E: rjohnson.birdart@gmail.com;
W: www.facebook.com/Richard-Johnson-Wildlife-Artist-318774484888727/

JONES, Kitty
E: via website; W: www.kittiejones.com

KEMP, Carolyn
E: via website; W: www.carolynkemp.co.uk

LANGMAN, Mike
E: mikelangman@blueyonder.co.uk;
W: www.mikelangman.co.uk

LEWINGTON, Ian
T: 01235 819 792; E: lewbirder@btinternet.com;
W: www.ian-lewington.co.uk

LEWINGTON, Richard
T: 01235 848 451; E: enquiries@richardlewington.co.uk;
W: www.richardlewington.co.uk

LOCKWOOD, Rachel
T: 01263 740 947; E: rachel@rachellockwoodartist.com;
W: www.rachellockwoodartist.co.uk

MACKAY, Andrew
E: via website; W: www.ajm-wildlife-art.co.uk

MANNING, Julia
T: 01458 223 025; E: julia@juliamanning.co.uk;
W: www.juliamanning.co.uk

McCALLUM, James
E: email@jamesmccallum.co.uk;
W: www.jamesmccallum.co.uk

WILDLIFE ART

MESSAGE, Steve
T: 07909 585 988; E: messagewildlifeart@btinternet.com;
W: www.message-wildlife-art.co.uk

MILLER, David
T: 01646 682 907; E: david@davidmillerart.co.uk;
W: www.davidmillerart.co.uk

NEILL, William
E: via website; W: www.william-neill.co.uk

NEWELL, Kerry
T: 07752 325 031; E: kerrynewell1@gmail.com;
W: www.kerrynewell.com

PAIGE, John & Jane
T: 01780 470 247; E: paiges@oldbrewerystudios.co.uk;
W: www.oldbrewerystudios.co.uk

PARRY, David
T: 01672 563 708; E: davidparryart@gmail.com;
W: www.davidparryart.com

PARTINGTON, Peter
T: 07966 579 592;
W: www.facebook.com/PeterPartingtonWildlifeArtist/

PAUL, Jeremy
T: 01624 832 980; E: jpaul@manx.net;
W: www.jeremypaulwildlifeartist.co.uk

PEARSON, Bruce
E: via website; W: www.brucepearson.net

PENDLETON, Chris
T: 07895 058 431; E: chris@pendleton.co.uk;
W: www.pendleton.co.uk

PHILLIPS, Antonia
T: 01308 420 423; E: via website;
W: www.antoniaphillips.co.uk

POMROY, Jonathan
T: 01439 788 014; E: jonathan@pomroy.plus.com;
W: www.jonathanpomroy.co.uk

POLLARD, Nick
E: info@nikpollard.co.uk; W: www.nikpollard.co.uk

POOLE, Greg
E: via website; W: www.gregpoole.co.uk

POWELL, Dan & Rosemary
T: 01329 668 465; E: danpowell11@btinternet.com;
W: www.powellwildlifeart.com

PROUD, Alastair
E: via website; W: www.alastairproud.co.uk

REES, Darren
T: 01786 870 538; E: darrenreesart@btinternet.com;
W: www.darrenrees.com

RIDLEY, Martin
T: 01764 670 695; E: art@martinridley.com;
W: www.martinridley.com

ROSE, Chris
T: 01835 822 547; E: chris@chrisrose-artist.co.uk;
W: www.chrisrose-artist.co.uk

SCOTT, Dafila
E: via website; W: www.dafilascott.co.uk

SINDEN, Chris
T: 01594 829 903; E: chrissinden@btinternet.com;
W: www.sindencox-art.co.uk/chris.html

STOCK, Andrew
E: andrew@andrewstock.co.uk;
W: www.andrewstock.co.uk

THRELFALL, John
T: 01556 630 262; E: john@johnthrelfall.co.uk;
W: www.johnthrelfall.co.uk

TRATT, Richard
E: rtratt@btinternet.com; W: www.richardtratt.co.uk

TRUSS, Jonathan
T: 07765 003 309; E: jon@jonathantruss.com;
W: www.jonathantruss.com

UNDERWOOD, Matthew
E: matt@mattunderwood.info; W: www.mattunderwood.info

WARREN, Michael
T: 01636 673 554; E: mike.warren@tiscali.co.uk;
W: www.mikewarren.co.uk

WATLING, Gareth
T: 01302 880 241; E: garethwatling@yahoo.com;
W: www.garethwatling.com

WHITE, Vicky
E: mail@vicky-white.co.uk; W: www.vicky-white.co.uk

WHITTLESTONE, Richard
T: 01246 582 720; E: art@richardwhittlestone.co.uk;
W: www.richardwhittlestone.co.uk

WILSON, Eric
E: via website; W: www.ericwilsonsart.com

WOOTTON, Tim
T: 01856 751 454; E: tim.wootton@tiscali.co.uk;
http://tim-wootton.blogspot.co.uk

WOODHEAD, Darren
T: 01620 823 213; E: via website;
W: www.darrenwoodheadartist.co.uk

WOOLF, Colin
T: 01852 500 232; E: sales@wildart.co.uk;
W: www.wildlifewatercolourpaintings.co.uk

Neil Gartshore

Why not head to the Scottish Highlands for a well earned break and for some of the UK's best wildlife watching - a number of Scottish-based holiday companies offering tours in the area are listed in this directory.

TRADE DIRECTORY

BIRD GARDEN SUPPLIERS

IN THIS SECTION you'll find a comprehensive guide to UK-based companies offering products or services of particular interest to active birdwatchers and wildlife enthusiasts. The aim is to make this directory as up-to-date and comprehensive as possible so if we've overlooked any companies that you feel should be included in future editions, please contact us (see page 6) with the relevant details.

If you contact any of these companies please mention *'The Birdwatcher's Yearbook'*.

BIRD GARDEN SUPPLIERS

ARK WILDLIFE LTD
Dog Kennel Farm, Charlton Road, Nr Hitchin, Herts SG5 2AB; T: 0800 085 4865; E: via website; W: www.arkwildlife.co.uk

BAMFORDS
Globe Mill, Midge Hall, Leyland, Lancashire PR26 6TN; T: 01772 456 300; E: sales@bamfords.co.uk; W: www.bamfords.co.uk

BRINVALE BIRD FOODS
Brinvale Farm, Broughton Lane, Long Clawson, Melton Mowbray, Leics LE14 4NB; T: 01664 823 230; E: info@brinvale.com; W: www.brinvale.com

CJ WILDBIRD FOODS LTD
The Rea, Upton Magna, Shrewsbury, Shropshire SY4 4UR; T: 0800 731 2820; E: sales@birdfood.co.uk; W: www.birdfood.co.uk

EYEBROOK WILD BIRD FEEDS
Rectory Farm, Great Easton, Market Harborough, Leics LE16 8SN; T: 01536 770 771; E: rectoryfarm@eyebrookwildbirdfeeds.co.uk; W: www.eyebrookwildbirdfeeds.co.uk

GARDENATURE
801 Fowler Road, Oakwood Business Park North, Clacton on Sea, Essex CO15 4AA; T: 01255 514 451; E: via website; W: www.gardennature.co.uk

GARDEN WILDLIFE DIRECT
Unit 1 Industrial, Millennium City Park, Millennium Road, Preston, Lancs, PR2 5BL; T: 01772 440 242; E: help@gardenwildlifedirect.co.uk; W: www.gardenwildlifedirect.co.uk

JACOBI JAYNE & CO
Wealden Forest Park, Herne Bay; Kent CT6 7LQ; T: 0800 072 0130; E: enquiries@livingwithbirds.com; W: www.livingwithbirds.com

KENNEDY WILD BIRD FOODS LTD
The Warehouse, 74 Station Rd, Deeping St James, Peterborough, PE6 8RQ; T: 01778 342 665; E: info@kennedywildbirdfood.co.uk; W: www.kennedywildbirdfood.co.uk

NATURE CAMERAS
176 Hungate Street, Aylsham, Norwich, Norfolk, NR11 6JZ; T: 07706 427 618; E: sales@stealthbirding.com; W: www.naturecameras.co.uk

NUTBAGS
7 Hampton Close, Blackfield, Southampton, SO45 1WQ; T: 02380 894 132; E: via website; W: www.nutbags.co.uk

THE NESTBOX COMPANY
Eastcote House, Barston Lane, Eastcote, Solihull, West Midlands B92 0HS; T: 01675 442 299; E: mail@nestbox.co.uk; W: www.nestbox.co.uk

THE OWL BOX
Tyddyn Waen, Nr Llangaffo, Isle of Anglesey LL60 6LP; T: 01248 421 091; E: info@theowlbox.co.uk; W: www.theowlbox.co.uk

SOAR MILL SEEDS
Globe Mill, Midge Hall Lane, Leyland, Lancs PR26 6TN; T: 01772 456 317; E: sales@soarmillseeds.co.uk; W: www.soarmillseeds.co.uk

VINE HOUSE FARM BIRD FOODS
Vine House Farm, Main Rd, Deeping St Nicholas, Spalding, Lincs PE11 3DG; T: 01775 630 208; E: via website; W: www.vinehousefarm.co.uk

WALTER HARRISON & SONS
Pedigree House, Ambleside, Gamston, Nottingham, NG2 6NQ; T: 0115 982 3900; E: via website; W: www.walterharrisons.com

BIRD & WILDLIFE PUBLICATIONS, BOOK PUBLISHERS, BOOK SELLERS

BIRD & WILDLIFE PUBLICATIONS

BBC WILDLIFE
Subscriptions: BBC Wildlife Magazine, PO Box 3320, 3 Queensbridge, Northampton, NN4 7BF;
T: 03330 162 121; E: bbcwildlife@buysubscriptions.com;
W: www.discoverwildlife.com

BIRDWATCH
Subscriptions: The Chocolate Factory, 5 Clarendon Road, London N22 6XJ; T: 01778 392027;
E: birdwatchsubs@warnersgroup.co.uk;
W: www.birdguides.com

BIRD WATCHING
Subscriptions: Tower House, Sovereign Park, Market Harborough, Leicestershire LE16 9EF;
T: 01858 438 884; E: bauer@subscription.co.uk;
W: www.birdwatching.co.uk

BRITISH BIRDS
Subscriptions: 4 Harlequin Gardens, St Leonards-on-Sea, East Sussex TN37 7PF; T: 01424 755 155;
E: subscriptions@britishbirds.co.uk;
W: www.britishbirds.co.uk

BRITISH WILDLIFE PUBLISHING (now part of NHBS Ltd)
Subscriptions: 1-6 The Stables, Ford Road, Totnes, Devon TQ9 5LE; T: 01803 467 166;
E: subs@britishwildlife.com;
W: www.britishwildlife.com

BOOK PUBLISHERS

BLOOMSBURY PUBLISHING
(inc Helm, Poyser, New Holland)
50 Bedford Square, London WC1B 3DP;
T: 0207 631 5600; E: contact@bloomsbury.com;
W: www.bloomsbury.com/uk/non-fiction/natural-history/

BRADT TRAVEL GUIDES LTD
31a High Street, Chesham, Buckinghamshire HP5 1BW; T: 01753 893 444;
E: info@bradtguides.com;
W: www.bradtguides.com

BRAMBLEBY BOOKS
15 Lyngford Square, Taunton, Somerset TA2 7ES;
T: 01823 259 615; E: info@bramblebybooks.co.uk;
W: www.bramblebybooks.co.uk

BUCKINGHAM PRESS LTD
55 Thorpe Park Road, Peterborough PE3 6LJ;
T: 01733 561 739; E: buckinghampress@btinternet.com;
W: www.buckinghampress.co.uk

COXTON PUBLICATIONS LTD
3 Home Farm, Saunders Lane, Walkington, Beverley, HU17 8TX; T: 01482 881 833;
E: info@coxton.alchemica.co.uk;
W: www.coxton.alchemica.co.uk

HARPER COLLINS PUBLISHERS
103 Westerhill Road, Bishopbriggs, Glasgow, G64 2QT; T: 0141 306 3100;
E: enquiries@harpercollins.co.uk;
W: www.harpercollins.co.uk

THE LANGFORD PRESS
27 Lodge Close, Ashby de-la-Zouch, LE65 1SJ;
T: 01530 417755; E: sales@langford-press.co.uk;
W: www.langford-press.co.uk

PELAGIC PUBLISHING
E: sales@pelagicpublishing.com;
W: www.pelagicpublishing.com

PRINCETON/WILDGUIDES LTD
The University Press Group, New Era Estate, Oldlands Way, Bognor Regis, W. Sussex PO22 9NQ;
T: 01243 842 165; E: via website;
W: www.press.princeton.edu/wildguides

THE SOUND APPROACH
Enefco House, 19 The Quay, Poole, Dorset BH15 1NF; T: 01202 641 004;
E: enquiries@soundapproach.co.uk;
W: www.soundapproach.co.uk

BOOK SELLERS

ATROPOS BOOKS
The Boat House, Church Cove, Lizard, Nr Helston, Cornwall TR12 7PH;
T: 01326 290 287; E: books@atropos.info;
W: www.atroposbook.co.uk

CALLUNA BOOKS
Moor Edge, 2 Bere Road, Wareham, Dorset BH20 4DD; T: 01929 552 560;
E: enquiries@callunabooks.co.uk;
W: www.callunabooks.co.uk

KEN MULLINS BOOKS
16 Heath Close, Tarvin, Chester, Cheshire CH3 8LT; T: 07866 479 010;
E: kendonago@hotmail.com

NHBS (Natural History Book Service + equipment)
1-6 The Stables, Ford Road, Totnes, Devon TQ9 5XN; T: 01803 865 913;
E: customer.service@nhbs.com;
W: www.nhbs.com

BOOK SELLERS, CLOTHING SUPPLIERS, EQUIPMENT SUPPLIERS, HOLIDAY COMPANIES

PANDION BOOKS
23 Wickham Close, Bideford, Devon
T: 01237 459 731; E: pandionbks@aol.com

PICTURE BOOK
6 Stanley Street, Leek, Staffs ST13 5HG;
T: 01538 399 033; E: info@leekbooks.co.uk;
W: www.leekbooks.co.uk

SECOND NATURE
Knapton Bookbarn, Back Lane, Knapton, York,
YO26 6QJ; T: 01904 795 489;
E: secondnatureyork@aol.com

STEVE HOLLIDAY (Bird Reports/Journals)
2 Larriston Place, Cramlington, Northumberland
NE23 8ER; T: 01670 731 963 (eves/w.ends);
E: birdreports@hotmail.co.uk

WILDSIDE BOOKS
29 Kings Avenue, Eastbourne, East Sussex
BN21 2PE; T: 01323 416 211;
E: wildsidebooks@hotmail.com

WILD SOUNDS & BOOKS (+ equipment)
Cross Street, Salthouse, Norfolk NR25 7XH;
T: 01263 741 100; E: isales@wildsounds.com;
W: www.wildsounds.com

CLOTHING SUPPLIERS

COUNTRY INNOVATION
The Granary, The Stables Business Park,
Rooksbridge, Somerset BS2 2TT; T: 01934 877 333;
E: sales@countryinnovation.com;
W: www.countryinnovation.com

FREET (shoes & boots)
16 High Garth, Richmond, North Yorkshire
DL10 4DG; T: 01748 900 421;
E: freet@freet.uk; W: www.freet.uk

PARAMO DIRECTIONAL CLOTHING SYSTEMS
Durgates Industrial Estate, Wadhurst, East Sussex
TN5 6DF; T: 01892 786 444; E: via website;
W: www.paramo-clothing.com

ROHAN
30 Maryland Road, Tongwell, Milton Keynes,
Bucks MK15 8HN; T: 0800 840 1412;
E: post@rohan.co.uk; W: www.rohan.co.uk

TILLEY ENDURABLES
6 Tresprison Court, Helston, Cornwall TR13 0QD;
T: 01326 574 402; E: via website;
W: www.tilley.com

EQUIPMENT SUPPLIERS

LOWEPRO
Vitec Imaging Distribution UK, Resolution Road,
Ashby-de-la-Zouch, Leicestershire LE65 1DW;
T: 01530 566 090; E: info@manfrotto.co.uk;
W: www.lowepro.com/uk-en/

(THE) BIRDERS STORE
Unit 4a King Charles Place, St Johns, Worcester,
WR2 5AJ; T: 01905 312 877;
E: sales@birders-store.co.uk;
W: www.birders-store.co.uk

(THE) ONE STOP NATURE SHOP
9 Dalegate Market, Burnham Deepdale,
Norfolk PE31 8FB; T: 01485 211 223;
E: sales@onestopnature.co.uk;
W: www.onestopnature.co.uk

OUTDOOR PHOTOGRAPHY GEAR
c/o Armadillo Storage, 73 Manchester Road,
Warrington, Cheshire WA1 4AE; T: 01925 555 727;
E: sales@outdoorphotographygear.co.uk;
W: www.outdoorphotographygear.co.uk

SCOPAC
T: 07810 560 916; E: enquiries@scopac.co.uk;
W: www.scopac.co.uk

WILDLIFE WATCHING SUPPLIES
Tiverton Way, Tiverton Business Park, Tiverton,
Devon EX16 6TG; T: 01884 254 191;
E: enquiries@wildlifewatchingsupplies.co.uk;
W: www.wildlifewatchingsupplies.co.uk

HOLIDAY COMPANIES

AIGAS FIELD CENTRE
Beauly, Inverness-shire IV4 7AD; T: 01463 782 443;
E: info@aigas.co.uk; W: www.aigas.co.uk

ART SAFARI
Harbourmaster's Office, Ferry Quay, Woodbridge,
Suffolk IP12 1BW; T: 01394 382 235;
E: via website; W: www.artsafari.co.uk

AVIAN ADVENTURES
49 Sandy Road, Norton, Stourbridge, Worcs
DY8 3AJ; T: 01384 372 013;
E: avianadventures@btinternet.com;
W: www.avianadventures.co.uk

BIRDFINDERS
Westbank, Cheselbourne, Dorset DT2 7NW;
T: 01258 839 066; E: birdfinders@aol.co.uk;
W: www.birdfinders.co.uk

HOLIDAY COMPANIES

BIRD HOLIDAYS LTD
10 Ivegate, Yeadon, Leeds, LS19 7RE;
T: 0113 3910 510; E: info@birdholidays.co.uk;
W: www.birdholidays.co.uk

(THE) BIRD ID COMPANY
Church Farm House, Church Lane,
Hindolveston, Norfolk NR20 5BT;
T: 01263 861 892; E: info@birdtour.co.uk;
W: www.birdtour.co.uk

BIRDWATCHING BREAKS
Cygnus House, Gordon's Mill, Balblair,
Ross-shire IV7 8LQ; T: 01381 610 495;
E: enquiries@birdwatchingbreaks.com;
W: www.birdwatchingbreaks.com

BIRD WATCHING & WILDLIFE CLUB
Grant Arms Hotel, 25 The Square,
Grantown-on-Spey, Highlands PH26 3HF;
T: 0800 043 8585; E: booking@bwwc.co.uk;
W: www.bwwc.co.uk

BIRDWATCHING TRIPS WITH THE BIGGEST TWITCH
Alan Davies & Ruth Miller, 12 Ormeside Court,
19 Church Walks, Llandudno, LL30 2HG;
T: 01492 872 407;
E: info@birdwatchingtrips.co.uk;
W: www.birdwatchingtrips.co.uk

BIRDQUEST LTD
Two Jays, Kemple End, Stonyhurst, Clitheroe,
Lancashire BB7 9QY; T: 01254 826 317;
E: birders@birdquest-tours.com;
W: www.birdquest-tours.com

BRITISH-BULGARIAN SOCIETY
Balkania Travel, Conex House, 148 Field End Road,
Eastcote, Middlesex HA5 1RJ; T: 020 7536 9400;
E: ognian@balkaniatravel.com;
W: www.bulgariatours.com

BUTEO WILDLIFE
14 Coolgardie Avenue, London E4 9HP;
T: 07527 454 683; E: info@buteowildlife.co.uk;
W: www.buteowildlife.co.uk

(THE) DORSET BIRDING AND WILDLIFE EXPERIENCE
Moor Edge, 2 Bere Road, Wareham, Dorset
BH20 4DD; T: 01929 552 560;
E: birding@callunabooks.co.uk;
W: www.callunabooks.co.uk

DUNGENESS & ROMNEY MARSH BIRD TOURS
Paul Trodd, Plovers, 1 Toby Road, Lydd-on-Sea,
Romney Marsh, Kent TN29 9PG;
T: 01797 366 935; E: troddy@plovers.co.uk;
W: www.plovers.co.uk

EXPERIENCE NATURE
16 Lint Meadow, Wythall, Worcestershire B47 5PH;
T: 07704 189 835;
E: experiencenaturetours@gmail.com;
W: www.experiencenature.co.uk

GLENLOY WILDLIFE
Glenloy Lodge, Banavie, Fort William,
Highlands PH33 7PD; T: 01397 712 700;
E: info@glenloywildlife.co.uk;
W: www.glenloywildlife.co.uk

GREENTOURS LTD
Kemp House,152-160 City Road, London EC1V 2NX;
T: 01298 83563; E: enquiries@greentours.co.uk;
W: www.greentours.co.uk

HEATHERLEA LTD
The Mountview Hotel, Nethy Bridge,
Inverness-shire PH25 3EB; T: 01479 821 248;
E: info@heatherlea.co.uk;
W: www.heatherlea.co.uk

LIMOSA HOLIDAYS
West End Farmhouse, Chapelfield, Stalham,
Norfolk NR12 9EJ; T: 01692 580 623;
E: enquiries@limosaholidays.co.uk;
W: www.limosaholidays.co.uk

NATURETREK
Mingledown Barn, Wolf's Lane, Chawton,
Alton, Hampshire GU34 3HJ; T: 01962 733 051;
E: info@naturetrek.co.uk; W: www.naturetrek.co.uk

NATURES IMAGES
4 Deer Park Drive, Newport, Shropshire
TF10 7HB; T: 01952 411 436; E: via website;
W: www.natures-images.co.uk

NORTH WEST BIRDS
Mike Robinson, Barn Close, Beetham, Cumbria
LA7 7AL; T: 01539 563 191;
E: mike@nwbirds.co.uk; W: www.nwbirds.co.uk

ORCADIAN WILDLIFE
Gerraquoy, St. Margaret's Hope, South Ronaldsay,
Orkney KW17 2TH; T: 01856 831 240;
E: enquiries@orcadianwildlife.co.uk;
W: www.orcadianwildlife.co.uk

ORIOLE BIRDING
The Manor House, Great Ryburgh, Norfolk NR21 0DX;
T: 0800 999 3036; E: info@oriolebirding.com;
W: www.oriolebirding.com

ORNITHOLIDAYS
[Managed by SKUA Nature Group, Italy]
T: 0208 144 9814; E: info@ornitholidays.com;
W: www.ornitholidays.com

TRADE DIRECTORY

HOLIDAY COMPANIES, OPTICAL DEALERS

SARUS BIRD TOURS
12 Walton Drive, Bury, Lancashire BL9 5JU;
T: 0161 761 7279; E: sarus@sarusbirdtours.co.uk;
W: www.sarusbirdtours.co.uk

SHETLAND NATURE
c/o Burkle, Fair Isle, Shetland ZE2 9JU;
T: 01595 760 333; E: info@shetlandnature.net;
W: www.shetlandnature.net

SHETLAND WILDLIFE
Windy Stacks, Quendale, Shetland ZE2 9JD;
T: 01950 460 939; E: info@shetlandwildlife.co.uk;
W: www.shetlandwildlife.co.uk

SPEYSIDE WILDLIFE
Wester Camerorie, Ballieward, Grantown-on-
Spey, Highlands PH26 3PR; T: 01479 812 498;
E: enquiries@speysidewildlife.co.uk;
W: www.speysidewildlife.co.uk

SUNBIRD
26B The Market Square, Potton, Sandy, Beds
SG19 2NP; T: 01767 262 522;
E: sunbird@sunbirdtours.co.uk;
W: www.sunbirdtours.co.uk

THINK GALAPAGOS
Millcote, Mill Lane, Bishop Burton, HU17 8QT;
T: 01964 552 292; E: info@thinkgalapagos.com;
W: www.thinkgalapagos.com

(THE) TRAVELLING NATURALIST
Long Barn South, Sutton Manor Farm, Bishop's
Sutton, Alresford, Hampshire SO24 0AA;
T: 01305 267 994;
E: sales@thetravellingnaturalist.com;
W: www.naturalist.co.uk

WILD ABOUT TRAVEL
25 Sapley Road, Hartford, Huntingdon, Cambs
PE29 1YG; T: 01480 370 593;
E: info@wildabouttravel.co.uk;
W: www.wildabouttravel.co.uk

WILD INSIGHTS
Yew Tree Farmhouse, Craignant, Selattyn,
Oswestry, Shropshire SY10 7NP;
T: 01691 718 740; E: keith@keithofford.co.uk;
W: www.wildinsights.co.uk

WILDFOOT TRAVEL
Travel House, 133 Gravel Lane, Wilmslow,
Cheshire SK9 6EG; T: 0800 195 3385;
E: via website; W: www.wildfoottravel.com

WILDLIFE TRAVEL
The Manor House, Broad St, Great Cambourne,
Cambridge, CB23 6DH; T: 01954 713 575;
E: wildlifetravel@wildlifebcn.org;
W: www.wildlife-travel.co.uk

WILDLIFE WORLDWIDE
Long Barn South, Sutton Manor Farm, Bishop's
Sutton, Alresford, Hampshire SO24 0AA;
T: 01962 302 086;
E: reservations@wildlifeworldwide.com;
W: www.wildlifeworldwide.com

WILDWINGS
PO Box 372, Bristol, BS16 0FD; T: 0117 9658 333;
E: tours@wildwings.co.uk;
W: www.wildwings.co.uk

WISE BIRDING HOLIDAYS
3 Moormead, Budleigh Salterton, Devon
EX9 6QA; T: 07973 483 227;
E: chris@wisebirding.co.uk;
W: www.wisebirding.co.uk

YORKSHIRE COAST NATURE
Highfield Farm, Southburn, Driffield, East
Yorkshire YO25 9AF; T: 01723 865 498;
E: enquiries@yorkshirecoastnature.co.uk;
W: www.yorkshirecoastnature.co.uk

OPTICAL DEALERS

ACE OPTICS
16 Green St, Bath, BA1 2JZ; T: 01225 466 364;
E: via website; W: www.aceoptics.co.uk

BIRDNET OPTICS LTD
5 Trenchard Drive, Harpur Hill, Buxton,
Derbyshire SK17 9JY; T: 01298 71844;
E: paulflint@birdnet.co.uk; W: www.birdnet.co.uk

BRESSER UK
Suite 3G, Eden House, Enterprise Way,
Edenbridge, Kent TN8 6HF; T: 01342 837 098;
E: sales@bresseruk.com;
W: www.bresseruk.com

CLEY SPY
Manor Farm Barns, Glandford, Holt, Norfolk
NR25 7JP; T: 01263 740 088; E: via website;
W: www.cleyspy.co.uk

CLIFTON CAMERAS
28 Parsonage Street, Dursley, Gloucestershire
GL11 4AA; T: 01453 548 128;
E: sales@cliftoncameras.co.uk;
W: www.cliftoncameras.co.uk

OPTICAL DEALERS

FOCALPOINT OPTICS
Sevenoaks Saw Mill, Antrobus, Cheshire CW9 6JB;
T: 01925 730 399; E: focalpoint@dial.pipex.com;
W: www.fpoint.co.uk

FOCUS OPTICS
Church Lane, Corley, Coventry, CV7 8BA;
T: 01676 540 501; E: enquiries@focusoptics.eu;
W: www.focusoptics.eu

H.A.BAKER (LEWES) LTD
44 High Street, Lewes, East Sussex BN7 2DD;
T: 01273 476 479; E: sales@habaker.co.uk;
W: www.habakerltd.co.uk

IN FOCUS
E: enquiries@infocusoptics.co.uk;
W: www.at-infocus.co.uk

Gloucestershire: The Wildfowl & Wetlands Trust, Slimbridge, Gloucestershire GL2 7BT; T: 01453 890 978

Hertfordshire: Willows Farm, Coursers Road, Colney Heath, Hertfordshire AL4 0PF; T: 01727 827 799

Lancashire: The Wildfowl & Wetlands Trust, Martin Mere, Burscough, Ormskirk, Lancashire L40 0TA; T: 01704 897 020

London, South West: The Wildfowl & Wetlands Trust, London Wetland Centre, Queen Elizabeth's Walk, Barnes, London SW13 9WT; T: 0208 409 4433

Norfolk: Main Street, Titchwell, Nr. King's Lynn, Norfolk PE31 8BB; T: 01485 210 101

Rutland: Anglian Water Birdwatching Centre, Egleton Reserve, Rutland Water, Rutland LE15 8BT; T: 01572 770 656

Yorkshire: Westleigh House, Wakefield Road, Denby Dale, West Yorkshire HD8 8QJ; T: 01484 864 729

LONDON CAMERA EXCHANGE
T: 01962 670 007 (online orders);
E: shops via website; W: www.lcegroup.co.uk

Bath: 13 Cheap Street, Bath, Avon BA1 1NB; T: 01225 462 234

Bristol (Baldwin Street): 3 Alliance House, Bristol, BS1 1SA; T: 0117 929 1935

Bristol (Broadmead): 53 The Horsefair, Bristol, BS1 3JP; T: 0117 927 6185

Cheltenham: 10-12 The Promenade, Cheltenham, GL50 1LR; T: 01242 519 851

Chester: 9 Bridge Street Row, Chester, CH1 1NW; T: 01244 326 531

Chichester: 17 Eastgate Square, Chichester, PO19 1JL; T: 01243 531 536

Colchester: 12 Eld Lane, Colchester, Essex CO1 1LS; T: 01206 573 444

Derby: 17 Sadler Gate, Derby, Derbyshire DE1 3NH; T: 01332 348 644

Exeter: 174 Fore Street, Exeter, Devon EX4 3AX; T: 01392 279 024

Gloucester: 12 Southgate Street, Gloucester, GL1 2DH; T: 01452 304 513

Guildford: 8/9 Tunsgate, Guildford, Surrey GU1 3QT; T: 01483 504 040

Hereford: 16 Widemarsh Street, Hereford, HR4 9EW; T: 01432 272 655

Leamington: 4C Lunn Poly House, Clarendon Avenue, Royal Leamington Spa, CV32 5PP; T: 01926 886 166

Lincoln (Silver Street): 6 Silver Street, Lincoln, LN2 1DY; T: 01522 514 131

London (Strand): 98 Strand, London WC2R 0EW; T: 0207 379 0200

Manchester: 16 Cross Street, Manchester, M2 7AE; T: 0161 834 7500

Newcastle: 76 High Street, Gosforth, Newcastle Upon Tyne, NE3 1HB; T: 0191 213 0060

Norwich: 12 Timber Hill, Norwich, Norfolk NR1 3LB; T: 01603 612 537

Nottingham: 7 Pelham Street, Nottingham, NG1 2EH; T: 0115 941 7486

Plymouth: 56 Cornwall Street, Plymouth, Devon PL1 1LR; T: 01752 664 894

Portsmouth: Kingswell Path, Cascades Shopping Centre, Portsmouth, PO1 4RR; T: 023 9283 9933

Reading: 7 Station Road, Reading, Berkshire RG1 1LG; T: 0118 959 2149

Salisbury: 6 Queen Street, Salisbury, Wiltshire SP1 1EY; T: 01722 335 436

Southampton (Civic Centre): 11 Civic Centre Road, Southampton, Hants SO14 7FJ; T: 023 8033 1720

Southampton (High Street): 10 High Street, Southampton, Hants SO14 2DH; T: 023 8022 1597

Taunton: 6 North Street, Taunton, Somerset TA1 1LH; T: 01823 259 955

OPTICAL DEALERS, OPTICAL IMPORTERS & MANUFACTURERS

Winchester: 15 The Square, Winchester, Hampshire SO23 9ES; T: 01962 866 203

Worcester: 8 Pump Street, Worcester WR1 2QT; T: 01905 22314

PARK CAMERAS
T: 01444 237 070; E: sales@parkcameras.com; W: www.parkcameras.com

Burgess Hill: York Road, Burgess Hill, West Sussex RH15 9TT

London: 53-54 Rathbone Place, London W1T 1JR

SHERWOODS
The Arden Centre, Little Alne, Wootton Wawen, Henley-in-Arden, Warwickshire B95 6HW; T: 01789 488 880; E: sales@sherwoods-photo.com; W: www.sherwoods-photo.com

SOUTH WEST OPTICS
22 River Street, Truro, Cornwall TR1 2SJ; T: 01872 263 444; E: internet@swoptics.com; W: www.swoptics.co.uk

UTTINGS
PO Box 672, Norwich, Norfolk NR3 2ZR; T: 01603 619 811; E: via website; W: www.uttings.co.uk

WEX PHOTOGRAPHIC
13 Frensham Road, Sweet Briar Industrial Estate, Norwich, Norfolk NR3 2BT; T: 01603 486 413; E: via website; W: www. wexphotographic.com

WILKINSON CAMERAS
Direct Sales: Unit 25 Charnley Fold, Bamber Bridge, Preston, PR5 6PS; T: 01772 252 188; E: sales@wilkinson.co.uk; W: www.wilkinson.co.uk

Burnley: 95 James Street, Burnley, Lancs BB11 1PY; T: 01282 424 524

Bury: 61 The Rock, Bury, Greater Manchester, BL9 0NB; T: 0161 764 3402

Carlisle: 13 Grapes Lane, The Lanes Centre, Carlisle, Cumbria CA3 8NH; T: 01228 538 583

Kendal: Unit 19a, The Westmorland Centre, Stricklandgate, Kendal, Cumbria LA9 4LR; T: 01539 735 055

Lancaster: 6 James Street, Lancaster, Lancs LA1 1UP; T: 01524 380 510

Liverpool: 4 Bold Street, Liverpool, L1 6DS; T: 0151 255 0345

Preston: 27 Friargate, St George's Centre, Preston, Lancs PR1 2NQ; T: 01772 556 250

Southport: 38 Eastbank Street, Southport, Merseyside PR8 1ET; T: 01704 534 534

Warrington: 10 The Mall, The Golden Square, Warrington, WA1 1QE; T: 01925 638 290

OPTICAL IMPORTERS & MANUFACTURERS

ALPHA OPTICAL DISTRIBUTION LTD (Kite Optics)
Unit 39, Unity Business Centre, 26 Roundhay Road, Leeds, LS7 1AB; E: via website: www.alphaodl.co.uk; W: www.kiteoptics.com

CANON UK LTD
Canon Support. T: 0207 660 0186; E: via website; W: www.canon.co.uk

CARL ZEISS LTD
ZEISS House, Building 1030, Cambourne Business Park, Cambourne, CB23 6DW; T: 01223 401 500; E: customercare.uk@zeiss.com; W: www.zeiss.co.uk

HAWKE
Avocet House, Wilford Bridge Rd, Melton, Woodbridge, Suffolk IP12 1RB; T: 0345 345 5555; E: uk@hawkeoptics.com; W: www.hawkeoptics.com

DAVID HINDS LTD (Celestron Optics)
Unit R, Cherrycourt Way, Leighton Buzzard, Bedfordshire LU7 4UH; T: 01525 852 696; E: astro@dhinds.co.uk; W: www.celestron.uk.com

INTRO 2020 (Steiner binos, Velbon & Slik tripods & more)
Unit 1, Priors Way, Maidenhead, Berks SL6 2HP; T: 01628 799 901; E: sales@intro2020.co.uk; W: www.intro2020.co.uk

KOWA OPTIMED
E: via website; W: www.kowaproducts.com

LEICA CAMERA LTD
64-66 Duke Street, Mayfair, London W1J 6JD; T: 0207 629 1351; E: customercare.uk@leica-camera.com; W: www.leica-camera.com

MANFROTTO IMAGE MORE
(inc. Manfrotto & Gitzo Tripods, Bushnell Optics)
Vitec Imaging Distribution, Resolution Rd, Ashby-de-la-Zouch, Leicestershire LE65 1DW; T: 01530 566 090; E: via website; W: www.manfrotto.co.uk

NEWPRO UK LTD (Vortex Optics, PhoneSkope)
3 Radcot Estate, Park Rd, Faringdon,
Oxfordshire SN7 7BP; T: 01367 242 411;
E: sales@newprouk.co.uk; W: www.newprouk.co.uk

NIKON UK LTD
380 Richmond Road, Kingston-upon-Thames,
Surrey KT2 5PR; T: 0330 123 0932;
E: via website; W: www.nikon.co.uk

OPTICAL VISION LTD (Barr & Stoud, Helios, Acuter Optics)
Unit 3, Woolpit Business Park, Woolpit,
Bury St Edmunds, Suffolk IP30 9UP;
E: info:opticalvision.co.uk;
W: www.opticalvision.co.uk

OPTICRON
Unit 21, Titan Court, Laporte way, Luton,
Befordshire LU4 8EF; T: 01582 726 522;
E: sales@opticron.co.uk;
W: www.opticron.co.uk

SWAROVSKI OPTIK
(Repair service) Tarbot House Unit 11,
Perrywood Business Park, Honeycrock Lane,
Salfords, Surrey RH1 5JQ; T: 01737 856 812;
Customer Service (Austria) T: 00800 3242 5056;
E: customerservice@swarovskioptik.com;
W: www.swarovskioptik.com

VANGUARD WORLD UK LTD
Unit 73, Basepoint Business Centre,
Enterprise Close, Aviation Business Park,
Christchurch, Dorset, BH23 6NX;
T: 01202 651 281; E: info@vanguardworld.co.uk;
W: www.vanguardworld.co.uk

VIKING OPTICAL LTD (Viking & RSPB Optics)
Blyth Road, Halesworth, Suffolk IP19 8EN;
T: 01986 875 315; E: sales@vikingoptical.co.uk;
W: www.vikingoptical.co.uk

OPTICAL REPAIRS & SERVICING

ACTION OPTICS
18 Butts Ash Gardens, Hythe, Southampton,
SO45 3BL; T: 023 8084 2801;
E: via website; W: www.actionoptics.co.uk

FIXATION UK LTD (Nikon/Canon repairs & servicing)
Unit C, 250 Kennington Lane, Lambeth,
London SE11 5RD; T: 0207 582 3294;
E: admin@fixationuk.com;
W: www.fixationuk.com

INTRASIGHTS
2 The Waggon Shed, Flaxdrayton Farm,
South Petherton, Somerset TA13 5LR;
T: 01460 929 291; E: intrasights@gmail.com;
W: www.intrasights.co.uk

OPTREP OPTICAL REPAIRS
16 Wheatfield Rd, Selsey, W. Sussex PO20 0NY;
T: 01243 601 365; E: info@opticalrepairs.com;
W: www.opticalrepairs.com

VIKING SERVICE & REPAIR CENTRE
Blyth Road, Halesworth, Suffolk IP19 8EN;
T: 01986 875 315; E: repairs@vikingoptical.co.uk;
W: www.vikingoptical.co.uk

TECHNOLOGY PRODUCTS

BIRD IMAGES (DVDS)
Paul Doherty, 28 Carousel Walk, Sherburn-in-
Elmet, North Yorkshire LS25 6LP;
T: 01977 684 666; E: paul@birdvideodvd.com;
W: www.birdvideodvd.com

BIRD JOURNAL (BLUEBIRD TECHNOLOGY)
1 Turnbridge Court, Swavesey, Cambridge,
CB24 4GH; W: www.birdjournal.com

BIRDGUIDES LTD
Warners Group Publications, The Chocolate
Factory, 5 Clarendon Road, London N22 6XJ;
T: 0208 881 0550; E: via website;
W: www.birdguides.com

EASYBIRDER DVDS
Dave Gosney, Valley View Cottage, 15 Low Rd,
Sheffield, S6 5FY; T: 0114 285 3712;
E: dave@easybirder.co.uk;
W: www.easybirder.co.uk

ISABELLINE FILMS
Steve Evans, 9 Milverton Close, Halesowen,
W.Midlands B63 3QL;
E: isabellineart@outlook.co.uk;
W: www.isabelline.co.uk

TRADE DIRECTORY

Joe Mitchell

The Kestrel (*Falco tinnunculus*) is widespread through the counties of the UK & is the logo of the Banbury Ornithological Society.

COUNTY DIRECTORY

COUNTY DIRECTORY

COUNTY DIRECTORY - EXPLANATION OF HEADINGS

THE INFORMATION IN this directory has been obtained from a number of sources - including the persons listed and the relevant national body. In some cases, where it has not proved possible to verify the details directly, alternative responsible sources have been used. When no satisfactory source was available, previously included entries have sometimes had to be deleted. Readers are requested to advise the editor of any errors, omissions or changes (see page 6).

(*Note:* for completeness, n/a has been used where information is not available or has been withheld)

Bird Atlas/Avifauna
The more recent county publications are listed here. Many of these titles should still be available to buy new but if out of print try the second hand market - check out the booksellers listed in the Trade Directory.

Bird Recorder
The County Bird Recorder is the key point of contact in the area to deal with all aspects of bird records including rarities & rare breeding birds.

Bird Report
The annual county bird report is usually, but not exclusively, published by the county bird club. In some counties, annual reports are also published covering smaller recording areas. The *(date-)* refers to the start of the current title or, in some cases, its predecessor. In the first instance, contact the relevant person/ club for the current report (& back issues). Check out the booksellers listed in the Trade Directory to look for 'out of print' reports.

BTO Regional Representative
Your local BTO Rep is the first point of contact if you wish to help with national bird surveys in your county - get involved, make a difference!

Club
Many counties have their own independent county-wide bird/natural history clubs & some have smaller clubs based on particular areas of the county. Contact details are provided along with information about the indoor meetings.

Get in touch/check out the club website for membership information, to confirm indoor meeting dates/venues & for details about field trips & other club activities.

Ringing Group/Bird Observatory
For more information about becoming a licenced ringer, contact the BTO (see National Directory).

Active groups of ringers are well represented around the counties. The names of the groups are listed under each county - for further details check out their website (if they have one) or contact the BTO to forward your enquiry.

Bird Observatories are a great place to see birds at close quarters, many offer accommodation/events.

If you find a ringed bird, contact the BTO/or other organisation - details will be on the ring.

RSPB Local Group
Groups are active in most counties offering an excellent programme of talks & field trips through the year. Contact details are provided along with information about the indoor meetings.

Get in touch/check out the group website to confirm indoor meeting dates/venues & for details about field trips & other activities the group offers.

Wetland Bird Survey (WeBS) Local Organiser
Get involved with your local monthly wetland bird counts - for details of how to help contact your local organiser or contact the WeBS Office, BTO, The Nunnery, Thetford, Norfolk IP24 2PU. T: 01842 750 050; E: webs@bto.org

Wildlife Trust
Don't forget to check out your local Wildlife Trust who organise/run many talks, walks, events & other activites. The network of 46 independent Wildlife Trusts also manage a wide range of nature reserves providing valuable habitats for birds & other wildlife.

ENGLAND

BEDFORDSHIRE

Bird Atlas/Avifauna
An Atlas of the Breeding Birds of Bedfordshire 1988-92. RA Dazley & P Trodd (Bedfordshire Natural History Society, 1994).

The Birds of Bedfordshire. P Trodd & D Kramer (Castlemead Publications, 1991).

Bird Recorder
Steve Blain, 9 Devon Drive, Biggleswade, SG18 0FJ. T: 07979 606 300;
E: recorder@bedsbirdclub.org.uk

Bird Report
BEDFORDSHIRE BIRD REPORT (1946-), from Mary Sheridan, 28 Chestnut Hill, Linslade, Leighton Buzzard, LU7 2TR.
T: 01525 378 245;
E: membership@bnhs.org.uk

BTO Regional Representative
Roger Hicks. T: 01462 816 028;
E: rogerkhicks@hotmail.com

Judith Knight (Regional Development Officer).
T: n/a; E: judithknight@waitrose.com

Club
BEDFORDSHIRE BIRD CLUB. (1992; 280).
Sheila Alliez (Hon Sec), Flat 61 Adamson Court, Adamson Walk, Kempston, Bedford, MK42 8QZ.
T: 01234 855 227; E: sjalliez12@btinternet.com;
W: www.bedsbirdclub.org.uk
Meetings: 8.00pm, last Tuesday of the month (Sep-Mar). Maulden Village Hall, Maulden, MK45 2DA.

RSPB Local Group
BEDFORD. (1970; 80).
Carolyn Hawkes. T: 01234 768 136;
E: BedfordRSPBlocalgroup@gmail.com;
W: www.rspb.org.uk/groups/bedford
Meetings: 7.30pm, 3rd Thursday of the month (Sep-May). Aircraft Research Association, The Sports & Social Club, Manton Lane, Bedford, MK41 7PF.

Wetland Bird Survey (WeBS) Local Organiser
BEDFORDSHIRE. Richard Bashford.
T: via WeBS Office.
E: richard.bashford@rspb.org.uk

Wildlife Trust. See Cambridgeshire.

BERKSHIRE

Bird Atlas/Avifauna
The Birds of Berkshire.
Neil Bucknell, Brian Clews, Renton Righelato & Chris Robinson
(Birds of Berkshire Atlas Group, 2nd ed 2013).

The Birds of Berkshire

Bird Recorder
Richard Burness,
20 Burlsdon Way, Bracknell, RG12 2PH. T: 07708 094 899;
E: records@berksoc.org.uk

Bird Report
NEWBURY DISTRICT BIRD REPORT: Covers a 10-mile radius from Newbury Museum incl. parts of N Hants, S Oxon *(1960-),* from Lesley Staves, 39 Priory Avenue, Hungerford, RG17 0BE.
T: 01488 682 301; E: dlsdroversdale@gmail.com

THE BIRDS OF BERKSHIRE (1974-),
from Sally Wearing, 9 Deans Farm, The Causeway, Reading, RG4 5JZ. E: secretary@berksoc.org.uk

BTO Regional Representative
Sean Murphy. T: n/a; E: s.murphy@cab1.org

Club
BERKSHIRE ORNITHOLOGICAL CLUB. (1947; 300).
Iain Oldcorn (Membership Sec), 28 Huntsman Meadow, Ascot, SL5 7PF. T: 01344 625 883;
E: membership@berksoc.org.uk;
W: www.berksoc.org.uk
Meetings: 8pm, alternate Wednesdays (Sep-Apr). Room 109, Palmer Building, University of Reading, RG6 6UR (usually).

NEWBURY DISTRICT ORNITHOLOGICAL CLUB. (1959; 90). Mrs Lesley Staves (Sec).
Address: n/a; T: 01488 682 301;
E: enquiries@newburybirders.co.uk;
W: www.newburybirders.co.uk
Meetings: 7.30pm, monthly on a Thursday (Oct-Mar). Greenham Church Hall, New Road, Greenham, Newbury, RG19 8RZ.

THEALE AREA BIRD CONSERVATION GROUP. (1988; 75).
Catherine McEwan (Club Sec). Address: n/a.
T: 0118 9415 792; E: tabcgsec@yahoo.com;
W: www.tabcg.webs.com/
Meetings: 8pm, 1st Tuesday of the month (all year). The Fox and Hounds Public House, Deans Copse Road, Reading, RG7 4BE.

ENGLAND

Ringing Group/Bird Observatory
BERKSHIRE DOWNS RG.

MIDDLE THAMES RINGING GROUP.
W: https://middlethames.wordpress.com/

NEWBURY RG. W: www.newburyrg.co.uk

RUNNYMEDE RG. W: www.runnymederinging.uk

RSPB Local Group
EAST BERKSHIRE. (1974; 170).
Kate Titford. T: 07753 840 573;
E: eastberks.rspb@gmail.com;
W: www.eastberksrspb.org.uk
Meetings: 7.30pm, 3rd Thursday of the month
(Sep-Jun). Methodist Church Hall, King Street,
Maidenhead, SL6 1EA.

READING. (1986; 130).
Carl Feltham. T: 0118 941 1713;
E: info@reading-rspb.org;
W: www.reading-rspb.org
Meetings: 8.00 pm, 2nd Tuesday of the month
(Sep-Jun). Pangbourne Village Hall, Station Road,
Pangbourne, Reading, RG8 7DY.

WOKINGHAM & BRACKNELL. (1979; 150).
Patrick Crowley. T: 01344 776 473;
E: RSPBwandb@gmail.com;
W: www.rspb.org.uk/groups/wokinghamandbracknell
Meetings: 7.45pm, 2nd Thursday of the month
(Sep-Jun). Finchampstead Memorial Hall,
The Village, Finchampstead, Wokingham, RG40 4JU.

Wetland Bird Survey (WeBS) Local Organiser
BERKSHIRE. Sean Murphy T: 01344 890 840;
E: seantmurphy8@gmail.com

Wildlife Trust. See Oxfordshire.

BUCKINGHAMSHIRE

BirdAtlas/Avifauna
The Birds of Buckinghamshire. David Ferguson
(Buckingham Bird Club, 2nd ed 2012).

Bird Recorder
Mike Wallen, 15 Bennetts Lane, Rowsham, HP22 4QU.
T: 07976 560 040;
E: Recorder@bucksbirdclub.co.uk

Bird Report
BUCKINGHAMSHIRE BIRD REPORT (1980-), from
Rob Andrews, 69 Stoke Road, Aylesbury, HP21 8BL.
T: 01442 827925; E: r.andrews18@btinternet.com
or E: conservation@bucksbirdclub.co.uk

BTO Regional Representative
Phil Tizzard. T: 01280 812 427;
E: phil.tizzard@care4free.net

Club
AMERSHAM BIRDWATCHING CLUB. (n/a; 80).
Eileen Tanner (Sec). Address: n/a. T: n/a;
E: abclubgeneral@gmail.com;
W: www.amershambirdwatchingclub.co.uk
Meetings: 7.45pm, 3rd Friday of the month
(Sep-May). Barn Hall Community Centre,
Chiltern Avenue, Amersham, HP6 5AH.

BUCKINGHAMSHIRE BIRD CLUB. (1981; 340).
Bill Parker (Sec). Address: n/a; T: n/a;
E: Secretary@bucksbirdclub.co.uk;
W: www.bucksbirdclub.co.uk
Meetings: 7.30pm, 1st Thursday of the month
(Oct-Dec/Feb-Apr). St Anne's Hall, Aylesbury Road,
Wendover, HP22 6JG.

Ringing Group/Bird Observatory
COLNE VALLEY RG.

HUGHENDEN RG.

RUNNYMEDE RG. See Berkshire.

RSPB Local Group
AYLESBURY. (1981; 160).
Anne Fisher. T: 01844 215 924;
E: anne.fisher50@yahoo.co.uk;
W: www.rspb.org.uk/groups/aylesbury
Meetings: 7.30pm, last Monday of the month
(Sep-May). Prebendal Farm Community Centre,
Fowler Road, Aylesbury, HP19 7QW.

NORTH BUCKS. (1976; 540).
Jane Grisdale. T: 01908 605 719;
E: jane.grisdale@googlemail.com;
W: www.rspb.org.uk/groups/northbucks
Meetings: 7.45pm, 2nd Thursday of the month
(Sep-May). Cruck Barn, City Discovery Centre, Alston
Drive, Bradwell Abbey, Milton Keynes, MK13 9AP.

Wetland Bird Survey (WeBS) Local Organiser
BUCKINGHAMSHIRE (NORTH).
Vacant - contact WeBS Office.

BUCKINGHAMSHIRE (SOUTH).
Vacant - contact WeBS Office.

Wildlife Trust. See Oxfordshire.

CAMBRIDGESHIRE

BirdAtlas/Avifauna
*Cambridgeshire Bird Atlas
2007-2011.*
Louise Bacon, Alison Cooper
& Hugh Venables
(Cambridge Bird Club, 2013).

The Birds of Cambridgeshire.
PMM Bircham
(Cambridge University Press,
1989/pbk ed 2009).

232

ENGLAND

Bird Recorder
Louise Bacon. Address: n/a. T: n/a;
E: recorder@cambridgebirdclub.org.uk

Bird Report
CAMBRIDGESHIRE BIRD REPORT (1927-), from
Bruce Martin, 178 Nuns Way, Cambridge, CB4 2NS.
E: bruce.s.martin@btinternet.com

BTO Regional Representative
CAMBRIDGESHIRE:
Rob Pople. T: n/a; E: robgpople@hotmail.com

HUNTINGDON & PETERBOROUGH.
Derek Langslow. T: 01733 232 153;
E: drldrl49@outlook.com

Club
CAMBRIDGESHIRE BIRD CLUB.
(1925; 350+).
Michael Holdsworth (Sec),
4a Cavendish Ave,
Cambridge, CB1 7US.
T: n/a; E: secretary@
cambridgebirdclub.org.uk;
W: www.cambridgebirdclub.org.uk
Meetings: 8pm, 2nd Friday of the month
(Sep-May). Either at St John's Church Hall,
Hills Road, Cambridge CB2 8RN or Cottenham
Village College, High Street, Cottenham,
Cambridge, CB24 8UA.

PETERBOROUGH BIRD CLUB. (1998; 135).
David Cromack, 55 Thorpe Park Road,
Peterborough, PE3 6LJ. T: 01733 566 815;
E: cromackd@gmail.com;
W: www.peterboroughbirdclub.com
Meetings: 7.30pm, last Tuesday of the month
(Sep-Nov, Jan-Apr). PO Social Club,
Bourges Boulevard, Peterborough, PE1 2AU.

Ringing Group/Bird Observatory
UPPER CAM RG.

WICKEN FEN RG.

RSPB Local Group
CAMBRIDGE. (1977; 80).
Andrew Law. T: 01799 501 790;
E: andylaw1954@gmail.com;
W: www.rspb.org.uk/groups/cambridge
Meetings: 7.30pm, 3rd Wednesday of the month
(Sep-Nov/Jan-May). Wilkinson Room, St John's
the Evangelist, Hills Road, Cambridge, CB2 8RN.

HUNTINGDONSHIRE. (1982; 100).
Mervyn Vickery. T: 01480 492 519;
E: mfvickery52@outlook.com;
W: www.rspb.org.uk/groups/huntingdonshire
Meetings: 7.30pm, last Wednesday of the month
(Sep-Apr, Dec may be earlier in month). The Free
Church, St Ives, Market Hill, St Ives, PE27 5AL.

Wetland Bird Survey (WeBS) Local Organiser
CAMBRIDGESHIRE (incl. HUNTINGDONSHIRE).
Bruce Martin. T: 01223 700 656;
E: brucemartin@virginmedia.com

NENE WASHES. Charlie Kitchin. T: 01733 205 140;
E: charlie.kitchin@rspb.org.uk

OUSE WASHES. Paul Harrington.
T: 01354 680 212; E: paul.harrington@rspb.org.uk

Wildlife Trust
THE WILDLIFE TRUST FOR BEDFORDSHIRE,
CAMBRIDGESHIRE AND NORTHAMPTONSHIRE.
(1994; 34,000).
The Manor House, Broad Street, Great
Cambourne, Cambs CB23 6DH.
T: 01954 713 500, (fax) 01954 710 051;
E: cambridgeshire@wildlifebcn.org;
W: www.wildlifebcn.org

CHESHIRE & WIRRAL

BirdAtlas/Avifauna
*Rare and Scarce Birds in
Cheshire and Wirral.*
Allan Conlin & Eddie Williams
(privately published, 2017).

*Birds in Cheshire and Wirral:
A Breeding and Wintering
Atlas.* David Norman
(Liverpool University Press,
2008).

Bird Recorder
CHESHIRE & WIRRAL. Hugh Pulsford,
6 Buttermere Drive, Great Warford,
Alderley Edge, SK9 7WA. T: 01565 880 171;
E: countyrec@cawos.org
[also the Secretary of Association of County
Recorders and Editors (ARCE)]

Bird Report
CHESHIRE & WIRRAL BIRD REPORT (1964), from
David Cogger, 71 Parkgate, Knutsford, WA16 8HF.
T: 01565 228 503; E: davidcogger@cawos.org

BTO Regional Representative
MID. Paul Miller. T: 01928 787 535;
E: paulandhilarymiller@live.co.uk

NORTH & EAST. Hugh Pulsford. T: 01565 880 171;
E: ahugh.pulsford@btinternet.com

SOUTH. Hugh Pulsford - see above.

THE WIRRAL. Paul Miller - see above.

ENGLAND

Club

CHESHIRE & WIRRAL ORNITHOLOGICAL SOCIETY. (1988; 310). Ted Lock (Sec), 2 Bourne Street, Wilmslow, SK9 5HD. T: 01625 540 466; E: info@cawos.org; W: www.cawos.org
Meetings: 7.45pm, 1st Friday of the month (Oct-Mar). St Vincent's Church Hall, Tatton Street, Knutsford, WA16 6HR.

KNUTSFORD ORNITHOLOGICAL SOCIETY. (1974; 45). Derek Pike (Sec). Address: n/a. T: 01565 653 811; Press Officer/Website - E: tony@10x50.com; W: www.10x50.com
Meetings: 8pm, 4th Friday of the month (Sept-Apr). Jubilee Hall, Stanley Road, Knutsford, WA16 0GP.

LANCASHIRE & CHESHIRE FAUNA SOCIETY. See Lancashire.

MID-CHESHIRE ORNITHOLOGICAL SOCIETY. (1962; 60). Ian Williams (Sec). Address: n/a. T: n/a; E: secretary@midcheshireos.co.uk; W: www.midcheshireos.co.uk
Meetings: 7:45pm, 2nd Friday of the month (Oct-Apr). Cuddington and Sandiway Village Hall, Norley Road, Cuddington, CW8 2LB.

NANTWICH NATURAL HISTORY SOCIETY. (1979; 65). Mike Holmes, 4 Tenchersfield, Nantwich, CW5 7GR. T: 01270 611 577; E: mike@do-ablesolutions.com; W: n/a
Meetings: No indoor meetings but regular social evenings relating to field work and surveys, usually in The Vine Pub, 42 Hospital Street, Nantwich, CW5 5RP.

SOUTH EAST CHESHIRE ORNITHOLOGICAL SOCIETY. (1964; 120). Colin Lythgoe (Chairman). Address: n/a. T: n/a; E: colin.lythgoe9@uwclub.net; W: www.secos.org.uk
Meetings: 7.30pm, 2nd Friday of the month (Sep-Apr). Ettiley Heath Church Community Centre, Elton Road, Ettiley Heath, Sandbach, CW11 3NE.

WILMSLOW GUILD BIRDWATCHING GROUP. (1965; 65). All members of the WGBG are required to be members of the Wilmslow Guild. T: 01625 523 936. E: via website; W: www.wilmslowguild.org

Brian Dyke (Chairman WGBG). T: 01625 525 936; W: http://wgbwcopy.wikidot.com/wgbg
Meetings: 7.30pm, usually last Friday of the month - but not always - (Sep-Apr). Wilmslow Guild, 1 Bourne Street, Wilmslow, SK9 5HD.

WIRRAL BIRD CLUB. (1977; 80). Bill Wonderley. Address: n/a. T: 07795 148 140; E: wirralbirdclub@gmail.com; W: www.wirralbirdclub.com
Meetings: 7.30pm, 4th Thursday of the month (Sep-Nov & Jan-Jul). Kingsmead School Hall, Bertram Drive, Hoylake, CH47 0LL.

Ringing Group/Bird Observatory

CHESHIRE SWAN GROUP. W: http://cheshireswanstudygroup.wordpress.com

SOUTH MANCHESTER RG.

HILBRE BIRD OBSERVATORY. Steve Williams. T: 07976 205 574; E: secretary@hilbrebirdobs.org.uk; W: http://hilbrebirdobs.blogspot.com

RSPB Local Group

CHESTER. (1988; 150). Norman Sadler. T: 01244 335 670; E: rspbchester@googlegroups.com; W: www.rspb.org.uk/groups/chester
Meetings: 7.30pm, 3rd Wednesday of the month (Sep-Apr). Christleton Parish Hall, Village Road, Christleton, CH3 7AS.

MACCLESFIELD. (1979; 220). Daryll Bailey. T: 01625 430 311; E: Secretary@macclesfieldRSPB.org.uk; W: www.rspb.org.uk/groups/macclesfield
Meetings: 7.45pm, 2nd Tuesday of the month (Sep-May). Macclesfield Senior Citizens Hall, Duke Street Car Park, Macclesfield, SK11 6UR.

NORTH CHESHIRE. (1976; 80). Paul Grimmett. T: 01925 268 770; E: paulwtwitcher@hotmail.com; W: www.rspb.org.uk/groups/north_cheshire
Meetings: 7.30pm, 3rd Friday of the month (Sep-Nov/Jan-Apr). Appleton Parish Hall, Dudlow Green Road, Appleton, Warrington, WA4 5EQ.

WIRRAL. (1982; 100). Jeremy Bradshaw. T: 07769 673 018; E: bradshaws1961@gmail.com; W: www.rspb.org.uk/groups/wirral
Meetings: 7.30pm, 1st Thursday of the month (Sep-Jun). Bromborough Civic Centre, 2 Allport Lane, Wirral, CH62 7HR.

Wetland Bird Survey (WeBS) Local Organiser

CHESHIRE (NORTH). Phil Hampson. T: n/a; E: pjhampers@me.com

CHESHIRE (SOUTH). Paul Miller. T: 01928 787 535; E: paulandhilarymiller@live.co.uk

Wildlife Trust

CHESHIRE WILDLIFE TRUST. (1962; 14,000). Bickley Hall Farm, Bickley, Malpas, SY14 8EF. T: 01948 820 728, (fax) 0709 2888 469; E: info@cheshirewt.org.uk; W: www.cheshirewildlifetrust.org.uk

CORNWALL & ISLES OF SCILLY

Bird Atlas/Avifauna
The Essential Guide to Birds of The Isles of Scilly.
Bob L Flood, N Hudson & B Thomas
(privately published, 2007).

The Birds of the Isles of Scilly. Peter Robinson
(Christopher Helm, 2003).

The Birds of Cornwall and the Isles of Scilly. RD Penhallurick
(Browsers Bookshop, 1978).

Bird Recorder
CORNWALL. Dave Parker,
2 Boslevan, Green Lane,
Marizion, TR17 0HQ.
T: 07932 354 711;
E: recorder@cbwps.org.uk

ISLES OF SCILLY. John Headon,
Hivernia, Jackson's Hill, St Mary's,
Isles of Scilly TR21 0JZ.
T: 01720 423 540; E: recorder@scilly-birding.co.uk

Bird Report
BIRDS IN CORNWALL (1931-), from Phil Taylor
(report editor). T: 01736 810 933;
E: shimoryu@mac.com
or E: birdsincornwall@cwps.org.uk

ISLES OF SCILLY BIRD REPORT and NATURAL HISTORY REVIEW (1969-), from Carole Cilia,
Hivemia, Jackson's Hill, St Mary's, Isles of Scilly
TR21 0JZ. T: 01720 423 540;
E: carole.cilia@btinternet.com

BTO Regional Representative
CORNWALL. Simon Taylor. T: n/a;
E: bto_cornwall@yahoo.com

ISLES OF SCILLY. Will Wagstaff. T: 01720 422 212;
E: will@islandwildlifetours.co.uk

Club
CORNWALL BIRD WATCHING & PRESERVATION SOC.
(1931; 1100).
Phil McVey (Sec), Little Boslymon, Bodmin, PL30 5AP.
T: 07740 923 385; E: secretary@cbwps.org.uk;
W: www.cbwps.org.uk
Meetings: contact/see website for details.

ISLES OF SCILLY BIRD GROUP.
(2000; 375).
Carole Cilia, (Membership Sec),
Hivemia, Jackson's Hill,
St Mary's, Isles of Scilly
TR21 0JZ. T: 01720 423 540;
E: membership@scilly-birding.co.uk;
W: www.scilly-birding.co.uk

Ringing Group/Bird Observatory
DEVON & CORNWALL WADER GROUP.
W: www.dcwrg.org.uk/

WEST CORNWALL RG.
W: http://cornishringing.blogspot.com/

RSPB Local Group
CORNWALL. (1972; 260).
Roger Hooper. T: 01209 820 610;
E: rogerwhooper@btinternet.com;
W: www.rspb.org.uk/groups/cornwall
Meetings: On a Friday, (Sep-Apr). Chacewater
Village Hall, Church Hill, nr Truro, TR4 8PZ -
contact/see website for details.

Wetland Bird Survey (WeBS) Local Organiser
CORNWALL (excl. TAMAR COMPLEX).
Peter Roseveare. T: via WeBS office;
E: peterroseveare@yahoo.com

TAMAR COMPLEX. Vacant - contact WeBS Office.

Wildlife Trust
CORNWALL WILDLIFE TRUST. (1962; 18,000).
Five Acres, Allet, Truro, TR4 9DJ.
T: 01872 273 939, (fax) 01872 225 476;
E: info@cornwallwildlifetrust.org.uk;
W: www.cornwallwildlifetrust.org.uk

THE ISLES OF SCILLY WILDLIFE TRUST. (1984).
Trenoweth, St Marys, Isles of Scilly TR21 0NS.
T/fax: 01720 422 153;
E: enquiries@ios-wildlifetrust.org.uk;
W: www.ios-wildlifetrust.org.uk

CUMBRIA

BirdAtlas/Avifauna
The Breeding Birds of Cumbria: A Tetrad Atlas 1997-2001. M Stott, J Callion, I Kinley, C Raven & J Roberts (Cumbria Bird Club, 2002).

Bird Recorder
Chris Hind, 2 Old School House, Hallbankgate,
Brampton, CA8 2NW. T: 01697 746 379;
E: chris.m.hind@gmail.com

Regional Recorders
ALLERDALE & COPELAND. Nick Franklin.
Address: n/a. T: 01228 810 413;
E: nickbirder66@gmail.com

BARROW & SOUTH LAKELAND.
Ronnie Irving, 24 Birchwood Close, Vicarage Park,
Kendal, LA9 5BJ. T: 01539 727 523;
E: ronnieirving2017@gmail.com

CARLISLE & EDEN. Chris Hind - see bird recorder.

ENGLAND

Bird Report

BIRDS AND WILDLIFE IN CUMBRIA (1970-),
from Dave Piercy,
64 The Headlands, Keswick,
CA12 5EJ. T: 01768 773 201;
E: daveandkathypiercy@
tiscali.co.uk

WALNEY BIRD OBSERVATORY REPORT (1964-),
from Keith Parke (Sec),
77 Dalton Lane, Barrow-in-Furness, LA14 4LB.
T: 01229 824 219;
E: keith.parkes5@btopenworld.com

BTO Regional Representative
Colin Gay. T: 01229 773 820;
E: colinathodbarrow@btinternet.com

Dave Piercy (Assistant Representative).
T: 01768 773 201; E: daveandkathypiercy@tiscali.co.uk

Peter Hearn (Regional Development Officer).
T: n/a; E: biarmicus@live.co.uk

Club
ARNSIDE & DISTRICT NATURAL HISTORY SOCIETY.
(1960's; 200). Gail Armstrong (Sec), 1 Bottoms Lane,
Silverdale, LA5 0TN. T: 01524 701 316;
E: arnsidenaturalhistorysociety@gmail.com;
W: www.arnsideanddistrictnhs.co.uk
Meetings: 7.30pm, 2nd Thursday of the month
(Sep-Mar). WI Hall, Orchard Rd, Arnside, LA5 0DP.

CUMBRIA BIRD CLUB. (1989; 330).
Dave Piercy (Sec), 64 The Headlands, Keswick,
CA12 5EJ. T: 01768 773 201;
E: daveandkathypiercy@tiscali.co.uk;
W: www.cumbriabirdclub.org.uk

Meetings: Various evenings
and venues (Oct-Mar) -
contact/see website for
details.

Ringing Group/Bird Observatory
EDEN RG.

MORECAMBE BAY WADER RG.

WATCHTREE RG. W: www.watchtree.co.uk

WALNEY BIRD OBSERVATORY.
Keith Parkes (Sec), 77 Dalton Lane,
Barrow-in-Furness, LA14 4LB. T: 01229 824 219;
E: keith.parkes5@btopenworld.com;
E (recorder): walneyobs@gmail.com;
W: http://walneybo.blogspot.co.uk

RSPB Local Group
NORTH CUMBRIA. (1974; 200).
Richard Dixon. T: 07720 067 283;
E: sunzeco@hotmail.co.uk;
W: www.rspb.org.uk/groups/carlisle
Meetings: 7.30pm, usually 2nd Wednesday
(Sep-Mar). Tithe Barn, (Behind Marks & Spencer's),
West Walls, Carlisle, CA3 8UF.

WEST CUMBRIA. (1986; 135).
Dave Smith. T: 01900 85347; E: smida@talktalk.net;
W: www.rspb.org.uk/groups/westcumbria
Meetings: 7.30pm, 1st Tuesday of the month
(Sep-Apr). United Reformed Church, Main St,
Cockermouth, CA13 9LU.

Wetland Bird Survey (WeBS) Local Organiser
CUMBRIA (excl. ESTUARIES). Dave Shackleton.
T: via WeBS Office; E: d.shackleton@btinternet.com

DUDDON ESTUARY. Colin Gay. T: 01229 773 820;
E: colinathodbarrow@btinternet.com

IRT/MITE/ESK ESTUARIES.
Peter Jones. T: via WeBS Office;
E: via WeBS Office

MORECAMBE BAY (NORTH).
Peter Hearn. T: 07789 483 601;
E: biarmicus@live.co.uk

SOLWAY ESTUARY (INNER SOUTH).
David Blackledge. T: via WeBS Office;
E: daveblackledge@rspb.org.uk

SOLWAY ESTUARY (NORTH). See Dumfries & Galloway.

SOLWAY ESTUARY (OUTER SOUTH).
Dave Shackleton - see above.

Wildlife Trust
CUMBRIA WILDLIFE TRUST. (1962; 13,000).
Plumgarths, Crook Road, Kendal, LA8 8LX.
T: 01539 816 300, (fax) 01539 816 301;
E: mail@cumbriawildlifetrust.org.uk;
W: www.cumbriawildlifetrust.org.uk

DERBYSHIRE

BirdAtlas/Avifauna
The Birds of Derbyshire. RA Frost & Steve Shaw
(Liverpool University Press, 2014).

Bird Recorder
Joint Recorder. Rodney Key, 3 Farningham Close,
Spondon, Derby DE21 7DZ. T: 01332 678 571 &
07710 770 195; E: r_key@sky.com

Joint Recorder (Annual Report). Anthony Garton.
Address: n/a. T: n/a; E: tonygarton13@sky.com

ENGLAND

Rare Breeding Birds Recorder. Roy Frost,
66 St Lawrence Road, North Wingfield,
Chesterfield, S42 5LL. T: 01246 850 037;
E: frostra66@btinternet.com

Bird Report
CARSINGTON BIRD CLUB ANNUAL REPORT (1992-),
from Paul Hickling (Sec), 12 Beaurepaire Crescent,
Belper, DE56 1HR.

DERBYSHIRE BIRD REPORT (1955-), from Bryan
Barnacle, Mays, Malthouse Lane, Froggatt, Hope
Valley, S32 3ZA. E: barney@mays1.demon.co.uk

OGSTON BIRD CLUB REPORT (1970-),
Mrs J Marshall, 94 Common Road, Huthwaite,
Sutton-in-Ashfield, Nottinghamshire NG17 2JT.
E: jen.marshall@birdinformation.co.uk

BTO Regional Representative
NORTH DERBYSHIRE. Dave Budworth.
T: 01283 215 188; E: dbud01@aol.com

SOUTH DERBYSHIRE. Dave Budworth - see above.

Club
BAKEWELL BIRD STUDY GROUP. (1987; 70).
Brian Shaw (Chairman). Address: n/a.
T: 07768 928 432; E: drgbshaw@gmail.com;
W: www.bakewellbirdstudygroup.org.uk
Meetings: 7.30pm, 2nd Monday of the month
(Sep-May). Friends Meeting House, Chapel Lane,
Bakewell, DE45 1EL.

BUXTON FIELD CLUB. (1946; 50).
Pat Thompson (Sec), Flat 6, Temple Court,
Temple Road, Buxton, SK17 9BA. T: 01298 938920;
E: 4acrylics9@gmail.com; W: n/a
Meetings: 7.30pm, usually fortnightly on a
Saturday (Oct-Mar). Buxton Methodist Church,
Chapel Street, Buxton, SK17 6HX.

CARSINGTON BIRD CLUB. (1992; 250).
Roger Carrington (Sec), Address: n/a. T: n/a.
E: rcarrington_matlock@yahoo.co.uk;
W: www.carsingtonbirdclub.co.uk
Meetings: 7.30pm,
3rd Tuesday of the month
(Sep-Mar). The Henmore
Room, Carsington Water
Visitor Centre, Big Lane,
Ashbourne, DE6 1ST.

DERBYSHIRE
ORNITHOLOGICAL SOCIETY. (1954; 550).
Steve Shaw (Sec), 84 Moorland View Road,
Walton, Chesterfield, S40 3DF. T: 01246 236 090;
E: steveshaw84mvr@btinternet.com;
W: www.derbyshireos.org.uk
Meetings: 7.30pm, usually last Friday of the
month (Sep-Mar), various venues - contact/see
website for details.

OGSTON BIRD CLUB. (1969; 125).
Jenny Marshall (Sec). Address: n/a.
T: 07533 973 809;
E: jen.marshall@birdinformation.co.uk;
W: www.ogstonbirdclub.co.uk
Meetings: Currently only an AGM is held -
contact/see website for details.

Ringing Group/Bird Observatory
SORBY-BRECK RG. See Yorkshire.

SOUDER RG.

RSPB Local Group
CHESTERFIELD. (1987; 275).
Stephen Williams. T: 01246 206 700;
E: stephen150williams@btinternet.com;
W: www.rspb.or.uk/groups/chesterfield
Meetings: 7.15pm, (usually) 1st Monday of the
month. St Thomass Centre, Chatsworth Road,
Chesterfield, S40 3AW.

DERBY. (1974; 270).
Max Maughan. T: 01332 511 825;
E: RSPBlocalgroupderby@gmail.com;
W: www.rspb.org.uk/groups/derby
Meetings: 7.30pm, 2nd Wednesday of the month
(Sep-Apr). The Grange Banqueting Suite,
457 Burton Rd, Littleover, Derby, DE23 6XX.

Wetland Bird Survey (WeBS) Local Organiser
DERBYSHIRE. Vacant - contact WeBS Office.

Wildlife Trust
DERBYSHIRE WILDLIFE TRUST. (1962; 14,000).
Sandy Hill, Main Street, Middleton, Matlock, DE4 4LR.
T: 01773 881 188, (fax) 01773 821 826;
E: enquiries@derbyshirewt.co.uk;
W: www.derbyshirewildlifetrust.org.uk

DEVON

BirdAtlas/Avifauna
Devon Bird Atlas 2007-2013.
Stella D Beavan & Mike Lock
(Devon Birdwatching &
Preservation Society, 2016).

The Birds of Devon.
Michael Tyler (Devon
Birdwatching & Preservation
Society, 2010).

The Birds of Lundy.
Tim Davis & Tim Jones
(Harpers Mill Publishing,
2007).

Bird Recorder
Kevin Rylands. Address: n/a. T: n/a;
E: recorder@devonbirds.org

ENGLAND

Bird Report

DEVON BIRDS (1929-), from Mike Daniels (Sec),
Devon Birds, 16 Erme Drive, Ivybridge, PL21 9BN.
T: 01752 690 278; E: info@devonbirds.org

LUNDY FIELD SOCIETY ANNUAL REPORT (1947-)
from Michael Williams (LFS Hon. Sec), 166 Wileman
Way, Cambridge CB3 1AR. E: secretary@lundy.org.uk

BTO Regional Representative
Stella Beavan. T: 07710 879 277;
E: stellabeavan@outlook.com

Club
DEVON BIRDS. (1928; 1200).
Mike Daniels (Sec, Devon Birds), 16 Erme Drive,
Ivybridge, PL21 9BN. T: 01752 690 278;
E: secretary@devonbirds.org; W: www.devonbirds.org

Branches
East Devon:
Geoffrey Green. T: 01404 813 127;
E: gdgreen@talktalk.net
Meetings: No indoor meetings.

Mid Devon:
Nick Armstrong. T: 01363 866 860;
E: armstronick@gmail.com
Meetings: Occassional, contact/see website for
details.

Plymouth:
Liz Harris. T: 01752 789 594;
E: elizmharris@yahoo.com
Meetings: 7.30pm, (Sep-Apr). Spurgeon Hall,
Mutley Baptist Church, Mutley Plain, Plymouth,
PL4 6LB for programme see W: www.devonbirds.org

South Devon:
Mike Goss. T: 01364 72539.
E: mike.goss@devonbirds.org
Meetings: 7.30pm, 3rd Monday of the month
(Jan-Nov). Church House, Slade Lane,
Abbotskerswell, TQ12 5NX.

Taw & Torridge:
Maxine White. T: 07894 998 718. E: n/a.
Meetings: 7.30pm, 2nd Tuesday of the month
(Sep-Apr). The Castle Centre, 25 Castle Street,
Barnstaple, EX31 1DR.

KINGSBRIDGE & DISTRICT
NATURAL HISTORY SOCIETY.
(1989; 80). Chris Klee
(Chairman), The Old School
House, 2 Ebrington Street,
Kingsbridge, TQ7 1DF.
T: 01548 288 397;
E: jcklee@pobroadband.co.uk; W: www.knhs.org.uk
Meeting: 7.30pm, 4th Monday of the month
(Sep-Apr). West Charleton Village Hall,
West Charleton, Kingsbridge, TQ7 2AJ.

LUNDY FIELD SOCIETY. (1946; 480).
Michael Williams (Sec), 166 Wileman Way, Cambridge
CB3 1AR. T: n/a; E: secretary@lundy.org.uk;
W: www.lundy.org.uk
Meeting: AGM, 2nd Saturday of Mar in Crediton.

TOPSHAM BIRDWATCHING & NATURALISTS' SOCIETY.
(1969; 115). Keith Chester (Membership Sec).
Address: n/a. T: 01392 877 817;
E: topshambns@gmail.com;
W: http://topshambns.blogspot.co.uk/
Meetings: 7.30pm, 2nd Friday of the month
(Sep-Apr). Matthews Hall, Fore Street,Topsham,
Exeter, EX3 0HF.

Ringing Group/Bird Observatory
AXE ESTUARY RG.
W: http://axeestuaryringinggroup.blogspot.co.uk

DEVON & CORNWALL WADER GROUP.
W: www.dcwrg.org.uk/

LUNDY FIELD SOCIETY.

SLAPTON BIRD OBSERVATORY RG.

RSPB Local Group
EXETER & DISTRICT. (1974; 400).
Richard Swinbank. T: 01404 813 666;
E: richard.swinbank@mac.com;
W: www.rspb.org.uk/groups/exeter
Meetings: 7.30 pm, 1st or 2nd Tuesday of the
month, (Sep-Apr). Southernhay United Reformed
Church Rooms, Southernhay East, Exeter, EX1 1QA.

PLYMOUTH. (1974; 200).
Vince Bedford. T: 01752 785 240;
E: vincebedford@live.co.uk;
W: www.rspb.org.uk/groups/plymouth
Meetings: 7.30pm, usually on a Wednesday
(Sep/Nov/Jan/Mar). Trinity United Reform Church,
Tor Lane, Plymouth PL3 5NY - contact/see
website for details.

TORBAY & SOUTH DEVON TEAM. (n/a; n/a).
Julie King. T: 01626 351 135;
E: King.julie@hotmail.co.uk;
W: www.rspb.org.uk/groups/torbayandsouthdevon
Meetings: Held at various locations in the area -
contact/see website for details.

Wetland Bird Survey (WeBS) Local Organiser
DEVON (OTHER SITES). Peter Reay.
T: 01364 73293; E: peter.p.j.reay@btinternet.com

EXE ESTUARY. Penny Avant. T: 01647 252 333;
E: penavant@yahoo.co.uk

TAMAR COMPLEX. See Cornwall

TAW/TORRIDGE. Tim Davis. T: via WeBS office;
E: tim.davis@djenvironmental.com

ENGLAND

Wildlife Trust
DEVON WILDLIFE TRUST. (1962; 32,000).
Cricklepit Mill, Commercial Road, Exeter, EX2 4AB.
T: 01392 279 244, (fax) 01392 433 221;
E: contactus@devonwildlifetrust.org;
W: www.devonwildlifetrust.org

DORSET

Bird Atlas/Avifauna
The Birds of Dorset. George Green
(Christopher Helm, 2004)

Bird Recorder
VACANT.
Dorset Bird Club - E: recorder@dorsetbirds.org.uk

Bird Report
DORSET BIRDS (1977-), from Dorset Bird Club.
E: admin@dorsetbirds.org.uk

PORTLAND BIRD OBSERVATORY REPORT (1963-),
from Martin Cade, The Old Lower Light,
Portland Bill, DT5 2JT. T: 01305 820 553;
E: obs@btinternet.com

THE BIRDS OF CHRISTCHURCH HARBOUR (1956-),
from Ian Southworth, 1 Bodowen Road, Burton,
Christchurch, BH23 7JL. E: ianbirder@aol.com

BTO Regional Representative
Jack Winsper. T: n/a;
E: jlwinsper@btopenworld.com

Greg Lambe (Assistant Representative).
T: n/a; E: greg.lambe1@gmail.com

Club
CHRISTCHURCH HARBOUR
ORNITHOLOGICAL GROUP. (1956; 440).
Dave Taylor (Gen Sec),
Dairy Cottage, Sopley,
Hampshire BH23 7AZ.
T: 01425 672 318;
E: david.dhtaylor@gmail.com;
W: www.chog.org.uk
Meetings: 7.30pm, (usually)   *CHOG*
2nd Wednesday of the
month (Oct-Mar). St Nicholas
Church Hall, The Broadway, Hengistbury Head,
Christchurch, BH6 4EP.

DORSET BIRD CLUB. (1987; 450).
Richard Charman (Membership Sec),
20 Stourpaine Road, Poole, BH17 9AT.
T: 07391 756 053
E: membership@dorsetbirds.org.uk;
W: www.dorsetbirds.org.uk
Meetings: Irregular indoor meetings/AGM usually
in Mar - contact/see website for details.

DORSET NATURAL HISTORY
& ARCHAEOLOGICAL SOCIETY. (1845; 2000).
Museum Secretary, The Old Warehouse,
31a Durngate Street, Dorchester, DT1 1JP.
T: 01305 262 735;
E: membership@dorsetcountymuseum.org;
W: www.dorsetcountymuseum.org

Ringing Group/Bird Observatory
CHRISTCHURCH HARBOUR RS.

RADIPOLE RG.

STOUR RG.

PORTLAND BIRD OBSERVATORY.
Martin Cade (Warden), The Old Lower Light,
Portland Bill, DT5 2JT. T: 01305 820 553;
E: obs@btinternet.com;
W: www.portlandbirdobs.com

RSPB Local Group
SOUTH DORSET. (1976; 420).
Michael Neely. T: 01305 262 869;
E: a.m.neely@btinternet.com;
W: www.rspb.org.uk/groups/southdorset
Meetings: 7.15pm, 4th Tuesday of the month
(Sep-Apr, not Dec). Meeting Room 2, County Hall,
Colliton Park, Dorchester, DT1 1XJ.

Wetland Bird Survey (WeBS) Local Organiser
DORSET (excl. ESTUARIES). Malcolm Balmer.
T: via WeBS Office;
E: malcolm.balmer@gmail.com

POOLE HARBOUR. Paul Morton.
T: via WeBS Office; E: paulolua@yahoo.co.uk

RADIPOLE & LODMOOR. Stephen Hales.
T: 07801 344 024; E: via WeBS Office

THE FLEET & PORTLAND HARBOUR. Stephen Groves.
T: 01305 871 684; E: cygnusolor@yahoo.co.uk

Wildlife Trust
DORSET WILDLIFE TRUST. (1961; 27,000).
Brooklands Farm, Forston, Dorchester, DT2 7AA.
T: 01305 264 620, (fax) 01305 251 120;
E: enquiries@dorsetwildlifetrust.org.uk;
W: www.dorsetwildlifetrust.org.uk

DURHAM

Bird Atlas/Avifauna
The Birds of Durham. Keith Bowey &
Mark Newsome (Durham Bird Club, 2012).

Birds of Cleveland. Martin Blick (Tees Valley
Wildlife Trust, 2009).

*The Breeding Birds of Cleveland: A Tetrad Atlas
1999-2006*. Graeme Joynt, James Fairbrother &
Ted Parker (Teesmouth Bird Club, 2008).

ENGLAND

A Summer Atlas of Breeding Birds of County Durham. Stephen Westerberg & Keith Bowey (Durham Bird Club, 2000).

Bird Recorder
CLEVELAND. Alan Crossley, 32 Sledwick Rd, Billingham, Cleveland TS23 3HU.
T: 07801 751 952; E: alancrossley11@outlook.com

DURHAM. Recorder. Andrew Kinghorn. Address: n/a.
T: n/a; E: andrew.kinghorn@hotmail.co.uk

Assistant Recorder (Rarities). Tom Middleton, 3 Tunstall Villas, Sunderland, SR3 2BE. T: n/a; E: t_middleton24@hotmail.co.uk

Bird Report
CLEVELAND BIRD REPORT (1974-), from John Fletcher, 43 Glaisdale Avenue, Tollesby, Middlesbrough, TS5 7PF. T: 01642 818 825; E: j.fletcher666@btinternet.com

BIRDS IN DURHAM (1970-), from D Sowerbutts, 9 Prebends Fields, Gilesgate Moor, Durham, DH1 1HH. E: dsowerbutts608@gmail.com

BTO Regional Representative
CLEVELAND. Michael Leakey. T: n/a; E: mikeaquila@hotmail.com

DURHAM. David Sowerbutts. T: 0191 386 7201; E: dsowerbutts608@gmail.com

Club
DURHAM BIRD CLUB. (1974; 350). Richard Cowen (Sec), Rose Cottage, Old Quarrington, DH6 5NN. T: 07882 782 833; E: durhambirdclub@gmail.com; W: www.durhambirdclub.org
Meetings: Contact/see website for details.

NORTHUMBERLAND & TYNESIDE BIRD CLUB. NATURAL HISTORY SOCIETY OF NORTHUMBRIA.
- See Northumberland

TEESMOUTH BIRD CLUB. (1960; 425).
Chris Sharp (Sec), 6 Maritime Avenue, Hartlepool, TS24 0XF. T: 01429 865 163; E: chrisandlucia@ntlworld.com; W: www.teesmouthbc.com
Meetings: 7.30pm, 1st Monday of the month (Sep-Apr). Stockton Library, Church Road, Stockton, TS18 1TU.

Ringing Group/Bird Observatory
DURHAM DALES RG.

SOUTH CLEVELAND RG.

TEES RG.

WHITBURN RG.

RSPB Local Group
CLEVELAND. (1974; 100).
Jenny Wright . T: 07952 419 897; E: jenny.wright@RSPB.org.uk; W: www.rspb.org.uk/groups/cleveland
Meetings: 7.30pm, 2nd Monday of the month (Sep-Apr). Middlesbrough Rugby Club, Green Lane, Middlesbrough, TS5 7SL.

DURHAM. (1974; 125).
Richard Cowen. T: 07397 862 833; E: richard.cowen313@gmail.com; W: www.rspb.org.uk/groups/durham
Meetings: 7.30pm, 2nd Tuesday of the month (Oct-Apr). Laurel Avenue Community Centre, Laurel Avenue, Durham, DH1 2EY.

Wetland Bird Survey (WeBS) Local Organiser
CLEVELAND (excl. TEES ESTUARY). Chris Sharp.
T: 01429 865 163; E: chrisandlucia@ntlworld.com

DURHAM. Vacant - contact WeBS Office.

TEES ESTUARY. Adam Jones. T: 07872 157 735; E: via WeBS Office

Wildlife Trust
DURHAM WILDLIFE TRUST. (1971; 9,000).
Rainton Meadows, Chilton Moor, Houghton-le-Spring, Tyne & Wear DH4 6PU. T: 0191 584 3112, (fax) 0191 584 3934; E: mail@durhamwt.co.uk; W: www.durhamwt.com

TEES VALLEY WILDLIFE TRUST. (1979; 5,000).
Margrove Heritage Centre, Margrove Park, Boosbeck, Saltburn, TS12 3BZ. T: 01287 636 382, (fax) 01287 636 383; E: info@teeswildlife.org; W: www.teeswildlife.org

ESSEX

Bird Atlas/Avifauna
The Birds of Essex. Simon Wood (Christopher Helm, 2007).

Tetrad Atlas of the Breeding Birds of Essex. MK Dennis (Essex Birdwatching Soc, 1996).

Bird Recorder
Michael Tracey, Robins, Hayhouse Rd, Earls Colne, Colchester, CO6 2PD.
T: 07500 866 335; E: micktrac@aol.com

Bird Report
ESSEX BIRD REPORT (1949/50-), from Peter Dwyer, EBWS, 48 Churchill Avenue, Halstead, CO9 2BE.
T: 01787 476 524; E: petedwyer@petedwyer.plus.com

ENGLAND

BTO Regional Representative
NORTH-EAST. Rod Bleach. T: 07799 547 192;
E: rod.bleach@sesl.eu

NORTH-WEST. Graham Smith. T: 01277 354 034;
E: silaum.silaus@tiscali.co.uk

SOUTH. Vacant - contact Dawn Balmer, BTO.
T: 01842 750 050; E: dawn.balmer@bto.org

Club
ESSEX BIRDWATCHING
SOCIETY. (1949; 510).
Peter Dwyer
(Membership Sec),
48 Churchill Avenue,
Halstead, CO9 2BE.
T: 01787 476 524;
E: info.ebws@gmail.com; W: www.ebws.org.uk
Meetings: 8pm, 1st Friday of the month (Sep-Apr).
Quaker Meeting House, 82 Rainsford Road,
Chelmsford, CM1 2QL.

Ringing Group/Bird Observatory
BRADWELL BIRD OBSERVATORY RG.

NORTH THAMES GULL GROUP. W: www.ntgg.org.uk

SOUTHERN COLOUR RINGING GROUP.
W: www.southern-colour-ringing-group.org.uk

RSPB Local Group
CHELMSFORD & CENTRAL ESSEX. (1975; 360).
Sue McClellan. T: 01245 471 576;
E: suem@idnet.com;
W: www.rspb.org.uk/groups/chelmsford
Meetings: 7.45pm, 2nd Thursday of the month
(Sep-Apr). Northumberland Theatre, Writtle
University College, Lordship Road, Writtle, CM1 3RP.

COLCHESTER. (1981; 40).
Ron Firmin. T: 07714 210 746;
E: ron.firmin@btinternet.com;
W: www.rspb.org.uk/groups/colchester
Meetings: 7.45pm (7.30pm Sep) 2nd Thursday of
the month (Sep-Apr). Shrub End Social Centre,
Shrub End Road, Colchester, CO3 4SA.

SOUTH EAST ESSEX. (1983; 200).
Graham Mee. T: 01702 525 152;
E: grahamm@southendrspb.co.uk;
W: www.southendrspb.co.uk
Meetings: 8.00pm, 1st Wednesday of the month
(Sep-May). The EWT Belfairs Woodland Centre,
Eastwood Road North, Leigh-on-Sea, SS9 4LR.

Wetland Bird Survey (WeBS) Local Organiser
CROUCH/ROACH ESTUARY and SOUTH DENGIE.
Stephen Spicer. T: 07515 651 736;
E: stephenspicer4@gmail.com

ESSEX (OTHER SITES). Anthony Harbott.
T: 01992 575 213; E: anthonyharbott@gmail.com

HAMFORD WATER. Leon Woodrow.
T: 07881 652 920; E: via WeBS Office

LEE VALLEY. See Hertfordshire.

NORTH BLACKWATER. John Thorogood.
T: 01206 768 771; E: via WeBS Office

SOUTH BLACKWATER AND NORTH DENGIE.
Mr A Harbott - see above.

SWALE, MEDWAY & NORTH KENT MARSHES.
See Kent.

THAMES ESTUARY (FOULNESS). Chris Lewis.
T: via WeBS Office. E: cpm.lewis@gmail.com

Wildlife Trust
ESSEX WILDLIFE TRUST. (1959; 37,000).
Abbotts Hall Farm, Maldon Road,
Great Wigborough, Colchester, CO5 7RZ.
T: 01621 862 960, (fax) 01621 862 990;
E: admin@essexwt.org.uk; W: www.essexwt.org.uk

GLOUCESTERSHIRE

Bird Atlas/Avifauna
The Birds of Gloucestershire.
Gordon Kirk &
John Phillips (Liverpool
University Press, 2013).

*Birds of The Cotswolds:
A New Breeding Atlas.*
Iain Main, Dave Pearce &
Tim Hutton (Liverpool
University Press 2009).

Bird Recorder
Richard Baatsen. Address: n/a. T: 07879 850 196;
E: Richard.Baatsen@gmail.com
(excl. S.Gloucs = Avon)

Bird Report
GLOUCESTERSHIRE BIRD REPORT (1948-),from
The Membership Secretary (GNS), 50 KIngsmead,
Abbymead, Gloucester, GL4 5DY.
E: gnsmembership@btinternet.com

BTO Regional Representative
Gordon Kirk. T: 01452 741 724;
E: GordonKirk@aol.com

Club
CHELTENHAM BIRD CLUB. (1976; 100).
Membership Sec. Address: n/a.
T: 01242 690 660; E: via website;
W: www.cheltenhambirdclub.org.uk
Meetings: 7.15pm, most Mondays (Oct-Mar),
Bournside School, Warden Hill Road, Cheltenham,
GL51 3EF.

COUNTY DIRECTORY

ENGLAND

DURSLEY BIRDWATCHING
& PRESERVATION SOCIETY. (1953; 240).
Brenda Usher (Sec). Address: n/a.
T: 01452 721 863; E: secretary@dbwps.org.uk;
W: www.dbwps.org.uk
Meetings: 7.45pm, 2nd and last Mondays of the
month (Sep-Apr). Dursley Community Centre,
Rednock Drive, Dursley, GL11 4BX.

GLOUCESTERSHIRE NATURALISTS' SOCIETY.
(1948; 500).
The Membership Secretary, 50 KIngsmead,
Abbymead, Gloucester, GL4 5DY.
T: 01452 610 085;
E: gnsmembership@btinternet.com;
W: www.glosnats.org

Meetings: 7.30pm, 2nd
Friday of the month
(Oct-Apr). Normally
at Watermoor Church
Hall, Watermoor Road,
Cirencester, GL7 1JR - some
may be held at: Parish
Rooms in Gosditch Street,
Cirencester, GL7 2AG -
contact/check website for
details.

Ringing Group/Bird Observatory
COTSWOLD WATER PARK RG.

SEVERN ESTUARY GULL GROUP.

RSPB Local Group
GLOUCESTERSHIRE. (1972; 400).
David Cramp. T: 01242 620 281;
E: djcramp@btinternet.com;
W: www.rspb.org.uk/groups/gloucestershire
Meetings: 7.30pm, 3rd Tuesday of the month
(Sep-Nov, Jan-Mar). The Gala Club, Fairmile Gardens,
Longford, Gloucester, GL2 9EB.

Wetland Bird Survey (WeBS) Local Organiser
GLOUCESTERSHIRE (inc. SEVERN ESTUARY,
excl. COTSWOLD WATER PARK).
Michael Smart. T: 01452 421 131;
E: smartmike143@gmail.com

COTSWOLD WATER PARK. Ben Welbourn.
T: via WeBS Office; E: ben.welbourn@waterpark.org

Wildlife Trust
GLOUCESTERSHIRE WILDLIFE TRUST. (1961; 28,000).
Conservation Centre, Robinswood Hill Country Park,
Reservoir Road, Gloucester, GL4 6SX.
T: 01452 383 333, (fax) 01452 383 334;
E: info@gloucestershirewildlifetrust.co.uk;
W: www.gloucestershirewildlifetrust.co.uk

HAMPSHIRE

Bird Atlas/Avifauna
*Hampshire Bird Atlas
2007-2012.* John Eyre (Ed).
(HOS, 2015).

Birds of Hampshire.
JM Clark & JA Eyre
(Hampshire Ornithological
Society, 1993).

Bird Recorder
Keith Betton, 8 Dukes Close,
Folly Hill, Farnham, Surrey
GU9 0DR. T: 01252 724 068 or 07809 671 468;
E: keithbetton@hotmail.com

Bird Report
HAMPSHIRE BIRD REPORT (1978-), from Bryan &
Sandy Coates, 8 Gardner Way, Chandler's Ford,
SO53 1JL. E: sandyandbryan@tiscali.co.uk

BTO Regional Representative
Glynne Evans. T: 01264 860 697;
E: hantsbto@hotmail.com

Brian Sharkey (Assistant Representative).
T: 01189 814 751; E: briansharkeyuk@yahoo.co.uk

John Shillitoe (Assistant Representative).
T: 01329 833 086; E: jshillitoe.googlemail.com

Club
HAMPSHIRE ORNITHOLOGICAL SOCIETY. (1979; 2000).
John Shillitoe (Sec), 'Westerly', Hundred Acres
Road, Wickham, PO17 6HY. T: 01329 833 086;
E: jshillitoe@googlemail.com; W: www.hos.org.uk
Meetings: Members' Day at the end of March -
contact/see website for details.

Ringing Group/Bird Observatory
FARLINGTON RG.

ITCHEN RG.

TITCHFIELD HAVEN RG.

RSPB Local Group
BASINGSTOKE. (1979; 65).
*** 40th Anniversary Year***
Peter E. Hutchins. T: 01256 770 831 or 07895 388 378;
E: RSPBbasingstoke@gmail.com;
W: www.rspb.org.uk/groups/basingstoke
Meetings: 7.45pm, 3rd Wednesday of the month
(Sep-May). The Barn, St Michael's Cottage, Church
Cottage, St Michael's Church, Church Square,
Basingstoke, RG21 7QW.

Hampshire
Bird Atlas
2007–2012

Hampshire Ornithological Society

NEW FOREST. (2000; 150).
T: n/a; E: enquiries@nfRSPB.org.uk;
W: www.rspb.org.uk/groups/newforest
W: www.nfrspb.org.uk
Meetings: 7.30pm, 2nd Wednesday of the month
(Sep-Jun). Lyndhurst Community Centre,
High Street, Lyndhurst, SO43 7NY.

NORTH EAST HANTS. (1976; 175).
Sue Radbourn. T: 01276 29434;
E: NehantsRSPB@gmail.com;
W: www.rspb.org.uk/groups/northeasthants
Meetings: 7.30pm, in halls in Church Crookham
and Fleet (Sep-Apr) - contact/see website for
details.

PORTSMOUTH. (1974; 210).
Gordon Humby. T: 023 9235 3949;
E: PortsmouthRSPB@gmail.com;
W: www.rspb.org.uk/groups/portsmouth
Meetings: 7.30pm, 4th Saturday of the month
(Jan-Nov). St Andrews Church Hall, Havant Road,
Farlington, Portsmouth, PO6 1AA.

WINCHESTER & DISTRICT (1974; 80).
Pam Symes. T: 01962 851 821;
E: WinchRSPB1974@gmail.com;
W: www.rspb.org.uk/groups/winchester
Meetings: 7.45pm, 1st Wednesday of the month
(not Jan or Aug). Shawford Parish Hall, Pearson
Lane, Shawford, Winchester, SO21 2AA.

Wetland Bird Survey (WeBS) Local Organiser
AVON VALLEY. John Clark. T: 01252 623 397;
E: johnclark50@sky.com

HAMPSHIRE (ESTUARIES/COASTAL).
John Shillitoe. T: 01329 833 086;
E: jshillitoe.googlemail.com

HAMPSHIRE (INLAND - excl. AVON VALLEY).
Keith Wills. T: via WeBS Office;
E: kwills57@btinternet.com

Wildlife Trust
HAMPSHIRE & ISLE OF WIGHT WILDLIFE TRUST.
(1960; 27,000).
Beechcroft, Vicarage Lane, Curdridge, SO32 2DP.
T: 01489 774 400, (fax) 01489 774 401;
E: feedback@hiwwt.org.uk; W: www.hiwwt.org.uk

HEREFORDSHIRE

Bird Atlas/Avifauna
The Birds of Herefordshire 2007-2012: An Atlas
of Their Breeding and Wintering Distributions.
Mervyn Davies, Peter Eldridge, Chris Robinson,
Nich Smith & Gerald Wells (Liverpool University
Press, 2014).

Bird Recorder
Mick Colquhoun, Old Gore House, Old Gore,
Ross on Wye, HR9 7QT. T: 07587 151 627;
E: recorder@herefordshirebirds.org

Bird Report
THE BIRDS OF HEREFORDSHIRE
(1951-), from
Mervyn Davies, Hunters Moon,
Bishopstone, Hereford,
HR4 7JE.
E: mervyn.davies88@gmail.com

BTO Regional Representative
Chris Robinson.
T: 01981 510 360;
E: herefordbtorep@btinternet.com

Club
HEREFORDSHIRE ORNITHOLOGICAL CLUB.
(1950; 400+). Josephine Spencer (Sec).
Address: n/a. T: 01432 350 764;
E: secretary@herefordshirebirds.org;
W: www.herefordshirebirds.org
Meetings: 7.30pm,
2nd Thursday of the
month (Sep-Mar),
Holmer Parish
Centre, Holmer,
Hereford, HR4 9RG.

Ringing Group/Bird Observatory
LLANCILLO RG.

Wetland Bird Survey (WeBS) Local Organiser
HEREFORDSHIRE. Chris Robinson.
T: 01981 510 360;
E: fredbloggs@btinternet.com

Wildlife Trust
HEREFORDSHIRE NATURE TRUST. (1962; 5,000).
Queenswood Country Park & Arboretum, Dinmore
Hill, Nr Leominster, HR6 0PY.
T: 01432 356 872, (fax) 01432 275 489;
E: enquiries@herefordshirewt.co.uk;
W: www.herefordshirewt.org

HERTFORDSHIRE

Bird Atlas/Avifauna
Birds of Hertfordshire. Ken W Smith, Chris W Dee,
Jack D Fearnside & Mike Ilett (Herts NHS, 2015).

Bird Recorder
Alan Gardiner, 199 Watford Rd, St Albans AL2 3HH.
T: 01727 863 945; E: birdrecorder@hnhs.org

Bird Report
HERTFORDSHIRE BIRD REPORT (1980-), not for
general sale but enquiries to David Utting (Sec).
E: secretary@hnhs.org

COUNTY DIRECTORY

ENGLAND

BTO Regional Representative
Martin Ketcher. T: n/a;
E: martinketcher@gmail.com

Club
HERTFORDSHIRE BIRD CLUB. (1971) part of
HERTFORDSHIRE NATURAL HISTORY SOCIETY.
(1875; 420)
VACANT (Sec). Address: n/a. T: n/a;
E: birdclubsecretary@hnhs.org;
W: www.hnhs.org/birds
Meetings: Annual Herts Bird Conference -
contact/see website for details.

Ringing Group/Bird Observatory
MAPLE CROSS RG.

RUNNYMEDE RG. W: www.runnymedering.uk

RYE MEADS RG. W: www.rmrg.org.uk

SOUTHERN COLOUR RINGING GROUP.
W: www.southern-colour-ringing-group.org.uk

TRING RG. W: www.tringringinggroup.org.uk
https://tringringinggroup.blogspot.co.uk/

RSPB Local Group
CHORLEYWOOD & DISTRICT. (1976; 90).
Carol Smith. T: 01923 897 885;
E: carolsmithuk@hotmail.com;
W: www.rspb.org.uk/groups/chorleywood
Meetings: 8.00pm, 3rd Thursday of the month
(Sep-May). The Russell School, Brushwood Drive,
Chorleywood, Rickmansworth, WD3 5RR.

HARPENDEN. (1974; 100).
Geoff Horn. T: 01582 765 443;
E: geoffrhorn@yahoo.co.uk;
W: www.rspb.org.uk/groups/harpenden
Meetings: 8.00pm, 2nd Thursday of the month
(Sep-Apr). All Saint's Church Hall, Station Road,
Harpenden, AL5 4UU.

HEMEL HEMPSTEAD. (1972; 100).
Ian Wilson. T: 01442 265 022;
E: ian.aeronautics@gmail.com;
W: www.rspb.org.uk/groups/hemelhempstead
Meetings: 8.00pm, 1st Monday of the month
(Sep-Jun). The Laureate Academy, Warners End
Road, Hemel Hempstead, HP1 3DW.

HITCHIN & LETCHWORTH. (1972; 85).
Martin Johnson. T: 01763 249 459;
E: martinrjspc@hotmail.com;
W: www.rspb.org.uk/groups/hitchinandletchworth
Meetings: 7.30pm, 1st Friday of the month (Sep-May).
Letchworth Settlement, 229 Nevells Rd,
Letchworth, SG6 4UB.

POTTERS BAR & BARNETS. (1977; 1400/area).
Ian Sharp. T: 01707 662 914;
E: Pbandb.RSPB@gmail.com;
W: www.rspb.org.uk/groups/pottersbarandbarnet
Meetings: 2.00pm, one Wednesday of the month
(Sep-Jun). St Johns URC Hall, Mowbray Rd,
Barnet, EN5 1RH & 7.45pm, one Friday of the
month (Sep-Jun), Tilbury Hall, United Reform
Church, Darkes Lane, Potters Bar, EN6 1BZ -
contact/see website for details.

SOUTH EAST HERTFORDSHIRE. (1971; 200).
Stan Kitchiner. T: 07821 875 419;
E: stan.kitchiner@hotmail.com;
W: www.rspb.org.uk/groups/southeasthertfordshire
Meetings: 8.00pm, last Tuesday of the month
(Sep-Jun, Dec = 3rd Tuesday). United Reformed
Church, Mill Lane, Broxbourne, EN10 7BG.

ST ALBANS. (1979; 80).
Colin Rose, T: 01727 767 282;
E: colin.rose20@ntlworld.com;
W: www.rspb.org.uk/groups/stalbans
Meetings: Indoor meetings currently suspended,
mainly run outdoor meetings - contact/see
website for details.

STEVENAGE. (1982; 50).
Trevor Storey. T: 01438 226 014;
E: trevorstorey54@gmail.com;
W: www.rspb.org.uk/groups/stevenage
Meetings: 7.30pm, 3rd Tuesday of the month
(Sep-May). Friends Meeting House, Cutty's Lane,
Stevenage, SG1 1UP.

STORT VALLEY. (2009; 40).
Simon Hurwitz. T: 01799 500 996;
E: simon.hurwitz@ntlworld.com;
W: www.rspb.org.uk/groups/stortvalley
Meetings: 7.30pm, 2nd Tuesday of the month
(Sep-Jun). Bishops Park Community Centre,
2 Lancaster Way, Bishop's Stortford, SM23 4DA.

WATFORD. (1974; 590).
Janet Reynolds. T: 01923 249 647;
E: WatfordRSPB@gmail.com;
W: www.rspb.org.uk/groups/watford
Meetings: 7.30pm, 2nd Wednesday of the month
(Sep-Jun). The Stanborough Centre,
609 St Albans Road, Watford, WD25 9JL.

Wetland Bird Survey (WeBS) Local Organiser
HERTFORDSHIRE (excl. LEE VALLEY).
Jim Terry. T: 0208 905 1461;
E: jimjoypaddy@virginmedia.com

LEE VALLEY (GREATER LONDON/ESSEX/
HERTFORDSHIRE). Cath Patrick.
T: 01992 709 882; E: cpatrick@leevalleypark.org.uk

ENGLAND

Wildlife Trust
HERTFORDSHIRE & MIDDLESEX WILDLIFE TRUST.
(1964; 23,000).
Grebe House, St Michael's Street, St Albans, Herts,
AL3 4SN. T: 01727 858 901, (fax) 01727 854 542;
E: info@hmwt.org; W: www.hertswildlifetrust.org.uk

ISLE OF MAN

Bird Atlas/Avifauna
*Manx Bird Atlas: An
Atlas of Breeding and
Wintering Birds on the
Isle of Man.*
Chris Sharpe (Liverpool
University Press, 2007).

Manx Bird Atlas

Bird Recorder
Allen Moore, 'Lyndale',
Derby Road, Peel, IOM
IM5 1HH. T: n/a;
E: allen.gobbag@manx.net

Bird Report
CALF OF MAN BIRD OBSERVATORY, from Manx
National Heritage Shop, Manx Museum, Kingswood
Grove, Douglas, IM1 3LY. T: 01624 648 000;
E: enquiries@mnh.gov.im

MANX BIRD REPORT (1972-), from Allen S Moore,
'Lyndale', Derby Road, Peel, IOM IM5 1HH.
E: allen.gobbag@manx.net

BTO Regional Representative
David Kennett. T: n/a; E: dtkennett@manx.net

Janet Thompson (Assistant Representative).
T: n/a; E: jthompson@manx.net

Club
MANX BIRDLIFE.
Laxey & Lanan Commissioners Offices, 35 New Road,
Laxey, Isle of Man IM4 7BG. T: 01624 861 130;
E: enquiries@manxbirdlife.im; W: http://manxbirdlife.im

MANX ORNITHOLOGICAL SOCIETY. (1997; 150).
Janet Thompson (Sec),
Cott ny Greiney,
Beach Road,
Port St Mary, IM9 5NF.
T: 01624 835 524;
E: jthompson@manx.net;
W: http://manxbirdlife.
im/manx-ornithological-
society
Meetings: 7.30pm, 1st
Tuesday of the month
(Oct-Mar). Union Mills
Methodist Chapel, Strang Road, Union Mills
IM4 4NL.

Ringing Group/Bird Observatory
MANX RG.

CALF OF MAN BIRD OBSERVATORY.
Aron Sapsford (Ornithological Warden).
T: 07624 497 179; E: aron.sapsford@sky.com;
W: www.manxnationalheritage.im/visit/stay-
with-us/calf-of-man-bird-observatory/

Accommodation Bookings Officer, Manx National
Heritage, Kingswood Grove, Douglas, IOM IM1 3LY.
T: 01624 648 015; E: staywithus@mnh.gov.im

Wetland Bird Survey (WeBS) Local Organiser
ISLE OF MAN. Patrick Cullen. T: 01624 676 774);
E: bridgeen@mcb.net

Wildlife Trust
MANX WILDLIFE TRUST. (1973; 1,000).
7-8 Market Place, Peel, Isle of Man IM5 1AB.
T: 01624 844 432, (fax) 01624 842 317;
E: enquiries@manxwt.org.uk; W: www.manxwt.org.uk

ISLE OF WIGHT

Bird Recorder
Jon Sparshott, Leopards, Main Road, Havenstreet,
IoW PO33 4DR. T: 01983 882 549; E: jon1a8@aol.com

Bird Report
ISLE OF WIGHT BIRD REPORT (1996-), from Dave
Hunnybun, 40 Church Hill Road, Cowes, IoW
PO31 8HH. E: davehunnybun@hotmail.com

BTO Regional Representative
Jim Baldwin. T: 01983 721 137 & 07528 586 683;
E: wightbto@hotmail.com

Club
ISLE OF WIGHT NATURAL HISTORY & ARCHAEOLOGICAL
SOCIETY. (1919; 350).
The Secretary, Unit 16, Prospect Business Centre,
Prospect Business Centre, West Cowes, IoW
PO31 7HD. T: 01983 282 596;
E: iwnhas@iwnhas.org; W: www.iwnhas.org
Meetings: Contact/see website for details.

ISLE OF WIGHT ORNITHOLOGICAL GROUP. (1986; 155).
Dave Hunnybun (Sec), 40 Churchill Road, Cowes,
IoW PO31 8HH. T: 01983 292 880;
E: davehunnybun@hotmail.com;
W: http://iowbirds.awardspace.biz/IWOG.htm
Meetings: Only held occasionally - contact/see
website for details.

Ringing Group/Bird Observatory
ISLE OF WIGHT RG.

Wetland Bird Survey (WeBS) Local Organiser
ISLE OF WIGHT. Jim Baldwin. T: 01983 721 137;
E: wightbto@hotmail.com

Wildlife Trust. See Hampshire.

ENGLAND

KENT

Bird Atlas/Avifauna
Kent Breeding Bird Atlas 2008-13. Rob Clements, Murray Orchard, Norman McCanch & Stephen Wood (Kent Ornithological Society, 2015).

The Birds of Kent: A Review of Their Status and Distribution. DW Taylor (Meresborough Books, 2nd ed 1984).

Bird Recorder
Barry Wright, 6 Hatton Close, Northfleet, DA11 8SD. T: 01474 32 918; E: umbrellabirds66@gmail.com

Bird Report
DUNGENESS BIRD OBSERVATORY REPORT (1989-), from David Walker, Dungeness BO, 11 RNSSS Cottages, Dungeness, Romney Marsh, TN29 9NA. T: 01797 321 309; E: dungenessobs@vfast.co.uk

KENT BIRD REPORT (1952-), from Chris Roome, Rowland House, Station Road, Staplehurst, TN12 0PY. E: chrisroome105@icloud.com

SANDWICH BAY BIRD OBSERVATORY REPORT (1962-), from SBBOT, Guildford Road, Sandwich Bay, Sandwich, CT13 9PF. T: 01304 617 341; E: sbbotmail@gmail.com

BTO Regional Representative
Bob Knight. T: n/a. E: rjknight53@gmail.com

Club
KENT ORNITHOLOGICAL SOCIETY. (1952; 650). Brendan Ryan (Hon Sec), 18 The Crescent, Canterbury, CT2 7AQ. T: 01227 471 121; E: brendan.ryan@yahoo.co.uk; W: www.kentos.org.uk
Meetings: AGM - contact/see website for details.

Ringing Group/Bird Observatory
DARTFORD RG.

EAST KENT WILDLIFE GROUP. W: www.ekwg.org

RECULVER RG.

SWALE WADER GROUP. W: www.swalewaders.co.uk

DUNGENESS BIRD OBSERVATORY. David Walker (Warden), Dungeness Bird Observatory, 11 RNSSS Cottages, Dungeness, Romney Marsh, TN29 9NA. T: 01797 321 309; E: dungenessobs@vfast.co.uk; W: www.dungenessbirdobs.org.uk

SANDWICH BAY BIRD OBSERVATORY. Steffan Walton (Warden), Sandwich Bay Bird Observatory, Guildford Road, Sandwich, CT13 9PF. T: 01304 617 341; E: sbbotmail@gmail.com; W: www.sbbot.org.uk

RSPB Local Group
CANTERBURY. (1973; 150). Babs Golding. T: 01227 470 151; E: babs@squirrels.plus.com; W: www.rspb.org.uk/groups/canterbury
Meetings: 7.30pm, 2nd Tuesday of the month (Sep-Apr). Canterbury Academy, Knight Avenue, Canterbury, CT2 8QA.

GRAVESEND. (1977; 170). Paul Yetman. T: 01474 332 417; E: groupleader@RSPBgravesend.org.uk; W: www.rspbgravesend.org.uk
Meetings: 7.30pm, 2nd Thursday of the month (Sep-May). Northfleet School for Girls, Hall Road, Northfleet, Gravesend, DA11 8AQ & 2.00pm, 4th Tuesday of the month (Sep-Nov, Jan-Mar). Masonic Hall, 25 Wrotham Road, Gravesend, DA11 0PA.

MAIDSTONE. (1973; 250). James Downer. T: 01622 739 475; E: maidstoneRSPB@gmail.com; W: www.rspb.org.uk/groups/maidstone
Meetings: 7.30pm, 3rd Thursday of the month (not Aug). Grove Green Community Hall, Penhurst Close, Grove Green, Bearsted, Maidstone, ME14 5BT.

MEDWAY. (1974; 135). Warren Mann. T: 01634 234 816; E: medwayrspb-leader@virginmedia.com; W: www.rspb.org.uk/groups/medway
Meetings: 7.30pm, 3rd Tuesday of the month (not Aug). Parkwood Community Centre, Parkwood Green, Gillingham, ME8 9PN.

SEVENOAKS. (1974; 180). Anne Chapman. T: 01732 456 459; E: anneanddave.chapman@outlook.com; W: www.rspb.org.uk/groups/sevenoaks
Meetings: 7.45pm, 1st Thursday of the month (Sep-May). Otford Memorial Hall, High Street, Otford, Sevenoaks, TN14 5PQ.

THANET. (1975; 165). Brian Short. T: 07721 452 294; E: theRSPBthanetlocalgroup@talktalk.net; W: www.rspb.org.uk/groups/thanet
Meetings: 7.30pm, 2nd Monday of the month (Jan-Dec). St Peter's Church Hall, Portland Centre, Hopeville Avenue, Broadstairs, CT10 2TR.

ENGLAND

TONBRIDGE. (1975; no formal membership).
Martin Ellis. T: 01892 521 413;
E: rspb.tonbridge@gmail.com;
W: www.rspb.org.uk/groups/tonbridge
Meetings: 7.30pm, one Wednesday each month
(Sep-Apr). St Philip's Church, Salisbury Road,
Tonbridge, TN10 4PA - contact/see website for
details.

Wetland Bird Survey (WeBS) Local Organiser
DUNGENESS AREA. David Walker.
T: 01797 321 309; E: dungenessobs@vfast.co.uk

KENT (WEST). Vacant - contact WeBS Office.

KENT (EAST). Vacant - contact WeBS Office.

MEDWAY ESTUARY. Robert Knight. T: 07801 449
077; E: rjknight53@gmail.com

PEGWELL BAY. Steffan Walton. T: via WeBS Office;
E: via WeBS Office

SWALE ESTUARY. Brian Watmough.
T: 01227 266 746; E: brianrwat@yahoo.co.uk

THAMES ESTUARY (FOULNESS). See Essex.

THAMES ESTUARY (HOO). Murray Orchard.
T: 07788 102 238; murray.orchard@live.co.uk

Wildlife Trust
KENT WILDLIFE TRUST. (1958; 32,000).
Tyland Barn, Sandling, Maidstone, ME14 3BD.
T: 01622 662 012, (fax) 01622 671 390;
E: info@kentwildlife.org.uk;
W: www.kentwildlifetrust.org.uk

LANCASHIRE & NORTH MERSEYSIDE

Bird Atlas/Avifauna
The Birds of Lancashire and North Merseyside.
Steve White, Barry McCarthy & Maurice Jones
(Hobby Publications, 2008).

*Atlas of Breeding Birds of Lancashire and North
Merseyside 1997-2000.* Robert Pyefinch &
Peter Golborn (Hobby Publications, 2001).

Bird Recorder
(Incl. North Merseyside). Steve White,
102 Minster Court, Crown Street, Liverpool, L7 3QD.
T: 0151 707 2744; E: stevewhite102@btinternet.com

Bird Report
BIRDS OF LANCASTER & DISTRICT (1959-), from
Peter Cook, 21 Threshfield Avenue, Heysham,
Morecambe, LA3 2DU. T: 01524 851 454 &
07880 541 798; E: peter.cook33@btinternet.com.

BLACKBURN & DISTRICT BIRD CLUB REPORT (1992-),
not for general sale but enquiries to Jonathan Fry,
20 Rhodes Avenue, Blackburn, BB1 8NP.
E: birdrecorder24@gmail.com

*CHORLEY AND DISTRICT NATURAL HISTORY
SOCIETY ANNUAL REPORT (1975-),* published
online. W: www.chorleynats.org.uk

*EAST LANCASHIRE ORNITHOLOGISTS' CLUB BIRD
REPORT (1982-),* from Tony Cooper, 28 Peel Park Ave,
Clitheroe, BB7 1ET. E: anthony.cooper34@btinternet.com

FYLDE BIRD REPORT (1983-), from Kinta Beaver,
22 Beach Road, Preesall, Poulton le Fylde, FY6 0HQ.
E: kinta.beaver@btinternet.com

LANCASHIRE BIRD REPORT (1914-), from Dave
Bickerton, 64 Petre Crescent, Rishton, Blackburn,
BB1 4RB. E: bickertond@aol.com

BTO Regional Representative
EAST. Tony Cooper. T: 01200 424 577;
E: bto.elancs@btinternet.com

MERSEYSIDE. Vacant - contact Dawn Balmer, BTO.
T: 01842 750 050; E: dawn.balmer@bto.org

NORTH-WEST. Jean Roberts. T: n/a;
E: jeanrbrts6@aol.com

SOUTH. Vacant - contact Dawn Balmer, BTO.
T: 01842 750 050; E: dawn.balmer@bto.org

Club
BLACKBURN BIRD CLUB. (1991; 100).
Anne Wilkinson (Sec). Address: n/a.
T: 01254 812 425;
E: blackburnbirdclub@gmail.com;
W: www.blackburnbirdclub.com

Blackburn
Bird Club

Meetings: 7.30pm, normally 1st Monday of the
month (Oct-Apr). Feniscowles Methodist Church,
Preston Old Road, Blackburn, BB2 5ER.

CHORLEY & DISTRICT NATURAL HISTORY SOCIETY.
(1979; 110). Paul Brennan (Sec). Address: n/a.
T: n/a; E: secretary@chorleynats.org.uk;
W: www.chorleynats.org.uk
Meetings: 7.30pm, 3rd Thursday of the month
(Sep-Apr). St Mary's Parish Centre, West Street,
off Devonshire Road, Chorley, PR7 2SR.

EAST LANCASHIRE ORNITHOLOGISTS' CLUB. (1955; 45).
David Chew (Sec), Lower Wheathead Barn,
Wheathead Lane, Blacko, Nelson, BB9 6PD.
T: 01282 695 649; E: via the website;
W: www.eastlancsornithologists.org.uk
Meetings: 7.30pm, 1st Tuesday of the month
(Sep-May). St Anne's Parish, Wheatley Lane Road,
Fence, BB12 9EE.

ENGLAND

FYLDE BIRD CLUB. (1982; 180).
Paul Ellis (Sec), 22 Beach Road, Preesall, Poulton le
Fylde, FY6 0HQ. T: 01253 811 726 (eves);
E: paul.ellis24@btopenworld.com;
W: www.fyldebirdclub.org
Meetings: 7.45pm, 4th Tuesday of the month (all year).
River Wyre Hotel, Breck Road, Poulton le Fylde, FY6 7JZ.

FYLDE NATURALISTS' SOCIETY. (1946; 90).
Julie McGough (Sec). Address: n/a. T: n/a;
E: secretary@fyldenaturalists.co.uk;
W: www.fyldenaturalists.co.uk
Meetings: 7.15pm, 2nd Wednesday of the month
(Sep-Mar). Forest Gate Baptist Church Hall,
off Whitegate Drive, Blackpool, FY3 9AW
(unless otherwise stated in the programme).

LANCASHIRE & CHESHIRE FAUNA SOCIETY. (1914; 200).
Dave Bickerton (Sec), 64 Petre Crescent, Rishton,
BB1 4RB. T: 01254 886 257;
E: sec@lacfs.org.uk; W: www.lacfs.org.uk
Meetings: No indoor meetings held.

LANCASTER & DISTRICT
BIRDWATCHING SOCIETY.
(1959; 200). Peter Cook (Sec),
21 Threshfield Ave, Heysham,
Morecambe, LA3 2DU.
T: 01524 851 454 &
07880 541 798;
E: peter.cook33@btinternet.com;
W: www.lancasterbirdwatching.org.uk
Meetings: 7.30pm, last Monday of the month
(Sep-Nov/Jan-Mar) - contact/see website for
details.

MERSEYSIDE NATURALISTS' ASSOCIATION. (1938; 140).
Sabena Blackbird (Chairman), 18 Ludlow Grove,
Bromborough, Wirral CH62 7JH. T: n/a.
E: chairman@mnapage.info; W: www.mnapage.info
Meetings: Contact/see website for details.

PRESTON SOCIETY BIRD WATCHING & NATURAL
HISTORY. (1876/Preston Scientific Society; 140).
John Finnan (Sec). Address: n/a.
T: 07565 497 065; E: prestonwildlife@gmail.com;
W: www.prestonsociety.co.uk
Meetings: 7.30pm, Monday evenings (Oct-Mar).
St. Mary's Church, Church Avenue, Penwortham,
PR1 0AH.

ROSSENDALE ORNITHOLOGISTS' CLUB.
(1976; 135 online). Ian Brady. T: 01706 222 120;
E: n/a; W: http://rocforum.activeboard.com
Meetings: 7.15pm, 3rd Monday of the month
(check the forum for details). Weavers Cottage,
Bacup Road, Rawtenstall, BB4 7NW.

Ringing Group/Bird Observatory
FYLDE RG.

MERSEYSIDE RG. W: www.merseysiderg.org.uk

NORTH LANCASHIRE RG (inc. North Heysham Bird Obs).

SOUTH WEST LANCS RG.

RSPB Local Group
BOLTON. (1978; 155).
Terry Delaney. T: 0161 794 4684.
E: terry.delaney@sky.com;
W: www.rspb.org.uk/groups/bolton
Meetings: 7.30pm, 2nd Thursday of the month
(Sep-Apr). St Catherine's Academy - Sports Centre
entrance on Newby Road, Breightmet, Bolton,
BL2 4HU.

LANCASTER. (1972; 130).
Val Hall. T: 07542 117 064;
E: RSPBlancaster@gmail.com;
W: www.rspb.org.uk/groups/lancaster
Meetings: 2.30pm, 4th Tuesday of the month
(Feb, Mar, Oct, Nov) & 7.30pm, 4th Tuesday of the
month (Apr, May, Sep). The United Reformed Church,
Sefton Road, Heysham, LA3 1TZ. Sep meeting/AGM
held at Leighton Moss.

LIVERPOOL. (1972; 180).
Chris Tynan. T: 07831 352 870;
E: christtynan@aol.com;
W: www.rspb.org.uk/groups/liverpool
Meetings: 7.30pm, 3rd Monday of the month
(Sep-Apr, 1st Monday in Dec). Mossley Hill Parish
Church Hall, Rose Lane, Liverpool, L18 8DB.

SOUTHPORT. (1974; 200).
Kathryn Hall. T: 01704 568 694;
E: SouthportRSPB@btinternet.com;
W: www.rspb.org.uk/groups/southport
Meetings: 7.45pm, 3rd Friday of the month
(Sep-May). Lord Street West Church Hall,
Duke Street, Southport, PR8 2FP.

WIGAN. (1973; 80).
Neil Martin. T: 01695 624 860;
E: neimaz07@yahoo.co.uk;
W: www.rspb.org.uk/groups/wigan
Meetings: 7.45pm, 2nd Tuesday of the month
(Sep-Apr). St Anne's Parish Hall, Church Lane,
Shevington, Wigan, WN6 8BD.

Wetland Bird Survey (WeBS) Local Organiser
ALT ESTUARY. Steve White. T: via WeBS Office.
E: stevewhite102@btinternet.com

DEE ESTUARY (CLWYD/MERSEYSIDE). Colin Wells.
T: via WeBS Office; E: colinewells@outlook.com

EAST LANCASHIRE AND FYLDE. Stephen Dunstan.
T: 07985 417 755;
E: stephendunstan76@googlemail.com

ENGLAND

LANCASHIRE - NORTH (INLAND). Peter Marsh.
T: 07532 433 043; E: pmrsh123@aol.com

LANCASHIRE - WEST (INLAND). Vacant - contact WeBS Office.

MERSEY ESTUARY. Dermot Smith.
T: 01925 602 397; E: dermot.smith71@gmail.com

MERSEYSIDE (INLAND). Kevin Feeney.
T: via WeBS Office; E: kvin@hotmail.co.uk

MORECAMBE BAY (NORTH). See Cumbria.

MORECAMBE BAY (SOUTH). Jean Roberts.
T: 01524 770 295; E: Jeanrbrts6@aol.com

RIBBLE ESTUARY. Ken Abram. T: via WeBS Office;
E: bonkser.ka@gmail.com

RIVER LUNE. Jean Roberts - see above.

Wildlife Trust
THE WILDLIFE TRUST FOR LANCASHIRE,
MANCHESTER & NORTH MERSEYSIDE. (1962; 29,000).
The Barn, Berkeley Drive, Bamber Bridge,
Preston, Lancs PR5 6BY. T: 01772 324 129;
E: info@lancswt.org.uk; W: www.lancswt.org.uk

LEICESTERSHIRE & RUTLAND

Bird Atlas/Avifauna
The Birds of Leicestershire and Rutland. Rob Fray,
Roger Davies, Dave Gamble,
Andrew Harrop & Steve Lister.
(Christopher Helm, 2009).

Rutland Breeding Bird Atlas 2008-2011. Terry Mitcham
(Spiegl Press, 2013)

Bird Recorder
Carl Baggott, 72 New Street, Earl Shilton,
LE9 7FR. T: n/a; E: cdbaggott@gmail.com

Bird Report
LEICESTERSHIRE & RUTLAND BIRD REPORT (1946-),
from Mrs S Graham, 5 Lychgate Close, Cropston,
LE7 7HU. T: 0116 236 6474; E: JSGraham83@aol.com

BTO Regional Representative
David Wright. T: 01530 231 102;
E: davewrightbto@gmail.com

Club
ROTHLEY & BIRSTALL BIRDWATCHING CLUB. (1976; 50).
Ken Goodrich (Sec), 6 Riversdale Close, Birstall,
Leicester, LE4 4EH. T: 0116 267 4813;
E: kjgood1532@aol.com; W: n/a
Meetings: 7.30pm, 2nd Tuesday of the month
(Oct-Apr). Rothley Centre, 12 Mountsorrel Lane,
Rothley LE7 7PR.

LEICESTERSHIRE & RUTLAND
ORNITHOLOGICAL SOCIETY.
(1941; 500).
Peter Williams (Sec),
Address: n/a.
T: 0116 236 4704;
E: peterwilliams23@btinternet.com;
W: www.lros.org.uk
Meetings: 7.30pm, 1st Friday
of the month (Oct-May). The Hall of St. Anne's,
Letchworth Road, Leicester LE3 6FN.

RUTLAND NATURAL HISTORY SOCIETY. (1965; 300+).
Margaret Conner (Membership Sec), 24 Burrough
Road, Somerby, Melton Mowbray, LE14 2PP.
T: 01664 454 532; E: rnhsmembers@gmail.com;
W: www.rnhs.org.uk
Meetings: 7.30pm, 1st Tuesday of the month
(Oct-Apr). Voluntary Action Rutland, Lands End Way,
Oakham, LE15 6RB.

SOUTH LEICESTER BIRDWATCHERS. (2006; 60).
Graham & Marion Turner. Address: n/a.
T: 07852 782 002; E: graham.turner@btinternet.com;
W: http://southleicesterbirdwatchers.uk/
Meetings: 7.15 pm, 2nd Wednesday of the month
(Sep-Jun). All Saints Parish Centre, Wigston Road,
Blaby, Leicester, LE8 4FA.

Ringing Group/Bird Observatory
CHARNWOOD RINGING GROUP.
W: http://charnwoodringers.blogspot.com/
RUTLAND WATER RG.
STANFORD RG. W: www.stanfordrg.org.uk

RSPB Local Group
LEICESTER. (1969; 1600/area).
Graham Heninghem. T: 01455 616 098;
E: graham.heninghem@hotmail.co.uk;
W: www.rspb.org.uk/groups/leicester
Meetings: 7.30pm, usually 3rd Friday of the
month (Sep-May). Trinity Methodist Hall,
Harborough Road, Oadby, Leicester, LE2 4LA.

LOUGHBOROUGH. (1970; 100).
Peter Farnworth. T: n/a;
E: Lboro.RSPBgroup@talktalk.net;
W: www.rspb.org.uk/groups/loughborough
Meetings: 7.45pm, 2nd Friday of the month
(Oct-May). Lecture Theatre U020, Brockington
Building, Loughborough University, Epinal Way,
Loughborough, LE11 3TZ.

Wetland Bird Survey (WeBS) Local Organiser
LEICESTERSHIRE & RUTLAND (excl. RUTLAND
WATER). Brian Moore. T: 0116 291 0411 (pm only);
E: b_moore@ntlworld.com

RUTLAND WATER. Tim Appleton.
T: 01572 770 651; E: tappleton@birdfair.org.uk

Wildlife Trust

LEICESTERSHIRE & RUTLAND WILDLIFE TRUST.
(1956; 16,000).
The Old Mill, 9 Soar Lane, Leicester, LE3 5DE.
T: 0116 262 9968, (fax) 0116 251 5426;
E: info@lrwt.org.uk; W: www.lrwt.org.uk

LINCOLNSHIRE

The Birds of Lincolnshire & South Humberside.
Stephen Lorand & Keith Atkin
(Leading Edge Press, 1989).

Bird Recorder

NORTH LINCS: VACANT - (contact Phil Hyde,
below, until replacement found).

SOUTH LINCS: Phil Hyde, Plot 6, Manor Park,
Legbourne, LN11 8NH. T:01507 607 998;
E: recorder_south@lincsbirdclub.co.uk

Bird Report

LINCOLNSHIRE BIRD REPORT (1979-), from Bill
Sterling, 'Newlyn', 5 Carlton Avenue, Healing,
NE Lincs DN41 7PW. E: wbsterling@hotmail.com

BTO Regional Representative

EAST. Philip Espin. T: 01507 605 448;
E: pmjespin@gmail.com

NORTH. Chris Gunn. T: 01777 818 742;
E: donandchris@hotmail.co.uk

Iain Turner (Assistant Representative). T: n/a;
E: iainturner80@gmail.co.uk

SOUTH. Hugh Dorrington. T: 01778 440 716;
E: hdorrington@btconnect.com

WEST. Mike Daly. T: 01522 820 105;
E: Mike.btorrwl@gmail.com;

LINCOLNSHIRE (E,N,S,W): Nicholas Watts
(Regional Development Officer). T: n/a;
E: nicholas@vinehousefarm.co.uk

Club

LINCOLNSHIRE BIRD CLUB. (1979; 300).
Jim Wright (Secretary), 33 Parker Street,
Cleethorpes, N.E. Lincolnshire DN35 8TH.
T: n/a; E: secretary@lincsbirdclub.co.uk;
W: www.lincsbirdclub.co.uk

Meetings: Held occasionally
- sometimes jointly with
other groups such as BTO or
Lincolnshire Naturalists' Union.
AGM in Mar or Apr with a guest
speaker. Contact/see website
for details.

LINCOLNSHIRE NATURALISTS' UNION. (1893; n/a)
c/o Lincolnshire Wildlife Trust, Banovallum
House, Manor House Street, Horncastle, LN9 5HF.
T: 01507 526 667; E: info@lnu.org;
W: https://lnu.org/
Meetings: 2pm, Saturdays (winter) - contact/see
website for details. Whisby Education Centre,
Whisby Nature Park, Moor Lane, Thorpe on the Hill,
Lincoln, LN6 9BW.

Ringing Group/Bird Observatory

MID LINCS RG.

WASH WADER RG. W: www.wwrg.org.uk

GIBRALTAR POINT BIRD OBSERVATORY.
Kevin Wilson (Warden) Gibraltar Point Field Centre,
Skegness, PE24 4SU. T: 01754 898 079;
E: kwilson@lincstrust.co.uk;
W: http://gibraltarpointbirdobservatory.blogspot.co.uk

RSPB Local Group

GRIMSBY. (1986; n/a).
Martin Francis. T: 01472 883 436;
E: martin.francis2@ntlworld.com;
W: www.rspb.org.uk/groups/grimsby
Meetings: 7.30pm, 3rd Monday of the month
(Sep-Jun). Holy Trinity Parish Hall, 2 Machray Place,
Grimsby Road, Cleethorpes, DN35 7LH.

LINCOLN. (1974; 250).
Peter Skelson. T: 01522 695 747;
E: peter.skelson@lincolnRSPB.org.uk;
W: www.lincolnrspb.org.uk
Meetings: 7.30pm, 2nd Thursday of the month
(Sep-May). Bishop Grosseteste University,
Longdales Road, Lincoln, LN1 3DY.

SOUTH LINCOLNSHIRE SOCIAL GROUP. (1987; n/a).
Robin Dobson. T: 01529 304 370;
E: ro.dobson@btinternet.com;
W: www.rspb.org.uk/groups/southlincolnshire
This is a social group rather than a Local Group -
contact/see website for details of activities.

Wetland Bird Survey (WeBS) Local Organiser

HUMBER ESTUARY (INNER SOUTH). Keith Parker.
T: via WeBS Office; E: keithparker69@gmail.com

HUMBER ESTUARY (MID-SOUTH). Richard Barnard.
T: 01484 868 425; E: richard.barnard@rspb.org.uk

HUMBER ESTUARY (NORTH). See Yorkshire.

HUMBER ESTUARY (OUTER SOUTH). John Walker.
T: 01507 338 038; E: johnwalkermbe@gmail.com

NORTH LINCOLNSHIRE (INLAND). Chris Gunn.
T: 01777 818 742; E: donandchris@hotmail.co.uk

SOUTH LINCOLNSHIRE (INLAND INC.
PETERBOROUGH). Robert Titman.
T: 01733 583 254; E: bob.titman@gmail.com

ENGLAND

THE WASH (LINCOLNSHIRE). Jim Scott.
T: 01485 542 689; E: jim.scott@rspb.org.uk

Wildlife Trust
LINCOLNSHIRE WILDLIFE TRUST. (1948; 28,000).
Banovallum House, Manor House Street,
Horncastle, LN9 5HF.
T: 01507 526 667, (fax) 01507 525 732;
E: info@lincstrust.co.uk; W: www.lincstrust.org.uk

LONDON (GREATER)

Bird Atlas/Avifauna
The London Bird Atlas.
Ian Woodward, Richard
Arnold & Neil Smith
(John Beaufoy Books,
2017).

The Birds of London.
Andrew Self
(Christopher Helm, 2014).

Bird Recorder
Andrew Self, 16 Harp Island Close, Neasden, London
NW10 0DF. T: 07443 221 382; E: a-self@sky.com

Bird Report
*LONDON BIRD REPORT: 20-mile radius of St Paul's
Cath. (1936-),* from Catherine Schmitt,
London Natural History Society, 4 Falkland Ave,
London N3 1QR. E: catherineschmitt20@gmail.com

BTO Regional Representative
LONDON, NORTH. Vacant - contact Dawn Balmer,
BTO. T: 01842 750 050; E: dawn.balmer@bto.org

LONDON, SOUTH. Richard Arnold.
T: 0208 224 1135; E: bto@thomsonecology.com

Club
MARYLEBONE BIRDWATCHING SOCIETY. (1981; 140).
Steve Ripley (Chair), 29 Berriman Road, Holloway,
London N7 7PN. T: 07929 966 705;
E: birdsmbs@yahoo.com;
W: www.birdsmbs.org.uk
Meetings: 7.15pm, usually 3rd Friday of the month
(Sep-Apr, not Dec). Gospel Oak Methodist Church,
Lisburne Road, London NW3 2NT.

THE LONDON BIRD CLUB (1858; 1000).
(Ornithology Section of London NHS).
Douglas Bilton (Sec), 75 Walcot Square, London
SE11 4UB. T: 07725 740585;
E: douglas.bilton@yahoo.com;
W: www.lnhs.org.uk/index.php/about-us/lnhs-
sections/london-bird-club
Meetings: 7.00pm, contact/see website
for details. Burgh House, New End Square,
Hampstead, London, NW3 1LT.

Ringing Group/Bird Observatory
RUNNYMEDE RG. W: www.runnymederinging.uk

SOUTHERN COLOUR RINGING GROUP.
W: www.southern-colour-ringing-group.org.uk

RSPB Local Group
BEXLEY. (1979; n/a).
Stuart Banks. T: 0208 854 7251;
E: bexleylocalRSPBgroup@gmail.com;
W: www.rspb.org.uk/groups/bexley
Meetings: 7.15pm, 2nd Friday of the month
(Sep-May). John Fisher Church Hall, 48 Thanet Road,
Bexley, DA5 1AP.

BROMLEY. (1972; 200).
Sandie Wood. T: 07392 790 719;
E: bromleyrspb@gmail.com;
W: www.rspb.org.uk/groups/bromley
Meetings: 7.00pm, 2nd Wednesday of the month
(Sep-Jun). United Reformed Church (Verrall Hall),
Widmore Road, Bromley, BR1 1RY.

CENTRAL LONDON. (1974; 250).
Andrew Peel. T: 0208 997 0072;
E: RSPB.centrallondongroup@gmail.com;
W: www.rspb.org.uk/groups/centrallondon
Meetings: 6.45pm, 2nd Thursday of the month
(Sep-May). St Columba's Church Hall, Pont St,
London SW1X 0BD.

CROYDON. (1973; 500).
John Davis. T: 0208 640 4578;
E: johndavis.wine@care4free.net;
W: www.rspb.org.uk/groups/croydon
Meetings: 2.00pm & 8.00pm, 2nd Monday of the
month (not Jun). Whitgift Sports Club, The Clubhouse,
Croham Manor Road, South Croydon, CR2 7BG.

NORTH EAST LONDON. (2009; 200).
David Littlejohns. T: 0208 989 4746;
E: NelondonRSPB@yahoo.co.uk;
W: www.rspb.org.uk/groups/northeastlondon
Meetings: 8.00pm, 2nd Tuesday of the month.
St Mary's Church - Gwinnell Room, 207 High Road,
South Woodford, London E18 2PA.

NORTH WEST LONDON. (1983; n/a).
Bob Husband. T: 0208 441 8742;
E: bobhusband@hotmail.co.uk;
W: www.rspb.org.uk/groups/nwlondon
Meetings: 8pm, usually the last Tuesday of the
month (Sep-Mar). Wilberforce Centre, St Paul's
Church, The Ridgeway, London NW7 1QU.

PINNER & DISTRICT. (1972; 300).
Ian Jackson. T: 0208 907 3513;
E: imjpinRSPB@gmail.com;
W: www.rspb.org.uk/groups/pinner
Meetings: 8pm, 2nd Thursday of the month
(Sep-May). St John The Baptist Church Hall,
Church Lane, Pinner, Middx HA5 3AA.

ENGLAND

RICHMOND & TWICKENHAM. (1979; 200).
Clare Million. T: 07794 835 571;
E: richmondRSPB@yahoo.co.uk;
W: www.rspb.org.uk/groups/richmond
Meetings: 7.30pm, 1st Wednesday of the month
& 2.00pm, 2nd Tuesday of the month (Sep-May).
York House, Richmond Road, Twickenham, TW1 3AA.

Wetland Bird Survey (WeBS) Local Organiser
GREATER LONDON (excl. THAMES ESTUARY/
see Essex). Andrew Moon. T: 07811 847 732;
E: andrew.moon@talk21.com

LEE VALLEY. See Hertfordshire.

SOUTH WEST LONDON. See Surrey.

Wildlife Trust
LONDON WILDLIFE TRUST. (1981; 15,000).
Dean Bradley House, 52 Horseferry Road, London
SW1P 2AF. T: 0207 261 0447, (fax) 0207 633 0811;
E: enquiries@wildlondon.org.uk;
W: www.wildlondon.org.uk

MANCHESTER (GREATER)

Bird Recorder
Ian McKerchar, 42 Green Ave, Astley, Manchester
M29 7EH. T: 01942 701 758 & 07958 687 481;
E: ianmckerchar1@gmail.com

Bird Report
BIRDS IN GREATER MANCHESTER (1959-), from
the Bird Recorder - see above.

LEIGH ORNITHOLOGICAL SOCIETY BIRD REPORT (1971-),
latest report available to members only, then download
from website after one year. W: www.leighos.org.uk

BTO Regional Representative
Nick Hilton. T: 07920 494 240; E: nmhilton71@aol.com

Steve Atkins (Assistant Representative).
T: 01706 645 097; E: svatkins38@gmail.com

Club
ALTRINGHAM AND DISTRICT
NATURAL HISTORY SOCIETY. (1908; 30)
Mike Pettipher (Chairman). Address: n/a. T: n/a;
E: info@altnats.org.uk; W: www.altnats.org.uk
Meetings: 7:30pm, 2nd Tuesday of the month
(Sep-Apr). Dunham Room, The Jubilee Centre,
The Firs, Bowdon, Altrincham, WA14 2TQ.

 LEIGH ORNITHOLOGICAL
SOCIETY. (1971; 115).
David Shallcross (Chairman),
28 Surrey Avenue, Leigh,
WN7 2NN. T: n/a;
E: leighos.chairman@gmail.com;
W: www.leighos.org.uk

LOS Young Birders. W: www.losybc.blogspot.co.uk
Meetings: 7.30pm, usually 1st Friday of the
month (ca. 10 talks Sep-May) - contact/see
website for details. Derby Room, Leigh Library,
Turnpike Centre, Civic Square, Leigh, WN7 1EB.

ROCHDALE FIELD NATURALISTS' SOCIETY. (1874; 100).
Joan Carter (Sec), 57 Plover Close, Bamford,
Rochdale, OL11 5PU. T: 07597 838 061;
E: rfnsenquiries@talktalk.co;
W: www.rochdalefieldnaturalists.org.uk
Meetings: 7.30pm, usually 2nd Thursday of
the month (Sep-Apr). Cutgate Baptist Church,
Edenfield Rd, Rochdale, OL11 5AQ.

STOCKPORT BIRDWATCHING SOCIETY. (1972; 70).
Dave Evans, 36 Tatton Road South, Stockport,
SK4 4LU. T: 0161 432 9513;
E: windhover1972@yahoo.co.uk;
W: http://stockportbirders.blogspot.com/
Meetings: 7.30pm, last Wednesday of the month
(Sep-Apr). The Heatons Sports Club, Heaton Moor,
Stockport, SK4 2NF.

Ringing Group/Bird Observatory
LEIGH RG.

SOUTH MANCHESTER RG.

RSPB Local Group
HIGH PEAK. (1974; 130).
Richard Stephenson. T: 0161 427 4187;
E: stephenson3rj@gmail.com;
W: www.rspb.org.uk/groups/highpeak
Meetings: 7.30pm, 3rd Monday of the month
(Sep-May). Marple Senior Citizens Hall,
Memorial Park, Marple, Stockport, SK6 6BA.

STOCKPORT. (1979; 140).
Jayne Skelhorn. T: 0161 879 4680;
E: jayne.skelhorn@talktalk.net;
W: www.rspb.org.uk/groups/stockport
Meetings: 7.30pm, 2nd Monday of the month
(Sep-May). Stockport Masonic Guildhall,
169 Wellington Road South, Stockport, SK1 3UA.

Wetland Bird Survey (WeBS) Local Organiser
GREATER MANCHESTER. Tim Wilcox.
T: via WeBS Office; E: tim.wilcox0@gmail.com

Wildlife Trust. See Lancashire & Noth Merseyside.

NORFOLK

Bird Atlas/Avifauna
*The Norfolk Bird Atlas: Summer and Winter
Distributions 1999-2007*. Moss Taylor &
John H Marchant (BTO 2011).

The Birds of Norfolk. Moss Taylor, Michael Seago,
Peter Allard & Don Dorling (Christopher Helm, 1999/
rep 2007).

ENGLAND

The Birds of Blakeney Point. Andy Stoddart, Steve Joyner & James McCallum (Wren Publishing, 2005).

Bird Recorder
Neil Lawton. Address: n/a. T: n/a;
E: norfolkbirdrecs@gmail.com

Bird Report
NAR VALLEY ORNITHOLOGICAL SOCIETY ANNUAL REPORT (1977-), from Ian Black, Three Chimneys, Tumbler Hill, Swaffham, PE37 7JG.
E: enquiries@narvos.org.uk

NORFOLK BIRD & MAMMAL REPORT (1953-), from Tony Leech, NNNS Publications, 3 Eccles Road, Holt, NR25 6HJ.
E: birdreport@nnns.org.uk

NORFOLK ORNITHOLOGISTS' ASSOCIATION ANNUAL REPORT (1962-), from NOA, Broadwater Rd, Holme Next the Sea, Hunstanton, PE36 6LQ.
E: info@noa.org.uk

BTO Regional Representative
NORTH-EAST. Chris Hudson. T: 01603 868 805;
E: chris697@btinternet.com

NORTH-WEST. Bob Osborne. T: 01553 670 430;
E: rtoclass40@yahoo.co.uk

Fred Cooke (Assistant Representative)
T: 01553 631 076; E: f.cooke1@btinternet.com

SOUTH-EAST. Rachel Warren. T: 01603 593 912;
E: campephilus@btinternet.com

SOUTH-WEST. Vince Matthews. T: 01953 884 125;
E: norfolksouthwest@gmail.co.uk

Club
CLEY BIRD CLUB. (1986; 620+).
John Dicks (Chairman), Cherry Tree House, Cherry Tree Road, Plumstead, NR11 7LQ.
T: 01263 577 354;
E: j48a@hotmail.com;
W: www.cleybirdclub.org.uk
Meetings: 7.30pm, one Wednesday monthly (Nov-Mar).
Cley Village Hall, The Fairstead, Cley, NR25 7RJ.

NAR VALLEY ORNITHOLOGICAL SOCIETY. (1976; 125).
Ian Black (Chairman), Three Chimneys, Tumbler Hill, Swaffham, PE37 7JG. T: 01760 724 092;
E: enquiries@narvos.org.uk; W: www.narvos.org.uk
Meetings: 7.30pm, last Tuesday of the month (Jul-Nov & Jan-May). Barn Theatre, Convent of The Sacred Heart, Mangate Street, Swaffham, PE37 7QW.

NORFOLK & NORWICH NATURALISTS' SOCIETY. (1869; 630).
The Secretary, 22 Springfield Close, Weybourne, Holt, NR25 7IB. T: n/a;
E: membership@nnns.org.uk;
W: www.NNNS.org.uk
Meetings: 7.30pm, 2nd Tuesday of the month (Oct-Mar), St Andrew's Hall, Church Lane, Eaton, NR4 6NW.

NORFOLK ORNITHOLOGISTS' ASSOCIATION. (1970; 1500).
Sophie Barker (Warden/Secretary), Broadwater Rd, Holme-next-Sea, Hunstanton, PE36 6LQ.
T: 01485 525 406; E: info@noa.org.uk;
W: www.noa.org.uk
Meetings: AGM held in Sep.

NORTH-EAST NORFOLK BIRD CLUB. (2015; 280).
Colin Blaxill, (Membership Sec), Caitlins, Bernard Close, High Kelling, Holt, NR25 6QY.
T: 01263 711 718; E: info@nenbc.co.uk;
W: www.nenbc.co.uk
Meetings: 7.30pm, last Thursday of the month (Sep-Nov, Jan-Apr, plus a social event in Dec & May). Aylmerton Village Hall, Aylmerton, NR11 8PX.

WENSUM VALLEY BIRDWATCHING SOCIETY. (2003; 130+).
Lin Pateman (Sec). Address: n/a. T: 01263 587 262:
E: wvbs.secretary@gmail.com; W: www.wvbs.co.uk
Meetings: 7.30pm, 3rd Thursday of the month (all year). Great Witchingham (Lenwade) Village Hall, Hubbards Loke, Lenwade, NR9 5AZ.

Ringing Group/Bird Observatory
BTO NUNNERY RG.

EAST ANGLIA GULL GROUP.

EAST NORFOLK RG.
W: http://eastnorfolkringinggroup.blogspot.co.uk/

NORTH NORFOLK RG.

NORTH WEST NORFOLK RG.
W: http://www.nwnrg.co.uk/

SHERINGHAM RG.

SOUTH WEST NORFOLK RG.

THETFORD FOREST RG.

UEA RG. W: http://uearg.blogspot.co.uk/

WASH WADER RG. W: www.wwrg.org.uk

HOLME BIRD OBSERVATORY (NOA RG). See Club - NOA.

RSPB Local Group
NORWICH. (1971; 230).
David Porter. T: 01603 745 310 (day);
E: RSPBnorwichgroup@virginmedia.com;
W: www.rspb.org.uk/groups/norwich
Meetings: 7.30pm, 2nd Monday of the month (Sep-Jun). Hellesdon Community Centre, (off Wood View Road), Middletons Lane, Norwich, NR6 5QB.

COUNTY DIRECTORY

ENGLAND

Wetland Bird Survey (WeBS) Local Organiser
BREYDON WATER. James Rowe.
T: via WeBS Office; E: via WeBS Office

NORFOLK (excl. ESTUARIES). Tim Strudwick.
T: via WeBS Office; E: tim.strudwick@rspb.org.uk

NORTH NORFOLK COAST. Neil Lawton.
T: via WeBS Office; E: neilscolt@yahoo.com

THE WASH (NORFOLK). See Lincolnshire.

Wildlife Trust
NORFOLK WILDLIFE TRUST. (1926; 36,000).
Bewick House, 22 Thorpe Road, Norwich, NR1 1RY.
T: 01603 625 540, (fax) 01603 598 300;
E: info@norfolkwildlifetrust.org.uk;
W: www.norfolkwildlifetrust.org.uk

NORTHAMPTONSHIRE

Bird Recorder
VACANT.

Bird Report
NORTHANTS BIRDS (1969-), from RW Bullock,
81 Cavendish Drive, Northampton, NN3 3HL.
E: robertbullock25@hotmail.com

BTO Regional Representative
Barrie Galpin. T: 01780 444 351;
E: barrie.galpin@zen.co.uk

Ben Reeve (Assistant Representative).
T: 01788 824 413; E: benreeve@outlook.com

Club
NORTHAMPTONSHIRE BIRD
CLUB. (1973; 50).
Eleanor McMahon (Sec),
Oriole House, 5 The Croft,
Hanging Houghton, NN6 9HW.
T: 01604 880 009;
E: eleanor1960@btinternet.com;
W: https://northantsbirdclub.blogspot.com/
Meetings: 7.30pm, 1st Wednesday of the month
(all year). The Lodge, Pitsford Water,
7 Brixworth Road, Holcot, NN6 9SJ.

Ringing Group/Bird Observatory
NORTHANTS RG.
STANFORD RG. W: www.stanfordrg.org.uk

RSPB Local Group
MID NENE. (1975; 280).
Ian Wrisdale. T: 01933 410 566;
E: wrisdale1@tiscali.co.uk;
W: www.rspb.org.uk/groups/midnene
Meetings: 7.30pm, 3rd Thursday of the month
(Sep-Mar). The Saxon Hall, Thorpe Street, Raunds,
Wellingborough, NN9 6LT.

Wetland Bird Survey (WeBS) Local Organiser
NENE VALLEY. Steve Brayshaw.
T: via WeBS Office; E: via WeBS Office

NORTHAMPTONSHIRE (excl. NENE VALLEY).
Barrie Galpin. T: 07776 337 201;
E: barrie.galpin@zen.co.uk

Wildlife Trust. See Cambridgeshire.

NORTHUMBERLAND

Bird Atlas/Avifauna
Northumbria Bird Atlas. Tim Dean, Dick Myatt,
Muriel Cadwallender, Tom Cadwallender
(Northumberland & Tyneside Bird Club, 2015).

Bird Recorder
Tim Dean, 2 Knocklaw Park, Rothbury, NE65 7PW.
T: 01669 621 460; E: t.r.dean@btinternet.com

Bird Report
BIRDS IN NORTHUMBRIA (1970-),
from Trevor Blake,
6 Glenside, Ellington,
Morpeth, NE61 5LS.
E: trevor.1958@live.co.uk

BIRDS ON THE FARNE
ISLANDS: in Northumbrian
Naturalist (1971-), from the
Natural History Society of
Northumbria, Great North
Museum, Hancock, Barras
Bridge, Newcastle upon Tyne, NE2 4PT.
T: 0191 208 2790; E: nhsn@ncl.ac.uk

BTO Regional Representative
Tom Cadwallender. T: 01665 830 884;
E: tomandmurielcadwallender@hotmail.com

Muriel Cadwallender
(Regional Development Officer). T: & E: as above.

Club
NATURAL HISTORY SOCIETY OF NORTHUMBRIA.
(1829; 1000+).
Natural History Society of Northumbria,
Great North Museum: Hancock, Barras Bridge,
Newcastle upon Tyne, NE2 4PT. T: 0191 208 2790;
E: nhsn@ncl.ac.uk; W: www.nhsn.ncl.ac.uk
Meetings: 7pm, Fridays (Oct-Mar). Ridley Building
Lecture Hall, Claremont Road, Newcastle upon
Tyne, NE1 7RU.

NORTH NORTHUMBERLAND BIRD CLUB. (1984; 180).
Glynis Gower (Sec). Address: n/a. T: 01289 330 969;
E: ringouzel@northnorthumberlandbirdclub.co.uk;
W: www.northnorthumberlandbirdclub.co.uk
Meetings: 7.30pm, 3rd Friday of the month (Sep)/
2nd Friday of the month (Oct-Jun). Bamburgh
Pavilion (corner of green below Bamburgh Castle).

ENGLAND

NORTHUMBERLAND & TYNESIDE BIRD CLUB. (1958; 270).
Andrew Brunt (Sec), South Cottage, West Road,
Longhorsley, Morpeth, NE65 8UY. T: 01670 788 352;
E: ntbcorg@gmail.com; W: www.ntbc.org.uk
Meetings: 7.00pm, 2nd Thursday of the month
(Sep-Apr). Northern Rugby Club, McCracken Park,
Great North Road, Newcastle upon Tyne, NE3 2DT.

Ringing Group/Bird Observatory
NHS OF NORTHUMBRIA.

NORTHUMBRIA RG.
W: https//:northumbriaringinggroup.com

RSPB Local Group
NEWCASTLE UPON TYNE. (1969; 250).
Jeff Mason. T: 0191 289 5058;
E: newcastlerspbgroup@gmail.com;
W: www.rspb.org.uk/groups/newcastle
Meetings: 7.00pm, 1st Tuesday of the month
(Oct-Mar). Jurys Inn, St James Gate,
Scotswood Road, Newcastle upon Tyne, NE1 4AD.

Wetland Bird Survey (WeBS) Local Organiser
LINDISFARNE. Andrew Craggs. T: 01289 381 470;
E: andrew.craggs@naturalengland.org.uk

NORTHUMBERLAND (COASTAL). Kathy Evans.
T: via WeBS Office; E: via WeBS Office

NORTHUMBERLAND (INLAND). Steve Holliday.
T: via WeBS Office; E: steveholliday@hotmail.co.uk

Wildlife Trust
NORTHUMBERLAND WILDLIFE TRUST. (1971; 12,000).
Garden House, St Nicholas Park, Jubilee Road,
Gosforth, Newcastle upon Tyne, NE3 3XT.
T: 0191 284 6884, (fax) 0191 284 6794;
E: mail@northwt.org.uk; W: www.nwt.org.uk

NOTTINGHAMSHIRE

Bird Atlas/Avifauna
Birds of Nottinghamshire.
Nick Crouch, Jason Reece,
Bernie Ellis, Chris du Feu,
David Parkin (Liverpool
University Press, 2019).

Bird Recorder
Andy Hall, 10 Staverton Road,
Bilborough, Nottingham,
NG8 4ET.
T: 0115 875 9043;
E: andy.h11@ntlworld.com

Bird Report
BIRDS OF NOTTINGHAMSHIRE (1943-), from Jenny
Swindells, 21 Chaworth Road, West Bridgford,
Nottingham, NG2 7AE. T: 0115 9812 432;
E: j.swindells@btinternet.com

BTO Regional Representative
Lynda Milner. T: 01623 862 025;
E: milner.lynda@googlemail.com

Club
LOUND BIRD CLUB. (1990; 60).
Paul Hobson (Chairman). Address: n/a.
T: 07415 671 346; E: hoblong@hotmail.co.uk;
W: facebook - Lound Bird Club
Meetings: last Wednesday of the month (Sep-Mar,
not Dec). Sutton-cum-Lound village hall - see
facebook or contact for details.

NETHERFIELD WILDLIFE GROUP. (1999; 130).
NWG, c/o 4 Shellburne Close, Heronridge,
Nottingham, NG5 9LL. T: n/a; E: via website;
W: www.gedlingconservationtrust.org/
netherfield-lagoons/netherfield-wildlife-group/
Meetings: No indoor meetings held.

NOTTINGHAMSHIRE BIRDWATCHERS. (1935; 290).
Jenny Swindells (Sec), 21 Chaworth Rd,
West Bridgford, Nottingham, NG2 7AE.
T: 0115 9812 432; E: j.swindells@btinternet.com;
W: www.nottsbirders.net
Meetings: Contact/see website for details.

WOLLATON NATURAL HISTORY SOCIETY. (1976; 70).
E: via website;
[Nigel Downes (Bird Group). T: 0115 944 4671]
W: www.spanglefish.com/wollatonnaturalhistory/
Meetings: 7.30pm, 3rd Wednesday of the month
(not Aug). St Leonards Community Centre,
Bramcote Lane, Wollaton, HG8 2ND.

Ringing Group/Bird Observatory
BIRKLANDS RG.

NORTH NOTTS RG.

SOUTH NOTTS RG.
W: http://southnottsringinggroup.blogspot.co.uk/

TRESWELL WOOD INTEGRATED POPULATION
MONITORING GROUP.
W: www.treswellwoodipmg.org

RSPB Local Group
MANSFIELD. (1986; 30).
Diane Bartlam. T: 07847 935 583;
E: dianeashplorers@hotmail.co.uk;
W: www.rspb.org.uk/groups/mansfield
Meetings: 7.30pm, 1st Wednesday of the month
(Sep-Jun). The Stanhope Centre, Rock Valley,
Mansfield, NG18 1AL.

NOTTINGHAM. (1974; 300).
Doreen Markam. T: 0115 978 2741;
E: RSPBnottmlgmem@gmail.com;
W: www.rspb.org.uk/groups/nottingham
Meetings: 7.30pm, 1st Wednesday of the month
(Sep-May). Nottingham Mechanics,
3 North Sherwood Street, Nottingham, NG1 4EZ.

ENGLAND

Wetland Bird Survey (WeBS) Local Organiser
NOTTINGHAMSHIRE. David Parkin.
T: 0115 932 0090; E: bluethroat@btinternet.com

Wildlife Trust
NOTTINGHAMSHIRE WILDLIFE TRUST. (1963; 11,000).
The Old Ragged School, Brook Street,
Nottingham, NG1 1EA. T: 0115 958 8242,
(fax) 0115 924 3175; E: info@nottswt.co.uk;
W: www.nottinghamshirewildlife.org

OXFORDSHIRE

Bird Atlas/Avifauna
Birds of the Heart of England (Banbury area).
TG Easterbrook (Liverpool University Press, 2013).

Birds of Oxfordshire. JW Brucker, AG Gosler &
AR Heryet (Pisces Publications, 1992).

Bird Recorder
Ian Lewington, 119 Brasenose Road, Didcot, OX11 7BP.
T: 01235 819 792; E: recorder@oos.org.uk

Bird Report
BIRDS OF OXFORDSHIRE (1915-), from Roy Overall,
30 Hunsdon Road, Iffley, Oxford, OX4 4JE.
E: roy.overall@oos.org.uk

BANBURY ORNITHOLOGICAL SOCIETY ANNUAL
REPORT (1966-), from Sandra Bletchly, 11 Orchard
Grove, Bloxham, Banbury, OXON OX15 4NZ.
E: sandra.banornsoc@btinternet.com

BTO Regional Representative
NORTH. Frances Buckel. T: 01608 644 425;
E: fran.buckel@btinternet.com

SOUTH. John Melling. T: 01865 820 867;
E: bto-rep@oos.org.uk

Alison Bunning (Assistant Representative).
T: n/a; E: allybirdy@hotmail.co.uk

Club
BANBURY ORNITHOLOGICAL SOCIETY (incl. parts
of Northants/Oxon/Warwick). (1952; 100).
Frances Buckel (Sec), Witts End, Radbones Hill,
Over Norton, Chipping Norton, OX7 5RA.
T: 01608 644 425;
E: fran.buckel@btinternet.com;
W: www.banburyornithologicalsociety.org.uk

Meetings: 7.30pm, 2nd Monday
of the month (Sep-May).
The Banbury Cricket Club,
White Post Road, Bodicote,
OX15 4BN.

OXFORD ORNITHOLOGICAL SOCIETY. (1921; 330).
Barry Hudson (Sec), Pinfold, 4 Bushey Row,
Bampton, Witney, OX18 2JU. T: 01993 200 790 &
07788 496 847; E: secretary@oos.org.uk;
W: www.oos.org.uk
Meetings: 7.45pm, 2nd Wednesday of the month
(Sep-May). Exeter Hall, Oxford Road, Kidlington,
OX5 1AB.

RSPB Local Group
OXFORD. (1977; 100).
Roy Grant. T: 01865 774 659;
E: roy.otters@hotmail.co.uk;
W: www.rspb.org.uk/groups/oxford
Meetings: 7.45pm, (usually) 1st Thursday of
the month (Sep-May). Sandhills Primary School,
Terrett Avenue, Sandhills, Oxford, OX3 8FN.

VALE OF WHITE HORSE. (1977; 160).
Bob Knight. T: 01235 818 072;
E: bob_knight@tiscali.co.uk;
W: www.rspb-vwh.org.uk
Meetings: 7.45pm, 3rd Monday of the month
(Sep-May). Didcot Civic Hall, Britwell Road,
Didcot, OX11 7JN.

Wetland Bird Survey (WeBS) Local Organiser
OXFORDSHIRE (NORTH). Sandra Bletchly.
T: 01295 721 048;
E: sandra.banornsoc@btinternet.com

OXFORDSHIRE (SOUTH). Ben Carpenter.
T: 07814 159 050; E: beniow@yahoo.co.uk

Wildlife Trust
BERKSHIRE, BUCKS. & OXON WILDLIFE TRUST.
(1959; 51,000).
The Lodge, 1 Armstrong Road, Littlemore, Oxford,
OX4 4XT. T: 01865 775 476, (fax) 01865 711 301;
E: info@bbowt.org.uk; W: www.bbowt.org.uk

SHROPSHIRE

Bird Atlas/Avifauna
The Birds of Shropshire. Leo Smith
(Liverpool University Press, 2019).

Bird Recorder
Ian Grant, 1 Audley Road, Newport, TF10 7DT;
T: 07590 422 568; E: soscountyrecorder@gmail.com

Bird Report
SHROPSHIRE BIRD REPORT (1956-), from
E: WebManager@shropshirebirds.com

BTO Regional Representative
Jonathan Groom. T: n/a;
E: bto.shropshire@gmail.com

ENGLAND

Club
SHROPSHIRE ORNITHOLOGICAL
SOCIETY. (1955; 800).
Helen J Griffiths (Sec).
Address: n/a. T: 07800 880 445;
E: secretary@shropshirebirds.co.uk;
W: www.shropshirebirds.com
Meetings: 7.15pm,
1st Wednesday of the month
(Oct-Mar). Bayston Hill Memorial Hall, Lyth Hill Road,
Bayston Hill, Shrewsbury, SY3 0DR.

Ringing Group/Bird Observatory
CHELMARSH RG.
W: http://chelmarshrg.blogspot.co.uk/

SHROPSHIRE RG.
W: http://shropshirerg.wordpress.com

WEST MIDLANDS RINGING GROUP.
W: www.westmidlandsringinggroup.co.uk

RSPB Local Group
SHROPSHIRE. (1991; 110).
Nadia Archer. T: 0121 262 6800;
E: ShrewsburyRSPBgroup@gmail.com;
W: www.rspb.org.uk/groups/shropshire
Meetings: 7.30pm, 4th Tuesday of the month
(Sep-Apr/2nd Tuesday in Dec).
Bayston Hill Memorial Hall, Lyth Hill Rd,
Shrewsbury, SY3 0DR.

SOUTH SHROPSHIRE. (2004; 75).
Carol Wood. T: 07807 068 304;
E: carolwood772@outlook.com;
W: www.rspbsouthshropshire.co.uk
Meetings: 7.30pm, 2nd Tuesday of the month
(Sep-Apr). Culmington Village Hall, on the B4365,
Culmington, SY8 2DA.

Wetland Bird Survey (WeBS) Local Organiser
SHROPSHIRE. Michael Wallace. T: 01743 369 035;
E: michaelwallace47@gmail.com

Wildlife Trust
SHROPSHIRE WILDLIFE TRUST. (1962; 11,000).
193 Abbey Foregate, Shrewsbury, SY2 6AH.
T: 01743 284 280, (fax) 01743 284 281;
E: enquiries@shropshirewildlifetrust.org.uk;
W: www.shropshirewildlifetrust.org.uk

SOMERSET & BRISTOL/AVON

Bird Atlas/Avifauna
The Birds of Exmoor and the Quantocks.
David Ballance, Brian Gibbs & Roger Butcher
(privately published, 2nd ed 2016).

*Somerset Atlas of Breeding and Wintering Birds
2007-2012.* David Ballance, Rob Grimmond,
Julian Thomas & Eve Tigwell (Somerset OS, 2014).

Avon Atlas 2007-11. Richard L Bland & M Dadds
(Bristol Naturalists' Society, 2012).

A History of the Birds of Somerset. DK Ballance
(Isabelline Books, 2006).

Bird Recorder
AVON. John Martin, 34 Cranmoor Green, Pilning,
Bristol, BS35 4QF. T: 01454 633 040 &
07443 544 962; E: avonbirdrecorder@gmail.com

SOMERSET. Brian Gibbs, 23 Lyngford Road,
Taunton, TA2 7EE. T: 01823 274 887;
E: brian.gibbs@somersetbirding.org.uk

Bird Report

AVON BIRD REPORT (1977-),
from Harvey Rose, Arncliffe,
Coast Road, Walton Bay,
Clevedon, BS21 7FW.
E: h.e.rose@bris.ac.uk

SOMERSET BIRDS (1912-),
from the Somerset Bird
Recorder - see above.

BTO Regional Representative
AVON. Gordon Youdale. T: 01454 881 690;
E: gordon.youdale@blueyonder.co.uk

Dave Stoddard (Assistant Representative).
T: 0117 924 698; E: dave.stoddard@tiscali.co.uk

SOMERSET. Eve Tigwell. T: 01373 451 630;
E: eve.tigwell@zen.co.uk

Club
BRISTOL NATURALISTS' SOCIETY. (1862; 500).
Lesley Cox (Ornithology Section Rep). Address: n/a.
T: 07786 437 528; E: secretary@bristolnats.org.uk;
W: www.bristolnats.org.uk
Meetings: 7.30pm, 2nd Wednesday of the month
(Oct-Mar). Westbury-on-Trym, Methodist Church,
46 Westbury Hill, Bristol, BS9 3AA.

BRISTOL ORNITHOLOGICAL CLUB. (1967; 580).
Judy Copeland (Membership Sec),
19 St George's Hill, Easton-in-Gordano,
North Somerset BS20 0PS. T: 01275 373 554;
E: bocsecretary@hotmail.com;
W: www.bristolornithologicalclub.co.uk
Meetings: 7.30pm, 3rd Thursday of the month
(Sep-Mar). Newman Hall, Grange Court Road,
Westbury-on-Trym, BS9 4DR.

257

ENGLAND

EXMOOR NATURAL HISTORY SOCIETY. (1974; 480). Caroline Giddens (Sec), 12 King George Road, Minehead, TA24 5JD. T: 01643 707 624; E: carol.enhs@talktalk.net; W: www.enhs.org.uk **Meetings:** 7.30pm, 1st Wednesday of the month (Oct-Mar). Methodist Church Hall, The Avenue, Minehead, TA24 5AY - check website for times. 10am, 2nd Tuesday of the month at Luckbarrow, West Luccombe. TA24 8HX.

SOMERSET ORNITHOLOGICAL SOCIETY. (1974; 475). Dick Best (Membership Sec), Quantock View Farm, Steart, TA5 2PXP. T: 01278 651 063; E: dick.best@somersetbirding.org.uk; W: www.somersetbirding.org.uk **Meetings:** 7.30pm, 3rd Thursday of the month (Oct-Apr, except Dec). Village Hall, Ruishton, Taunton, TA3 5JD.

Ringing Group/Bird Observatory
CHEW VALLEY RS.
W: www.chewvalleyringingstation.co.uk

GORDANO VALLEY RG.

RSPB Local Group
BATH AND DISTRICT. (1969; 260). Jean Melksham. T: 01225 404985; E: jeanmelksham@blueyonder.co.uk; W: www.rspb.org.uk/groups/bath **Meetings:** 7.30pm, 3rd Wednesday of the month (Sep-Apr). St Andrew's Community Church, Hawthorn Grove, Combe Down, Bath, BA2 5QA.

SOUTH SOMERSET. (1979; 240). Denise Chamings. T: 01460 240 740; E: denise.chamings@talktalk.net; W: www.rspb.org.uk/groups/southsomerset **Meetings:** 7.30pm, 3rd Thursday of the month (Sep-May). The Millennium Hall, Seavington St. Mary, Ilminster, TA19 0QH.

Wetland Bird Survey (WeBS) Local Organiser
AVON (OTHER SITES). Rupert Higgins. T: 0117 944 1034; E: rupert@wessexeco.co.uk

SEVERN ESTUARY (SOMERSET & BRISTOL). Harvey Rose. T: via WeBS Office; E: H.E.Rose@bristol.ac.uk

SOMERSET LEVELS. Eve Tigwell. T: 01373 451 630; E: eve.tigwell@zen.co.uk

SOMERSET (OTHER SITES). Eve Tigwell - see above.

Wildlife Trust
AVON WILDLIFE TRUST. (1980; 19,000). 32 Jacobs Wells Road, Bristol, BS8 1DR. T: 0117 917 7270, (fax) 0117 929 7273; E: mail@avonwildlifetrust.org.uk; W: www.avonwildlifetrust.org.uk

SOMERSET WILDLIFE TRUST. (1964; 19,000). 34 Wellington Road, Taunton, Somerset TA1 5AW. T: 01823 652 400, (fax) 01823 652 411; E: enquiries@somersetwildlife.org; W: www.somersetwildlife.org

STAFFORDSHIRE

Bird Atlas/Avifauna.
See West Midlands.

Bird Recorder
Nick Pomiankowski, 22 The Villas, West End, Stoke-on-Trent, ST4 5AQ. T: 01782 849 682; E: staffs-recorder@westmidlandbirdclub.org.uk

Bird Report.
See West Midlands.

BTO Regional Representative
NORTH: Scott Petrek. T: n/a; E: scott.petrek@gmail.com

Gerald Gittens (Assistant Representative). T: 01785 815 141; E: gerald.gittens1@btopenworld.com

SOUTH: Scott Petrek/Gerald Gittens - see above.

WEST: Scott Petrek/Gerald Gittens - see above.

Club
WEST MIDLAND BIRD CLUB (STAFFORD BRANCH). David Dodd (Chairman). Address: n/a. T: n/a; E: stafford@westmidlandbirdclub.org.uk; W: www.westmidlandbirdclub.org.uk/stafford **Meetings:** 7.45pm, 1st Tuesday of the month (Nov-Mar). Perkins Engines Sport & Social Club, Tixall Road, Stafford, ST16 3UB.

Ringing Group/Bird Observatory
WEST MIDLANDS RINGING GROUP.
W: www.westmidlandsringinggroup.co.uk

RSPB Local Group
BURTON & SOUTH DERBYSHIRE. (1973; 50). Dave Lummis. T: 01283 219 902; E: david.lummis@btinternet.com; W: www.basd-rspb.co.uk **Meetings:** 7.30pm, 2nd Wednesday of some months between Sep-May - contact/see website for details. All Saint's Church Hall, Branston Road, Burton-on-Trent, DE14 3BY.

LICHFIELD & DISTRICT. (1977; 1150). Dennis Muxworthy. T: 0121 353 6886; E: dennis.muxworthy@btinternet.com; W: www.rspb.org.uk/groups/lichfield **Meetings:** 7.30pm, 2nd Tuesday of the month (Sep-May). Guildhall, Bore Street, Lichfield, WS13 6LU.

NORTH STAFFS. (1982; 200).
Geoff Sales. T: 0121 262 6800;
E: sgeoff31@gmail.com;
W: www.rspb.org.uk/groups/northstaffordshire
Meetings: 7.30pm, 3rd Wednesday of the month
(Sep-May). North Staffs Conference Centre
(Medical Institute), Hartshill Road, Stoke-on-Trent,
ST4 7NY.

SOUTH WEST STAFFORDSHIRE. (1972; 120).
Theresa Dorrance. T: 01902 847 041;
E: tmidorrance@gmail.com;
W: www.rspb.org.uk/groups/southweststaffs
Meetings: 8.00pm, 2nd Tuesday of the month
(Sep-May). Codsall Village Hall, Wolverhampton Road,
Codsall, WV8 1PW.

Wetland Bird Survey (WeBS) Local Organiser
STAFFORDSHIRE. Scott Petrek. T: 07914 647 755;
E: scott.petrek@gmail.com

Wildlife Trust
STAFFORDSHIRE WILDLIFE TRUST. (1969; 16,000).
The Wolseley Centre, Wolseley Bridge, Stafford,
ST17 0WT. T: 01889 880 100, (fax) 01889 880 101;
E: info@staffs-wildlife.org.uk;
W: www.staffs-wildlife.org.uk

SUFFOLK

Bird Atlas/Avifauna
The Birds of Suffolk. Steve
Piotrowski (Christopher Helm,
2003).

Bird Recorder
NORTH EAST. Andrew Green,
17 Cherrywood, Harleston,
Norfolk IP20 9LP.
T: 07766 900 063;
E: waveney@yahoo.com

SOUTH EAST. Scott Mayson, 8 St Edmunds Close,
Woodbridge, IP12 4UY. T: n/a;
E: smsuffolkbirder@gmail.com

WEST. Colin Jakes, 7 Maltward Avenue,
Bury St Edmunds, IP33 3XN. T: 01284 702 215;
E: colin@jakes.myzen.co.uk

SUFFOLK. National Rarities Co-ordinator.
David Walsh, 20 Netley Close, Ipswich, IP2 9YB.
T: 07947 051 223; E: davidfwalsh@hotmail.co.uk

Bird Report
SUFFOLK BIRDS (1950-), from Suffolk Naturalist's
Society, c/o The Museum, High St, Ipswich,
IP1 3QH. E: enquiries@sns.org.uk

BTO Regional Representative
Mick Wright. T: 01473 721 486;
E: kupe1515@sky.com

Club
SUFFOLK BIRD GROUP. (1973; 400).
Gi Grieco. Address: n/a.
T: 07951 482 547;
E: info@suffolkbirdgroup.org;
W: www.suffolkbirdgroup.org
Meetings: 7.30pm, last Thursday of
the month (Sep-Nov, Jan-Apr).
Ipswich Hotel, Old London Road,
Copdock, IP8 3JD or The Cedars Hotel,
Needham Road, Stowmarket, IP14 2AJ
- contact/check website for details.

WAVENEY BIRD CLUB. (n/a; 185).
Rebecca Bedwell (Sec), Garden Cottage, Great
Common Lane, Ilketshall St Andrew, NR34 8JB.
T: 01986 781 436;
E: secretary@waveneybirdclub.com;
W: www.waveneybirdclub.com
Meetings: 7.30pm,
usually the last Tuesday
of the month
(Sep-Mar). The Maltings
Sports Ground,
Pirnhow Street,
Ditchingham, NR35 2RU.

Ringing Group/Bird Observatory
DINGLE BIRD CLUB.

EAST ANGLIA GULL GROUP.

KESSINGLAND RG.

LACKFORD RG.

LANDGUARD RG.

LITTLE OUSE RG.

WAVENEY RG.

LANDGUARD BIRD OBSERVATORY.
Landguard Bird Observatory, View Point Road,
Felixstowe, IP11 3TW. T: 01394 673 782;
E: langardbo@yahoo.co.uk;
W: www.lbo.org.uk

RSPB Local Group
IPSWICH. (1975; 150).
Timothy Kenny. T: 01394 809 236;
E: IpswichRSPBlocalgroup@yahoo.com;
W: www.rspb.org.uk/groups/ipswich
Meetings: 7.30pm, 2nd Thursday of the month
(Sep-Apr). St Andrews Church Hall, The Street,
Rushmere,Ipswich, IP5 1DH.

LOWESTOFT. (1976; n/a).
Howard Bayliss. T: n/a;
E: LowestoftRSPBlocalgroup@gmail.com;
W: www.rspb.org.uk/groups/lowestoft
Meetings: 7.30pm, 1st Friday of the month
(Jan-Dec). St Marks Church Centre, Bridge Road,
Oulton Broad, Lowestoft, NR33 9JX.

COUNTY DIRECTORY

ENGLAND

WOODBRIDGE. (1987; 320).
Paul Hetherington. T: 01728 724 504;
E: RSPBwoodbridge@paulandgill.com;
W: www.rspb.org.uk/groups/woodbridge
Meetings: 7.30pm, 1st Thursday of the month
(Oct-May). Woodbridge Community Hall,
Station Road,Woodbridge, IP12 4AU.

Wetland Bird Survey (WeBS) Local Organiser
ALDE COMPLEX. Ian Castle. T: 01394 450 188;
E: ian@castle-hamlett.co.uk

ALTON WATER. John Glazebrook.
T: via WeBS Office;
E: johnglazebrook@btopenworld.com

BLYTH ESTUARY (SUFFOLK). Will Russell.
T: 07876 796 143;
E: will.russell@naturalengland.org.uk

DEBEN ESTUARY. Nick Mason. T: 07876 086 039;
E: nick.mason4@btinternet.com

ORWELL ESTUARY. Mick Wright.
T: 01473 720 032; E: kupe1515@sky.com

STOUR ESTUARY. Rick Vonk. T: 01206 391 153;
E: rick.vonk@rspb.org.uk

SUFFOLK (OTHER SITES). Alan Miller.
T: 01728 833 405;
E: alan.miller@suffolkwildlifetrust.org

Wildlife Trust
SUFFOLK WILDLIFE TRUST. (1961; 28,000).
Brooke House, The Green, Ashbocking, Ipswich,
IP6 9JY. T: 01473 890 089, (fax) 01473 890 165;
E: info@suffolkwildlifetrust.org;
W: www.suffolkwildlifetrust.org

SURREY

Bird Atlas/Avifauna
Birds of Surrey Bird Atlas 2007-2012.
Surrey Bird Club (Surrey Bird Club, 2018).

Birds of Surrey. Jeffery J Wheatley
(Surrey Bird Club, 2007).

Bird Recorder
Steve Chastell, 8 Burnet Ave, Guildford, GU1 1YD.
T: 07826 544 221; E: surrey.recorder@btinternet.com

Bird Report
*SURBITON AND DISTRICT BIRD WATCHING SOCIETY
ANNUAL BIRD REPORT (1970-),* from Thelma Caine,
21 More Lane, Esher, KT10 8AJ.
E: thelmacaine512@btinternet.com

SURREY BIRD REPORT (1953-), from Jeremy Gates,
5 Hillside Road, Weybourne, Farnham, GU9 9DW.
T: 01252 315 047; E: jeremygates@live.com

BTO Regional Representative
Penny Williams. T: 01276 857 736;
E: penny@waxwing.plus.com

Club
SURBITON & DISTRICT BIRDWATCHING SOCIETY.
(1954; 130).
Alice Laird (Membership enquiries). Address: n/a.
E: alicesdbws@martinhwatson.co.uk;
W: http://surbitonbirds.org/
Meetings: 8pm, 3rd Tuesday of each month
(not Aug). The Main Hall, Surbiton Library,
Ewell Rd, Surbiton, KT6 6AG.

SURREY BIRD CLUB. (1957; 375).
Penny Williams (Membership Sec),
Bournbrook House, Sandpit Hall Lane, Chobham,
GU24 8HA. T: 01276 857 736;
E: membership@surreybirdclub.org.uk;
W: www.surreybirdclub.org.uk
Meetings: Contact/see website for details.

Ringing Group/Bird Observatory
HERSHAM RG.

RUNNYMEDE RG. W: www.runnymederinging.uk

RSPB Local Group
DORKING & DISTRICT. (1982; 230).
Roy Theobald. T: 01306 889 976;
E: roytheobald@yahoo.co.uk;
W: www.rspb.org.uk/groups/dorkinganddistrict
Meetings: 8.00pm, 3rd Friday of the month
(Sep-Apr). Christian Centre, Church Street,
Dorking, RH4 1DW.

EAST SURREY. (1984; 7000+/area).
John Lawrence. T: 01737 553 316;
E: jfjlawrence@gmail.com;
W: www.eastsurreyrspb.co.uk
Meetings: 8.00pm, 2nd Wednesday of the month
(not Aug). White Hart Barn, Godstone, RH9 8DT.

EPSOM & EWELL. (1974; 50).
Timothy Tomkins. T: 0208 391 0116;
E: timothy.tomkins@yahoo.co.uk;
W: www.rspb.org.uk/groups/epsom
Meetings: 7.45pm, 2nd Friday of the month
(Oct-Jun). All Saints Church Hall, 7 Church Road,
West Ewell, KT19 9QY.

GUILDFORD & DISTRICT. (1974; 400).
Margo Scott. T: 01483 767 546;
E: info@RSPBguildford.org.uk;
W: www.rspbguildford.org.uk
Meetings: Generally - 2.00pm, 1st Thursday of
the month (Oct-Mar). Shalford Village Hall,
Kings Road, Shalford, GU4 8JU &
7.30pm, 4th Wednesday of the month (Sep-May).
Onslow Village Hall, The Square, Wilderness Road,
Guildford, GU2 7QR.

NORTH WEST SURREY. (1974; 150).
Alan Sharps. T: 01784 244 665;
E: nwsleader@yahoo.co.uk;
W: www.rspb.org.uk/groups/nwsurrey
Meetings: 7.45pm, 4th Thursday of the month
(Sep-Nov, Jan-Jun). St Charles Borromeo School,
Portmore Way, Weybridge, KT13 8JD.

Wetland Bird Survey (WeBS) Local Organiser
SURREY & SW LONDON. Penny Williams.
T: via WeBS Office; E: penny@waxwing.plus.com

Wildlife Trust
SURREY WILDLIFE TRUST. (1959; 26,000).
School Lane, Pirbright, Woking, GU24 0JN.
T: 01483 795 440, (fax) 01483 486 505;
E: info@surreywt.org.uk;
W: www.surreywildlifetrust.org

SUSSEX

Bird Atlas/Avifauna
The Birds of Sussex. Sussex Ornithological
Society/Adrian LR Thomas (BTO, 2014).

Bird Recorder
Mark Mallalieu, 29 Cobbetts Mead, Haywards Heath,
West Sussex RH16 3TQ. T: 01444 441 425
& 07736 788 077; E: recorder@sos.org.uk

Bird Report
SUSSEX BIRD REPORT
(1948-), from John Trowell,
'Lorrimer', Main Road,
Icklesham, Winchelsea,
E. Sussex TN36 4BS.
E: membership@sos.org.uk

**BTO Regional
Representative**
Helen Crabtree.
T: 01444 441 687;
E: hcrabtree@gmail.com

Dave Boddington (Assistant Representative).
T: n/a; E: davebodds@yahoo.co.uk

Club
FRIENDS OF RYE HARBOUR NATURE RESERVE.
(1973; 2000+).
Friends of Rye Harbour;
E: via website;
W: www.rhnrfriends.co.uk
& www.sussexwildlifetrust.org.uk/ryeharbour
Meetings: Special events, including winter talks,
held for Friends (info in newsletter).

HENFIELD BIRDWATCH. (1998; 150+).
Mike Russell, Tor-Est-In, Lower Station Road,
Henfield, West Sussex BN5 9UG.
T: 01273 649 246;
E: mikerussell51@yahoo.co.uk;
W: http://henfieldbirdwatch.co.uk/

SHOREHAM DISTRICT ORNITHOLOGICAL SOCIETY.
(1953; 200).
SDOS Hon. Sec, 24 Chancellors Park, Hassocks,
West Sussex BN6 8EZ. T: n/a;
E: membership@sdos.org; W: www.sdos.org
Meetings: 7.30pm, 2nd Tuesday of the month
(Oct-Apr). St Peter's Church Hall, West Street,
Shoreham-by-Sea, East Sussex BN43 5GZ.

SUSSEX ORNITHOLOGICAL SOCIETY. (1962; 1900+).
Chris Davis (Sec),
27 Salisbury Road,
Seaford, East Sussex
BN25 2BD.
T: 01323 891 267;
E: secretary@sos.org.uk;
W: www.sos.org.uk
Meetings: Annual
conference (Jan)
Haywards Heath. AGM
(Apr) - contact/see website for details.

Ringing Group/Bird Observatory
BEACHY HEAD RS.

CUCKMERE RG.

RYE BAY RG.

STEYNING RG.

RSPB Local Group
BRIGHTON & DISTRICT. (1974; 200).
Mark Weston. T: 01903 606 581;
E: markweston64@talktalk.net;
W: www.rspb.org.uk/groups/brighton
Meetings: 7.30pm, 4th Thursday of the month
(Sep-May, for Dec contact/see website). New venue
trialled for Sep-Nov 2019, probably permanent
thereafter: North Barn of West Blatchington
Windmill, Holmes Avenue, Hove, BN3 7LH.

COUNTY DIRECTORY

ENGLAND

CHICHESTER. (1979; 245).
Chris Furlepa. T: 01243 261 591;
E: chichesterbirds@gmail.com;
W: www.rspb.org.uk/groups/chichester
Meetings: 7.30pm, 4th Thursday of the month
(Sep-May). The Masonic Hall, 7 South Pallant,
Chichester, West Sussex PO19 1SY.

CRAWLEY & HORSHAM. (1978; 65).
Andrea Saxton. T: 01403 242 218;
E: andrea.saxton@sky.com;
W: www.rspb.org.uk/groups/crawley
Meetings: 8.00pm, 3rd Wednesday of the month
(Sep-Apr). The Friary Hall, Haslett Avenue West,
Crawley, West Sussex RH10 1HR.

EAST GRINSTEAD. (1998; 185).
Shaun Taylor. T: 01342 719 456;
E: eastgrinsteadRSPB@gmail.com;
W: www.rspb.org.uk/groups/egrinstead
Meetings: 8.00pm, last Wednesday of the month
(Sep-Jun, not Dec). Main Hall, East Court,
College Lane, East Grinstead, West Sussex RH19 3LT.

EASTBOURNE & DISTRICT. (1994; 200).
Tony Vass. T: 01424 844 304;
E: eastbourneRSPB@gmail.com;
W: www.rspb.org.uk/groups/eastbourne
Meetings: 2.15pm & 7.30pm, 1st Wednesday of
the month (Sep-Jun). St. Wilfrid's Church Hall,
Eastbourne Rd, Pevensey Bay, East Sussex BN24 6HL.

HASTINGS & ST LEONARDS. (1983; 65).
Ros Leigh. T: 07557 345 894;
E: rosalindhl@talktalk.net;
W: www.rspb.org.uk/groups/hastings
Meetings: 7.30pm, 3rd Friday of the month. The
Taplin Centre, Upper Maze Hill, St Leonards-on-Sea,
East Sussex TN38 0LQ.

Wetland Bird Survey (WeBS) Local Organiser
CHICHESTER HARBOUR. Peter Hughes.
T: 01243 510 985;
E: peter.hughes@conservancy.co.uk

SUSSEX (OTHER SITES - COASTAL).
Dave Boddington. T: 07771 758 105;
E: davebodds@yahoo.co.uk

SUSSEX (OTHER SITES - INLAND). Helen Crabtree.
T: 01444 441 687; E: hcrabtree@gmail.com

Wildlife Trust
SUSSEX WILDLIFE TRUST. (1961; 34,000).
Woods Mill, Shoreham Road, Henfield, West Sussex
BN5 9SD. T: 01273 492 630, (fax) 01273 494 500;
E: enquiries@sussexwt.org.uk;
W: www.sussexwildlifetrust.org.uk

WARWICKSHIRE

Bird Atlas/Avifauna.
See West Midlands.

Bird Recorder
Chris Hill. 17 Brampton
Crescent, Shirley, Solihull,
B90 3SY. T: 07900 473 911;
E: warks-recorder@
westmidlandbirdclub.org.uk

Bird Report.
See West Midlands.

BTO Regional Representative
Annette Jarratt-Knock. T: n/a;
E: annettejk@oneuk.com

Club
NUNEATON & DISTRICT BIRDWATCHERS' CLUB
(NUNEATON BIRD CLUB). (1950; 30).
Address: n/a. T: n/a;
E: nuneatonbirdclub@outlook.com;
W: http://nuneatonbirdclub.wordpress.com/
Meetings: 7.30pm, 3rd Thursday of the month
(Sep-May). Hatters Space Community Centre,
Upper Abbey Street, Nuneaton, CV11 5DN.

Ringing Group/Bird Observatory
ARDEN RG.

BRANDON RG.

RSPB Local Group
COVENTRY & WARWICKSHIRE. (1969; 120).
Peter Worthy. T: 01926 497 967;
E: pete@cpworthy.plus.com;
W: www.rspb.org.uk/groups/coventryandwarwickshire
Meetings: 7:30pm, 4th Friday of the month (Sep-May).
Baginton Village Hall, Frances Rd, Baginton, Coventry,
CV8 3AB.

Wetland Bird Survey (WeBS) Local Organiser
WARWICKSHIRE. Matthew Griffiths.
T: via WeBS Office; E: matt_avesmaster@hotmail.com

Wildlife Trust
WARWICKSHIRE WILDLIFE TRUST. (1970; 24,000).
Brandon Marsh Nature Centre, Brandon Lane,
Coventry, CV3 3GW. T: 02476 302 912,
(fax) 02476 639 556; E: enquiries@wkwt.org.uk;
W: www.warwickshire-wildlife-trust.org.uk

WEST MIDLANDS

Bird Atlas/Avifauna
The New Birds of the West Midlands. Graham
& Janet Harrison - covers Staffordshire,
Warwickshire, Worcestershire & the former West
Midlands County (West Midland Bird Club, 2005).

ENGLAND

Bird Recorder
Kevin Clements, 26 Hambrook Close, Dunstall Park, Wolverhampton, West Midlands WV6 0XA.
T: 01902 568 997;
E: west-mids-recorder@westmidlandbirdclub.org.uk

Bird Report
WEST MIDLAND BIRD REPORT (inc Staffs, Warks, Worcs & West Mids) (1934-), from Focus Optics www.focusoptics.eu/publications and The Birders Store www.birders-store.co.uk or further info from E: secretary@westmidlandbirdclub.org.uk

BTO Regional Representative
BIRMINGHAM & WEST MIDLANDS. Steve Davies.
T: 07782 891 726;
E: stevedaviesbtorep@hotmail.co.uk

Club
WEST MIDLAND BIRD CLUB (1929; 1400).
(Staffs, Warks, Worcs & the West Midlands.)
Mark Rickus (Sec), 27 Ringmere Avenue, Castle Bromwich, Birmingham, B36 9AT. T: 0121 749 5348;
E: secretary@westmidlandbirdclub.org.uk;
W: www.westmidlandbirdclub.org.uk
Meetings: Contact/see website for branch details.

Field Trips only:
Liz Palmer. T: 01827 54557 & 07947 456 448;
E: Wmbcfieldtrips.liz@westmidlandbirdclub.org.uk

WEST MIDLAND BIRD CLUB (SOLIHULL BRANCH). Richard Harvey (Chairman). Address: n/a.
T: 0789 556 125;

E: solihull@westmidlandbirdclub.org.uk;
W: www.westmidlandbirdclub.org.uk/solihull
Meetings: 7.30 pm, on a Friday (Oct-Mar).
Guild House, 1715 High Street, Knowle, Solihull, B93 0LN.

Ringing Group/Bird Observatory
BIRMINGHAM UNIVERSITY RG.
W: http://www.birmingham.ac.uk/research/activity/ornithology/people/ringing-group/index.aspx

MERCIAN RG.

WEST MIDLANDS RINGING GROUP.
W: www.westmidlandsringinggroup.co.uk

RSPB Local Group
SOLIHULL. (1983; 2600).
John Roberts. T: 0121 707 3101;
E: johnbirder@care4free.net;
W: www.rspb.org.uk/groups/solihull
Meetings: 7.30pm, (usually) 1st Thursday of the month (Sep-Apr). Bentley Heath Community Hall, Widney Road, Bentley Heath, Solihull, B93 9BQ.

STOURBRIDGE. (1978; 150).
David Bradford. T: 01384 390 035;
E: djbstourbridge@yahoo.co.uk;
W: www.rspb.org.uk/groups/stourbridge
Meetings: 7.30pm, 2nd Wednesday of the month (Sep-May). St Thomas' Church Hall, Market Street, Stourbridge, DY8 1HQ.

SUTTON COLDFIELD. (1986; 250).
Tony Green. T: 01827 750 633;
E: tonygreen777@hotmail.co.uk;
W: www.rspb.org.uk/groups/suttoncoldfield
Meetings: 7.30pm, usually 1st Monday of the month (Sep-May). Bishop Vesey's Grammer School, Lichfield Road, Sutton Coldfield, B74 2NH.

WALSALL. (1971; n/a).
Michael Pittaway. T: 01922 710 568;
E: michaelpittaway34@gmail.com;
W: www.rspb-walsall.org.uk
Meetings: 7.30pm, 3rd Wednesday of the month (Sep-May). St Marys RC Primary School, Jesson Rd, Walsall, WS1 3AY.

Wetland Bird Survey (WeBS) Local Organiser
WEST MIDLANDS. Nick Lewis. T: 0121 783 0874;
E: nick.r.lewis@virginmedia.com

Wildlife Trust
WILDLIFE TRUST FOR BIRMINGHAM AND THE BLACK COUNTRY. (1980; 8,000).
Centre of the Earth, 42 Norman Street, Winson Green, Birmingham, B18 7EP. T: 0121 523 0094;
E: info@bbcwildlife.org.uk; W: www.bbcwildlife.org.uk

WILTSHIRE

Bird Atlas/Avifauna
Birds of Wiltshire.
J Ferguson-Lees, P Castle & P Cranswick (Wiltshire Ornithological Society, 2007).

Bird Recorder
Nick Adams (standing down March 2020, e-mail will remain the same). Address: n/a. T: n/a;
E: recorder@wiltshirebirds.co.uk

Bird Report
WILTSHIRE BIRD REPORT (HOBBY) (1975-), from John Osborne, 4 Fairdown Avenue, Westbury, BA13 3HS. E: josb@talktalk.net

BTO Regional Representative
NORTH: Bill Quantrill. T: 01225 866 245;
E: william.quantrill@btinternet.com

Claire Jones (Assistant Representative). T: n/a;
E: wiltshirebto@gmail.com

SOUTH: Bill Quantrill/Claire Jones - see above.

ENGLAND

Club
SALISBURY & DISTRICT
NATURAL HISTORY SOCIETY. (1952; 140).
John Pitman (Ornithology Section). Address: n/a.
T: 01722 327 395; E: jacpitman@btinternet.com;
W: www.salisburynaturalhistory.com
Meetings: 7.30pm, 3rd Thursday of the month
(Sep-Apr). The Meeting Room, Salisbury Baptist
Church, Brown Street, Salisbury, SP1 2AS.

WILTSHIRE ORNITHOLOGICAL SOCIETY. (1974; 500+).
Matt Prior (Chair). Address: n/a. T: n/a;
E: chair@wiltshirebirds.co.uk;
W: www.wiltshirebirds.co.uk
Meetings: Contact/see website for details.

Ringing Group/Bird Observatory
COTSWOLD WATERPARK RG.

NORTH WILTS RG.

WEST WILTS RG.

RSPB Local Group
SOUTH WILTSHIRE. (1986; 500).
Tony Goddard. T: 01722 712 713;
E: goddard543@hotmail.com;
W: www.rspb.org.uk/groups/southwiltshire
Meetings: 7.30pm, 2nd Tuesday of the month
(Sep-May). Salisbury Arts Centre, Bedwin Street,
Salisbury, SP1 3UT.

Wetland Birds Survey Organiser
AVON VALLEY. See Hampshire.

COTSWOLD WATER PARK. See Gloucestershire.

WILTSHIRE. Claire Jones. T: via WeBS Office;
E: wiltshirebto@gmail.com

Wildlife Trust
WILTSHIRE WILDLIFE TRUST. (1962; 19,000).
Elm Tree Court, Long Street, Devizes, SN10 1NJ.
T: 01380 725 670, (fax) 01380 729 017;
E: info@wiltshirewildlife.org;
W: www.wiltshirewildlife.org

WORCESTERSHIRE

Bird Atlas/Avifauna. See West Midlands.

Bird Recorder
Steven Payne, 6 Norbury Close, Redditch, B98 8RP.
T: 01527 60169;
E: steven.payne@tiscali.co.uk

Bird Report. See West Midlands.

BTO Regional Representative
Steve Davies. T: 01562 885 789;
E: stevedaviesbtorep@hotmail.co.uk

Harry Green (Assistant Representative).
T: 01386 710 377; E: zen130501@zen.co.uk

Club
WEST MIDLAND BIRD CLUB (KIDDERMINSTER BRANCH).
Roger Pannell (Chairman). Address: n/a. T: n/a;
E: kidderminster@westmidlandbirdclub.org.uk;
W: www.westmidlandbirdclub.org.uk/kidderminster
Meetings: 7.30pm, 4th Wednesday of the month
(Sep-Apr). St Oswalds Church Centre,
off Broadwaters Drive, Kidderminster, DY10 2RY.

Ringing Group/Bird Observatory
WYCHAVON RG.

RSPB Local Group
WORCESTER & MALVERN. (1980; 150).
Nick Skilbeck. T: 07540 328 945;
E: nickskilbeck@btinternet.com;
W: www.rspb.org.uk/groups/worcester
Meetings: 7.30pm, 2nd Wednesday of the month
(Sep-May). Powick Village Hall, on A449, Powick,
WR2 4RT.
Club projects: 1: winter feeding corn buntings &
other farmland birds in Pershore area. 2: winter
feeding farmland birds in south Worcestershire.
3: working with Worcester hospital breast unit &
mental health unit connecting people to nature.

Wetland Bird Survey (WeBS) Local Organiser
WORCESTERSHIRE. Andrew Warr.
T: via WeBS Office;
E: andrew.warr3@btopenworld.com

Wildlife Trust
WORCESTERSHIRE WILDLIFE TRUST. (1967; 21,000).
Lower Smite Farm, Smite Hill, Hindlip, Worcester,
WR3 8SZ. T: 01905 754 919, (fax) 01905 755 868;
E: enquiries@worcestershirewildlifetrust.org;
W: www.worcswildlifetrust.co.uk

YORKSHIRE

Bird Atlas/Avifauna
The Birds of Spurn. Andy Roadhouse
(Spurn Observatory Trust, 2016).

*Breeding Birds of the
Sheffield Area including
the North-east Peak
District.* David Wood &
Richard Hill (Sheffield Bird
Study Group, 2013).

*Birds of the Huddersfield
Area.* Paul & Betty Bray
(Huddersfield Birdwatchers
Club, 2008).

The Birds of Yorkshire. J Mather (Croom Helm, 1986).

Bird Recorder
YORKSHIRE. Recorder, rarities. Chris Robinson.
Address: n/a. T: n/a; E: sabsgull@hotmail.co.uk

ENGLAND

EAST YORKSHIRE. James Spencer. Address: 22 Mill Chase, Nafferton, East Yorkshire YO25 4PE. T: 07795 081 804; E: eastyorksynu@gmail.com

NORTH YORKSHIRE. Ian Court, 2 Burley Mews, Steeton, Keighley, BT20 6TX. T: 01535 658 582; E: ian.court@mypostoffice.co.uk

SOUTH YORKSHIRE. Martin Wells, 715 Manchester Road, Stocksbridge, Sheffield, S36 1DQ. T: 0114 288 4211; E: martinwells@barnsleybsg.plus.com

WEST YORKSHIRE. Andy Jowett. Address: n/a. T: n/a; E: jowett.a@sky.com

Bird Report
BIRDS IN HUDDERSFIELD (1966-), from Helen Sill, Wards End Farm, Marsden, Huddersfield HD7 6NJ; T: 07854 739 646; E: hazel.sill@btinternet.com

BIRDS IN THE SHEFFIELD AREA (1973-), from Martin Hodgson, 142 Hangingwater Road, Sheffield, S11 7ET.
W: mjhodgson43@btinternet.com

BRADFORD ORNITHOLOGICAL GROUP REPORT (1987-), online - download from:
http://www.bradfordbirding.org/reports or further info Mr CJ King, E: bogmembership@live.co.uk

FILEY BIRD REPORT (1976-), from Janet Robinson, 31 Wharfedale, Filey, YO14 0DG. T: 01723 513 991; E: janetrobinson@yorkshire.net

FLAMBOROUGH HEAD BIRD OBSERVATORY, from Tony Hood. 9 Hartendale Close, Flamborough, East Yorkshire YO15 1PL.
E: tonyhood74@gmail.com

HARROGATE & DISTRICT NATURALISTS' SOCIETY BIRD REPORT (1958-), from Jill Warwick, Sharow Grange, Sharow, Ripon, HG4 5BN. T: 01765 602 832; E: jill@swland.co.uk

SPURN WILDLIFE (1991-), from Spurn Bird Observatory Trust, Kew Villa, Kilnsea, HU12 0UB. T: 01964 650 479; E: friendsofspurn@hotmail.com

YORK ORNITHOLOGICAL CLUB REPORT (1966-), from Jane Chapman, 12 Moorland Road, York, YO10 4HF. T: 01904 633 558; E: secretary@yorkbirding.org.uk

YORKSHIRE BIRD REPORT (1940-), from Jill Warwick, Sharow Grange, Sharow, Ripon, HG4 5BN. T: 01765 602 832; E: jill@swland.co.uk

BTO Regional Representative
BRADFORD. Mike Denton. T: 01484 646 990; E: michael@atheta.plus.com

CENTRAL. Mike Brown. T: 01423 567 382; E: mikebtorep@gmail.com

EAST. Vacant - contact Dawn Balmer, BTO. T: 01842 750 050; E: dawn.balmer@bto.org

HULL. Vacant - contact Dawn Balmer, BTO. T: 01842 750 050; E: dawn.balmer@bto.org

LEEDS & WAKEFIELD. Rachael Dixey. T: n/a; E: rachael.dixey@btopenworld.com

NORTH-EAST. Graham Oliver. T: 01947 811 290; E: g.h.oliver@btinternet.com

John McEachen (Assistant Representative). T: 01947 810 251; E: mceachen@btinternet.com

NORTH-WEST. Alex Gould. T: n/a; E: alexgould2011@hotmail.co.uk

RICHMOND. Mike Gibson. T: 01677 450 542; E: mkgibson@btinternet.com

SOUTH-EAST: Aidan Gill. T: 07961 079 995; E: aidanpgill@gmail.com

SOUTH-WEST: Grant Bigg. T: n/a; E: gr_bigg@tiscali.co.uk

YORK. Rob Chapman. T: 01904 633 558; E: robert.chapman@tinyworld.co.uk

Club
BRADFORD ORNITHOLOGICAL GROUP. (1987; 100). Shaun Radcliffe (Chairman), 8 Longwood Avenue, Bingley, Bradford, BD16 2RX. T: 01274 770 960; E: shaun.radcliffe@btinternet.com; W: www.bradfordbirding.org
Meetings: 7.30pm, 1st Tuesday of the month (all year). The Link, 35 Cliffe Avenue, Baildon, Shipley, BD17 6NX.

FILEY BIRD OBSERVATORY & GROUP. (1977; 165). Chris Blakeley (Membership Sec), Cottage 1, Skipster Hagg Farm, Sinnington, YO62 6SP. T: n/a. E: membership.fbog@gmail.com; W: www.fbog.co.uk

Filey Bird Observatory and Group

HARROGATE & DISTRICT NATURALISTS' SOCIETY. (1947; 210). Sue Coldwell (Gen Sec), 4 Abbots Way, Knaresborough, HG5 8EU. T: 01423 868 043; E: gensec@hdns.org.uk; W: www.hdns.org.uk
Meetings: 7.30pm, fortnightly, on a Wednesday (Oct-Mar). St. Roberts Centre, 2/3 Robert Street, Harrogate, HG1 1HP.

ENGLAND

HUDDERSFIELD BIRDWATCHERS' CLUB. (1966; 80).
Chris Abell (Sec), 57 Butterley Lane, New Mill,
Holmfirth, HD9 7EZ. T: 01484 681 499;
E: cdabell@gmail.com;
W: www.huddersfieldbirdwatchersclub.co.uk
Meetings: 7.30pm, Tuesday's fortnightly
(Sep-May). The Old Court Room, Town Hall,
Ramsden St, Huddersfield, HD1 2TA.

ROTHERHAM & DISTRICT ORNITHOLOGICAL SOCIETY.
(1974; 80). RDOS, c/o Galaxy Four, 493 Glossop Road,
Sheffield, S10 2QE; T: n/a; E: via website;
W: www.rotherhambirds.co.uk
Meetings: 7.30pm, 2nd Friday of the month
(Sep-Apr). Herringthorpe United Reform Church
Hall, Wickersley Road, Rotherham, S60 4JN.

SCARBOROUGH BIRDERS. (1993; 70).
Nick Addey (Chairman). Address: n/a. T: n/a;
E: nickaddey@dsl.pipex.com;
W: www.scaroughbirding.co.uk
Meetings: None planned 2019/20.

SHEFFIELD BIRD STUDY GROUP. (1972; 350).
Richard Hill (Sec), 22 Ansell Road, Sheffield, S11 7PE.
T: n/a; E: Secretary@sbsg.org; W: www.sbsg.org
Meetings: 7.15pm, 2nd Wednesday of the month
(Sep-May). Diamond Building - Lecture Theatre 2,
Sheffield University, 32 Leavygreave Road, Sheffield,
S3 7RD. Offers free membership to under-25's.

SK58 BIRDERS. (1992; 50).
Paul Tennyson (Chairman),
16/18 Sheffield Road,
South Anston, Sheffield,
S25 5DT. T: 01909 569 409;
E: p.tennyson@sky.com;
W: www.sk58birders.com
Meetings: 7.30pm, last
Wednesday of the month
(Sep-Nov & Jan-May). The Loyal Trooper Inn,
Sheffield Road, South Anston, Sheffield, S25 5DT.

SK58 BIRDERS

SORBY NATURAL HISTORY SOCIETY. (1918; 400).
General enquiries: E: secretary@sorby.org.uk;
W: www.sorby.org.uk
(Ornithology Group): Secretary - position vacant.
E: ornithology@sorby.org.uk; Acting bird recorder:
Harold Smith. E: birdrecords@sorby.org.uk
Meetings: Regularly held - contact/see website
for details.

SWILLINGTON INGS BIRD GROUP. (1989; 230).
Martin Robinson (Sec). Address: n/a; T: n/a;
E: via website; W: http://sibg1.wordpress.com
Meetings: 7.30pm, usually 1st Thursday of the
month (Feb, Apr, Jun, Aug, Oct, Dec).
Two Pointers, 69 Church Street, Woodlesford,
LS26 8RE.

WAKEFIELD NATURALISTS' SOCIETY. (1851; 30).
Address: n/a; T: n/a; E: via website;
W: http://wakefieldnaturalists.org
Meetings: 7.30pm, 2nd Tuesday of the month
(Sep-Apr). Quaker Meeting House, Thornhill Street,
Wakefield, WF1 1NQ.

YORK ORNITHOLOGICAL CLUB. (1965; 100).
Jane Chapman (Sec), 12 Moorland Road, York
YO10 4HF. T: 01904 633 558;
E: secretary@yorkbirding.org.uk;
W: www.yorkbirding.org.uk
Meetings: 7.30pm, 1st Tuesday of the month
(Sep-May). St Olaves Church Hall, Marygate Lane,
Marygate, York, YO30 7DS.

YORKSHIRE NATURALISTS' UNION (1861; 500).
Becky Bailey (Bird Section - Sec), 38 Birch Drive,
Kippax, West Yorkshire LS25 7DU.
T: 07809 461 331; E: beckybailey101@gmail.com;
W: www.ynu.org.uk
Meetings: No indoor meetings held.

Ringing Group/Bird Observatory
BARNSLEY RG.

DONCASTER RG.

EAST DALES RG.
W: https://eastdalesringinggroup.wordpress.com

EAST YORKSHIRE RG
(inc. Filey & Flamborough Bird Observatories)
HUMBER WADER RG.

PICKERING FORESTS RG.

SORBY BRECK RG. W: www.britishringers.co.uk

FILEY BIRD OBSERVATORY. See Club.

FLAMBOROUGH BIRD OBSERVATORY.
Tony Hood, (Sec) 9 Hartendale Close,
Flamborough, East Yorkshire YO15 1PL.
T: n/a; E: tonyhood74@gmail.com;
W: http://fbo.org.uk/

SPURN BIRD OBSERVATORY.
Paul Collins (Warden), Spurn Bird Observatory,
Easington Road, Kilnsea, Hull, HU12 0UB.
T: 01964 650 479; E: pcnfa@hotmail.com;
W: www.spurnbirdobservatory.co.uk

Acommodation enquiries: T: as above;
E: accommodation.spurnbirdobs@hotmail.com.

RSPB Local Group
AIREDALE & BRADFORD. (1972; 3500/area).
Paul Barrett. T: 01274 582 078;
E: abRSPB@blueyonder.co.uk;
W: www.rspb.org.uk/groups/airedaleandbradford
Meetings: 7.30pm, 2nd Friday of the month
(Sep-Apr). The Kirkgate Centre, 39A Kirkgate,
Shipley, BD18 3EH.

ENGLAND

DONCASTER. (1984; 70).
Steve Pynegar. T: 01302 834 443;
E: steve.pynegar@gmail.com;
W: www.rspbdoncaster.com
Meetings: 7.00pm, 2nd Wednesday of the month
(Sep-May). Castle Park Rugby Club, Armthorpe Road,
Doncaster, DN2 5QB.

EAST YORKSHIRE. (1986; 120).
Paul Leyland. T: 01723 891 507;
E: EastyorksRSPB@yahoo.co.uk;
W: www.rspb.org.uk/groups/eastyorkshire
Meetings: 7.30pm, 4th Tuesday of the month
(Sep-Apr, not Dec). North Bridlington Library,
Martongate, Bridlington, YO16 6YD.

HARROGATE DISTRICT. (2005; 100).
Bill Sturman. T: 01423 870 883;
E: billsturman@outlook.com;
W: www.rspb.org.uk/groups/harrogate
Meetings: 7.30pm, 2nd Monday of the month
(Sep-Apr). Christ Church Parish Centre, The Stray,
Harrogate, HG1 4SW.

HUDDERSFIELD & HALIFAX. (1981; 90).
David Hemingway. T: 01484 301 920;
E: d.hemingway@ntlworld.com;
W: www.rspb.org.uk/groups/huddersfieldandhalifax
Meetings: 7.30pm, 3rd Wednesday of the month
(Sep-Jun). New North Road Baptist Church,
New North Parade, Huddersfield, HD1 5JU.

HULL & DISTRICT. (1983; 85).
John Hallam. T: 01482 354 595;
E: jobar.hull@hotmail.co.uk;
W: www.rspb.org.uk/groups/hull
Meetings: 7.30pm, 2nd Tuesday of the month
(Sep-Apr). Christchurch United Reformed Church,
South Ella Way, Kirk Ella, Hull, HU10 7HB.

LEEDS. (1974; 430).
Ian Willoughby. T: 0113 258 6555;
E: RSPBleeds@googlemail.com;
W: www.rspb.org.uk/groups/leeds
Meetings: 7.30pm, various Wednesdays (Sep-Apr).
Friends Meeting House, 188 Woodhouse Lane,
Leeds, LS2 9DX.

RICHMONDSHIRE & HAMBLETON. (2005; n/a).
Ted Cooper. T: 07767 886 358;
E: croftbirder@hotmail.co.uk; W: www.rspb.org.uk/
groups/richmondshireandhambleton
Meetings: Various - contact/see website for details.

SHEFFIELD. (1981; 300).
Helen Ensor. T: 07749 932 806;
E: ensorhelen@gmail.com;
W: www.rspb.org.uk/groups/sheffield
Meetings: 7.30pm, 1st Thursday of the month
(Sep-May). Central United Reformed Church,
Norfolk Street, Sheffield, S1 2JB.

SKIPTON. (1986; 300).
Ewart Dawson. T: 01729 840 601;
E: ewartdawson1@gmail.com;
W: www.rspb.org.uk/groups/skipton
Meetings: 7.30pm, 2nd Wednesday of the month
(Sep-Apr). The Church Hall, Skipton Baptist Church,
Rectory Lane, Skipton, BD23 1ER.

WAKEFIELD. (1987; 70).
Duncan Stokoe. T: 01924 280 458;
E: duncanstokoe@gmail.com;
W: www.rspb.org.uk/groups/wakefield
Meetings: 7.30pm, 4th Thursday of the month
(Sep-Apr). Ossett Community Centre, Prospect Road,
Ossett, WF5 8AN.

YORK. (1972; 600).
Barry Bishop. T: 07746 596 690;
E: LeaderyorkRSPB@outlook.com;
W: www.rspb.org.uk/groups/york
Meetings: 7.30pm, usually 2nd week of the month
on a Tues, Wed or Thurs (Sep-May). Also afternoon
meetings, 2.30pm - contact/check website for
details. Clements Hall, Nunthorpe Road, York,
YO23 1BW.

Wetland Bird Survey (WeBS) Local Organiser
EAST YORKSHIRE AND SCARBOROUGH (excl.
THE HUMBER). Stephen Morgan. T: 01965 544 947;
E: jimmygpz@hotmail.com

HARROGATE AND YORKSHIRE DALES.
Vacant - contact WeBS Office.

HUDDERSFIELD & HALIFAX AREA.
Vacant - contact WeBS Office.

HUMBER ESTUARY (NORTH). Nick Cutts.
T: via WeBS Office; E: via WeBS Office

LEEDS AREA. Paul Morris. T: via WeBS Office;
E: paulr.morris8@outlook.com

SOUTH YORKSHIRE. Grant Bigg. T: 01433 639 631;
E: gr_bigg@tiscali.co.uk

WAKEFIELD AREA. Peter Smith. T: 01924 375 082;
E: via WeBS Office

Wildlife Trust
SHEFFIELD AND ROTHERHAM WILDLIFE TRUST.
(1985; 6,000).
37 Stafford Road, Sheffield, S2 2SF.
T: 0114 263 4335, (fax) 0114 263 4345;
E: mail@wildsheffield.com;
W: www.wildsheffield.com

YORKSHIRE WILDLIFE TRUST. (1946; 42,000).
1 St George's Place, Tadcaster Road, York,
YO24 1GN. T: 01904 659 570;
E: info@ywt.org.uk; W: www.ywt.org.uk

COUNTY DIRECTORY

267

SCOTLAND

The Birds of Scotland

Bird Atlas/Avifauna
The Birds of Scotland.
Ron Forrester & Ian Andrews
(Scottish Ornithologist's Club,
2007).

Bird Report
SCOTTISH BIRD REPORT
(1968-, data online), from W:
www.the-soc.org.uk/about-us/
online-scottish-bird-report

Club
SCOTTISH
ORNITHOLOGISTS' CLUB.
W: www.the-soc.org.uk
See National Directory.

Wildlife Trust
SCOTTISH WILDLIFE TRUST.
(1964; 41,000)
W: www.scottishwildlifetrust.org.uk
See National Directory.

SOC

ANGUS & DUNDEE

Bird Recorder
Jon Cook, 76 Torridon Road, Broughty Ferry,
Dundee, DD5 3JH. T: 01382 738 495;
E: 1301midget@tiscali.co.uk

Bird Report
ANGUS & DUNDEE BIRD REPORT (1985-), from the
Bird Recorder - see above.

BTO Regional Representative
ANGUS. Vacant - contact Dawn Balmer, BTO.
T: 01842 750 050; E: dawn.balmer@bto.org

Ken Slater (Regional Development Officer).
T: n/a; E: alisonslater19@aol.com

Club
ANGUS & DUNDEE BIRD CLUB. (1997; 200+).
Gus Guthrie. Address: n/a. T: 01575 574 548;
E: gusguthrie@btinternet.com;
W: www.angusbirding.com/html/adbc.html
Meetings: 7.30pm, 3rd Tuesday of the month
(Sep-Apr). Panbride Church Hall, 8 Arbroath Road,
Carnoustie, Angus DD7 6BL.

SOC TAYSIDE BRANCH. (1960's; 150).
Brian Brocklehurst. Address: n/a.
T: 01382 778 348;
E: brian.brocklehurst1@btinternet.com;
W: www.the-soc.org.uk/local-branches/tayside
Meetings: 7.30pm, 1st Thursday of the month
(Sep-Apr, 2nd Thursday in Jan). Methodist Church
Halls, 20 Marketgait, Dundee, DD1 1QR.

Ringing Group/Bird Observatory
TAY RG. W: www.tayringinggroup.org/

RSPB Local Group
DUNDEE. (1972; 100).
Darell Berthon. T: 01382 541 524;
E: darell.berthon@icloud.com;
W: www.rspb.org.uk/groups/dundee
Meetings: 7.30 pm, 2nd or 3rd Wednesday of
the month (Sep-Nov/Jan-Mar plus AGM Apr &
xmas social Dec). Methodist Church,
20 West Marketgait, Dundee, DD1 1QR.

Wetland Bird Survey (WeBS) Local Organiser
ANGUS (excl. MONTROSE BASIN).
Vacant - contact WeBS Office.

MONTROSE BASIN. Anna Cheshier.
T: via WeBS Office;
E: acheshier@scottishwildlifetrust.org.uk

ARGYLL

Bird Atlas/Avifauna
Birds of Argyll. Tristan
ap Rheinallt, Clive Craik,
P Daw, B Furness, S Petty &
D Wood (Argyll Bird Club, 2007).

The Birds of Bute

*The Birds of Bute: A Bird Atlas
and Local Avifauna.*
Ronald Forrester, Ian Hopkins
& Doug Menzies
(Buteshire NHS, 2012).

Bird Recorder
Jim Dickson, 11 Pipers Road, Cairnbaan,
Lochgilphead, Argyll PA31 8UF. T: 01546 603 967;
E: Argyllbirder@outlook.com

Assistant Recorder. Malcolm Chattwood,
1 The Stances, Kilmichael Glassary, Lochgilphead,
Argyll PA31 8QA. T: 01546 603 389;
E: abcrecorder@outlook.com
For submission of all non-rare bird records.

Bird Report
ARGYLL BIRD REPORT (1980/83-),
from Peter Hogbin, South Craleckan, Furnace,
Inveraray, PA32 8XN. E: treasurer@argyllbirdclub.org

ISLE OF MULL BIRD REPORT (2003-), from Mr Alan
Spellman, 'Maridon', Lochdon, Isle of Mull, Argyll
PA64 6AP. T: 01680 812 448;
E: mullbirds19@gmail.com; W: www.mullbirds.com

BTO Regional Representative
ARGYLL MAINLAND, BUTE & GIGHA. Nigel Scriven.
T: 07901 636 353; E: njscriven@gmail.com.

ARGYLL (MULL, COLL, TIREE & MORVERN).
Ewan Miles. T: n/a; E: ebm.gww@gmail.com

Sue Dewar (Regional Development Officer).
T: n/a; E: suedewar123@btinternet.com

ISLAY, JURA & COLONSAY. David Wood.
T: 01496 300 118; E: david.wood@rspb.org.uk

Club
ARGYLL BIRD CLUB. (1985; 270).
Anne Archer (Sec), Sealladh Breagha,
Gallanach Road, Oban, PA34 6PD. T: 01631 566 276;
E: secretary@argyllbirdclub.org;
W: www.argyllbirdclub.org
Meetings: All-day indoor meetings are held on
a Saturday in early Mar & early Nov each year -
contact/see website for details.

ISLE OF MULL BIRD CLUB. (2001; 150+).
Nancy Somerville (Sec). Address: n/a.
T: 01680 812 527; E: secretary@mullbirdclub.org.uk;
W: www.mullbirdclub.org.uk
Meetings: 7.30pm, usually 3rd Friday of the month
(Sep-Apr). Craignure Village Hall, PA65 6BE.
Contact/see website for details.

Ringing Group/Bird Observatory
TRESHNISH ISLES AUK RG.

RSPB Local Group
HELENSBURGH. (1975; 35). John Clark.
T: 01436 821 178; E: laighfield@gmail.com;
W: www.rspb.org.uk/groups/helensburgh
Meetings: 7.30 pm, 3rd Wednesday of the month
(Sep-Apr). The Guide Halls, Lower John Street,
Helensburgh.

Wetland Bird Survey (WeBS) Local Organiser
ARGYLL MAINLAND. Nigel Scriven.
T: 01505 706 652; E: njscriven@gmail.com

BUTE. Ian Hopkins. T: 01700 504 042;
E: hopkins0079@btinternet.com

ISLAY, JURA & COLONSAY. David Wood.
T: 01496 300 118; E: david.wood@rspb.org.uk

MULL. Nigel Scriven - see above.

TIREE & COLL. John Bowler. T: 01879 220 748.
E: john.bowler@rspb.org.uk

AYRSHIRE

Bird Atlas/Avifauna
*Arran Bird Atlas 2007-2012: Mapping the breeding and
wintering birds of Arran.* Jim Cassels (Arran NHS, 2014).

Bird Recorder
Fraser Simpson, 4 Inchmurrin Drive, Kilmarnock,
KA3 2JD; T: n/a; E: recorder@ayrshire-birding.org.uk

Assistant Recorder. Angus Hogg, 11 Kirkmichael Road,
Crosshill, Maybole, KA19 7RJ.
T: 01655 740 317. E: dcgos@globalnet.co.uk

Bird Report
ARRAN BIRD REPORT (1980-),
from ANHS c/o Lindsey &
Robert Marr, Tiree,
Brodick Road, Lamlash,
Isle of Arran, KA27 8JU.
E: arrannaturalhistorysociety@
gmail.com

*AYRSHIRE BIRD REPORT
(1976-),* from Anne Dick,
Rowanmyle House, Tarbolton,
Mauchline, KA5 5LU.
E: a_m_dick@hotmail.com

BTO Regional Representative
ARRAN ONLY. James Cassels (Assistant Representative).
T: 01770 860 316; E: james.cassels@virgin.net

AYRESHIRE & CUMBRAE. Vacant - contact
Dawn Balmer, BTO. T: 01842 750 050;
E: dawn.balmer@bto.org

Club
SOC AYRSHIRE BRANCH. (1962; 120).
Anne Dick, Rowanmyle House, Tarbolton,
Mauchline, KA5 5LU. T: 01292 541 981;
E: a_m_dick@btinternet.com;
W: www.the-soc.org.uk/local-branches/ayrshire
Meetings: 7.30pm, 2nd Tuesday of the month
(Sep-Apr). Monkton Community Church,
Main Street, Monkton by Prestwick, KA9 2RN.

RSPB Local Group
CENTRAL AYRSHIRE. (1978; 85).
Anne Dick. T: 01292 541 981;
E: a_m_dick@btinternet.com;
W: www.ayrshire-birding.org.uk
Meetings: 7.30pm. 3rd Monday of the month
(Sep-Apr). Newton Wallacetown Church Hall,
60 Main Street, Ayr, KA8 8EF.

NORTH AYRSHIRE. (1976; 60).
John Tedd. T: 01294 823 434;
E: johntedd48@gmail.com; W: www.narspb.org.uk
Meetings: 7.30pm, 2nd Friday of the month
(Sep-Apr). Argyle Centre, Donaldson Avenue,
Saltcoats, Ayrshire KA21 5AG.

Wetland Bird Survey (WeBS) Local Organiser
ARRAN. Jim Cassels. T: via WeBS Office;
E: jim@arranbirding.co.uk

AYRSHIRE (excl. ISLE OF CUMBRAE). Dave Grant.
T: via WeBS Office; E: daveg466@gmail.com

ISLE OF CUMBRAE. Vacant - contact WeBS Office.

SCOTLAND

BORDERS

Bird Atlas/Avifauna
The Breeding Birds of South-east Scotland:
A tetrad atlas 1988-1994. Ray Murray,
Mark Holling, Harry Dott & Peter Vandome.
(Scottish Ornithologists' Club, 1998).

Bird Recorder
Martin Moncrieff. Address: n/a; T: 01835 822 398;
E: bordersrecorder@gmail.com

David Parkinson. Address: n/a; T: 01896 822 028;
E: bordersrecorder@gmail.com

Borders Bird Report
No. 54
2017

Bird Report
BORDERS BIRD REPORT (1979-),
from Malcolm Ross,
24 Netherbank, Galashiels,
TD1 3DH.
E: eliseandmalcolm@
btinternet.com

BTO Regional Representative
Dave McGarvie. T: n/a;
E: 7askja@gmail.com

Club
SOC BORDERS BRANCH. (1980; 150).
Neil Stratton, Heiton Mains, Heiton, Kelson,
TD5 8JR. T: 01573 450 695;
E: neildstratton@btinternet.com;
W: www.the-soc.org.uk/local-branches/borders
Meetings: 7.30pm, 2nd Monday of the month
(Sep-Apr, except Jan). The Townhouse Hotel,
Market Square, Melrose, TD6 9PQ.

Ringing Group/Bird Observatory
BORDERS RG.

Wetland Bird Survey (WeBS) Local Organiser
SCOTTISH BORDERS. Andrew Bramhall.
T: 01896 755 326; E: andrewtbramhall@gmail.com

CLYDE

Bird Recorder
Recorder. Iain Gibson, 8 Kenmure View, Howwood,
Johnstone, Renfrewshire PA9 1DR.
T: 01505 705 874; E: iaingibson.soc@btinternet.com

Assistant Recorder. Val Wilson, Flat 2/1,
12 Rawcliffe Gardens, Langside, Glasgow,
G41 3DA. T: n/a; E: val.wilson38@btinternet.com

CLYDE ISLANDS (ARRAN, BUTE & CUMBRAE).
Bernard Zonfrillo, 28 Brodie Road, Glasgow,
G21 3SB. T: n/a; E: b.zonfrillo@bio.gla.ac.uk

Bird Report
CLYDE BIRDS (Clyde & Clyde Islands) (1973-),
Val Wilson, Flat 2/1 12 Rawcliffe Gardens,
Glasgow, G41 3DA. T: 0141 649 4512;
E: val.wilson38@btinternet.com

BTO Regional Representative
LANARK, RENFREW & DUNBARTON.
Gordon Brady. T: n/a;
E: gordonbrady@outlook.com

Club
SOC CLYDE BRANCH. (n/a; 300).
Ian Fulton. Address: n/a. T: 0141 773 4329;
E: clydesecretary@the-soc.org.uk;
W: www.the-soc.org.uk/ local-branches/clyde
Meetings: 7.30pm, 1st Monday of the month
(Sep-Apr, except Sep & Jan/2nd Mon). Zoology Dept,
Graham Kerr Building, University of Glasgow,
G12 8QQ [venue may change - contact/check
website for udpate].

Ringing Group/Bird Observatory
CLYDE RG.

RSPB Local Group
GLASGOW. (1972; 140).
Neil Rankine. T: 07986 580 116;
E: rspbglasgowgroupleader@gmail.com;
W: www.rspb.org.uk/groups/glasgow
Meetings: 7.30pm, 2nd Wednesday of the month
(Sep-Apr). Renfield St Stephens Church Centre,
260 Bath Street, Glasgow, G2 4JP.

LANARKSHIRE. (1976; 50).
Jim Lynch. T: 0141 583 1044;
E: contactlanarkshireRSPBgroup@gmail.com;
W: www.rspb.org.uk/groups/lanarkshire
Meetings: 7.30pm, 3rd Thursday of the month
(Sep-May). Motherwell South Parish Church,
11 Gavin Street, Motherwell, ML1 2RL.

RENFREWSHIRE. (1986; 70).
Shelley Mellor. T: n/a;
E: shemellor@gmail.com;
W: www.rspb.org.uk/groups/renfrewshire
Meetings: 7.30pm, 1st Friday of the month
(Sep-May, 2nd Friday in Jan). The McMaster Centre,
2a Donaldson Drive, Renfrew, PA4 8LX.

Wetland Bird Survey (WeBS) Local Organiser
CLYDE ESTUARY (GLASGOW, RENFREWSHIRE,
LANARKSHIRE). John Clark. T: 01436 821 178;
E: laighfield@gmail.com

GLASGOW, RENFREWSHIRE, LANARKSHIRE.
John Clark - see above.

SCOTLAND

DUMFRIES & GALLOWAY

Bird Recorder
Paul Collin, 'Gairland', Old Edinburgh Road,
Minnigaff, Newton Stewart, DG8 6PL.
T: 01671 402 861; E: pncollin@live.co.uk

Bird Report
BIRDS IN DUMFRIES & GALLOWAY (1987-), from
Peter Swan, 13 Robb Place, Castle Douglas,
DG7 1LW. T: 01556 502 144;
E: pandmswan@btinternet.com

BTO Regional Representative
DUMFRIES. Andy Riches. T: 07792 142 446 or
07570 915 630; E: slioch69@aol.com or
websdg@aol.com

KIRKCUDBRIGHT. Andrew Bielinski.
T: 01644 430 418; E: redcanoe57@gmail.com

WIGTOWN. Vacant - contact Dawn Balmer, BTO.
T: 01842 750 050; E: dawn.balmer@bto.org

Club
SOC DUMFRIES BRANCH. (1964; 75).
Lesley Creamer, Braeside, Virginhall, Thornhill,
DG3 4AD. T: 01848 330 821;
E: dumfriessecretary@the-soc.org.uk;
W: www.the-soc.org.uk/local-branches/dumfries
Meetings: 7.30pm, 2nd Wednesday of the month
(Sep-Apr). Dumfries Baptist Church Centre,
Gillbrae Rd, Dumfries, DG1 4EJ.

SOC STEWARTRY BRANCH. (1976; 80).
Joan Howie, The Wilderness, High Street,
New Galloway, Castle Douglas, DG7 3RL.
T: 01644 420 280; E: joanospreys1@btinternet.com;
W: www.the-soc.org.uk/local-branches/stewartry
Meetings: 7.30pm, 2nd Thursday of the month
(Sep-Mar) except 3rd Thursday in Sep, Mar date
will vary depending on easter. Kells School,
New Galloway, DG7 3RU.

SOC WEST GALLOWAY BRANCH. (1975; 35).
Geoff Sheppard, The Roddens, Leswalt, Stranraer,
DG9 0QR. T: 01776 870 685;
E: geoff.roddens@btinternet.com;
W: www.the-soc.org.uk/local-branches/west-galloway
Meetings: 7.30pm, usually 1st or 2nd Tuesday of
the month (Oct-Apr). Stranraer Library,
North Strand Street, Stranraer, DG9 7LD.

Ringing Group/Bird Observatory
NORTH SOLWAY RG.

RSPB Local Group
GALLOWAY. (1985; 120).
David Henshilwood. T: 01566 650 129;
E: david.henshilwood@btinternet.com;
W: www.rspb.org.uk/groups/galloway
Meetings: 7.30pm, irregular Mondays (Sep-Apr).
The Gordon Memorial Hall, adjoining St Ninian's
Scottish Episcopal Church, Whitepark Road, Castle
Douglas, DG7 1EX.

Wetland Bird Survey (WeBS) Local Organiser
AUCHENCAIRN AND ORCHARDTON BAYS.
Euan MacAlpine. T: 01556 640 244;
E: js.eamm@gmail.com

DUMFRIES AND GALLOWAY (OTHER SITES).
Andy Riches. T: 07792 142 446;
E: slioch69@aol.com

FLEET BAY. David Hawker. T: 01557 814 249;
E: davidhawker3@gmail.com

LOCH RYAN. Paul Collin. T: 01671 402 861;
E: pncollin@live.co.uk

ROUGH FIRTH. Andy Riches - see above.

SOLWAY ESTUARY (NORTH). Andy Riches - see above.

WIGTOWN BAY. Paul Collin - see above.

FIFE

Bird Atlas/Avifauna
The Fife Bird Atlas.
Norman Elkins, Jim Reid,
Allan Brown, Derek Robertson
& Anne-Marie Smout.
(privately published, 2003).

Bird Recorder
FIFE inc.OFFSHORE ISLANDS
(NORTH FORTH) -
(excl. Isle of May).
Graham Sparshott,
19 Inverewe Place, Dunfermline, KY11 8FH;
T: 07770 225 440; E: grahamspa@aol.com

ISLE OF MAY. Iain English, 19 Nethan Gate,
Chantinghall Road, Hamilton, South Lanarkshire
ML3 8NH; T: 01698 891 788; E: i.english@talk21.com

Bird Report
FIFE BIRD REPORT (1988-), from Malcolm Ware,
88 Dewar Street, Dunfermline, KY12 8AA;
E: malware74@icloud.com [from the 2014 report
(pub 2018) - only available online, free for
members W: www.fifebirdclub.org.uk].

ISLE OF MAY BIRD OBSERVATORY REPORT (1985-),
from Stuart Rivers, Flat 8 (2F2), 10 Waverley Park,
Edinburgh, EH8 8EU.
E: slr.bee-eater@blueyonder.co.uk

SCOTLAND

BTO Regional Representative
FIFE & KINROSS. Norman Elkins. T: 01334 654 348;
E: jandnelkins@btinternet.com

ISLE OF MAY. Vacant - contact Dawn Balmer, BTO.
T: 01842 750 050; E: dawn.balmer@bto.org

Club
FIFE BIRD CLUB. (1985; 200).
The Secretary. Address: n/a. T: n/a;
E: via website; W: www.fifebirdclub.org.uk
Meetings: Held regularly through the year -
contact/see website for details.
Dean Park Hotel, Kirkcaldy, KY2 6HF.

Fife Bird Club

LOTHIANS AND FIFE SWAN &
GOOSE STUDY GROUP. (1978; 12)
Allan & Lyndesay Brown, 61 Watts Gardens, Cupar,
Fife KY15 4UG. T: 01334 656 804;
E: swans@allanwbrown.co.uk

SOC FIFE BRANCH. (1950; 170).
Caroline Gordon. Address: n/a. T: 01592 750 230;
E: fifesecretary@the-soc.org.uk;
W: www.the-soc.org.uk/local-branches/fife
Meetings: 7.30pm, 2nd Wednesday of the month
(Sep-Apr). Supper Room of St Andrews Town Hall
(at corner of South Street & Queen's Gardens),
St Andrews, KY16 9TA.

Ringing Group/Bird Observatory
TAY RG. W: www.tayringinggroup.org/

ISLE OF MAY BIRD OBSERVATORY.
Mark Newell (Booking Sec). T: 07909 707971;
E: bookings@isleofmaybirdobs.org;
W: www.isleofmaybirdobs.org

Wetland Bird Survey (WeBS) Local Organiser
FIFE (excl. ESTUARIES). Allan Brown.
T: 01334 656 804; E: swansallan@gmail.com

FORTH ESTUARY (NORTH). Alastair Inglis.
T: 01383 822 115; E: aandjinglis@hotmail.com

TAY & EDEN ESTUARY. Norman Elkins.
T: 01334 654 348; E: jandnelkins@btinternet.com

FORTH

Bird Atlas/Avifauna
The Birds of Clackmannanshire. Neil Bielby,
Keith Broomfield & John Grainger
(Scottish Ornithologist's Club, 2014).

Bird Recorder
UPPER FORTH. Chris Pendlebury, 23 Ochlochy Park,
Dunblane, FK15 0DU. T: 07798 711 134;
E: chris@upperforthbirds.co.uk

Bird Report
FORTH AREA BIRD REPORT (1975-), published in
The Forth Naturalist & Historian, from
Roy Sexton, 22 Alexander Drive, Bridge of Allan,
Stirling, FK9 4QB. T: 01786 833 409;
E: RoyGravedigger@aol.com

BTO Regional Representative
CENTRAL SCOTLAND. Neil Bielby. T: 01786 823 830;
E: neil.bielby@gmail.com

Club
SOC CENTRAL SCOTLAND BRANCH. (1968; 100).
Neil Bielby, 56 Ochiltree, Dunblane, FK15 0DF.
T: 01786 823 830; E: neil.bielby@gmail.com;
W: www.the-soc.org.uk/local-branches/central-scotland
Meetings: 7.30pm, 1st Thursday of the month
(Oct-Mar). The Allan Centre, Fountain Road,
Bridge of Allan, FK9 4AT [except Jan 2020 - 7pm
Braeport Community Centre, Dunblane, FK15 0AT].

RSPB Local Group
FORTH VALLEY. (1995; 50).
Richard Knight. T: 07941 298 688;
E: richard.knight@blueyonder.co.uk;
W: www.rspb.org.uk/groups/forthvalley
Meetings: 7.30pm, 3rd Thursday of the month
(Sep-Apr). Hillpark Community Centre,
Morrison Drive, Bannockburn, Stirling, FK7 0HZ.

Wetland Bird Survey (WeBS) Local Organiser
CENTRAL SCOTLAND (excl FORTH ESTUARY).
Neil Bielby. T: 01786 823 830;
E: neil.bielby@gmail.com

FORTH ESTUARY (INNER). Michael Bell.
T: via WeBS Office; E: mvbell34@gmail.com

HIGHLAND & CAITHNESS

Bird Atlas/Avifauna
The Birds of Eigg.
John Chester
(Isle of Eigg Heritage Trust,
2013).

Skye Birds. RL McMillan.
(Skye-Birds.com, 2nd ed 2009)

*A History of Caithness Birds
1979 to 2001.* Manson Sinclair
(Privately published, 2002).

The Birds of Sutherland. Alan Vittery
(Colin Baxter Photography Ltd, 1997).

The Birds of Badenoch and Strathspey.
Roy Dennis (Colin Baxter Photography Ltd, 1995).

SCOTLAND

Bird Recorder
CAITHNESS. Sinclair Manson, 7 Duncan Street,
Thurso, KW14 7HZ. T: 01847 892 379;
E: sinclairmanson@btinternet.com

HIGHLAND [excludes Caithness, covers ROSS-SHIRE,
INVERNESS-SHIRE, SUTHERLAND, BADENOCH &
STRATHSPEY, LOCHABER, LOCHALSH & SKYE].
Peter Stronach, Clachan, Boat of Garten,
Inverness-shire PH24 3BX; T: 07470 984 937;
E: highlandrecorder@protonmail.com

Bird Report
CAITHNESS BIRD REPORT
(1983-97), no longer
published but the latest
report can be downloaded
from website
W: www.the-soc.org.uk
(local branches link)

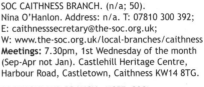

HIGHLAND BIRD REPORT
(1995-), from Lynda Graham,
9 Burn Brae Terrace,
Westhill, Inverness,
IV2 5HD.
E: ljgraham50@btinternet.com

BTO Regional Representative
CAITHNESS. Donald Omand. T: 01847 811 403;
E: achreamie@yahoo.co.uk

INVERNESS (EAST & SPEYSIDE). Hugh Insley.
T: 01463 230 652; E: hugh.insley@btinternet.com

INVERNESS (WEST). Hugh Insley - see above.

ROSS-SHIRE. Simon Cohen. T: n/a;
E: saraandsimon@hotmail.com

RUM, EIGG, CANNA & MUCK. Bob Swann.
T: 01862 894 329; E: robert.swann@homecall.co.uk

SKYE. Carol Hawley. T: n/a; E: bto.skye@gmail.com

Stephen Bentall (Regional Ambassador/Asst Rep).
E: s.bentall@talk21.com

SUTHERLAND. Lesley Mitchell. T: 07817 281 352;
E: colourflow@btinternet.com

Club
EAST SUTHERLAND BIRD GROUP. (1976; 120).
Fraser Symonds, Old Schoolhouse, Balvraid,
Dornoch, Sutherland IV25 3JB. T: 01408 633 922;
E: esbirdgroup@gmail.com; W: n/a
Meetings: 7.30pm, last Monday of the month
(Oct/Nov, Jan-Mar). Golspie Community Centre,
Back Rd, Golspie, Highland KW10 6TL.

SOC CAITHNESS BRANCH. (n/a; 50).
Nina O'Hanlon. Address: n/a. T: 07810 300 392;
E: caithnesssecretary@the-soc.org.uk;
W: www.the-soc.org.uk/local-branches/caithness
Meetings: 7.30pm, 1st Wednesday of the month
(Sep-Apr not Jan). Castlehill Heritage Centre,
Harbour Road, Castletown, Caithness KW14 8TG.

SOC HIGHLAND BRANCH. (1955; 230).
Kathy Bonniface, Alt Dubh, North End,
Tomatin, IV13 7YP. T: 01808 511 740;
E: highlandsecretary@the-soc.org.uk;
W: www.the-soc.org.uk/local-branches/highland;
W: www.highlandbirds.scot
Meetings: 7.30pm, 1st or 2nd Tuesday of the
month (Sep-Apr). Culloden Library, Keppoch Road,
Culloden, IV2 7LL.

Ringing Group/Bird Observatory
HIGHLAND RG.

RSPB Local Group
HIGHLAND. (1987; 110).
Maureen MacDonald. T: 01463 220 013,
E: macdonald456@btinternet.com;
W: www.rspb.org.uk/groups/highland
Meetings: 7.30pm, last Thursday of the month
(Sep-Apr). Greyfriars Free Church, Balloan Road,
Inverness, IV2 4PP.

Wetland Bird Survey (WeBS) Local Organiser
BADENOCH AND STRATHSPEY. Keith Duncan.
T: via WEBS Office; E: via WeBS Office

CAITHNESS. Sinclair Manson. T: 01847 892 387;
E: sinclairmanson@btinternet.com

LOCHABER. Calum Ross. T: 07729 128 144;
E: funkyhaywood@yahoo.co.uk

SKYE & LOCHALSH. Jonathan Jones.
T: 01478 611 328; E: jjonskye@yahoo.co.uk

SUTHERLAND (excl. MORAY BASIN).
Vacant - contact WeBS Office.

WEST INVERNESS AND WESTER ROSS.
Andy Douse. T: 01463 725 241;
E: andyandbronwen@gmail.com

LOTHIAN

Bird Atlas/Avifauna. See Borders.

Bird Recorder
Stephen Welch, 25 Douglas Road, Longniddry,
EH32 0LQ. T: 01875 852 802 or 07931 524 963;
E: lothianrecorder@the-soc.org.uk

Bird Report
LOTHIAN BIRD REPORT (1979-),
from Gillian Herbert, 19 Cammo Grove, Edinburgh,
EH4 8EX. E: gillianiherbert@btinternet.com

SCOTLAND

BTO Regional Representative
Alan Heavisides. T: 0131 449 3816;
E: alanheavisides@yahoo.com

Club
LOTHIANS AND FIFE SWAN AND GOOSE STUDY
GROUP. See Fife.

SOC LOTHIAN BRANCH. (1936; 500).
Alison Creamer, Waterston House, Aberlady,
East Lothian, EH32 0PY. T: 01875 871 330;
E: lothiansecretary@the-soc.org.uk;
W: www.the-soc.org.uk/local-branches/lothian
Meetings: 7.30pm, 2nd Tuesday of the month
(Sep-Apr). The Guide Hall, 33 Melville Street,
Edinburgh, EH3 7JF. [Two meetings a year are
held at Waterston House, Aberlady.]

Ringing Group/Bird Observatory
LOTHIAN RG.

RSPB Local Group
EDINBURGH. (1974; 480).
Brian Robertson. T: 01875 340 580;
E: brianedinburghrspb@btinternet.com;
W: www.rspb.org.uk/groups/edinburgh/
Meetings: 7.30pm, alternating between a Tuesday
& a Wednesday each month (Sep-Apr).
Lindsay Stewart Lecture Theatre, Napier University,
Craiglockhart Campus, Colinton Road, Edinburgh
ED14 1DJ.

Wetland Bird Survey (WeBS) Local Organiser
FORTH ESTUARY (OUTER SOUTH). Duncan Priddle.
T: 01620 827 459; E: dpriddle@eastlothian.gov.uk

LOTHIAN (excl ESTUARIES). Allan Brown.
T: 01334 656 804; E: swansallan@gmail.com

TYNINGHAME ESTUARY. Tara Sykes.
T: via WeBS Office; E: tsykes@eastlothian.gov

MORAY & NAIRN

Bird Atlas/Avifauna
The Birds of Moray and Nairn. Martin Cook
(Mercat Press, 1992).

Bird Recorder
Martin Cook, Rowanbrae, Clochan, Buckie,
Banffshire AB56 5EQ. T: 01542 850 296;
E: martin.cook99@btinternet.com

Bird Report
*BIRDS IN MORAY AND NAIRN (1999-), online since
2010)*, download from website
W: www.birdsinmorayandnairn.org

BTO Regional Representative
MORAY & NAIRN. Melvin Morrison. T: 01542 882 940;
E: wmmorrison@btinternet.com

Club
SOC MORAY BRANCH (Moray Bird Club). (2013; 60).
Alison Richie. Address: n/a. T: 01309 674 379;
E: moraysecretary@the-soc.org.uk;
W: www.the-soc.org.uk/local-branches/moray;
W: www.birdsinmorayandnairn.org
Meetings: 7.30pm, 2nd Thursday of the month
(Oct-Feb). Elgin Museum Hall, 1 High Street,
Elgin, IV30 1EQ.

Wetland Bird Survey (WeBS) Local Organiser
LOSSIE ESTUARY. Bob Proctor. T: 07976 456 657;
E: bobproctor8246@gmail.com

MORAY & NAIRN (INLAND). David Law.
T: 01463 725 200; E: jdavidlaw@btinternet.com

MORAY BASIN COAST. Bob Swann.
T: via WEBS Office;
E: robert.swann@homecall.co.uk

NORTH EAST SCOTLAND

Bird Atlas/Avifauna
*The Birds of North-East
Scotland Then and Now.*
Adam Watson & Ian Francis
(Paragon Publishing, 2012).

*The Breeding Birds of
North-East Scotland.*
Ian Francis & Martin Cook
(Scottish Ornithologist's
Club, 2011).

The Birds of North-East Scotland. ST Buckland,
MV Bell & N Picozzi (North-East Scotland
Bird Club, 1990).

Bird Recorder
Ian Broadbent, 18 Abbotshall Drive, Cults,
Aberdeen, AB15 9JD. T: 07790 562 892;
E: NEScotlandRecorder@the-soc.org.uk

Bird Report
NORTH-EAST SCOTLAND BIRD REPORT (1974-),
from Dave Gill, Quarmby, Neathermuir Road,
Maud, Peterhead, Aberdeenshire AB42 4ND.
E: davidgill1928@john-lewis.com

NORTH SEA BIRD CLUB ANNUAL REPORT (1979-),
from Andrew Thorpe, Oceanlab & Centre
for Ecology, Aberdeen University, Newburgh,
Aberdeenshire AB41 6AA. E: nsbc@abdn.ac.uk

BTO Regional Representative
ABERDEEN. Moray Souter. T: 01358 788 828;
E: bto_aber_rr@btintrnet.com

KINCARDINE & DEESIDE. Graham Cooper.
T: 01339 882 706; E: grm.cooper@btinternet.com

SCOTLAND

Club
SOC NORTH-EAST SCOTLAND BRANCH. (1956; 150).
John Wills, Bilbo, Monymusk, Inverurie,
Aberdeenshire AB51 7HA. T: 01467 651 296;
E: grampian.secretary@the-soc.org.uk;
W: www.the-soc.org.uk/local-branches/north-east-scotland
Meetings: 7.30pm, 1st Monday of the month
(Oct-Apr). Sportsman's Club, 11 Queens Road,
Aberdeen, AB15 4YL.

Ringing Group/Bird Observatory
GRAMPIAN RG.
W: http://grampianringing.blogspot.co.uk

RSPB Local Group
ABERDEEN & DISTRICT. (1975; 260).
Mark Sullivan. T: 01224 861 446;
E: geolbird_abz@btinternet.com;
W: www.rspb.org.uk/groups/aberdeen
Meetings: 7.30pm, 2nd Tuesday of the month
(Oct-Apr). Aberdeen University, Main Lecture
Theatre, Zoology Building, Tillydrone Ave,
Aberdeen, AB24 2TZ.

Wetland Bird Survey (WeBS) Local Organiser
ABERDEENSHIRE. Moray Souter. T: 01358 788 828;
E: bto_aber_rr@btinternet.com

ORKNEY

Bird Atlas/Avifauna
The Birds of Orkney. C Booth, M Cuthbert &
P Reynolds. (The Orkney Press, 1984).

Bird Recorder
Russ Neave & Emma Neave-Webb, East Thrave
Cottage, Sanday, Orkney KW17 2AZ.
T: 01857 600 272; E: orkbird.recorder@gmail.com

Bird Report
*NORTH RONALDSAY BIRD OBSERVATORY BIRD
REPORT (2011-), from* Alison Duncan, NRBO,
Twingness, North Ronaldsay, Orkney KW17 2BE.
T: 01857 633 200; E: enquiries@nrbo.org.uk

ORKNEY BIRD REPORT (1974-), from Jim Williams,
Fairholm, Finstown, Orkney KW17 2EQ.
E: jim.geniefea@btinternet.com

BTO Regional Representative
Colin Corse. T: 01856 874 484;
E: ccorse@btinternet.com

Club
SOC ORKNEY BRANCH. (1993; n/a).
Helen Aiton. Address: n/a. T: 01856 751 482;
E: helendavidaiton@hotmail.co.uk;
W: www.the-soc.org.uk/local-branches/orkney
Meetings: 7.30pm, 1st Thursday of the month
(Oct & Nov) and 2nd Thursday of the month
(Feb & Mar). St Magnus Centre, Kirkwall.

Ringing Group/Bird Observatory
ORKNEY RG. W: www.orkneyrg.co.uk

SULE SKERRY RG.

NORTH RONALDSAY BIRD
OBSERVATORY.
Alison Duncan (Warden),
Twingness, North Ronaldsay,
KW17 2BE. T: 01857 633 200;
E: enquiries@nrbo.org.uk;
W: www.nrbo.co.uk

RSPB Local Group
ORKNEY. (1985; 300/area).
Dick Matson. T: 01856 751 426;
E: P.wilson410@btinternet.com; W: n/a
Meetings: Meetings advertised in newsletter and
local press, or phone/e-mail for details.

Wetland Bird Survey (WeBS) Local Organiser
ORKNEY. Sarah Money. T: via WeBS Office;
E: via WeBS Office.

OUTER HEBRIDES

Bird Recorder
Yvonne Benting, Suthainn, Askernish, South Uist,
HS8 5SY. T: 07501 332 803;
E: recorder@outerhebridesbirds.org.uk
W: www.outerhebridesbirds.org.uk

Bird Report
OUTER HEBRIDES BIRD REPORT (1997-), from
bird recorder - see above.

BTO Regional Representative
BENBECULA & THE UISTS. Yvonne Benting.
T: 07501 332 803; E: uistbto@gmail.com

LEWIS & HARRIS. Chris Reynolds.
T: 01851 672 376 (summer) / 01202 854 629
(rest of year); E: cmreynolds@btinternet.com

Ringing Group/Bird Observatory
SHIANTS AUK RG.

Wetland Bird Survey (WeBS) Local Organiser
HARRIS AND LEWIS. Yvonne Benting.
T: 01878 700 849 E: uistbto@gmail.com

UISTS AND BENBECULA. Yvonne Benting - see above.

PERTH & KINROSS

Bird Recorder
Scott Paterson, 12 Ochil View, Kinross, KY13 8TN.
T: 01577 864 248 & 07501 640 518;
E: pkrecorder@the-soc.org.uk

Bird Report
PERTH & KINROSS BIRD REPORT (1974-), digital
reports from the Bird Recorder - see above.

SCOTLAND

BTO Regional Representative
PERTHSHIRE. Michael Bell. T: 01786 822 153;
E: mvbell34@gmail.com

Club
PERTHSHIRE SOCIETY OF NATURAL SCIENCE
(1867; Ornithological Section: 25).
Jeanne Freeman, 14 St Mary's Drive, Perth,
PH2 7BY. T: 01738 620 914;
E: birdsatpsns@btinternet.com;
W: www.psns.org.uk
Meetings: 7.30pm, Wednesday - dates vary
(Oct-Mar), Sandeman Room, AK Bell Library,
17 York Place, Perth, PH2 8EP - contact/see
website for details.

Wetland Bird Survey (WeBS) Local Organiser
LOCH LEVEN. Jeremy Squire. T: via WeBS Office;
E: jeremy.squire@snh.gov.uk

PERTH AND KINROSS (INLAND). Michael Bell.
T: via WeBS Office; E: mvbell34@gmail.com

TAY & EDEN ESTUARY. See Fife.

SHETLAND

Bird Atlas/Avifauna
The Birds of Shetland.
P Harvey, M Pennington,
K Osborn, R Riddington,
P Ellis, M Huebeck & D Okill
(Christopher Helm, 2004).

Bird Recorder
FAIR ISLE. David Parnaby,
Fair Isle Bird Observatory,
Fair Isle, Shetland, ZE2 9JU.
T: 01595 760 258;
E: fibo@btconnect.com

[If the landline is unavailable use the e-mail to make contact].

SHETLAND. Rob Fray, The Meadows, Bakkasetter,
Quendale, Shetland ZE2 9JD. T: 07775 647 463;
E: recorder@shetlandbirdclub.co.uk

Bird Report
*FAIR ISLE BIRD OBSERVATORY
REPORT (1949-),* from
Susannah Parnaby, Fair Isle
Bird Observatory, Fair Isle,
Shetland, ZE2 9JU.
T: 01595 760 258;
E: fibo@btconnect.com

*SHETLAND BIRD REPORT
(1969-),* from Bird Recorder
- see above.
E: reports@shetlandbirdclub.co.uk

BTO Regional Representative
Dave Okill. T: 01595 880 450;
E: david@auroradesign.plus.com

Club
SHETLAND BIRD CLUB. (1973; 200+).
Helen Moncrieff (Sec), Scholland, Virkie, ZE3 9JL.
T: 01950 460 249;
E: secretary@shetlandbirdclub.co.uk;
W: www.shetlandbirdclub.co.uk
Meetings: Occasional - contact/see website for
details.

Ringing Group/Bird Observatory
SHETLAND RG.

FAIR ISLE BIRD OBSERVATORY.
David Parnaby (Warden), Fair Isle Bird
Observatory, Fair Isle, Shetland ZE2 9JU.
T: 01595 760 258;
E: fibo@btconnect.com;
W: www.fairislebirdobs.co.uk

*Due to the fire that destroyed the Observatory in
March 2019 accommodation will not be available
for the forseeable future, check out the
Observatory website for alternative options.
If the Observatory landline is unavailable use
the e-mail address (or write) to make contact.*

Wetland Bird Survey (WeBS) Local Organiser
SHETLAND. Paul Harvey. T: 01595 694 688;
E: paul@shetlandamenity.org

WALES

Bird Report
The WELSH BIRD REPORT is published in 'BIRDS IN WALES', from the Welsh Ornithological Society, available to members of WOS for downloading
W: www.birdsin.wales/what-we-do/our-journals/

BTO Wales Officer
John Lloyd. T: 01550 750 202;
E: johnvlloyd2000@gmail.com

Club
WELSH ORNITHOLOGICAL SOCIETY.
See National Directory.

EASTERN AREA OF WALES

Bird Atlas/Avifauna
The Birds of Radnorshire. Peter Jennings (Fidedula Books, 2014).

The Birds of Gwent. WA Venables, AD Baker, RM Clarke, C Jones, JMS Lewis & SJ Tyler (Christopher Helm, 2008).

The Birds of Montgomeryshire. B Holt & G Williams (privately published, 2008).

Bird Recorder
BRECONSHIRE. Andrew King, Heddfan, Pennorth, Brecon, Powys LD3 7EX. T: 01874 658 351; E: andy@breconbirds.wales

GWENT. Darryl Spittle. Address: n/a. T: n/a; E: countyrecorder@gwentbirds.org.uk

MONTGOMERYSHIRE. Mike Haigh, Tynewydd Ketch, Llanfyllin, Powys SY22 5EU. T: 01691 648 746; E: montbird@gmail.com

RADNORSHIRE (VC43). Pete Jennings, The Old Farmhouse, Choulton, Lydbury North, Shropshire SY7 8AH. T: 01588 680 631; E: radnorshirebirds@hotmail.com

Bird Report
BRECONSHIRE BIRDS (1962-), from Wildlife Trust of South and West Wales, The Nature Centre, Fountain Road, Tondu, Bridgend, Mid-Glamorgan CF32 0EH. T: 01656 724 100; E: info@welshwildlife.org

GWENT BIRD REPORT (1973-), from Andrew Cormack, 29 Chestnut Drive, Abergavenny, Monmouthshire NP7 5JZ. E: treasurer@gwentbirds.org.uk

MONTGOMERYSHIRE BIRD REPORT (1981/82-), from 2013 report, now available as a download from montgomerybirdblog.blogspot.co.uk/p/county-reports.html

BTO Regional Representative
BRECKNOCK. Andrew King. T: 01874 658 351; E: andy@breconbirds.wales

GWENT. Richard Clarke. T: n/a; E: chykembro2@aol.com

MONTGOMERY. Jane Kelsall. T: 01970 872 019; E: janekelsall@phonecoop.coop

RADNOR. Carlton Parry. T: 01597 824 050; E: cj.parry@tiscali.co.uk

Club
GWENT ORNITHOLOGICAL SOCIETY. (1964; 420). Catherine Gregory (Sec). Address: n/a. T: n/a; E: secretary@gwentbirds.org.uk; W: www.gwentbirds.org.uk
Meetings: 7.30pm, 1st & 3rd Saturdays of the month (Sep-Apr). Goytre Village Hall, Newtown Road, Penperlleni, Pontypool, NP4 0AW.

MONTGOMERYSHIRE WILDLIFE TRUST BIRD GROUP. (1997; 110). Sally Davies (Sec). Address: n/a.
T: 01938 580 278; E: montbird@gmail.com; W: www.montgomerybirdblog.blogspot.co.uk
Meetings: 7.30pm, 3rd Wednesday of the month (Sep-Apr). Welshpool Methodist Hall, 13 High Street, Welshpool, Powys SY21 7JP.

RADNORSHIRE BIRD GROUP. (1988; 75). Pete Jennings, The Old Farmhouse, Choulton, Lydbury North, Shropshire SY7 8AH.
T: 01588 680 631; W: n/a; E: radnorshirebirds@hotmail.com
Co-ordinates bird recording and surveys in the county through the Bird Recorder.

Ringing Group/Bird Observatory
GOLDCLIFF RG.

LLANGORSE RG.

MID-WALES RG.

Wetland Bird Survey (WeBS) Local Organiser
BRECONSHIRE. Andrew King. T: 01874 658 351; E: andy@breconbirds.wales

GWENT (excl. SEVERN ESTUARY). Al Venables. T: via WeBS Office; E: via WeBS Office

WALES

MONTGOMERYSHIRE. Jane Kelsall.
T: 01970 832 625; E: janekelsall@phonecoop.coop

RADNORSHIRE. Pete Jennings. T: 01597 811 522;
E: ppjennings@hotmail.co.uk

SEVERN ESTUARY (NORTH (GWENT/GLAMORGAN).
Al Venables - see above.

Wildlife Trust
GWENT WILDLIFE TRUST. (1963; 10,000).
Seddon House, Dingestow, Monmouth, NP25 4DY.
T: 01600 740 600, (fax) 01600 740 299;
E: info@gwentwildlife.org;
W: www.gwentwildlife.org

MONTGOMERYSHIRE WILDLIFE TRUST. (1982; 3,000).
42 Broad St, Welshpool, Powys, SY21 7RR.
T: 01938 555 654, (fax) 01938 556 161;
E: info@montwt.co.uk; W: www.montwt.co.uk

RADNORSHIRE WILDLIFE TRUST. (1987; 1,000).
Warwick House, High St, Llandrindod Wells, Powys
LD1 6AG. T: 01597 823 298, (fax) 01597 823 274;
E: info@rwtwales.org; W: www.rwtwales.org

NORTHERN AREA OF WALES

Bird Atlas/Avifauna
*Scarce and Rare Birds in
North Wales: historic records
up to and including 2016.*
Robin Sandham (privately
published, 2018).

Birds of Caernarfonshire.
Rhion Pritchard (Cambrian
Ornithological Society, 2017).

*The Breeding Birds of
North Wales.* Anne Brenchley, Geoff Gibbs,
Rhion Pritchard & Ian M Spence (Liverpool
University Press, 2013).

The Birds of Meirionnydd. Rhion Pritchard
(Cambrian Ornithological Society, 2012).

The Birds of Anglesey. Peter Hope Jones &
P Whalley (Menter Mon, 2004).

Bird Recorder
ANGLESEY. David Wright. Graig Eithin, Mynydd
Bodafon, Llanerchymedd, Anglesey LL71 8BG.
T: 07973 568 096; E: bodafondavid@yahoo.co.uk

CAERNARFONSHIRE. Rhion Pritchard, Pant Afonig,
Hafod Lane, Bangor, Gwynedd LL57 4BU.
T: 01248 671 301;
E: rhion678pritchard@gmail.com

DENBIGHSHIRE. Ian M Spence, 43 Blackbrook,
Sychdyn, Mold, Flintshire CH7 6LT.
T: 01352 750118; E: ian.spence@zen.co.uk

FLINTSHIRE. Ian M Spence - see above.

MEIRIONNYDD. Jim Dustow, Afallon, 7 Glan y Don,
Rhiwbryfdir, Blaenau Ffestiniog, Gwynedd LL41 3LW.
T: 01766 830 976; E: meinirowen@live.co.uk

Bird Report
*BARDSEY BIRD AND FIELD OBSERVATORY REPORT
(1953-),* from Jo Jones, 70 Newmarket Road,
Burwell, Cambridgeshire CB25 0AE.
E: jojones14@btinternet.com

CAMBRIAN BIRD REPORT (NW Wales) (1953-), from
Geoff Gibbs, Fronwen, Llanfairfechan, LL33 0ET.
T: 01248 681 936; E: geoffgibbs058@gmail.com

NORTH-EAST WALES BIRD REPORT (2004-), from
Ian Spence, 43 Blackbrook, Sychdyn, Mold,
Flintshire CH7 6LT. E: ian.spence@zen.co.uk

*WREXHAM BIRDWATCHERS' SOCIETY ANNUAL
REPORT (1981-),* from Marian Williams,
10 Lake View, Gresford, Wrexham, LL12 8PU.
T: 01978 854 633

BTO Regional Representative
ANGLESEY. Ian Hawkins. T: 01248 430 590;
E: ian.hawkins590@btinternet.com

CAERNARFON. Geoff Gibbs. T: 01248 681 936;
E: geoffgibbs058@gmail.com

Rhion Pritchard (Assistant Representative).
T: 01248 671 301;
E: rhion678pritchard@btinternet.com

CLWYD EAST. Anne Brenchley. T: 01352 750 118;
E: annebrenchley@imsab.myzen.co.uk

Jane Hemming (Assistant Representative). T: n/a;
E: jane@hemming.myzen.co.uk

CLWYD WEST. Mel ab Owain. T: 01745 826 528;
E: melabowain@gmail.com

Glen Heaton (Assistant Representative). T: n/a;
E: n/a.

MEIRIONNYDD. Dave Anning. T: n/a;
E: davidanning1@btinternet.com

Club
BANGOR BIRD GROUP. (1947; 70).
Ian Wright (Membership Sec). Address: n/a.
T: 01407 860 471; E: bangorbirdgroup@gmail.com;
W: https://birdsin.wales/counties/bird-clubs/
bangor-bird-group/

Meetings: 7.30pm, every
Wednesday, Autumn
& Spring terms (Oct-Mar).
Room 101, Alun Bldg.,
The Management Centre,
College Road, Bangor,
LL57 2DG.

WALES

BIRD RECORDING NORTH WALES

CAMBRIAN ORNITHOLOGICAL SOCIETY. (1952; 160).
Julian Thompson (Sec), Pensychnant, Sychnant Pass,
Conwy, LL32 8BJ. T: 01492 592 595;
E: julian.pensychnant@btinternet.com;
W: www.brnw.cymru/cos
Meetings: 7.30pm, 1st Friday of the month
(Sep-May). Pensychnant Centre, Sychnant Pass,
Conwy, LL32 8BJ.

CLWYD BIRD RECORDING GROUP (a committee
of local birders who produce the North-East
Wales Bird Report). Giles Pepler (Sec), Rosedan,
Coleshill Fechan, Bagillt, Flintshire CH6 6DH.
T: 01352 732 876; E: gilesp64@gmail.com;
W: www.brnw.cymru/cbrg
Meetings: No indoor meetings held.

CLWYD ORNITHOLOGICAL SOCIETY. (1956; 45).
Angela Ross, 25 Leonard Avenue, Rhyl, LL18 4LN.
T: 01745 338 493;
E: angela.ross@talktalk.net; W: n/a.
Meetings: 7.30pm, last Tuesday of the month
(Sep-Nov & Jan-Apr). Rhuddlan Community Centre,
Parliament Street, Rhuddlan, LL18 5AW.

DEESIDE NATURALISTS' SOCIETY. (1973; 400+).
The Secretary. Address: n/a. T: n/a;
E: secretary@deenats.org.uk;
W: www.deenats.org.uk
Meetings: 7.30pm, 3rd Friday of the month
(Sep-Mar). Connah's Quay Community Centre,
Tuscan Way, off Chapel Street, Connah's Quay,
CH5 4DZ.

WREXHAM BIRDWATCHERS' SOCIETY. (1974; 90).
Kevin Smith. Address: n/a. T: 01978 354 551;
E: kevjsmith3@hotmail.com;
W: https://birdsin.wales/counties/bird-clubs/
Meetings: 7.30pm, 1st Friday of the month
(Sep-Apr). Gresford Memorial Hall, High Street,
Gresford, Wrexham, LL12 8PS.

Ringing Group/Bird Observatory
BARDSEY BIRD OBSERVATORY.

Steve Stansfield
(Warden), Cristin,
Bardsey Island,
Pwllheli, Gwynedd
LL53 8DE.
T: 07855 264 151;
E: warden@bbfo.org.uk; W: www.bbfo.org.uk

Alicia Normand (Booking Sec), 46 Maudlin Drive,
Teignmouth, Devon TQ14 8SB. T: 01626 773 908;
E: stay@bbfo.org.uk

CHESHIRE SWAN GROUP.
W: http://cheshireswanstudygroup.wordpress.com

MERSEYSIDE RG. W: www.merseyiderg.org.uk

SCAN RG.

RSPB Local Group
NORTH WALES. (1986; n/a).
John Beagan. T: 01492 531 409;
E: colwynbooks@waitrose.com;
W: www.rspb.org.uk/groups/northwales
Meetings: 7.30pm, 3rd Friday of the month
(Sep-Apr). St Davids Church Hall, Penrhyn Bay,
Llandudno, Conwy, LL30 3NT.

Wetland Bird Survey (WeBS) Local Organiser
ANGLESEY. Ian Sims. T: 01248 421 100;
E: ian.sims@rspb.org.uk

CAERNARFONSHIRE.
Rhion Pritchard. T: via WeBS Office;
E: rhion678pritchard@gmail.com

CLWYD (COASTAL).
Henry Cook. T: 07976 377 215;
E: henerz1@yahoo.co.uk

CLWYD (INLAND). Vacant - contact WeBS Office.

DEE ESTUARY. Mr CE Wells - see Lancashire.

FORYD BAY. Simon Hugheston-Roberts.
T: 01248 385 500; E: simon.hr@btinternet.com

MEIRIONNYDD (ESTUARIES). Jim Dustow.
T: 01691 870 278; E: meinirowen@live.co.uk

MEIRIONNYDD (OTHER SITES). Jim Dustow - see above.

Wildlife Trust
NORTH WALES WILDLIFE TRUST. (1963; 6,000).
Llys Garth, Garth Road, Bangor, Gwynedd LL57 2RT.
T: 01248 351 541, (fax) 01248 353 192;
E: nwwt@wildlifetrustswales.org;
W: www.northwaleswildlifetrust.org.uk

SOUTHERN AREA OF WALES

Bird Atlas/Avifauna
Birds of Glamorgan. Clive Hurford &
Peter Lansdown (Privately Published, 1995).

An Atlas of Breeding Birds in West Glamorgan.
DK Thomas (Gower Ornithological Society, 1992).

Bird Recorder
EAST GLAMORGAN. Phil Bristow, 2 Forest Oak Close,
Cyncoed, Cardiff CF23 6QN. T: 07769 973 890;
E: phlbrstw@gmail.com

WEST GLAMORGAN. Rob Taylor. Address: n/a.
T: n/a. E: robthebirder@gmail.com

WALES

Bird Report
EAST GLAMORGAN BIRD REPORT (1985-), from
John Wilson, 122 Westbourne Road, Penarth, Vale of
Glamorgan, CF64 3HH. E: johndw1948@gmail.com

GOWER BIRDS (1968-), from Jeremy Douglas-Jones,
14 Alder Way, West Cross, Swansea, SA3 5PD.
T: 01792 551 331; E: jeremy@douglas-jones.biz

BTO Regional Representative
EAST GLAMORGAN (MID). Wayne Morris.
T: 01443 430 284; E: eastglambto@gmail.com

Daniel Jenkins-Jones (Assistant Representative).
T: 01292 062 1394; E: jenkinsjones@btinternet.com

GLAMORGAN (SOUTH). Wayne Morris/
Daniel Jenkins-Jones - see above.

GLAMORGAN (WEST). Lyndon Jeffery.
T: 01792 874 337; E: norma.jeffery@virginmedia.com

Rob Jones (Assistant Representative). T: n/a;
E: rob.jones27@outlook.com

Club
CARDIFF NATURALISTS' SOCIETY. (1867; 150).
Mike Dean (Sec), 36 Rowan Way, Lisvane, Cardiff,
CF14 0TD. T: n/a;
E: secretary@cardiffnaturalists.org.uk;
W: www.cardiffnaturalists.org.uk
Meetings: 7.30pm, various evenings (Sep-May).
Room 0.23 (ground floor) of the Cardiff School of
Management Building, Llandaff Campus,
Western Ave, Cardiff, CF5 2YB.

GLAMORGAN BIRD CLUB.
(1990; 400).
Alan Rosney
(Membership Sec),
10 Parc-y-Nant, Nantgarw,
RCT, CF15 7TJ.
T: 01443 841 555 &
07906 558 489;
E: alanrosney@gmail.com;
W: www.glamorganbirds.org.uk
Meetings: 7.45pm, generally 1st Tuesday of the
month (Oct-Apr). Kenfig NNR Visitor Centre,
Ton Kenfig, Bridgend, Mid Glamorgan CF33 4PT.

GOWER ORNITHOLOGICAL
SOCIETY. (1956; 100).
Jeremy Douglas-Jones (Sec),
14 Alder Way, West Cross,
Swansea, SA3 5PD.
T: 01792 551 331;
E: jeremy@douglas-jones.biz;
W: www.glamorganbirds.org.uk
Meetings: 7.15pm, generally held on Fridays
(Sep-Mar, not Dec). The Environment Centre,
Pier Street, Swansea, SA1 1RY. Contact/see
website for details.

Ringing Group/Bird Observatory
FLAT HOLM RG.

GOWER RG.
W: http://gowerbirdringinggroup.blogspot.co.uk

KENFIG RG. W: http://kenfigrg.blogspot.co.uk

RSPB Local Group
CARDIFF & DISTRICT. (1973; n/a).
Huw Moody-Jones. T: 01446 760 757;
E: huwmoodyjones@hotmail.com;
W: www.RSPB.org.uk/groups/cardiff
Meetings: 7.30pm, 2nd Friday of the month
(Sep-May). Llandaff Parish Hall, (next car park off)
High St, Llandaff, Cardiff, CF5 2DX.

WEST GLAMORGAN. (1985; 180).
Maggie Cornelius. T: 01792 229 244;
E: RSPBwglamgrp@gmail.com;
W: www.rspb.org.uk/groups/westglamorgan
Meetings: Contact/see website for details.
Environment Centre, Pier Street, Swansea,
SA1 1RY.

Wetland Bird Survey (WeBS) Local Organiser
BURRY INLET (NORTH). Lyndon Jeffery.
T: 01792 874 337; E: norma.jeffery@virginmedia.com

EAST GLAMORGAN. Daniel Jenkins-Jones.
T: 02920 353 011; E: eastglamwebs@gmail.com

SEVERN ESTUARY (NORTH (GWENT/GLAMORGAN).
See Eastern Area.

WEST GLAMORGAN. Lyndon Jeffery - see above.

Wildlife Trust
WILDLIFE TRUST OF SOUTH AND WEST WALES.
(2002; 11,000).
The Nature Centre, Fountain Road, Tondu,
Bridgend, Mid-Glamorgan CF32 0EH.
T: 01656 724 100, fax 01656 726 980;
E: info@welshwildlife.org;
W: www.welshwildlife.org

WESTERN AREA OF WALES

Bird Atlas/Avifauna
Birds of Ceredigion.
Hywel Roderick & Peter Davis
(Wildlife Trust, S & SW Wales,
2010).

Atlas of Breeding Birds in
Pembrokeshire 2003-07.
Annie Haycock et al
(Pembrokeshire Bird Group,
2009).

Birds of Pembrokeshire.
Jack Donovan &
Graham Rees (Dyfed Wildlife Trust, 1994).

WALES

Bird Recorder
CARMARTHENSHIRE. Gary Harper, Maesteg,
Capel Seion, Drefach, Llanelli, SA14 7BS.
T: 01269 831 496 & 07748 970 124;
E: gary.harper3@gmail.com

CEREDIGION. Russell Jones, Bron y Gan, Talybont,
Ceredigion SY24 5ER. T: 07753 774 891;
E: russell.jones@rspb.org.uk

PEMBROKESHIRE. Joint Recorder, Rarities.
Jon Green, Crud Yr Awel, Bowls Road, Blaenporth,
Ceredigion SA43 2AR. T: 01239 811 561;
E: jonrg@tiscali.co.uk

PEMBROKESHIRE. Joint Recorder. Stephen Berry,
The Old Mill, Llanychaer, Pembrokeshire SA65 9TB.
T: 01348 875 604; E: stepheneb@icloud.com

Bird Report
CARMARTHENSHIRE BIRDS (1982-), from
Wendell Thomas, 48 Glebe Road, Loughhor,
Swansea, SA4 6QD. E: wendellthomas57@gmail.com

CEREDIGION BIRD REPORT
(1982/85), from Ynys-hir RSPB,
Naturequest in Market Hall,
Aberystwyth & Teifi Marshes
Nature Reserve Centre - or
by post from Arfon Williams,
Abernaint, Ffarmers, Llanwrda,
Carmarthenshire SA19 8JR.

Ceredigion Bird Report
2017

PEMBROKESHIRE BIRD REPORT
(1981-), download from
website -
http://pembrokeshirebirdgroup.blogspot.com/
p/reports.html

SKOKHOLM BIRD REPORT (1981-), download from
website - https://www.welshwildlife.org/
about-us/skokholm-reports/

BTO Regional Representative
CARDIGAN. Moira Convery. T: 01970 612 998;
E: moira.convery@gmail.com

Naomi Davis (Assistant Representative). T: n/a;
E: naomi.davis25@gmail.com

CARMARTHEN. Vacant - contact Dawn Balmer,
BTO. T: 01842 750 050; E: dawn.balmer@bto.org

Danielle Rouse (Assistant Representative). T: n/a;
E: danrouse@live.co.uk

PEMBROKESHIRE. Bob Haycock. T: 01834 891 667;
E: bob.rushmoor1@tiscali.co.uk

Annie Haycock (Assistant Representative). T: n/a;
E: rushmoor1@tiscali.co.uk

Club
CARMARTHENSHIRE BIRD CLUB.
(2003; 140+).
Sian Rees-Harper (Sec), Maesteg,
Capel Seion, Drefach, Llanelli,
SA14 7BS. T: 01269 831 496;
E: gary.harper3@gmail.com;
W: www.carmarthenshirebird.club
Meetings: 7.30pm, on a
Wednesday (Oct-Mar).
Llanelli Cricket Club, Stradey Park, Llanelli,
SA15 4BT. Contact/see website for details.

PEMBROKESHIRE BIRD GROUP. (1983; 60).
Peter Royle (Sec), Orlandon Kilns, St. Brides,
Haverfordwest, SA62 3AP. T: 01646 636 970;
E: pdroyle@orlandon.co.uk;
W: http://pembrokeshirebirdgroup.blogspot.co.uk/
Meetings: No indoor meetings held.

Ringing Group/Bird Observatory
SKOKHOLM RG.

PEMBROKESHIRE RG.
W: http://birdringingpembrokeshire.blogspot.com/

TEIFI RG. W: www.teifimarshbirds.blogspot.co.uk

SKOKHOLM BIRD OBSERVATORY.
Richard Brown/Giselle Eagle (Wardens),
The Welsh Wildlife Centre, Cilgerran, Cardigan
SA43 2TB; T: 01239 621 212 (wardens: 07971 114 303);
E: skokholmwarden@gmail.com;
W: http://skokholm.blogspot.co.uk
Accommodation: T: 01656 724 100;
E: islands@welshwildlife.org
W: www.welshwildlife.org/staying-on-skokholm/

Wetland Bird Survey (WeBS) Local Organiser
CARMARTHENSHIRE. Vacant - contact WeBS Office.

CEREDIGION (incl DYFI ESTUARY). Russell Jones.
T: 07753 774 891; E: russell.jones@rspb.org.uk

PEMBROKESHIRE. Annie Haycock.
T: via WeBS Office;
E: annie@rushmoorphotos.co.uk

Wildlife Trust
WILDLIFE TRUST OF SOUTH AND WEST WALES.
See Southern Area of Wales.

CHANNEL ISLANDS

ALDERNEY

Atlas/Avifauna
The Birds of Alderney.
Jeremy G Sanders.
(Privately Published, 2007).

Bird Recorder
John Horton, c/o Alderney
Bird Observatory - see below.

BTO Regional Representative
Chris Mourant. T: n/a;
E: chris.mourant@yahoo.co.uk

Ringing Group/Bird Observatory
ALDERNEY BIRD OBSERVATORY.
The Warden, Alderney Bird Observatory,
The Nunnery, Longis Road, Alderney, GY9 3YB.
T: 01481 822 954 or 07815 549 191;
E: abo.warden@outlook.com;
W: www.alderneybirdobservatory.org

Wetland Bird Survey (WeBS) Local Organiser
Alderney Wildlife Trust RAMSAR Officer.
T: 07781 423 635; E: ramsar@alderneywildlife.org

Wildlife Trust
ALDERNEY WILDLIFE TRUST. (2002)
Slades, 48 Victoria Street, St Anne, Alderney
GY9 3TA. T/fax: 01481 822 935;
E: info@alderneywildlife.org;
W: www.alderneywildlife.org

GUERNSEY

Bird Atlas/Avifauna
*Birds of the Bailiwick: Guernsey, Alderney, Sark
and Herm.* Duncan Spencer & Paul Hillion
(Jill Vaudin Publishing 2011).

Bird Recorder
Mark Lawlor, St Etienne, Les Effards, St Sampsons,
Guernsey GY2 4YN. T: 07781 122 313;
E: mplawlor@cwgsy.net

Bird Report
GUERNSEY BIRD REPORT (1992-), download from
website: W: www.guernseybirds.org.gg

BTO Regional Representative
Chris Mourant. T: n/a;
E: chris.mourant@yahoo.co.uk

Club
LA SOCIÉTÉ GUERNESIAISE. (1882).
Secretary, La Société Guernesiaise, Candie Gardens,
St Peter Port, Guernsey GY1 1UG.
T: 01481 725 093; E: societe@cwgsy.net;
W: www.societe.org.gg

Chris Mourant (Sec, Ornithology Section).
Address: n/a. T: 07911 130 415;
E: ornithology@societe.org.gg;
W: www.guernseybirds.org.gg
Meetings: (Ornithology Section). 7.30pm,
1st Thursday of the month. Frossard Theatre,
Candie - address, as above.

RSPB Local Group
GUERNSEY BAILIWICK. (1975; 200+).
Tim Hughes. T: n/a;
E: tchughes@hotmail.co.uk;
W: www.rspbguernsey.co.uk
Meetings: Several during the year - contact/
see website for details. La Villette Hotel,
St Martins, Guernsey GY4 6QG.

Wetland Bird Survey (WeBS) Local Organiser
GUERNSEY COAST. Mary Simmons.
T: 01481 256 016; E: msim@cwgsy.net

JERSEY

Bird Recorder
Tony Paintin, 1 Ficquet House, La Verte Rue,
St Brelade, Jersey JE3 8EL. T: 01534 741 928;
E: cavokjersey@hotmail.com

Bird Report
JERSEY BIRD REPORT (1991-), from Ornithology
Section, La Société Jersiaise - see below.

BTO Regional Representative
Tony Paintin. T: 01534 741 928;
E: cavokjersey@hotmail.com

Club
SOCIÉTIÉ JERSIAISE. (1873).
La Société Jersiaise, 7 Pier Road, St Helier,
Jersey JE2 4XW. T: 01534 758 314;
E: info@societe-jersiaise.org;
W: www.societe-jersiaise.org

Roger Noel (Sec, Ornithology Section).
Address: n/a. T: n/a;
E: rogernoel1@googlemail.com
Meetings: (Ornithology Section). 8pm, 1st & 3rd
Thursdays of the month. Arthur Mourant Room -
address as above.

Wetland Bird Survey (WeBS) Local Organiser
JERSEY COAST. Roger Noel. T: 01534 481 409;
E: rogernoel1@googlemail.com

JERSEY INLAND. Vacant - contact WeBS Office.

NORTHERN IRELAND

Bird Recorder
George Gordon, 2 Brooklyn Avenue, Bangor,
Co Down BT20 5RB. T: 028 9145 5763;
E: nimbus10111947@gmail.com

Bird Report
IRISH BIRD REPORT (1953-), included in Irish Birds,
see BirdWatch Ireland in Republic of Ireland.

COPELAND BIRD OBSERVATORY REPORT, from
David Galbraith, Bookings Sec. T: 028 9338 2539 &
07934 416 668; E: davidgalbraith903@btinternet.com

BTO Regional Representative
BTO IRELAND OFFICER. Shane Wolsey.
T: 028 9146 7947; E: shane.wolsey@bto.org

ANTRIM & BELFAST. Adam McClure.
T: 028 9346 2562 & 07793 038 211;
E: adamdmcclure@yahoo.co.uk

ARMAGH. Stephen Hewitt. T: n/a;
E: sjameshewitt@hotmail.com

DOWN. Vacant - contact Dawn Balmer, BTO.
T: 01842 750 050; E: dawn.balmer@bto.org

FERMANAGH. Michael Stinson. T: 07890 358 239;
E: mick.stinson@hotmail.com

LONDONDERRY. John Clarke. T: 028 7032 7675;
E: jclarke48@gmail.com

TYRONE. Michael Stinson - see above.

Club
NORTHERN IRELAND BIRDWATCHERS' ASSOCIATION.
See National Directory.
W: http://nibirds.blogspot.co.uk/

NORTHERN IRELAND ORNITHOLOGISTS' CLUB.
See National Directory. W: nioc.co.uk

Ringing Group/Bird Observatory
BELFAST AND DOWN RG.
W: https://www.facebook.com/BogMeadowsCes

COPELAND BIRD OBSERVATORY.
David Galbraith (Booking Secretary).
T: 028 9338 2539 or 07934 416 668;
E: davidgalbraith903@btinternet.com;
W: www.thecbo.org.uk

RSPB Local Group
ANTRIM. (1977; 25).
Brenda Campbell. T: 028 9332 3657;
E: brendacampbell961@gmail.com;
W: www.rspb.org.uk/groups/antrim
Meetings: 7.30pm, 2nd Monday of the month
(Sep-May). College of Agriculture Food & Rural
Enterprise, 22 Greenmount Road, Antrim, BT41 4PU.

BELFAST. (1970; 50).
Eleanor Brennan. T: 02890 647 571;
E: eleanor.brennan@btinternet.com;
W: www.rspb.org.uk/groups/belfast
Meetings: 7.30pm, 1st Monday of the month
(Sep-Apr). Cooke Centenary Church Hall,
Park Road, Belfast, BT7 2FW.

COLERAINE. (1978; 45).
Jim McDowell. T: 028 7034 2747;
E: jdmcdowell12@talktalk.net; W: n/a
Meetings: 7.30pm, 3rd Monday of the month
(Sep-Nov, Jan-Apr). Ballysally Youth and
Community Centre, Ballysally Road, Coleraine,
BT52 2QA.

FERMANAGH. (1977; 30).
Rozy McConkey. T: 028 6632 0794;
E: harry_mcconkey@yahoo.co.uk; W: n/a
Meetings: 8pm, 4th Tuesday of the month
(Sep-Apr, not Dec). St Macartins Cathedral Hall,
Halls Lane, Enniskillen, BT74 7DR.

LARNE. (1974; 35).
Jimmy Christie. T: 028 2858 3223;
E: jameschristie310@gmail.com; W: n/a
Meetings: 7.30pm, 1st Wednesday of the month
(Sep-Mar). Larne Grammar School,
4-6 Lower Cairncastle Rd, Larne, BT40 1PQ.

LISBURN. (1978; 30).
Richard Crothers. T: 028 9262 1866;
E: Richardcrothers@btinternet.com;
W: www.rspb.org.uk/groups/lisburn
Meetings: 7.30pm, 4th Monday of the month
(Sep-May). Harmony Hill Presbyterian Church,
Moss Road, Lambeg, Lisburn, BT27 4NW.

Wetland Bird Survey (WeBS) Local Organiser
ANTRIM (OTHER SITES). Adam McClure.
T: 028 2827 1875;
E: adamdmcclure@yahoo.co.uk

ARMAGH (excl. LOUGHS NEAGH & BEG).
Stephen Hewitt. T: via WeBS Office;
E: sjameshewitt@hotmail.com

BANN ESTUARY. Hill Dick. T: 028 7032 9720;
E: hdcoleraine@googlemail.com

NORTHERN IRELAND

BELFAST LOUGH. Shane Wolsey.
T: 07831 697 371; E: shane.wolsey@bto.org

CARLINGFORD LOUGH. Jennifer Lynch.
T: via WeBS Office; E: jenny.lynch9@gmail.com

DUNDRUM BAY. Patrick Lynch. T: 028 4375 1467;
E: patrick.lynch@nationaltrust.org.uk

FERMANAGH. Michael Stinson.
T: 07890 358 239; E: mick.stinson@hotmail.com

LARNE LOUGH. Doreen Hilditch.
T: via WeBS Office; E: mail18brae@btinternet.com

LOUGH FOYLE. Matthew Tickner.
T: 028 9049 1547;
E: matthew.tickner@rspb.org.uk

STRANGFORD LOUGH. Kerry Mackie.
T: 07719 537 275; E: kerrymackie9@gmail.com

Vacant sites - contact WeBS Office:

DOWN (OTHER SITES).
LONDONDERRY (OTHER SITES).
LOUGHS NEAGH AND BEG.
OUTER ARDS.
SOUTH DOWN COAST.
TYRONE (excl. LOUGHS NEAGH AND BEG).

Wildlife Trust
ULSTER WILDLIFE. (1978; 14,000).
McClelland House, 10 Heron Road, Belfast, BT3 9LE.
T: 028 9045 4094; E: info@ulsterwildlife.org;
W: www.ulsterwildlife.org

REPUBLIC OF IRELAND

BirdWatchIreland
protecting birds and biodiversity

BirdWatch Ireland
Unit 20, Block D
Bullford Business Campus
Kilcoole, Greystones
Co. Wicklow, A63 RW83,
Eire.
T: +353 (0)1 281 9878;
E: info@birdwatchireland.ie;
W: www.birdwatchireland.ie

Bird Recorder
IRELAND (all non-rarities): BirdWatch Ireland,
P.O.Box 12, Greystones, Co. Wicklow.
E: info@birdwatchireland.ie

CLARE. John Murphy. E: murphyjohn@gmail.com

CORK. Mark Shorten. E: mshorten@gmail.com

DONEGAL. Ralph Sheppard. E: rsheppard@eircom.net

DUBLIN, LOUTH, MEATH & WICKLOW.
Dick Coombes. E: rcoombes@birdwatchireland.ie

GALWAY. Chris Peppiatt. E: chris.peppiatt@iol.ie

KERRY. Michael O'Clery & Jill Crosher.
E: moclery@tinet.ie

LIMERICK. Tony Mee, Ballyorgan, Kilfinane,
Co. Limerick.

MAYO. National Parks and Wildlife, Lagduff More,
Ballycroy, Westport.

MID-SHANNON. Stephen Heery. E: sheery@eircom.net

MONAGHAN. Joe Shannon. E: joeshan@eircom.net

WATERFORD. Paul Walsh, 16 Castlepoint,
Crosshaven, Co. Cork.
E: pmwalsh@waterfordbirds.com

WEXFORD. Tony Murray, Wexford Wildfowl
Reserve, North Slob. E: murraytony@hotmail.com

Bird Report
IRISH BIRD REPORT (1977),
contact BirdWatch Ireland.

BirdWatch Ireland Branches
There is a network of local branches around the
country who organise events including field trips
and talks - they can be contacted via BirdWatch
Ireland.

Ringing Group/Bird Observatory
GREAT SALTEE RS.

IRISH MIDLANDS RG.

MUNSTER RG.

CAPE CLEAR BIRD OBSERVATORY.
Birdwatch Ireland - see above.
E: info@birdwatchireland.ie;
W: https://birdwatchireland.ie/our-work/cape-
clear-bird-observatory/

WILDLIFE WELFARE

A number of organisations work towards the care and rehabilitation of injured, sick and abandoned birds/wildlife across the UK, and individual wildlife hospitals carry out the same role on a local basis - some of these are listed below. The RSPCA (England & Wales), SSPCA (Scotland) and USPCA (Northern Ireland) are the national charities that help and advise on injured wildlife (NOT the RSPB). You can also find an independent local rescue centre on www.helpwildlife.co.uk

ORGANISATIONS

BRITISH WILDLIFE REHABILITATION COUNCIL (1987)
Promoting the care and rehabilitation of wildlife casualties through the exchange of information between people such as rehabilitators, zoologists and veterinary surgeons who are active in this field. Organises symposiums and regional workshops. Periodically issues a newsletter, *The Rehabilitator*. Website includes a list of rehabilitators.
Contact: BWRC, PO Box 8686, Grantham, Lincolnshire NG31 0AG; E: admin@bwrc.org.uk; W: www.bwrc.org.uk

HELPWILDLIFE.CO.UK (2005)
HelpWildlife.co.uk is maintained by a very small team of people involved in British wildlife rehabilitation to fully utilise the internet to help with wildlife issues. The site aims to provide informed, unbiased advice about caring for sick or injured birds and animals. Volunteers trawl the internet for details of those who might be able to help so that assistance can be offered quickly in an emergency. Visitors to the site are invited to provide feedback on listings published to ensure they are kept as up to date as possible.
Contact: for general enquiries NOT for a specific wildlife rescue - E: enquiries@helpwildlife.co.uk; W: www.helpwildlife.co.uk

INTERNATIONAL CENTRE FOR BIRDS OF PREY (1967)
The ICBP works for the conservation of birds of prey and their habitats through public education, captive breeding, treatment and rehabilitation of wild injured birds of prey. Education is on-going to visitors and specific groups and parties, from first schools to universities. The Centre continues its captive breeding aims; to research species; maintain the collection and provide birds for demonstrations. The Centre also works with many other groups and facilities to continue to support worldwide field research projects and international conservation programmes. It accepts, treats and rehabilitates injured wild birds of prey. Membership available. The Centre is open from Feb-Nov, 10.30am-5.30pm (4.30pm Feb/early Mar & Nov) and closed in Dec/Jan.
Contact: ICBP, Boulsdon House, Newent, Gloucs GL18 1JJ. T: 01531 820 286; E: info@icbp.org; W: www.icbp.org

PEOPLE'S DISPENSARY FOR SICK ANIMALS (1917)
Provides free veterinary treatment for sick/injured animals whose owners qualify for this charitable service and promotes responsible pet ownership.
Contact: PDSA, Whitechapel Way, Priorslee, Telford, Shropshire TF2 9PQ. T: 0800 917 2509; W: www.pdsa.org.uk

RAPTOR FOUNDATION (1989)
Provides mediacl care for injured raptors and returns rehabilitated birds back to the wild or provides a sanctuary for un-releasable birds. Researches into environmental and conservation matters. A full 24-hour rescue service is available for injured raptors and owls and the centre assists in breed-and-release schemes to rebuild populations across Europe. Centre is open daily, 10am-5pm (4pm mid Oct-mid-Feb), closed Jan 1 & Dec 25/26.
Contact: The Raptor Foundation, The Heath, St Ives Road, Woodhurst, Cambs PE28 3BT. T: 01487 741 140; E: via website; W: www.raptorfoundation.org.uk

RAPTOR RESCUE (1978)
Raptor Rescue has evolved into one of the UK's foremost organisations dedicated to ensuring all sick and injured birds of prey are cared for by suitably qualified people, and wherever possible, released back into the wild.
Contact: Raptor Rescue. T: 0870 241 0609; E: secretary@raptorrescue.org.uk; W: www.raptorrescue.org.uk

ROYAL SOCIETY FOR THE PREVENTION OF CRUELTY TO ANIMALS (1824): RSPCA
The oldest welfare charity looking out for the needs of animals on farms, in research labs, in the wild in paddocks and in our homes. The RSPCA also operate four wildilfe centres providing specialist care for the rehabilitation of wildlife throughout England and Wales (see wildlife hospitals below). In cases of animal cruelty, inspectors are contacted through their National Communication Centre, which can be reached via the Society's 24-hour national cruelty and advice line: T: 0300 1234 999
Contact: RSPCA Headquarters, Willberforce Way, Southwater, Horsham, West Sussex RH13 9RS. W: www.rspca.org.uk

WILDLIFE WELFARE

SCOTTISH SOCIETY FOR THE PREVENTION OF CRUELTY TO ANIMALS (1839): SCOTTISH SPCA

Represents animal welfare interests to Government, local authorities and others. Educates young people to realise their responsibilities. Maintains an inspectorate to patrol and investigate and to advise owners about the welfare of animals and birds in their care. Maintains a National Wildlife Rescue Centre. Bird species, including birds of prey, are rehabilitated and where possible released back into the wild.
Contact: Scottish SPCA, Kingseat Road, Halbeath, Dunfermline, Fife KY11 8RY.
T: 03000 999 999 (animal helpline 7am-10pm); E: via website; W: www.scottishspca.org

SWAN SANCTUARY (1980s)

Founded by Dorothy Beeson, this registered charity is the largest and only completely self-contained swan hospital in the UK. It has several nursing ponds and rehabilitation lakes. 24-hr rescue service, with volunteers on hand to recover swans (and other animals).
Contact: The Swan Sanctuary, Felix Lane, Shepperton, Middlesex TW17 8NN.
T: 01932 240 790 (emergency); E: via website; W: www.theswansanctuary.org.uk

ULSTER SOCIETY FOR THE PREVENTION OF CRUELTY TO ANIMALS (1836): USPCA

Represents animal welfare in Northern Ireland with the purpose of preventing cruelty and revlieve suffering to all animals, both pets and wildlife.
Contact: UPSCA, Unit 6, Carnbane Industrial Estate (East), Newry, Co Down BT35 6HQ.
T: 028 3025 1000; E: enquiries@uspca.co.uk; W: www.uspca.co.uk

---

WILDLIFE HOSPITALS

England

SWAN LIFELINE.
Swan Rescue HQ & Treatment Centre, Cuckoo Weir Island, South Meadow Lane, Eton, BERKSHIRE SL4 6SS.
T: 01753 859 397 (24hr emergency line); E: enquiries@swanlifeline.org.uk (non-emergency); W: www.swanlifeline.org.uk
Thames Valley 24-hour swan rescue & treatment service. Veterinary support & hospital unit. Membership available.

TIGGYWINKLES, THE WILDLIFE HOSPITAL TRUST.
Tiggywinkles, Aston Road, Haddenham, Aylesbury, BUCKINGHAMSHIRE HP17 8AF.
T: 01844 292 292 (24hr helpline); E: mail@tiggywinkles.org (non-emergency); W: www.sttiggywinkles.org.uk
All British species. Veterinary referrals & helpline for vets & others on wild bird treatments. Full veterinary unit & staff. Membership available.

RSPCA WILDLIFE CENTRES (not 24-hours).
EAST WINCH, Gayton Rd, East Winch, NORFOLK PE32 1LG. T: 0300 123 0709 (9am-4pm, Mon-Fri).

MALLYDAMS WOOD, Peter James Lane, Hastings, EAST SUSSEX TN35 4AH. T: 0300 123 0723 (8am-8pm Apr-Sep, 9am-5pm Oct-Mar).

STAPELEY GRANGE, London Road, Stapeley, Nantwich, CHESHIRE CW5 7JW. T: 0300 123 0722 (8am-9pm May-Oct, 8am-8pm Nov-Apr).

WEST HATCH, Cold Road,Taunton SOMERSET TA3 5RT. 0300 123 0721 (8am-9pm daily).

T: 0300 1234 999 (24-hr national cruelty line); W: https://www.rspca.org.uk/whatwedo/care/wildlifecentres

SWAN RESCUE SANCTUARY.
The Widgeons, Crooked Withies, Holt, Wimborne, DORSET BH21 7LB. T: 01202 828 166; W: www.swan-rescue.co.uk
Rescue service for swans. Large sanctuary of ponds/lakes. Hospital and intensive care. Veterinary support. Free advice and help line. Rescue water craft for emergencies. Viewing by appointment only.

VALE WILDLIFE HOSPITAL & REHABILITATION CENTRE. Station Road, Beckford, Tewkesbury, GLOUCESTERSHIRE GL20 7AN.
T: 01386 882 288; E: info@valewildlife.org.uk; W: www.valewildlife.org.uk
All wildlife. Intensive care. Veterinary support.

HAWK CONSERVANCY TRUST.
Visitor Centre, Sarson Lane, Weyhill, Andover, HAMPSHIRE SP11 8DY. T: 01264 773 850;
E: info@hawkconservancy.org;
W: www.hawk-conservancy.org
The HCT is an important centre for receiving injured birds of prey and has one of the only specialist birds of prey hospitals in the UK.

WILDLIFE WELFARE

RAPTOR CENTRE.
c/o Hobbledown, Horton Lane, Epsom, SURREY
KT19 8PT. T: 01372 848 990; E: via website;
W: www.raptorcentre.co.uk
Birds of prey. Veterinary support. Rescue service
for sick and injured birds of prey that covers the
South-East.

BERWICK SWAN & WILDLIFE TRUST.
Windmill Way East, Ramparts Business Park,
Berwick-upon-Tweed, NORTHUMBERLAND
TD15 1TU. T: 01289 302 882;
E: swan-trust@hotmail.co.uk;
W: www.swan-trust.org
All categories of wildlife. Pools for swans, other
waterfowl. Veterinary support. Membership
available.

BRITISH WILDLIFE RESCUE CENTRE.
The centre has moved and is currently undergoing
development. STAFFORDSHIRE. T: 01889 271 308;
E: admin@thebwrc.com; W: www.thebwrc.com
All species, including imprints and permanently
injured. Hospital, large aviaries and caging.
Veterinary support.

GENTLESHAW BIRD OF PREY & WILDLIFE CENTRE.
Fletcher's Country Garden Centre, Stone Road,
Eccleshall, STAFFORDSHIRE ST21 6JY.
T: 01785 850 379; E: gentleshaw1@btconnect.com;
W: www.gentleshawwildlife.co.uk
All birds of prey (incl. owls). Hospital cages and
aviaries; release sites. Veterinary support. Open
to the public.

THE WILDLIFE AID FOUNDATION.
Randalls Farm House, Randalls Road,
Leatherhead, SURREY KT22 0AL. 24-hr Wildlife
Help & Enquiries line: 09061 800 132 (50p/min);
E: via website; W: www.wildlifeaid.org.uk
Wildlife hospital and rehabilitation centre helping
all native British species. Special housing for birds
of prey. Membership scheme and fund raising
activities. Veterinary support.

BRENT LODGE BIRD & WILDLIFE TRUST.
Cow Lane, Sidlesham, Chichester, WEST SUSSEX
PO20 7LN. T: 01243 641 672 (emergency number);
E: enquiries@brentlodge.org; W: www.brentlodge.org
All species of wild birds and small mammals.

ANIMAL HOUSE BIRDS OF PREY.
58 Dale Edge, Eastfield, Scarborough,
NORTH YORKSHIRE YO11 3EP.
T: 07807 038 553; E: via website;
W: www.animalhousewildlifewelfare.com
Specialises in the rescue and rehabilitation of
birds of prey.

Scotland

HESSILHEAD WILDLIFE RESCUE CENTRE.
Gateside, Beith, AYRSHIRE KA15 1HT.
T: 01505 502 415; E: info@hessilhead.org.uk;
W: www.hessilhead.org.uk
All species. Releasing aviaries. Veterinary
support. Visits on open days. Membership
available.

NATIONAL WILDLIFE RESCUE CENTRE.
Scottish SPCA, National Wildlife Rescue Centre,
Fishcross, CLACKMANNANSHIRE FK10 3AN.
T: 03000 999 999 (7am-10pm); E: via website;
W: www.scottishspca.org/rehome/our-centres/
national-wildlife-rescue-centre/
No visiting, but casualties accepted at any time.

Wales

GOWER BIRD HOSPITAL.
Sandy Lane, Pennard, SWANSEA,
SA3 2EW. T: 01792 371 630;
E: info@gowerbirdhospital.org.uk;
W: www.gowerbirdhospital.org.uk
All species of wild birds, also small mammals.
Cares for sick, injured and orphaned wild birds
and animals with the sole intention of returning
them to the wild.

Channel Islands

GUERNSEY.
GSPCA ANIMAL SHELTER, Les Fiers Moutons,
St Andrews, GUERNSEY GY6 8UD.
T: 01481 257 261; (T: 07781 104 082 emergency);
E: admin@gspca.org.gg; W: www.gspca.org.gg
All species. 24-hour emergency service. Veterinary
support.

JERSEY.
JSPCA ANIMALS' SHELTER, 89 St Saviour's Road,
St Helier, JERSEY JE2 4GJ. T: 01534 724 331;
(T: 07797 720 331 emergency);
E: via website; W: www.jspca.org.je
All species. 24-hour emergency service. Veterinary
support. Educational Centre.

~~~~~

In an emergency, DO NOT send an e-mail,
use the emergency phone numbers.

All of the organisations and wildife hospitals
that look after the health and welfare of our
wildlife rely on funding from memberships
and/or donations.

BIRD INFORMATION SERVICES & BIRDLINE NUMBERS

Bird Forum
Free to join, online forum. W: www.birdforum.net

BirdGuides
Offers subscription bird news services online and via e-mail, text message and apps for Apple and Android devices. T: 01778 392 027;
E: subscriptions@warnersgroup.co.uk;
W: www.birdguides.com

Flightline
Northern Ireland's daily bird news service.
T: 028 91467408; E: nibirds@live.co.uk;
http://nibirds.blogspot.co.uk

Rare Bird Alert
Offers subscription instant bird news service - available online, by pager or phone app.
T: 01603 457 016; E: admin@rarebirdalert.co.uk;
W: www.rarebirdalert.co.uk

Birdline   09068 700 222 (National number)

Scotland   09068 700 234
W: https://www.the-soc.org.uk/content/
    bird-recording/birdline-scotland

South East   09068 700 240
W: www.southeastbirdnews.co.uk

South West   closed

East Anglia   09068 700 245
W: www.birdlineeastanglia.co.uk

North East   09068 700 246

Midlands   09068 700 247

Wales   closed

North West   closed

Note:
The 09068 Birdline numbers are charged at premium line rates (65p per minute from landline or mobile + any connection charges your mobile provider may charge).

NOTES

Joe Mitchell

The American White Pelican (*Pelecanus erythrorhynchos*) breeds in the interior of North America & moves to the estuaries & lakes of southern USA & Central America for the winter, covering the territories of a number of BirdLife Partners.

DIRECTORY OF ORGANISATIONS

UK/UK-BASED ORGANISATIONS

MANY BIRD ORGANISATIONS operate across, or are based in, the UK. Some cater for specialist groups of people/interests, others are open to a wider audience. The majority are membership-based - contact them directly for more information about their work and subscription rates. A selection of other organisations and govermental departments are also listed in this directory. Have a browse.

AFRICAN BIRD CLUB (1994)
Provides a worldwide focus for African Ornithology and raises funds to support conservation projects through its Conservation Fund. Liaises and promotes the work of existing regional societies. Holds an annual meeting in London, publishes a colour bulletin twice yearly.
Contact: c/o BirdLife International, The David Attenborough Building, Pembroke Street, Cambridge, CB2 3QZ. T: n/a. E: info@africanbirdclub.org; E (membership): membership@africanbirdclub.org; W: www.africanbirdclub.org

AMPHIBIAN & REPTILE CONSERVATION TRUST (2009)
Formed out of The Herpetological Conservation Trust (1989) to widen its role (HCT still runs as an functioning charity). ARC conserves amphibians and reptiles and their habitats, including a number of reserves.
Contact: ARC, 655a Christchurch Rd, Boscombe, Bournemouth BH1 4AP. T: 01202 391 319; E: enquiries@arc-trust.org; W: www.arc-trust.org

ARMY ORNITHOLOGICAL SOCIETY (1960)
Open to any serving and ex-Army personnel, other Services and their families, MOD civil servants and members of the Commonwealth Forces who have an interest in birdlife, either on a casual basis or in more depth. Activities include field meetings, expeditions, assistance with bird surveys and ringing projects, and a long term survey of seabirds on Ascension Island. AOS newsletter & annual journal *Adjutant*.
Contact: The Army Ornithological Society, Prince Consort's Library, Knollys Road, South Camp, Aldershot, Hampshire GU11 1PS. E: via website; W: www.armybirding.org.uk

ASSOCIATION FOR THE PROTECTION OF RURAL SCOTLAND (1926)
Works to protect Scotland's world renown landscape and the amenity of the countryside from unnecessary or inappropriate development. APRS recognise the needs of those who live and work in rural Scotland and the necessity of reconciling these needs with the sometimes competing requirements of industry and recreation. Members have access to specialist advice, newsletters and regular e-bulletins.
Contact: Association for the Protection Rural Scotland, Dolphin House, 4 Hunter Square, Edinburgh EH1 1QW. T: 0131 225 7012; E: info@aprs.scot; W: http://aprs.scot/

ASSOCIATION OF COUNTY RECORDERS & EDITORS (1993)
ACRE's basic aim is to promote best practice in the work of County Recorders, providing a forum for discussions on producing county bird reports and in problems arising in assessing records, managing county databases systems and archives. Also provides a discussion medium for interactions of the County Recorders and report Editors with British Birds Rarities Committee (BBRC), Rare Breeding Bird Panel (RBBP) and the British Trust for Ornithology (BTO).
Contact: Hugh Pulsford (Secretary). T: 01565 880 171; E: countyrec@cawos.org

BARN OWL TRUST (1988)
A registered charity dedicated to conserving the Barn Owl and its environment - it is the main source of Barn Owl information in the UK. The Trust, and its members, erect nestboxes and are closely involved in habitat creation both on its own land and through farm visits. Also offers practical guidance to developers and planners - advising on Barn Owl mitigation measures, undertakes research and provides care for injured owls. Produces a number of publications inc. 'The Barn Owl Conservation Handbook'. Events held.
Contact: Barn Owl Trust, Waterleat, Ashburton, Devon TQ13 7HU. T: 01364 653 026; E: info@barnowltrust.org.uk; W: www.barnowltrust.org.uk

BAT CONSERVATION TRUST (1991)
Supports local bat groups across the UK. Their vision includes: learning more about bats and how they use the landscape; taking action to protect bats and to enhance the landscapes they rely on; and inspiring people about bats and their environment.
Contact: Bat Conservation Trust, 5th floor, Quadrant House, 250 Kennington Lane, London SE11 5RD. T: Bat Helpline 0345 1300 228 (9.30am-4.30pm Mon-Fri & up to 10.30pm daily May-Sep for emergencies only); E: enquiries@bats.org.uk; W: www.bats.org.uk

BIRD OBSERVATORIES COUNCIL (1946)
The BOC co-ordinates and promotes the work of bird observatories at a national level. All accredited bird observatories (20 at present) affiliated to the Council undertake a ringing programme and provide a ringing experience to those interested. Most are also able to provide accommodation for visiting birdwatchers.
Contact: Alison Duncan, The Secretary BOC, North Ronaldsay Bird Observatory, Twingness, North Ronaldsay, Orkney KW17 2BE. T: 01857 633200; E: info@birdobscouncil.org.uk; W: www.birdobscouncil.org.uk

BIRD STAMP SOCIETY (1986)
Quarterly magazine *Flight* contains philatelic and ornithological articles. Lists all new issues and identifies species. Runs a quarterly Postal Auction - number of lots of between 500-700 per auction, depending on stock levels.
Contact: Graham Horsman (Mem Sec), 23A East Main Street, Blackburn, West Lothian EH47 7QR. T: 01506 651 029; E: graham_horsman7@msn.com; W: www.birdstampsociety.org

UK/UK-BASED ORGANISATIONS

BIRDING FOR ALL (2000)

Formally known as The Disabled Birder's Association, Birding For All (2010) is a registered charity and international movement, which aims to promote access to reserves and other birding places and to a range of services, so that people with different needs can follow the birding obsession as freely as able-bodied people. Membership is currently free (donations welcomed) and is open to everyone - new members are needed to help send a stronger message to those who own and manage nature reserves to improve access when they are planning and improving facilities. BFA also seeks to influence those who provide birdwatching services and equipment.
Contact: Bo Beolens (Chairman), Birding For All, 18 St Mildreds Road, Cliftonville, Margate, Kent CT9 2LT. E: birdingforall@gmail.com; W: www.birdingforall.com

BIRDLIFE INTERNATIONAL (1993)

Formally ICBP - International Committee for Bird Preservation (1922). See page 306.

BIRDWATCH IRELAND (1968, network of over 30 branches)

The largest independent conservation organisation in Ireland with over 15,000 members. Its primary objective is the protection of wild birds and their habitats in Ireland through the efforts of its staff, members and volunteers alike. It carries out extensive research and survey work, operates applied conservation projects and manages a network of reserves nationwide. It publishes *Wings* (quarterly magazine), *eWings* (electronic) magazine, *Irish Birds* (annual journal) and *Bird Detectives* (children's magazine, twice yearly).
Contact: BirdWatch Ireland, Unit 20, Block D, Bullford Business Campus, Kilcoole, Greystones, Co. Wicklow, A63 RW83 Ireland. T: +353 (0)1 2819 878; Fax: +353 (0)1 281 0997; E: info@birdwatchireland.ie; W: www.birdwatchireland.ie

BRITISH BIRDS RARITIES COMMITTEE (1959)

The Committee (with 10 experts who vote) adjudicate records of species of rare occurrence in Britain (these are marked 'R' in the Checklists, P.55) and publishes its annual report in B*ritish Birds*. The BBRC also assesses records from the Channel Islands. In the case of rarities trapped for ringing, records should be sent to the Ringing Office of the British Trust for Ornithology, who will in turn forward them to the BBRC.
Contact: Chas Holt (Secretary), British Birds Rarities Committee, 307 St John's Way, Thetford, Norfolk IP24 3PA. E: secretary@bbrc.org.uk; W: www.bbrc.org.uk

BRITISH DECOY & WILDFOWL CARVERS ASSOCIATION (1990)

The Association is a non-profitmaking organisation, run by carvers to promote all aspects of their art. It produces three *Wingspan* magazines p.a.; keeps members in touch with the art; promotes regional groups; generates local interest; holds competitions and exhibitions; and cares for the interests of bird carvers. Each Sept the BDWCA stages the 'Festival of Bird Art' in Bakewell, in the Peak District, and includes the National Bird Carving Championships.
Contact: E: bdwcaenquiries@bdwca.org.uk; W: www.bdwca.org.uk

BRITISH DRAGONFLY SOCIETY (1983)

The BDS aims to promote the recording and the conservation of dragonflies. Members receive two issues of *Dragonfly News* and *BDS Journal* each year and *Hawker*, a monthly e-newsletter. Dragonfly recorders also receive

Darter, an annual magazine. There are countrywide field trips, an annual members' day, and training is available on aspects of dragonfly identification and ecology.
Contact: Henry Curry (Sec), British Dragonfly Society, 23 Bowker Way, Whittlesey, Cambs PE7 1PY. T: 01733 204 286; E: secretary@british-dragonflies.org.uk; W: www.british-dragonflies.org.uk

BRITISH ENTOMOLOGICAL & NATURAL HISTORY SOCIETY (1872)

The Society promotes and advances research in entomology. Holds a number of indoor and outdoor meetings, publishes a journal (4pa) and makes small grants. Its HQ has a library and reference collections.
Contact: The Secretary, c/o The Pelham-Clinton Building, Dinton Pastures Country Park, Davis Street, Hurst, Reading, Berkshire RG10 0TH. T: n/a; E: enquiries@benhs.org.uk; W: www.benhs.org.uk

BRITISH FALCONERS' CLUB (1927)

The BFC is the oldest and largest falconry club in Europe and has 13 regional branches in the UK. Its aim is to encourage responsible falconers and conserve birds of prey by breeding, holding educational meetings and providing facilities, guidance and advice to those wishing to take up the sport. Publishes *The Falconer* and a newsletter.
Contact: British Falconers' Club, Westfield Meeting Hill, Worstead, North Walsham, Norfolk NR28 9LS. T: 01692 404 057; E: admin@britishfalconersclub.co.uk; W: www.britishfalconersclub.co.uk

BRITISH LIBRARY SOUND ARCHIVE - WILDLIFE SOUNDS (1969)

The most comprehensive collection of bird sound recordings in existence. Consists of 240,000+ wildlife recordings inc. 10,000+ species (birds, mammals, amphibians, reptiles, fish & insects) from around the world, many accessible for free listening. Copies or sonograms of most recordings can be supplied for private study or research and, subject to copyright clearance, for commercial uses. Contribution of new material and enquiries on all aspects of wildlife sounds and recording techniques are welcome. Publishes a number of magazines and periodicals, CD guides to bird songs and other wildlife, inc. ambience titles. Catalogue available on-line at http://cadensa.bl.uk/uhtbin/cgisirsi/x/x/0/49/
Contact: Cheryl Tipp, Curator, Wildlife & Environmental Sounds, The British Library, 96 Euston Road, London NW1 2DB. T: 020 7412 7403; E: wildlifesound@bl.uk; W: www.bl.uk/collection-guides/wildlife-and-environmental-sounds

UK/UK-BASED ORGANISATIONS

BRITISH NATURALISTS' ASSOCIATION (1905)

The association was founded to promote the interests of nature lovers and bring them together. It encourages and supports schemes and legislation for the protection of the country`s natural resources. It organises meetings, field weeks, lectures and exhibitions to help popularise the study of nature. BNA publishes two magazines, *Country-Side* and *British Naturalist* and has ten local branches.
Contact: General Secretary, British Naturalists' Association BM 8129, London WC1N 3XX.
T: 0844 892 1817; E: info@bna-naturalists.org;
W: www.bna-naturalists.org

BRITISH ORNITHOLOGISTS' CLUB (1892)

The Club's objects are 'the promotion of scientific discussion between members of the BOU, and others interested in ornithology, and to facilitate the publication of scientific information in connection with ornithology'. The Club maintains a special interest in avian systematics, taxonomy and distribution and publishes the B*ulletin of the British Ornithologists' Club* quarterly (online only), as well as a continuing series of publications. It also holds a number of evening meetings each year (see website for details).
Contact: BOC, c/o Natural History Museum at Tring, Akeman Street, Tring, Herts HP23 6AP.
T: 0220 8876 4728 & 07919 174 898;
E: info@boc-online.org; W: www.boc-online.org

BRITISH ORNITHOLOGISTS' UNION (1858)

The BOU is one of the world's oldest and most respected ornithological societies. It aims to promote ornithology within the scientific and birdwatching communities, in Britain and around the world - this is largely achieved by the publication of its quarterly international journal, *Ibis*, featuring work at the cutting edge of our understanding of the world's birdlife. It also runs an active programme of meetings, seminars and conferences covering major ornithological topics and issues of the day - the proceedings are published free on the BOU website. Via social media (see website for links) the BOU acts as a global ornithological hub providing details of newly published research articles, conferences, jobs, PhD opportunities and more. Work being undertaken around the world can include research projects that have received financial assistance from the BOU's on-going programme of Small Research Grants and Career Development Bursaries (for ornithological students). The BOU's Records Committee (see below) maintains the official British List. It has also published a series of country/island group 'checklists'.
Contact: British Ornithologists' Union, P.O. Box 417, Peterborough, PE7 3FX. E: via website;
W: www.bou.org.uk

BRITISH ORNITHOLOGISTS' UNION RECORDS COMMITTEE

A standing committee of the BOU, the BOURC's function is to maintain the British List, the official list of birds recorded in Great Britain (the up-to-date list can be viewed on the BOU website). The British List follows the International Ornithological Union's (IOU) IOC World Bird List. Where vagrants are involved it is concerned only with those which relate to potential additions to the British List (i.e. first records) - in this it differs from the British Birds Rarities Committee. It also examines, where necessary, important pre-1950 records, monitors introduced species for possible admission to, or deletion from, the List. BOURC reports are published in Ibis and are also available via the BOU website. **Contact:** as above (BOU).

BRITISH TRUST FOR ORNITHOLOGY (1933)

The BTO is an independent charitable research institute that combines professional and citizen science aimed at using evidence of change in wildlife populations, particularly birds, to inform the public, opinion-formers and environmental policy/decision makers. Through the fieldwork of 60,000 volunteer birdwatchers, in partnership with professional research scientists, the BTO collects high quality monitoring data on birds and other wildlife. Surveys include the National Ringing Scheme, the Nest Record Scheme, the Breeding Bird Survey (in collaboration with JNCC/RSPB), the Wetland Bird Survey, in particular Low Tide Counts (in collaboration with WWT/RSPB/JNCC) which all contribute to an integrated programme of population monitoring. The BirdTrack recording system is an important resource for recording bird data and all birdwatchers are encouraged to use it to log their bird sightings.

The Trust has a network of voluntary regional representatives (see County Directory) who organise fieldworkers for the BTO's programme of national surveys in which members participate. The results of these co-operative efforts are communicated to government departments, local authorities, industry and conservation bodies for effective action. For details of current activities see National Projects. Members receive *BTO News* regularly throughout the year and have the option of subscribing to *Bird Study* (four times yearly) and *Ringing & Migration* (twice yearly). Local meetings are held in conjunction with bird clubs and societies, there are regional and national birdwatchers' conferences, and specialist courses in bird identification and modern censusing techniques. Grants are made for research, and members have the use of a lending and reference library at Thetford.
Contact: British Trust for Ornithology, The Nunnery, Thetford, Norfolk IP24 2PU. T: 01842 750 050;
Fax: 01842 750 030; E: info@bto.org; W: www.bto.org

BTO IRELAND

The role of the Northern Ireland team is to develop the BTO presence in the country, particularly to assist the voluntary reps to find enough volunteers to undertake key bird monitoring surveys.
Contact:
W: www.bto.org/about-bto/national-offices/ireland

UK/UK-BASED ORGANISATIONS

BTO SCOTLAND
BTO Scotland's main functions are to promote the work of the Trust and develop wider coverage for surveys in Scotland, by encouraging greater participation in survey work. With a landscape and wildlife so different from the rest of the UK, BTO Scotland ensure that the Trust's work is not just related to the priorities of the UK as a whole but is also focused on the priorities of Scotland.
Contact: BTO Scotland, Unit 15, Beta Centre, Stirling University Innovation Park, Stirling, FK9 4NF.
T: 01786 458 021; E: scot.info@bto.org;
W: www.bto.org/about-bto/national-offices/scotland

BTO WALES/CYMRU
For many years much has been achieved in Wales through efforts of volunteers. An office is now located in Bangor Univerity to provide more support to provide a Welsh voice for the BTO and to focus on Welsh priorities.
Contact: BTO Wales, Thoday Building, Deiniol Rd, Bangor, Gwynedd LL57 2UW. T: 01248 383 285;
W: www.bto.org/about-bto/national-offices/wales

BRITISH WATERFOWL ASSOCIATION
The BWA is an association of enthusiasts interested in keeping, breeding and conserving all types of waterfowl, inc. wildfowl and domestic ducks and geese. It is a registered charity, without trade affiliations, dedicated to educating the public about waterfowl and the need for conservation as well as to raising the standards of keeping and breeding ducks, geese and swans in captivity. Publishes *Waterfowl* magazine for members three times a year.
Contact: Kate Elkington, BWA Secretary, The Old Bakehouse, Ashperton, Ledbury, Herts HR8 2SA. T: 01531 671 250; E: info@waterfowl.org.uk; W: www.waterfowl.org.uk

BUGLIFE (2000)
The only organisation in Europe devoted to the conservation of all invertebrates, actively engaged in halting the extinction of Britain's rarest slugs, snails, bees, wasps, ants, spiders, beetles and many more. It works to achieve this through practical conservation projects; promoting the environmental importance of invertebrates and raising awareness about the challenges to their survival; assisting in the development of helpful legislation and policy; developing and disseminating knowledge about how to conserve invertebrates; and encouraging and supporting invertebrate conservation initiatives by other organisations in the UK, Europe and worldwide.
Contact: Buglife, Age UK, The Lindens, 86 Lincoln Road, Peterborough, PE1 2SN. T: 01733 201 210; E: info@buglife.org.uk; W: www.buglife.org.uk

BUTTERFLY CONSERVATION (1968)
One of the largest insect conservation organisations in the world. Their core aims: to recover threatened butterflies and moths; to increase numbers of widespread species; to promote international conservation actions; and to inspire people to understand and deliver species conservation. Runs 36 nature reserves and are involved in 73 landscape-scale projects to conserve habitats. There are 32 volunteer-run branches through the British Isles.

Contact: Head Office, Manor Yard, East Lulworth, Wareham, Dorset, BH20 5QP. T: 01929 400 209 ; E: info@butterfly-conservation.org; W: www.butterfly-conservation.org
Northern Ireland: Ned's Place, 66 Dublin Road, Kilcoo, Newry, BT34 5JG. T: 028 4377 1497; E: northernireland@btconnect.com
Scotland: Balallan House, Allan Park, Stirling, FK8 2QG. T: 01786 447 753; E: scotland@butterfly-conservation.org
Wales: 4D Cwm Road, Hafod, Swansea, SA1 2AY. T: 01792 642 972; E: wales@butterfly-conservation.org

Butterfly Conservation
Saving butterflies, moths and our environment

CAMPAIGN FOR THE PROTECTION OF RURAL WALES (1928)
Its aims are to help the conservation and enhancement of the landscape, environment and amenities of the countryside, towns and villages of rural Wales and to form and educate opinion to ensure the promotion of its objectives. It gives advice and information upon matters affecting protection, conservation and improvement of the visual environment. Publishes *Rural Wales* (usually 2 p.a.).
Contact: Tŷ Gwyn, 31 High Street, Welshpool, Powys SY21 7YD. T: 01938 552 525; E: info@cprwmail.org.uk; W: www.cprw.org.uk

CENTRE FOR ECOLOGY & HYDROLOGY (CEH)
The work of the CEH, a component body of the Natural Environment Research Council, includes a range of ornithological research, covering population studies, habitat management and work on the effects of pollution. The CEH has a long-term programme to monitor pesticide and pollutant residues in the corpses of predatory birds sent in by birdwatchers, and carries out detailed studies on affected species. The Biological Records Centre (BRC), which is part of the CEH, is responsible for the national biological data bank on plant and animal distributions (except birds) - see BRC website.
Contact: Centre for Ecology & Hydrology, Maclean Building, Benson Lane, Crowmarsh Gifford, Wallingford, Oxfordshire OX10 8BB. T: 01491 838 800; E: via website; W: www.ceh.ac.uk; W: www.brc.ac.uk

CLA (Country Land & Business Association) (1907)
The CLA is at the heart of rural life and is the voice of the countryside for England and Wales, campaigning on issues which directly affect those who live and work in rural communities. Anyone who owns rural land or runs a rural business will benefit from joining the CLA and its members range from some of the largest landowners, with interests in forest, moorland, water and farming, to some with little more than a paddock or garden.
Contact: Country Land and Business Association Ltd, 16 Belgrave Square, London SW1X 8PQ. T: 020 7235 0511; E: mail@cla.org.uk; W: www.cla.org.uk

UK/UK-BASED ORGANISATIONS

CONSERVATION FOUNDATION (1982)
Created by David Bellamy and David Shreeve, it provides a means for people in public, private and not-for-profit sectors to collaborate on environmental causes. Over the years its programme has included award schemes, conferences, promotions, special events, field studies, school programmes, media work, seminars and workshops etc. The Conservation Foundation has created and managed environmental award schemes of all kinds. For information about how to apply for current award schemes visit the website. **Contact:** Conservation Foundation, 1 Kensington Gore, London SW7 2AR. T: 020 7591 3111; E: info@conservationfoundation.co.uk; W: www.conservationfoundation.co.uk

CPRE (Campaign to Protect Rural England) (1926)
CPRE campaigns at all levels for a beautiful and living countryside by working to protect, promote and enhance our towns and countryside to make them better places to live, work and enjoy, and to ensure the countryside is protected for now and future generations. **Contact:** Campaign to Protect Rural England, 5-11 Lavington Street, London SE1 0NZ. T: 020 7981 2800; Fax: 020 7981 2899; E: info@cpre.org.uk; W: www.cpre.org.uk

EARTHWATCH INSTITUTE (1971)
Earthwatch developed the innovative idea of engaging the general public into the scientific process by bringing together individual volunteers and scientists on field research projects, thereby providing an alternative means of funding, as well as a dedicated labour force for field scientists. Earthwatch have invested in nearly 1400 conservation research projects in more than 120 countries. **Contact:** Earthwatch (Europe), Mayfield House, 256 Banbury Road, Oxford, OX2 7DE. T: 01865 318 838; E: hello@earthwatch.org.uk; W: http://eu.earthwatch.org

EDWARD GREY INSTITUTE OF FIELD ORNITHOLOGY (1937)
The EGI takes its name from Edward Grey, first Viscount Grey of Fallodon, a life-long lover of birds and former Chancellor of the University of Oxford. The Institute now has a permanent (research) staff of research students, senior visitors and post-doctoral research workers. The Institute houses the Alexander Library of Ornithology, one of the largest collections of 20th Century material on birds in the world, which is supported by the British Ornithologists' Union who provide much of the material. It also houses the British Falconers Club library. The Library is open for reference use only to all holders of a university card or valid Bodleian Library card. External visitors are welcome on a one-off day pass by arrangement by contacting: Sophie Wilcox, Alexander Library, Radcliffe Science Library, Parks Road, Oxford, OX1 3QP; T: 01865 272 844; E: sophie.wilcocx@bodleian.ox.ac.uk **Contact:** Lynne Bradley, PA to Prof. Ben Sheldon, The EGI, Department of Zoology, University of Oxford, The John Krebs Field Starion, Wytham, Oxford, OX2 8QJ; T: 01865 271 234; E: ben.sheldon.pa@zoo.ox.ac.uk; W: www.zoo.ox.ac.uk/egi/

ENVIRONMENT AGENCY (1996)
A non-departmental body which aims to protect and improve the environment and to contribute towards the delivery of sustainable development through the integrated management of air, land and water. Functions include pollution prevention and control, waste minimisation, management of water resources, flood defence, improvement of salmon and freshwater fisheries, conservation of aquatic species, navigation and use of inland and coastal waters for recreation. **Contact:** Environment Agency, National Customer Contact Centre, PO Box 544, Rotherham, S60 1BY. General enquiries T: 03708 506 506 (Mon-Fri, 8am-6pm) Environment incident hotline T: 0800 80 70 60; Floodline (24 hrs) T: 0345 988 1188; E: enquiries@environment-agency.gov.uk; W: www.gov.uk/government/organisations/environment-agency

EURING (European Union for Bird Ringing) (1963)
EURING co-ordinates bird-ringing schemes throughout Europe. It aims to promote and encourage: Scientific and administrative co-operation between national ringing schemes; development and maintenance of high standards in bird ringing; scientific studies of birds, in particular those based on marked individuals; and the use of data from bird ringing for the management and conservation of birds. These objectives are achieved mainly through co-operative projects, the organisation of meetings and the collection of data in the EURING Data Bank. **Contact:** E: enquiries@euring.org; W: www.euring.org

EUROPEAN COLOUR-RING BIRDING
This is a platform enabling field observers to find out who the project leaders are if they find a colour-ringed bird. W: www.cr-birding.org

FAUNA & FLORA INTERNATIONAL (1903)
Their mission is to conserve threatened species and ecosystems worldwide by finding sustainable solutions based on sound science and taking human needs into account. They work in over 40 countries, supporting over 320 partners. Members receive a regular newsletter update and *Flora & Fauna (magazine)*. Also publish *Oryx (journal)* **Contact:** The David Attenborough Building, Pembroke Street, Cambridge CB2 3QZ. T: 01223 571 000; E: info@fauna-flora.org; W: www.fauna-flora.org

FIELD STUDIES COUNCIL (1943)
Manages a UK wide network of centres where students from schools, universities and colleges, as well as individuals of all ages, can stay to study various aspects of the environment under expert guidance. Courses include many bird related themes. Research workers and naturalists wishing to use the records and resources are welcome. There are centres in England, Scotland, Wales and Northern Ireland - see website for contacts/courses available. Publishes many identification charts, guides and handbooks.

UK/UK-BASED ORGANISATIONS

Contact: Field Studies Council, Preston Montford, Montford Bridge, Shrewsbury, SY4 1HW.
T: 01743 852 100; T (FSC publications): 01952 208 910;
E: enquiries@field-studies-council.org;
E: publications @field-studies-council.org;
W: www.field-studies-council.org

FORESTRY COMMISSION (1919)
Supports the delivery of English forestry operations inc. grants for forestry activities and felling licences.
Contact: National Office, 620 Bristol Business Park, Coldharbour Lane, Bristol, BS16 1EJ. T: 0300 067 4000;
E: nationalenquiries@forestrycommission.gov.uk;
W: www.gov.uk/government/organisations/forestry-commission

FORESTRY ENGLAND (2019)
Looks after England's public forests by carrying out management for people, wildlife and the economy.
Contact: National Office, 620 Bristol Business Park, Coldharbour Lane, Bristol, BS16 1EJ.
T: 0300 067 4000; E: fe.england@forestryengland.uk;
W: www.forestryengland.uk

FORESTRY & LAND SCOTLAND (2019)
Looks after national forests and land to enhance biodiversity, support tourism and increase access to the green spaces that will help improve Scotland's physical and mental health and well-being.
Contact: Head Office, 1 Highlander Way, Inverness Business Park, Inverness, IV2 7GB. T: 0131 370 5541;
E: enquiries@forestryandland.gov.scot;
W: www.forestryandland.gov.scot

SCOTTISH FORESTRY (2019)
Supports the delivery of sustainable Scottish forestry operations inc. grants for forestry activities and felling permissions.
Contact: Silvan House, 231 Corstorphine Road, Edinburgh EH12 7AT. T: 0131 370 5250;
E: Scottish.Forestry@forestry.gov.scot;
W: www.forestry.gov.scot

FORESTRY - Wales
See under listing for Natural Resources Wales.

FRESHWATER HABITATS TRUST (1988)
Formally Pond Conservation, Freshwater Habitats Trust aim is to protect freshwater life in ponds, streams, rivers and lakes through research, surveys and practical conservation work. Practical projects are targeted on the places that will bring the greatest benefits for freshwater life at regional and UK scale.
Contact: Freshwater Habitats Trust, Bury Knowle House, North Place, Headington, Oxford, OX3 9HY.
T: 01865 595 505; E: info@freshwaterhabitats.org.uk;
W: www.freshwaterhabitats.org.uk

FRIENDS OF THE EARTH (1971)
The largest international network of environmental groups in the world, represented in over 75 countries. In the UK it has a unique network of campaigning local groups, working in communities in England, Wales, Northern Ireland and Scotland. It is largely funded by supporters with more than 90% of income coming from individual donations, the rest from special fundraising events, grants and trading.
Contact: Friends of the Earth, The Printworks, 139 Clapham Road, London SW9 0HP.
T: 020 7490 1555; W: www.foe.co.uk

Friends of the Earth Cymru
33 Castle Arcade Balcony, Cardiff, CF10 1BY.
T: 029 2022 9577; E: cymru@foe.co.uk;
W: www.foe.cymru

Friends of the Earth Northern Ireland
W: www.friendsoftheearth.uk/northern-ireland

Friends of the Earth Scotland
Thorn House, 5 Rose Street, Edinburgh EH2 2PR.
T: 0131 243 2700; E: via website; W: https://foe.scot/

FWAG ASSOCIATION (2011)
The FWAG Association succeeded the Farming & Wildlife Advisory Group (FWAG - established in the 1960's) to represent local Farming & Wildlife Advisory Groups across the UK. FWAG's provide trusted, independent environmental advice to farmers helping them to understand the environmental value of their land and make the most of the agri-environment options available.
Contact: FWAG Association. E: hello@fwag.org.uk;
W: www.fwag.org.uk

Local FWAG Groups:
Chris Seabridge & Associates Limited (West Midlands)
T: 01785 710 564; E: info@chrisseabridge.co.uk;
W: www.chrisseabridge.co.uk

East Midlands FWAG (Derbys, Notts, Leics, Rutland, Northants, Lincs)
E: info@eastmidlandsfwag.co.uk;
W: www.eastmidlandsfwag.co.uk

FWAG Cymru
T: 01341 421 456; E: fwagcymru@btconnect.com

FWAG East (Cambs, Herts, Essex, Beds)
T: 01223 841 507; E: hello@fwageast.org.uk;
W: www.fwageast.org.uk

FWAG South East (Kent, Sussex, Surrey, Hants, IoW, Oxon)
T: 01483 810 887 & 07713 333 182;
E: shaun.page@fwagsoutheast.co.uk;
W: www.fwagadvice.co.uk

FWAG South West (Glous, Somerset, Dorset, Wilts, Devon, Cornwall)
T: 01823 660 684; E: info@fwagsw.org.uk;
W: www.fwagsw.org.uk

Norfolk FWAG
T: 01603 814 869; E: advice@norfolkfwag.co.uk;
W: www.norfolkfwag.co.uk

Suffolk FWAG
T: 01728 748 030; E: tim.schofield@suffolkfwag.co.uk;
W: www.suffolkfwag.co.uk

UK/UK-BASED ORGANISATIONS

GAME & WILDLIFE CONSERVATION TRUST (1931)

A registered charity which uses science to promote game and wildlife management as an essential part of nature conservation and support best practice for field sports that contribute to improving the biodiversity of the countryside. 100+ staff, inc. many scientists, run over 60 research projects. The results are used to advise government, landowners, farmers and conservationists on practical management techniques which will benefit game species, their habitats and other wildlife. In June the *Annual Review* lists papers published in the peer-reviewed scientific press. Members receive *Gamewise* magazine three times a year.
Contact: Game & Wildlife Conservation Trust, Burgate Manor, Fordingbridge, Hampshire SP6 1EF. T: 01425 652 381; Fax: 01425 655 848; E: info@gwct.org.uk; W: www.gwct.org.uk

GAY BIRDERS CLUB (1994)

A voluntary society for gay, lesbian, bisexual or transgender birdwatchers, their friends and supporters, over the age of consent, in the UK and worldwide. The club has a network of regional contacts and organises (up to 100 p.a.) day trips, weekends and longer events at notable birding locations in the UK and abroad. Members receive a quarterly newsletter *Out Birding* with details of all events. There is a 'Grand Get Together' every two years.
Contact: E: contact@gbc-online.org.uk; W: www.gbc-online.org.uk

HAWK & OWL TRUST (1969)

A registered charity dedicated to the conservation and appreciation of wild birds of prey and their habitats. Publishes a members' magazine, *Peregrine* and educational materials for all ages. The Trust achieves its major aim of creating and enhancing nesting, roosting and feeding habitats for birds of prey through projects which involve practical research, creative conservation and education, both on its own reserves and in partnership with landowners, farmers and others. Members are invited to take part in fieldwork, population studies, surveys, etc. The Trust manages two reserves: Sculthorpe Moor in Norfolk and Shapwick Moor on the Somerset Levels.
Contact: Hawk and Owl Trust, Turf Moor Road, Sculthorpe, Fakenham, Norfolk NR21 9GN. T: 01328 856 788; E: enquiries@hawkandowl.org; W: http://hawkandowl.org

INTERNATIONAL WADER STUDY GROUP (1970)

An association of wader enthusiasts, both amateur and professional, from all parts of the world, the Group aims to maintain contact between them, help organise co-operative studies, and provide a vehicle for the exchange of information. Publishes *Wader Study* three times a year and holds annual meetings throughout Europe.
Contact:
E: membership@waderstudygroup.org;
W: www.waderstudygroup.org

IRISH RARE BREEDING BIRDS PANEL

In Ireland, the (UK) RBBP is responsible for collating data on rare breeding species rare within the whole of the UK which breed or attempt to breed in Northern Ireland, but not in the Republic of Ireland. The IRBBP operates across the whole of Ireland.
Contact: E: secretary.irbbp@gmail.com; W: www.irbbp.org

IRISH RARE BIRDS COMMITTEE (1985)

Assesses records of species of rare occurrence in the Republic of Ireland. Details of records accepted and rejected have been published annually since 2004 in the *Irish Rare Bird Report* and previously (1953-2003) in the *Irish Bird Report*, published annually in *Irish Birds*. The Committee operates under the auspices of BirdWatch Ireland and also works closely with the Northern Ireland Birdwatchers' Association Rarities Committee to maintain a comprehensive record of birds found on the island of Ireland.
Contact: E: secretary@irbc.ie; W: www.irbc.ie

JOINT NATURE CONSERVATION COMMITTEE (1990)

A committee with members from Natural Resourses Wales, Northern Ireland's Council for Nature Conservation and the Countryside, Natural England and Scottish Natural Heritage as well as the Northern Ireland Environment Agency and independent members. Their role is to provide evidence, information and advice so that decisions are made to protect natural resources and systems, specifically to work on nature conservation issues the UK as a whole and internationally. The committee is the UK Government's nature conservation advisor in European and global fora, taking issues forward from the four home countries to inform policy development and then provide support to ensure that European and international requirements are met.
Contact: Joint Nature Conservation Committee, Monkstone House, City Road, Peterborough, PE1 1JY. T: 01733 562 626; Fax: 01733 555 948; E: comment@jncc.gov.uk; W: www.jncc.defra.gov.uk

LINNEAN SOCIETY OF LONDON (1788)

Named after Carl Linnaeus, the 18th Century Swedish biologist, who created the modern system of scientific biological nomenclature, the Society promotes all aspects of pure and applied biology. It houses Linnaeus' collection of plants, insects and fishes, library and correspondence. The Society has a major reference library consisting of books, journals and archives. Publishes the *Biological, Botanical* and *Zoological* Journals, and the *Synopsis of the British Fauna* series.
Contact: Linnean Society of London, Burlington House, Piccadilly, London W1J 0BF. T: 020 7434 4479 (ext. 210); E: info@linnean.org; W: www.linnean.org

LIPU-UK (1989)

(Italian League for the Protection of Birds)
A voluntary organisation that supports the work of LIPU in Italy by raising funds to carry out projects in the country. Members receive *Ali (Wings)* four times a year.
Contact: David Lingard, Fernwood, Doddington Road, Whisby, Lincs LN6 9BX. T: 01522 689 030; E: mail@lipu-uk.org; W: www.lipu-uk.org

UK/UK-BASED ORGANISATIONS

MAMMAL SOCIETY (1954)

The Mammal Society is the only organisation solely dedicated to the study and conservation of all British mammals. It seeks to raise awareness of mammal ecology and conservation needs, to survey British mammals and their habitats to identify the threats they face, and to promote mammal studies in the UK.
Contact: The Mammal Society, 18 St John's Church Road, London, E9 6EJ.T: 0238 001 0981;
E: info@themammalsociety.org; W: www.mammal.org.uk

MARINE CONSERVATION SOCIETY (1983)

MCS is the UK charity that campaigns for clean seas and beaches around the British coastline, sustainable fisheries, and protection for all marine life. MCS is consulted on a wide range of marine issues and provides advice primarily to government, but also to industry, on topics ranging from offshore wind, oil and gas, to marine strategies and fisheries reform. It provides advice to ensure that further action is taken to conserve our seas and reduce the effect of marine activities on marine habitats and species. It has an extensive programme for volunteers, ranging from fund-raising and an annual clean-up of UK beaches, to surveys of species such as basking shark.
Contact: Marine Conservation Society, Overross House, Ross Park, Ross-on-Wye, HR9 7US.
T: 01989 566 017; E: info@mcsuk.org;
W: www.mcsuk.org

NATIONAL TRUST (1895)

The charity works for the preservation of places of historic interest or natural beauty in England, Wales and Northern Ireland. It has a membership of over five million and over 65,000 volunteers (contributing nearly five million hours of work). Over 25 million visits are made to the pay-for-entry sites and it is estimated that 200 million visits are made to the open air properties. The Trust protects over 248,000ha of land, 780 miles of coastline and over 500 historic houses, castles, ancient monuments, gardens and parks and nature reserves (many of the latter SSSIs/ASSIs, NNRs, Ramsar sites and SPAs).
Contact: The National Trust (Membership), PO Box 574, Manvers, Rotherham, S63 3FH. T: 0344 800 1895;
E: enquiries@nationaltrust.org.uk;
W: www.nationaltrust.org.uk

NATIONAL TRUST FOR SCOTLAND (1931)

The charity protects and promotes Scotland's natural and cultural heritage for present and future generations to enjoy. Amongst its responsibilities it looks after 271 listed buildings, 38 gardens and designed landscapes, 76,000ha of countryside - inc. eight National Nature Reserves and 46 Munro mountains.
Contact: The National Trust for Scotland, Hermiston Quay, 5 Cultins Rd, Edinburgh EH11 4DF.
T: 0131 458 0200; E: via website; W: www.nts.org.uk

NATURAL ENGLAND

Natural England is the government's adviser for the natural environment in England, helping to protect England's nature and landscape for people to enjoy and for the services they provide. Responsibilities include helping land managers and farmers to protect wildlife and landscapes; improving public access to the coastline; managing about two thirds of the 224 National Nature Reserves; managing programmes that help restore and create wildlife habitats; and providing evidence to help make decisions affecting the natural environment.
Contact: Natural England (Enquiries), County Hall, Spetchley Road, Worcester, WR5 2NP.
T: 0300 060 3900 (enquiries);
E: enquiries@naturalengland.org.uk;
W: www.gov.uk/government/organisations/natural-england

NATURAL HISTORY MUSEUM AT TRING (1937)

Founded by Lord Rothschild, the museum has 80 million specimens inc. many rarities and extinct species, only a tiny fraction ever go on display. The galleries are open daily 10am-5pm (2pm-5pm on Sun) except Dec 24-26. Bird Group: the Museum at Tring looks after one of the largest ornithological collections in the world - with over a million skins, skeletons, nests, sets of eggs and specimens preserved in spirit, and there is an extensive ornithological library with 75,000 works. The Bird Group collection and library are not open to the public but can be visited by researchers (enquire by E: via website).
Contact: The Walter Rothschild Building, Akeman Street, Tring, Herts HP23 6AP. T: 020 7942 5000;
W: www.nhm.ac.uk/visit/tring.html

NATURAL RESOURCES WALES (2013)

Natural Resources Wales brought together the work of the Countryside Council for Wales, Environment Agency Wales and Forestry Commission Wales, as well as some functions of Welsh Government. Its purpose is to ensure that the natural resources of Wales are sustainably maintained, enhanced and used, now and in the future.
Contact: Natural Resources Wales, c/o Customer Care Centre, Tŷ Cambria, 29 Newport Road, Cardiff CF24 0TP.
T: 0300 065 3000 (Mon-Fri, 9am-5pm);
environmental incident -
T: 0300 065 3000, 1 for welsh, 2 for english (24 hrs);
floodline - T: 0345 988 1188 (24 hrs);
E: enquiries@naturalresourceswales.gov.uk;
W: https://naturalresources.wales/

NEOTROPICAL BIRD CLUB (1994)

(Middle & South America and the Caribbean)
An international organisation for those interested in

birds of the Neotropics, the NBC aims to foster an interest in the region and to increase awareness of the importance of support for conservation there. Publishes *Neotropical Birding* and *Cotinga*.
Contact: Neotropical Bird Club, c/o The Lodge, Sandy, Bedfordshire SG19 2DL. T: 01255 821 083;
E: secretary@neotropicalbirdclub.org;
W: www.neotropicalbirdclub.org

UK/UK-BASED ORGANISATIONS

NORTH SEA BIRD CLUB (1979)
The Club aims to: provide a recreational pursuit for people employed offshore; obtain, collate and analyse observations of all birds seen offshore; produce reports of observations, inc. an annual report; promote the collection of data on other wildlife offshore. Currently it holds over 120,000 records of birds, cetaceans and insects reported since 1979.
Contact: The North Sea Bird Club, Ocean Laboratory and Culterty Field Station, Newburgh, Aberdeenshire AB41 6AA. T: 01224 274 428; E: nsbc@abdn.ac.uk; W: www.abdn.ac.uk/nsbc/

NORTHERN IRELAND BIRDWATCHERS' ASSOCIATION (1991)
NIBA publishes the Northern Ireland Bird Report and is responsible for Flightline, a local rate telephone hotline for rare bird sightings. The NIBA Records Committee assesses the records in N Ireland.
Contact: NIBA. T: 028 9146 7408 (Flightline); E: nibirds@live.co.uk; W: http://nibirds.blogspot.com

NORTHERN IRELAND ORNITHOLOGISTS' CLUB (1965)
Formed to focus the interests of active birdwatchers in Northern Ireland. There is a regular programme of lectures (Oct-Apr) and field trips for members and the Club organises an annual photographic competition.
Contact: Carol Gillespie (Hon Sec), NIOC, 4 Demesne Gate, Saintfield, Co. Down BT24 7BE. T: 028 9751 9371; E: carolgillespie@btinternet.com; W: www.nioc.co.uk

NORTHERN IRELAND RARE BIRDS COMMITTEE (1997)
NIRBC manages the records of rare birds in Northern Ireland and maintains the Northern Ireland Bird List.
Contact: NIRBC. E: NIRBComm@gmail.com; W: https://nirbc.blogspot.co.uk

ORIENTAL BIRD CLUB (1984)
Membership is open to anyone who has an interest in birds of the Oriental region and their conservation. This interest in encouraged; the work of regional bird and nature societies is promoted; and information on Oriental birds is collated and published. Publishes *Forktail* and *BirdingASIA*.
Contact: Oriental Bird Club, P.O.Box 324, Bedford, MK42 0WG. E: mail@orientalbirdclub.org; W: www.orientalbirdclub.org

ORNITHOLOGICAL SOCIETY OF THE MIDDLE EAST, THE CAUCASUS & CENTRAL ASIA (OSME) (1978)
Encourages birdwatchers to visit the region; to particpate in surveys; and to work with others involved there. A conservation and research fund offers small grants. Publishes *Sandgrouse*.
Contact: OSME, c/o The Lodge, Sandy, Bedfordshire SG19 2DL. E: via website; W: www.osme.org

PLANTLIFE (1989)
Works nationally and internationally to save threatened wild flowers, plants and fungi - this includes working with others to protect rare flora and to ensure familiar flowers and plants continue to thrive; managing 23 nature reserves; and identifying 165 IPA's (Important Plant Areas) across the UK.

Contact: Plantlife, Brewery House, 36 Milford Street, Salisbury, Wiltshire SP1 2AP. T: 01722 342 730; E: enquiries@plantlife.org.uk; W: www.plantlife.org.uk/uk

RARE BREEDING BIRDS PANEL (1972)
With a representative from BTO, JNCC, RSPB, three independent members and a Secretary, the RBBP collects all information on rare breeding birds in the UK, so that changes in status can be monitored as an aid to conservation and is stored for posterity. Bespoke recording forms are used (obtainable from the website). Records should be submitted via county and regional recorders.
RBBP also monitor breeding by scarcer non-native species and seek records of these in the same way. An Annual report is published in *British Birds*. For details of species covered by RBBP see 'Checklists' section (P.57).
Contact: The Secretary, Rare Breeding Birds Panel, The Old Orchard, Grange Road, North Berwick, East Lothian EH39 4QT. T: 01620 894 037; E: secretary@rbbp.org.uk; W: www.rbbp.org.uk

ROYAL AIR FORCE ORNITHOLOGICAL SOCIETY (1965)
Open to any serving and ex-RAF personnel, other Services, MOD civil servants and their families. Organises field meetings and expeditions at home and abroad and undertakes surveys and ringing operations. Publishes a newsletter and a journal.
Contact: Jan Knight (Gen Sec). E: rafos_secretary@hotmail.com; W: www.rafornithology.org.uk

ROYAL ENTOMOLOGICAL SOCIETY (1833)
The RES promotes and develops entomological science and supports international collaboration, research and publication - demonstrating the importance of studying insects to everyone.
Contact: Royal Entomological Society, The Mansion House, Chiswell Green Lane, St Albans, AL2 3NS. T: 01727 899 387; E: info@royensoc.co.uk; W: www.royensoc.co.uk

ROYAL NAVAL BIRDWATCHING SOCIETY (1946)
RNBWS is open to anyone with a common interest in birds at sea. Maintains an extensive seabird database with records received from most sea areas of the world. Publishes a newsletter four times a year and an annual report - *The Sea Swallow*. The RNBWS administers a fund left by the late Cpt David Simpson with small grants available for scientific seabird studies.
Contact: Warrant Officer Steve Copsey RN (Gen Sec). E: secretary@rnbws.org.uk; W: www.rnbws.org.uk

ROYAL PIGEON RACING ASSOCIATION (1897)
Promotes the sport of pigeon racing and controls pigeon racing within the Association. Organises liberation sites, issues rings, calculates distances between liberation sites and home lofts, and assists in the return of strays. May be able to assist in identifying owners of ringed birds found.
Contact: Royal Pigeon Racing Association, The Reddings, Cheltenham, GL51 6RN. T: 01452 713 529; E: via website; W: www.rpra.org

ROYAL SOCIETY FOR THE PROTECTION OF BIRDS (1889)

UK Partner of BirdLife International and, with over 1.2 million members (inc. 200,000+ youth members - see RSPB Phoenix/RSPB Wildlife Explorers), is Europe's largest voluntary wildlife conservation body. The RSPB, a registered charity, is governed by an elected body. Its work in the conservation of wild birds and habitats covers a range of areas including: the acquisition and management of nature reserves; research and surveys; monitoring; responding to development proposals, land use practices and pollution which threaten wild birds and biodiversity; and the provision of an advisory service on wildlife law enforcement.

The RSPB currently manages over 200 nature reserves in the UK, covering ca.130,000ha and home to 80% of Britain's rarest or most threatened bird species. The aim is to conserve a countrywide network of reserves with all examples of the main bird communities and with due regard to the conservation of plants and other animals. There is an active network of 140 local groups (see County Directory) which hold regular indoor and outdoor meetings. Over 12,000 people volunteer in a wide range of capacities, inc. working on the RSPB's nature reserves. The RSPB's International Dept works closely with Birdlife International and its partners in other countries and is involved with numerous projects overseas, especially in Europe and Asia.

Contact: RSPB, The Lodge, Potton Road, Sandy, Bedfordshire SG19 2DL. T: 01767 680 551; E: individual members of staff (firstname.surname)@rspb.org.uk;

Membership enquiries: T: 01767 693 680 (9am-5.15pm, Mon-Fri); E: membership@rspb.org.uk

Wildlife enquiries: T: 01767 693 690 (9.30am-4.30pm, Mon-Fri); E: wildlife@rspb.org.uk

W: www.rspb.org.uk

Regional Offices:

ENGLAND

Eastern England: Stalham House, 65 Thorpe Road, Norwich, NR1 1UD. T: 01603 660 062.
Covers: Bedfordshire, Cambridgeshire, Essex, Hertfordshire, Lincolnshire, Norfolk, Suffolk.

London Office: 5th Floor, 50 Southwark Street, London SE1 1UN. T: 0207 940 3050.

Midlands: 1st Floor, One Cornwall Street, Birmingham, B3 2JN. T: 01767 693 777.
Covers: Buckinghamshire, Derbyshire, Herefordshire, Leicestershire, Northamptonshire, Nottinghamshire, Oxfordshire, Rutland, Shropshire, Staffordshire, Warwickshire, West Midlands, Worcestershire.

Northern England:
Denby Dale Office, Westleigh Mews, Wakefield Road, Denby Dale, Huddersfield, HD8 8QD. T: 0300 7772 676.

Newcastle Office, 1 Sirius House, Amethyst Road, Newcastle Business Park, Newcastle-upon-Tyne, NE4 7YL. T: 0300 7772 676.

Lancaster Office, 7.3.1 Cameron House, White Cross Estate, Lancaster, LA1 4XF. T: 0300 7772 676.
Covers: Cheshire, Cleveland, County Durham, Cumbria, East Riding of Yorkshire, Greater Manchester, Lancashire, Merseyside, Middlesbrough, North Yorkshire, North East Lincolnshire, North Lincolnshire, Northumberland, South Yorkshire, Tyne & Wear, West Yorkshire.

South East: 1st Floor, Pavilion View, 19 New Road, Brighton, BN1 1UF. T: 01273 775 333.
Covers: East Sussex, Hampshire, Isle of Wight, Kent, Surrey, Berkshire, West Sussex.

South West: 4th Floor (North Block), Broadwalk House, Southernhay West, Exeter, EX1 1TS. T: 01392 432 691.
Covers: Bristol, Cornwall, Devon, Dorset, Gloucestershire, Somerset, Wiltshire.

NORTHERN IRELAND

Northern Ireland Headquarters: Belvoir Park Forest, Belfast, BT8 7QT. T: 028 9049 1547.
Covers: Co. Antrim, Co. Armagh, Co. Down, Co. Fermanagh, Co. Londonderry, Co. Tyrone.

SCOTLAND

Scotland Headquarters: 2 Lochside View, Edinburgh Park, Edinburgh EH12 9DH. T: 0131 317 4100.

East Scotland: 10 Albyn Terrace, Aberdeen, Aberdeenshire AB10 1YP. E: esro@rspb.org.uk; T: 01224 624 824.
Covers: Aberdeen, Aberdeenshire, Angus, Dundee, Fife, Moray, Orkney, Perth and Kinross, Shetland.

North Scotland: Etive House, Beechwood Park, Inverness, IV2 3BW. T: 01463 715 000; E: nsro@rspb.org.uk
Covers: Eilean Siar, Highland.

South and West Scotland: 10 Park Quadrant, Glasgow, G3 6BS. T: 0141 331 0993; E: glasgow@rspb.org.uk
Covers: Argyll and Bute, Clackmannanshire, Dumfries and Galloway, East Ayrshire, East Lothian, East Dunbartonshire, East Renfrewshire, Edinburgh, Falkirk, Glasgow, Interclyde, Midlothian, North Ayrshire, North Lanarkshire, Renfrewshire, Scottish Borders, South Ayrshire, South Lanarkshire, Stirling, West Dunbartonshire, West Lothian.

WALES

Wales Headquarters: Castlebridge 3, 5-19 Cowbridge Road East, Cardiff CF11 9AB. T: 029 2035. 3000; E: cymru@rspb.org.uk
Covers: Blaenau Gwent, Bridgend, Caerphilly, Cardiff, Carmarthenshire, Ceredigion, Merthyr Tydfil, Monmouthshire, Neath Port Talbot, Newport, Pembrokeshire, Powys, Rhondda Cynon Taff, Swansea, Torfaen, Vale of Glamorgan.

North Wales Office: Uned 14, Llys Castan, Ffordd Y Parc, Parc Menai, Bangor, Gwynedd LL57 4FD. T: 01248 672 850.
Covers: Conwy, Denbighshire, Flintshire, Gwynedd, Isle of Anglesey, Wrexham.

RSPB WILDLIFE EXPLORERS (4-19) / RSPB PHOENIX (13+)

Junior section of the RSPB (formally the YOC), with a local network of around 80 youth groups. Activities include projects, holidays, roadshows, competitions, and local events for children, families and teenagers. All members receive *Wild Explorer* (6 pa.), Pheonix members also receive *Wingbeat*, the only environmental magazine written by teenagers for teenagers (4 pa.).
Contact: RSPB - as above.
W: www.rspb.org.uk/fun-and-learning/for-kids

SCOTTISH BIRDS RECORDS COMMITTEE (1984)

Set up by the Scottish Ornithologists' Club to ensure that records of species not deemed rare enough to be considered by the British Birds Rarities Committee, but which are rare in Scotland, are fully assessed; also maintains the official list of Scottish birds.
Contact: Chris McInerny (Sec), SBRC, 10 Athole Gardens, Glasgow, G12 9AZ E: chris.mcinerny@glasgow.ac.uk;
W: www.the-soc.org.uk/bird-recording/about-sbrc

SCOTTISH NATURAL HERITAGE (1991)

SNH is funded by the Scottish Government. Its purpose is to promote and care for Scotland's natural heritage; to enable people to enjoy the outdoors; and to support those who manage it.
Contact: SNH HQ, Great Glen House, Leachkin Road, Inverness, IV3 8NW. T: 01463 725 000;
E: enquiries@nature.scot; W: www.nature.scot

SCOTTISH ORNITHOLOGISTS' CLUB (1936)

The SOC promotes the study, enjoyment and conservation of wild birds and their habitats across Scotland. The Club has 15 branches (see County Directory), each with a programme of indoor meetings and field trips. The SOC organises an annual weekend conference in the autumn and a joint SOC/BTO one-day birdwatchers' conference in spring. *Scottish Birds* is published quarterly. The SOC is based in a large resource centre offering panoramic views of Aberlady Bay and houses the George Waterston Library.
Contact: The SOC, Waterston House, Aberlady, East Lothian EH32 0PY. T: 01875 871 330;
E: via website; W: www.the-soc.org.uk

SCOTTISH WILDLIFE TRUST (1964)

A member of The Wildlife Trusts partnership. The Trust's vision is for 'healthy, resilient ecosystems across Scotland's land and seas.' Its main activities focus on managing 120 wildlife reserves, and four visitor centres, undertaking practical conservation tasks; influencing and campaigning for better wildlife-related policy and action; inspiring people to enjoy and find out more about wildlife - offering a network of 19 local groups.
Contact: Scottish Wildlife Trust, Harbourside House, 110 Commercial Street, Edinburgh, EH6 6NF.
T: 0131 312 7765;
E: enquiries@scottishwildlifetrust.org.uk;
W: www.scottishwildlifetrust.org.uk

SEABIRD GROUP (1966)

The group promotes and helps to coordinate the study and conservation of seabirds. It maintains close links with other national and international ornithological bodies and organises regular conferences on seabird biology and conservation topics. Small grants available to assist with research/survey work on seabirds. Publishes regular newsletters and the journal '*Seabird*'.
Contact: Holly Klrk (Secretary).
E: secretary@seabirdgroup.org.uk;
W: www.seabirdgroup.org.uk

SWIFT CONSERVATION (2009)

An advice service aiming to reverse the decline in the UK's Swifts. Swift Conservation runs a website providing extensive information on Swifts, and on how to both preserve existing and set up new Swift nest sites. Swift Conservation also runs a lecture and training service, providing guidance for the general public, planners, developers and architects. It supplies advice and help both directly and via volunteers, and has links to similar assistance across Europe, the Middle East, Central Asia and North America. It campaigns for better protection of Swifts and other birds that rely on nest places in or on buildings.
Contact: E: mail@swift-conservation.org;
W: www.swift-conservation.org

THE CONSERVATION VOLUNTEERS (formerly BTCV) (1959)

The Conservation Volunteers helps thousands of people each year to reclaim local green spaces. Through their own environmental projects and through a network of community groups people are enabled to take responsibility for their local environments. TCV has published a series of practical handbooks (digital format/subscribe online).
Contact: TCV, Sedum House, Mallard Way, Potteric Carr, Doncaster, DN4 8DB. T: 01302 388 883;
E: information@tcv.org.uk; W: www.tcv.org.uk

TRAFFIC International (1976)
(the wildlife trade monitoring network)

Works globally on trade in wild animals and plants in the context of biodiversity conservation and sustainable development, ensuring that this trade is not a threat to the conservation of nature. Publishes *The TRAFFIC Bulletin*.
Contact: Traffic Global Office, The David Attenborough Building, Pembroke Street, Cambridge CB2 3QZ.
T: 01223 277 427; E: traffic@traffic.org;
W: www.traffic.org

WADER QUEST (2012)

A voluntary charity dedicated to supporting wader conservation through fundraising and increasing awareness about the acute problems facing wader populations around the world. Specialises in supporting community wader conservation projects by purchasing equipment and materials from the charity's Grants Fund. Members (Friends of Wader Quest & Sponsors) receive a quarterly e-newsletter. Talks and events are undertaken throughout the year in partnership with other organisations.

UK/UK-BASED ORGANISATIONS

Contact: Rick and Elis Simpson, Wader Quest,
20 Windsor Avenue, Newport Pagnell, Bucks, MK16 8HA.
T: 07484 186 443; E: waderquest@gmail.com;
W: www.waderquest.net

WELSH ORNITHOLOGICAL SOCIETY (1988)
Promotes the study, conservation and enjoyment of
birds throughout Wales. Runs the Welsh Records Panel
which maintains then Welsh bird list and produces
an annual report of accepted rare birds in Wales.
Publishes the journal *Birds In Wales* twice a year and
organises an annual conference.
Contact: E: membership@birdsin.wales;
W: www.birdsin.wales

WEST AFRICAN ORNITHOLOGICAL SOCIETY (1964)
Grew out of the Nigerian Ornithologists' Society. The
Society's aim is to promote scientific interest in the
birds of West Africa (comprising 28 countries) and to
further the region's ornithology, mainly through its
journal - *Malimbus*.
Contact: Tim Dodman (Membership Secretary),
Hundland, Papa Westray, Orkney KW17 2BU.
E: tim@timdodman.co.uk; W: malimbus.free.fr

for **EAST AFRICA NATURAL HISTORY SOCIETY (1909)**
(see Kenya/Nature Kenya under BirdLife Africa, P307)

WILDFOWL & WETLANDS TRUST (1946)
Founded by Sir Peter Scott to conserve wetlands and
their biodiversity, WWT has 10 wetland centres
(see below). The centres are nationally, or
internationally, important for wintering wildfowl.
Walks, talks and events are available for visitors,
and resources and programmes are provided for
school groups. Most of the centres have collections
of wildfowl from around the world, inc. many
endangered species. The Trust's conservation
programmes focus on a variety of aspects inc. science
and processes that underpin conservation action,
threats to wetlands and their wildlife and threatened
species. WWT Consulting undertakes commercial
contracts and Wetland Link International promotes
the role of wetland centres for education and public
awareness. Publishes the journal *Wildfowl* annually.
Contact: Wildfowl and Wetlands Trust, Slimbridge,
Gloucestershire GL2 7BT. T: 01453 891 900;
E: enquiries@wwt.org.uk; W: www.wwt.org.uk

WWT Wetland Centres:
Arundel, Mill Road, Arundel, Sussex BN18 9PB.
T: 01903 883 355; E: info.arundel@wwt.org.uk

Caerlaverock, Eastpark Farm, Caerlaverock,
Dumfriesshire DG1 4RS. T: 01387 770 200;
E: info.caerlaverock@wwt.org.uk

Castle Espie, 78 Ballydrain Road, Comber,
Co Down, N Ireland BT23 6EA. T: 028 9187 4146;
E: info.castleespie@wwt.org.uk

London, Queen Elizabeth's Walk, Barnes, London
SW13 9WT. T: 020 8409 4400;
E: info.london@wwt.org.uk

Martin Mere, Fish Lane, Burscough, Lancashire
L40 0TA. T: 01704 895 181;
E: info.martinmere@wwt.org.uk

National Wetland Centre Wales, Llwynhendy, Llanelli,
Carmarthenshire SA14 9SH. T: 01554 741 087;
E: info.llanelli@wwt.org.uk

Slimbridge, Bowditch, Slimbridge, Gloucs
GL2 7BT. T: 01453 891 900;
E: info.slimbridge@wwt.org.uk

Steart Marshes, Steart, Somerset, TA5 2PU.
T: 01278 651 090; E: info.steart@wwt.org.uk

Washington, Pattinson, Washington, Tyne & Wear
NE38 8LE. T: 0191 416 5454;
E: info.washington@wwt.org.uk

Welney, Hundred Foot Bank, Welney, Nr. Wisbech,
PE14 9TN. T: 01353 860 711;
E: info.welney@wwt.org.uk

WILDLIFE SOUND RECORDING SOCIETY (1968)
Works closely with the Wildlife Section, British Library
Sound Archive. Members carry out recording work
for scientific purposes as well as for pleasure. A field
weekend is held each spring, and members organise
meetings locally. Four CD sound magazines of members'
recordings are produced for members each year, and a
journal, *Wildlife Sound*, is published twice a year.
Contact: David Mellor (Hon Membership Secretary),
WSRS, Fuchsia Cottage, Helperthorpe, Nr Malton,
North Yorks YO17 8TQ;
E: membership@wildlife-sound.org;
W: www.wildlife-sound.org

WILDLIFE TRUSTS (1995)
Founded in 1912 and now the largest UK charity
dedicated to conserving all habitats and species, with a
membership of 800,000+ in 46 individual county trusts
(see County Directory). Collectively, they manage
2,300 nature reserves covering more than 98,000 ha.
The Trusts also lobby for better protection of the
UK's natural heritage and are dedicated to protecting
wildlife for the future. Members receive their local Trust
magazine which includes a UK News section.
Contact: The Wildlife Trusts, The Kiln, Waterside,
Mather Road, Newark, NG24 1WT. T: 01636 677 711;
Fax: 01636 670 001; E: enquiry@wildlifetrusts.org;
W: www.wildlifetrusts.org

WILDLIFE WATCH (1977)
Junior branch of the Wildlife Trusts with 150,000 members.
There are ca.300 Wildlife Watch groups across the UK
where children can join in a wide range of activities.
Membership is through a local Trust as a junior member.
Contact: Wildlife Watch - address as above.
T: 01636 670 000; E: watch@wildlifetrusts.org;
W: www.wildlifewatch.org.uk

UK/UK-BASED ORGANISATIONS

WOODLAND TRUST (1972)

The UK's larges woodland conservation charity works to protect, and campaign on behalf of, the country's woods inc. creating new native woodlands and restoring ancient woodland for the benefit of wildlife and people. Manages over 1000 sites.

Contact:

England: Kempton Way, Grantham, Lincolnshire NG31 6LL. T: 0330 33300; E: england@woodlandtrust.org.uk; W: www.woodlandtrust.org.uk

Northern Ireland: 1 Dufferin Court, Bangor, Co. Down BT20 3BX. T: 028 9127 5787; E: northernireland@woodlandtrust.org.uk

Scotland: South Inch Business Centre, Perth, PH2 8BW. T: 01738 635 544; E: scotland@woodlandtrust.org.uk

Wales: Castle Court, 6 Cathedral Road, Cardiff, CF11 9LJ. T: 029 2002 7732; E: wales@woodlandtrust.org.uk

WORLD OWL TRUST

Works on owl conservation nationally and internationally. Their conservation programmes protect populations of endangered owls until their habitat has been restored. A new World Owl Centre is under construction to house its owl collection.

Contact: World Owl Trust, Millstones, Bootle, Cumbria LA19 5TJ. T: 01229 718 080; E: jen@owls.org; W: www.owls.org

WORLD PHEASANT ASSOCIATION (1975)

WPA is committed to the conservation of *Galliformes* and their habitats which they do by: promoting the conservation of those species that are rare or in danger of extinction; advancing the education of the public and the knowledge of such species; and conducting research and studying captive and wild species. Publishes *WPA News*.

Contact: Barbara Ingman (administrator), WPA, Middle, Nimebanks, Hexham, Northumberland NE47 8DL. T: 01434 345 526; E: office@pheasant.org.uk; W: www.pheasant.org.uk

WWF-UK (1961)

WWF is the world's largest independent conservation organisation, working in more than 100 countries. It works to conserve habitats and species, protect endangered spaces, and address global threats to nature by seeking long-term solutions with people in government and industry, education and civil society. Members receive *Action* magazine three times a year.

Contact: WWF-UK, The Living Planet Centre, Rufford House, Brewery Road, Woking, Surrey GU21 4LL. T: 01483 426 444; E: via website; W: www.wwf.org.uk; W: www.panda.org

WWF Cymru, Churchill House, 17 Churchill Way, Cardiff, CF10 2HH. T: 029 2045 4970; E: wales@wwf.org.uk

WWF Scotland, The Tun, 4 Jackson's Entry, Holyrood Road, Edinburgh, EH8 8PJ. T: 0131 659 9100; E: scotland@wwf.org.uk

ZOOLOGICAL PHOTOGRAPHIC CLUB (1899)

Circulates black and white and colour prints of zoological interest via a series of postal portfolios. Membership limited to 28.

Contact: John Tinning (Hon. Secretary). E: john.tinning@btinternet.com; W: www.zpc-naturefolio.org.uk

ZOOLOGICAL SOCIETY OF LONDON (1826)

Carries out research, organises symposia and holds scientific meetings. Manages the Zoological Gardens in Regent's Park (first opened in 1828) and Whipsnade Wild Animal Park near Dunstable, Beds, each with extensive collections of birds. The Society's library has a large collection of ornithological books and journals. Publications include *Journal of Zoology* and *The International Zoo Yearbook*.

Contact: Zoological Society of London, Regent's Park, London NW1 4RY. T: 0344 225 1826; E: generalenquiries@zsl.org; W: www.zsl.org

NATIONAL PROJECTS

Namateur birdwatchers. In return they provide birdwatchers with an excellent opportunity to contribute in a positive and worthwhile way to the scientific study of birds and their habitats, which is the vital basis of all conservation programmes. The following entries provide a description of a number of ongoing projects and who to contact for further information.

BIG GARDEN BIRDWATCH
An RSPB Survey
The Big Garden Birdwatch, first launched in 1979, has grown into fun for all the family. The long-term trends of birds coming into gardens can be monitored. All you need to do is count the birds in your garden, or a local park, for one hour during (usually) the last weekend of January. In 2019 over 472,000 people counted a total of 7,669,138 birds, with House Sparrow, Starling and Blue Tit in 1st, 2nd and 3rd places.
Contact: RSPB.

BIRDTRACK
Organised by BTO on behalf of BTO, RSPB, BirdWatch Ireland, SOC, WOS & BirdLife International
BirdTrack is a free, online bird recording system for birdwatchers to store and manage bird records from anywhere in Britain and Ireland. The idea is simple: make a note of the birds that you see/hear at any time and then enter your observations on an easy-to-use web page:
https://app.bto.org/birdtrack/main/data-home.jsp

Registration is required - complete lists are preferred but casual records and incomplete lists can also be entered.There's also a free App for Android and iPhone smartphones through which you can log your sightings whilst you're in the field and upload them at the click of a button.
Exciting real-time outputs are generated by BirdTrack, including species reporting-rate graphs and animated maps of sightings, all freely-available online. The data collected are used by researchers to investigate migration movements and the distribution of scarce birds, and to support species conservation at local, national and international scales.
Contact: BTO. E: birdtrack@bto.org

BREEDING BIRD SURVEY (BBS)
Supported by BTO, JNCC & RSPB
First started in 1994, the BBS is the main scheme for monitoring population changes of the UK's common breeding birds and provides an indicator of the health of the countryside. It is dependent on volunteer birdwatchers throughout the country. Two visits (early-Apr/mid-May and mid-May/late-Jun) of about five hours in total, are made to survey the breeding birds in a 1x1km square. Survey squares are picked at random by computer to ensure that all habitats and regions are covered. BBS trends are produced annually for nearly 120 species.
Since its inception, BBS has been a tremendous success - now nearly 3000 volunteers cover nearly 4000 squares recording more than 200 species annually.
Contact: BTO, Sarah Harris (National Organiser)
E: bbs@bto.org or your local BTO Regional Representative (see County Directory).

CONSTANT EFFORT SITES (CES) SCHEME
Funded by a partnership between BTO, JNCC, The National Parks & Wildlife Service (Ireland) & ringers
The CES scheme, run since 1983, coordinates standardised mist-netting at over 130 sites across Britain and Ireland (12 visits between May-Aug). The scheme allows the BTO to monitor trends on abundance of adults and juveniles, productivity and adult survival rates for 24 species of common songbirds.
Information from CES complements demographic information collected by other BTO surveys and feeds into the BTO's Integrated Population Monitoring programme which highlights the causes of changes in bird populations. Results are updated annually and published on-line as part of the BirdTrends Report.
Contact: BTO. E: ces@bto.org

GARDEN BIRD FEEDING SURVEY (GBFS)
A BTO project
Starting in 1970/71, the Garden Bird Feeding Survey is the longest-running study of garden birds in Britain. Each year, a network of householders record the numbers and variety of birds using the different food supplements, feeders and water that they have provided in their garden - the results examine the effects on birds using these resources. Participation is limited to about 250 gardens each year. Observations are made on a weekly basis from October to March inclusive, with two recording periods (Oct/Dec & Jan/Mar). Gardens are selected by region and by type - from city flats to suburban semis, rural houses to outlying farms - to give a good spread of sites. The project is funded through an annual subscription.
Contact: BTO. E: gwb@bto.org

BTO GARDEN BIRDWATCH (GBW)
A BTO project
Started in January 1995, this project is a year-round survey that monitors the use that birds and other species groups of wildlife make of gardens. Participants from all over the UK and Ireland keep a weekly log of species using their gardens. The data collected are used to monitor regional, seasonal and year-to-year changes in the garden populations of our commoner birds, mammals, butterflies, reptiles and amphibians. The project is funded through an annual subscription, participants recieve a magazine four times a year.
Contact: BTO. E: gbw@bto.org

Sign up for Birdtrack...
make your sightings count

NATIONAL PROJECTS

GARDEN WILDLIFE HEALTH
A joint scheme of Zoological Society of London, BTO, Froglife & RSPB
This project aims to monitor the health of, and identify disease threats to, British garden wildlife. The particular focus is on garden birds, amphibians, reptiles and hedgehogs. Members of the public are asked to submit reports of sick or dead wildlife and may be to submit samples for analysis (contact first).
Contact: Garden Wildlife Health vets
T: 0207 449 6685; E: report sick/dead wildlife via a website link; other enquiries E: GWH@zsl.org
W: www.gardenwildlifehealth.org

GOOSE AND SWAN MONITORING PROGRAMME (GSMP)
Organised by WWT and funded in partnership with JNCC & Scottish National Heritage
Geese and swans are a cornerstone of the Wildfowl and Wetland Trust's conservation work. The UK supports 14 native goose and migratory swan populations, 13 are monitored through the GSMP network. During winter, geese and swans from Canada to central Russia undertake arduous migrations to reach their wintering grounds in the UK. In order to safeguard them WWT tracks how many individuals are in each population, where they are found, and the overall trend of the population (increasing, decreasing or remaining stable). Other demographic measures - most importantly productivity (how many young are born each year) and survival (or mortality) rates - help to understand the reasons behind any increases or decreases. To gather the information the WWT use a number of techniques and tools, including counts and capture/marking. A large amount of this work is carried out by volunteer birdwatchers who give their time to assist with the data collection.
Contact: WWT. E: enquiries@wwt.org.uk;
W: http://monitoring.wwt.org.uk/our-work/

HERONRIES CENSUS
A BTO project
This survey, started in 1928, has been carried out under the auspices of the BTO since 1934 and represents the longest continuous series of population data for any European breeding bird (Grey Heron). Counts of apparently occupied nests are made at as many UK heronries as possible each year, to provide an index of current population levels.
Data from Scotland and Wales is relatively scant, and more contributions from these countries would be especially welcomed, as would notification of new colonies elsewhere. Herons may be hit hard during periods of severe weather and are vulnerable to pesticides and pollution. Little Egret and other incoming species of colonial waterbird such as Cattle Egret are now fully included, whether nesting with Grey Herons, or on their own. Counts of Cormorant nests at heronries are also encouraged. Periodically Heronries Surveys are undertake and the data added to the Heroneries Census database. The 2018 Heroneries Survey was the most complete survey ever recorded in one year - producing a population estimate of just over 10,000 Grey Herons and over 1000 Little Egrets (apparently occupied nests).
Contact: BTO. E: herons@bto.org

IRISH WETLAND BIRD SURVEY (I-Webs)
A joint project of BirdWatch Ireland, the National Parks & Wildlife Service and the Dept of Arts, Culture & the Gaeltacht
The Irish Wetland Bird Survey (I-WebS) is the scheme that monitors wintering waterbirds in the Republic of Ireland. The survey runs from September to March each winter. Wetlands of all types and sizes are monitored, including estuaries, coastlines, bays, rivers, turloughs, lakes, streams and flooded fields. Each winter, more than 400 people take part counting waterbirds at over 250 wetlands throughout the country. The counts are undertaken once a month on predefined count days by skilled volunteers, as well as by professional staff of the National Parks and Wildlife Service and BirdWatch Ireland. New counters welcomed!
Contact: I-WebS Office, BirdWatch Ireland.
T: 353 (0)1 281 9878; E: iwebs@birdwatchireland.ie

NATIONAL BEACHED BIRD SURVEY
An RSPB project
In its current format the NBBS has been running since 1971. The results of the annual survey are used in conjunction with those from other European countries and aim to contribute to international monitoring efforts to document trends in chronic marine oil pollution and to promote adequate methods of controlling illegal oil discharge to help reduce seabird mortality.
Contact: RSPB.

NEST BOX CHALLENGE
A BTO project
NBC is an on-line survey which aims to monitor the breeding success of birds in Britain's green spaces. Participants are asked to register one or more nests, or nest boxes, in their garden or local green space, monitoring their progress via regular nest inspections and recording the number of eggs and/or chicks present at each visit. Records of unused boxes are also valuable as they can be used to determine next box occupancy rates. Anyone who has a nest box or nest in their garden or local park can take part.
Contact: BTO. E: nbc@bto.org

NEST RECORD SCHEME
A BTO Project carried out with support from JNCC
The scheme monitors changes in the nesting success and the timing of breeding of Britain's bird species by gathering information on nests found anywhere in the country, from a Blackbird in a garden to an Oystercatcher on a Scottish loch. Participants locate nests and monitor their progress over several visits, making counts of the number of eggs and/or chicks on each occasion and recording whether they are successful.
Information from NRS complements demographic information collected by other BTO surveys and feeds into the BTO's Integrated Population Monitoring, highlighting the causes of changes in bird populations. Since the scheme started in 1939, 1.25 million nest record histories have been collected from 232 species.

NATIONAL PROJECTS

Now more than 30,000 nest records (of 160-170 species) are submitted each year by over 600 volunteer surveyors. The results are updated annually and published online as part of the BirdTrends Report. Guidance on how to become a BTO nest recorder, including best practice guidelines on minimising disturbance while visiting nests, is available online. Free starter pack available on request.
Contact: BTO. E: nrs@bto.org

RETRAPPING ADULTS FOR SURVIVAL (RAS) SCHEME
Funded by a partnership between BTO, JNCC, The National Parks & Wildlife Service (Ireland) & ringers
Under the RAS scheme, started in 1999, ringers aim to catch or re-sight at least 50 adult birds of a single species in a study area in the breeding season. This data allows the BTO to monitor survival rates in adult birds and is particularly useful for those species not widely covered by CES scheme. and forms part of the BTO's Integrated Population Monitoring framework.
Contact: BTO. E: ras@bto.org

RINGING SCHEME
Funded by a partnership between BTO, JNCC (on behalf of the Country Agencies), The National Parks & Wildlife Service (Ireland) & ringers
Marking birds with individually numbered metal rings allows us to study survival, productivity and movements of British and Irish birds. Over 2,600 trained and licensed ringers operate in Britain and Ireland, marking nearly a million birds annually. Training to be a ringer takes at least a year, but more often two or more years, depending on the aptitude of the trainee and the amount of ringing they do. A restricted permit can usually be obtained more quickly. E: ringing.licensing@bto.org
Anyone can contribute to the scheme by reporting ringed or colour-marked birds seen or found W: http://blx1.bto.org/euring/main/index.jsp or contact BTO HQ. Anyone finding a ringed bird should note the ring number, species, when and where found and, if possible, what happened to it. If the bird is dead, it may also be possible to remove the ring, which should be kept in case there is a query. Anyone reporting a ringed bird will be sent details of where and when the bird was originally ringed.
Check out the 'Demog Blog' for up to date news and stories: http://btoringing.blogspot.co.uk
Contact: BTO. E: ringing@bto.org

WATERWAYS BREEDING BIRD SURVEY
A BTO project, supported by the Environment Agency
WBBS uses transect methods of surveying, like those of the Breeding Bird Survey, to record bird populations along more than 500 randomly chosen stretches of rivers and canals throughout the UK. Just two survey visits are needed during April-June, all birds seen or heard are recorded. WBBS began in 2008 taking over from the Waterways Bird Survey (which started in 1974) as the main monitoring scheme for birds in this habitat.
Contact: BTO Regional Representative to enquire if any local stretches require coverage (see County Directory), otherwise BTO HQ. E: wbbs@bto.org

WETLAND BIRD SURVEY (WeBS)
Run by BTO in a partnership funded by BTO, RSPB, JNCC and in association with WWT
The Wetland Bird Survey (WeBS) is the monitoring scheme for non-breeding waterbirds in the UK. The principal aims of the scheme are:
1. To identify population sizes of waterbirds.
2. To determine trends in numbers and distribution.
3. To identify important sites for waterbirds.

WeBS Core Counts are made annually at around 2000 wetland sites of all habitats, although estuaries and large still waters predominate. Monthly coordinated counts are made mostly by volunteers, principally between September and March, with fewer summer observations.
Estuaries in the UK provide an important habitat for non-breeding waterbirds. Low Tide Counts are made on about 20 of them each winter to identify important feeding areas (Core Counts tend to quantify birds present at high tide roosts).
Counts are relatively straightforward and can take from a few minutes up to a few hours, depending on the size of the site - numbers of all target species in the count area are recorded.
The WeBS data is used to designate important waterbird sites and protect them against adverse development, for research into the causes of declines, for establishing conservation priorities and strategies, and to formulate management plans for wetland sites and waterbirds.
WeBS participants receive an annual newsletter and a comprehensive annual report. New counters are always welcome - contact the local WeBS Organiser (see County Directory).

Contact: Gillian Birtles (General WeBS enquiries), WeBS Office, BTO. E: webs@bto.org

INTERNATIONAL/BIRDLIFE ORGANISATIONS

The BirdLife Partnership: www.birdlife.org
BirdLife is a Partnership of non-governmental organisations (NGOs) with a special focus on nature and people. Each NGO Partner represents a unique geographic territory/country. Publishes *World Birdwatch*.

The BirdLife Network explained:

Secretariat: The co-ordinating and servicing body of BirdLife International.

Partners: Membership-based NGOs who represent BirdLife in their own territory. Vote holders and key implementing bodies for BirdLife's Strategy and Regional Programmes in their own territories.

Partners Designate: Membership-based NGOs who represent BirdLife in their own territory, in a transition stage to becoming full Partners. Non-vote holders.

Affiliates: Usually NGOs, but also individuals, foundations or governmental institutions when appropriate. Act as a BirdLife contact with the aim of developing into, or recruiting, a BirdLife Partner in their territory.

SECRETARIAT ADDRESSES

BirdLife Global Office
The David Attenborough Building
1st Floor, Pembroke Street
Cambridge CB2 3QZ, UK
T: 01223 277 318
Fax: 01223 281 441
E: birdlife@birdlife.org

Birdlife Africa Regional Office
Volker's Garden on Terrace Close
off Rhapta Road
Westlands
Kenya

Postal Address
PO Box 3502 - 00100 GPO
Nairobi, Kenya
T: +254 020 247 3259
T: +254 020 806 8314
Fax: +254 020 806 8315
E: birdlife-africa@birdlife.org

Birdlife West Africa Sub-Regional Office
35A Sam Nujoma Rd
North Ridge
Accra, Ghana

Postal Address
PO Box GP 22521
Accra, Ghana
T: +233 (0) 302 255 015
T: +233 (0) 261 737 101

BirdLife Americas Regional Office
Av. Julio Zaldumbide N25-82 y
Valladolid
2do Piso
La Floresta 170109, Ecuador

Postal address
BirdLife International
Casilla 17-17-717
Quito, Ecuador
T: +593 2 2255 361
Fax +593 2 2233 086
E: americas@birdlife.org

BirdLife Asia Regional Office
[Japan]
Unizo Kakigara-cho Kitajima Bldg
1F, 1-13-1 Nihonbashi Kakigara-cho,
Chuo-ku, Tokyo 103-0014, Japan
T: +81 (3) 6206 2941
Fax.+81 (3) 6206 2942
E: info@birdlife-asia.org

[Singapore]
354 Tanglin Road
#01-16/17
Tanglin International Centre
Singapore 247672
T: +65 6479 3089
Fax: +65 6479 3090
E: singapore.office@birdlife.org

BirdLife Europe
Avenue de la Toison d'Or 67
(2nd floor)
B-1060 Brussels, Belgium
T: +32 2280 08 30
Fax +32 2230 38 02
E: europe@birdlife.org

BirdLife Middle East Regional Office
Khalda
Salameh El-Ma'aaytah Street
Building No 6.
Amman, Jordan

Postal address
PO Box 2295
Amman 11953, Jordan
T: +962 6 554 8173
Fax: +962 6 554 8172
E: me@birdlife.org

BirdLife Pacific Regional Office
10 MacGregor Road
Suva, Fuji

Postal address
GPO Box 18332
Suva, Fuji
T: +679 331 3492
Fax: +679 331 9658
E: suva.office@birdlife.org

AFRICA

Burkina Faso
NATURAMA 01 B.P. 6133, 01, Ouagadougou.
E: info@naturama.bf; W: www.naturama.bf

Ethiopia
Ethiopian Wildlife and Natural History Society (EWNHS), PO Box 13303, Addis Ababa. E: ewnhs.ble@gmail.com; W: www.ewnhs.org.et; Pub: *Agazen (school magazine); Ethiopian Wildlife & Nat. Hist. Soc. (quarterly newsletter); Walia (semi-scientific journal)*

Ghana
Ghana Wildlife Society (GWS), PO Box 13252, Accra.
E: info@ghanawildlifesociety.org;
W: www.ghanawildlifesociety.org; Pub: *NKO (magazine)*

Kenya
NatureKenya, PO Box 44486, 00100 GPO, Nairobi.
E: office@naturekenya.org; www. naturekenya.org;
Pub: *Nature Net (newsletter); Kenya Birding (magazine); Journal of East African Natural History (scientific); Scopus (scientific)*

INTERNATIONAL/BIRDLIFE ORGANISATIONS

Mauritania
Nature Mauritania, 2647, Nouakchott.
E: nature.mauritanie@laposte.net; W: www.natmau.org/en/

Nigeria
Nigerian Conservation Foundation (NCF), PO Box 74638, Victoria Island, Lagos. E: info@ncf-nigeria.org; W: www.ncfnigeria.org/

Seychelles
Nature Seychelles, Roche Caiman, Box 1310, Victoria, Mahe. E: nature@seychelles.net; W: www.natureseychelles.org; W: www.cousinisland.net; Pub: *Zwazo (magazine)*

Sierra Leone
Conservation Society of Sierra Leone (CSSL), 86 Main Road, Congo Town, Freetown. E: cssl_03@yahoo.com

South Africa
BirdLife South Africa (BLSA), Private Bag X5000, Gauteng, ZA, 2121. E: info@birdlife.org.za; W: www.birdlife.org.za; Pub: *e-newsletter*; *African BirdLife (magazine)*; *Ostrich (scientific)*

Tunisia
Association Les Amis des Oiseaux (AAO), Bureau No 4 au 2eme etage, 14 Rue Ibn El Heni, 2080 Ariana. E: aao.org@gmail.com; W: www.aao.org.tn; Pub: *(newsletter)*

Uganda
NatureUganda (NU), The EANHS, PO Box 27034, Kampala. E: nature@natureuganda.org; W: www.natureuganda.org; Pub: *The Naturalist (newsletter)*

*Nature*Uganda

Zimbabwe
BirdLife Zimbabwe (BLZ), PO Box RVL 100, Runiville, Harare. E: birds@zol.co.zw; W: www.birdlifezimbabwe.org; Pub: *The Babbler (newsletter); Honeyguide (scientific)*

PARTNERS DESIGNATE

Botswana
BirdLife Botswana (BLB), Kgale Siding, Plot K1069, Unit B1, Gaborone. E: blb@birdlifebotswana.org.bw; W: www.birdlifebotswana.org.bw; Pub: *The Babbler (scientific); Familiar Chat (newsletter); Birds and People (conservation newsletter)*

Burundi
Association Burundaise pour la Protection de la Nature (ABN), PO Box 7069, Bujumbura. E: info@aboconservation.org; W: http://www.abn.bi

Madagascar
Asity Madagascar, Lot IIN 83DM Analamahitsy, Antananarivio. E: contact@asity-madagascar.org; W: www.asity-madagascar.org

Zambia
BirdWatch Zambia, Box 33944, Lusaka 10101. E: birdwatch.zambia@gmail.com; W: www.birdwatchzambia.org; Pub: *BirdWatch Zambia (newsletter)*

AFFILIATES

Cameroon
Cameroon Biodiversity Conservation Society (CBCS), PO Box 3055, Messa, Yaoundé. E: cbcs_cam@yahoo.fr

Djibouti Nature
Djibouti Nature, Nasser A. Othman Building, Marabou-Djibouti, PO Box 3088, Djibouti. E: naturedjibouti@gmail.com; W: www.djoutinature.org; Pub: *The Eye (newsletter/quasi-scientific journal)*

Egypt
Nature Conservation Egypt, 56A Mahrousa St, Aguouza, 1st Floor, Apt 20, Giza. E: info@natureegypt.org; W: www.natureegypt.org; Pub: *(newsletter)*

Ivory Coast
SOS-FORETS (SF), 22 BP 918, Abidjan 22. E: sosforets@hotmail.com; W: www.sosforets.ci

Liberia
Society for Conservation of Nature in Liberia (SCNL), Monrovia, PO Box 2628, Monrovia, LR, 1000. E: scnlliberia@yahoo.com; W: www.scnlliberia.org

Malawi
Wildlife & Environmental Society of Malawi (WESM), Private Bag 578, Limbe. E: wesmhq@wesm.mw; W: www.wildlifemalawi.org; Pub: *WESM News (newsletter)*

Mauritius
Mauritian Wildlife Foundation, Grannum Road, Vacoas. E: executive@mauritian-wildlife.org; W: www.mauritian-wildlife.org

Morocco
GREPOM, Scientific Institutre Av Ibn Battota, BP 703, Agdal, 10090, Rabat. E: grepom@grepom.org; W: www.grepom.org

Rwanda
Association pour la Conservation de la Nature au Rwanda (ACNR), PO Box 4290, Kigali. E: conserverwanda@yahoo.com; W: www.acnrwanda.org

AMERICAS

PARTNERS

Argentina
Aves Argentina (AOP), Matheu 1246/8 (C1249AAB), Buenos Aires. E: info@avesargentinas.org.ar; W: www.avesargentinas.org.ar; Pub: *Aves Argentinas (magazine); Nuestras Aves (magazine); The Hornero (scientific)*

Bahamas
Bahamas National Trust (BNT), PO Box 4105, Nassau. E: bnt@bnt.bs; W: www.bnt.bs; Pub: *Trust Notes (newsletter)*

Belize
Belize Audubon Society (BAS), PO Box 1001, 12 Fort St, Belize City. E: base@btl.net; W: www.belizeaudubon.org; Pub: *Belize Audubon Society (newsletter)*

Bolivia
Asociacion Armonia, Avenida Lomas de Arena 400, Casilla 3566, Santa Cruz. E: armonia@armonia-bo.org; W: www.armoniabolivia.org

INTERNATIONAL/BIRDLIFE ORGANISATIONS

Canada
Bird Studies Canada (BSC), PO Box 160, 115 Front Street, Port Rowan, Ontario N0E 1M0. E: generalinfo@bsc-eoc.org; W: www.birdscanada.org; Pub: *Bird Studies Canada (annual report)*; *Birdwatch Canada (magazine)*

Canada
Nature Canada, 85 Albert Street, Suite 900, Ottawa, K1P 6A4. E: info@naturecanada.ca; W: www.naturecanada.ca; Pub: *(annual report)*

Colombia
Asociación Calidris, Cra. 24 #420, Cali, Valle del Cauca. E: calidris@calidris.org.co; W: www.calidris.org.uk

Ecuador
Aves y Conservación, Calle Mariana de Jesús E7-69 y La Pradera (2do piso), Quito. E: aves_direccion@avesconservacion.org; W: www.avesconservacion.org

Falkland Islands
Falklands Conservation, 41 Ross Road, Jubilee Villas, Stanley, FIQQ 1ZZ. E: info@falklandsconservation.com; W: www.falklandsconservation.com; Pub: *Falklands Conservation (newsletter)*; *Wildlife Conservation (magazine)*

Panama
Panama Audubon Society (PAS), Apartado 0843-03076, Panama City. E: info@panamaaudubon.org; W: www.audubonpanama.org; Pub: *Toucan (newsletter)*

Paraguay
Guyra, Av. Cnel. Carlos Bóveda, Parque Ecológico Capital Verde, Viñas Cué, Asunción, CC 1132. E: guyra.paraguay@guyra.org.py; W: www.guyra.org.py; Pub: *Memoria Anual (annual report)*

United States
Audubon, 225 Varick Street, 7th Floor New York, NY, 10004. E: international@audubon.org; W: www.audubon.org; Pub: *Audubon (magazine)*

AFFILIATES

Brazil
SAVE Brasil, Rua Fernão Dias, 219 conj 2 Pinheiros, São Paulo SP, 05427-010. E: aves@savebrasil.org.br; W: www.savebrasil.org.br; Pub: *(annual report)*; *(newsletter)*

Chile
Comité Nacional Pro Defensa de la Flora y Fauna (CODEFF), Ernesto Reyes 035, Providencia, Santiago. E: administra@codeff.cl; W: www.codeff.cl; Pub: *Ecos Codeff (newsletter)*

Cuba
Centro Nacional de Áreas Protegidas (CNAP), Calle 18a, No 1441, 41 y 47, Playa, Havana. E: cnap@snap.cu; W: www.snap.cu

Dominican Republic
Grupo Jaragua (GJI), Calle El Vergel No 33, Ensanche, El Vergel, Santo Domingo. E: jaragua@tricom.net; W: www.grupojaragua.org.do

El Salvador
SalvaNATURA (SN), Finca Vista Alegre Km 3½, Planes de Randeros, San Salvador. E: info@salvanatura.org; W: www.salvanatura.org

Mexico
Pronatura, 1 Calle Pedro Moreno esq. Benito Juárez, Barrio Santa Lucia, San Cristobal de las Casas, Chiapas, 29200. E: pronatura@pronatura.org.mx; W: www.pronatura.org.mx; Pub: *(annual report)*

Puerto Rico (to USA)
Sociedad Ornitológica Puertorriqueña, Inc. (SOPI), PO Box 195166, San Juan, 00919-5166. E: directivasopi@yahoo.com; W: www.sopipr.org; Pub: *El Bien-Te-Veo (magazine)*

Uruguay
Aves Uruguay (GUPECA), Canelones 1164, Montevideo. E: info@avesuruguay.org.uy; W: www.avesuruguay.org.uy; Pub: *Achara (magazine)*

ASIA

PARTNERS

Bhutan
Royal Society for the Protection of Nature, PO Box 325, Building #25, Lhado Lam Kawajangsa, Thimphu-11001. E: rspn@rspnbhutan.org; W: www.rspnbhutan.org; Pub: *Rangzhin (newsletter)*; *(annual report)*

Hong Kong
Hong Kong Birdwatching Society, (HKBS) 7C, V Ga Building, 532 Castle Peak Road, Lai Chi Kok, Kowloon. E: hkbws@hkbws.org.hk; W: www.hkbws.org.hk; Pub: *Hong Kong Bird Report*; *HKBWS (bulletin)*. HKBWS currently operates BirdLife's Direct Action Programme in China.

India
Bombay Natural History Society (BNHS), Hornbill House, Shaheed Bhagat Singh Road, Mumbai, 400 001. E: director@bnhs.org; W: www.bnhs.org; Pub: *Hornbill (magazine)*; *Journal of BNHS (scientific)*

Japan
Wild Bird Society of Japan (WBSJ), Maruw Bldg, 3-9-23, Nishi-Gotanda, Shinagawa-ku, Tokyo 141-0031. E: hogo@wbsj.org; W: www.wbsj.org; Pub: *Wild Bird (magazine)*; *Toriino (magazine)*; *Strix (scientific)*

Malaysia
Malaysian Nature Society (MNS), PO Box 10750, Kuala Lumpur 50724. E: mns@mns.org.my; W: www.mns.my; Pub: *Pencinta Alam (newsletter)*; *Malaysian Naturalist (magazine)*; *Malayan Nature Journal (scientific)*

Myanmar
Biodiversity and Nature Conservation Association (BANCA), No.943, Second Floor (right), Kyeikwine Pagoda Road, Ward (3), Mayangone Township, Yangon. E: bancamayanmar@gmail.com; W: www.banca-env.org

Nepal
Bird Conservation Nepal (BCN), PO Box 12465, Uttardhoka,Lazimpat, Kathmandu. E: bcn@birdlifenepal.org; W: www.birdlifenepal.org

Philippines
Haribon Foundation, 2/F, Santos and Sons Building, 973 Aurora Blvd, Cubao, Quezon CIty 1109. E: act@haribon.org.ph; W: www.haribon.org.ph

Singapore
Nature Society (Singapore) (NSS), 510 Geylang Road, #02-05, The Sunflower, 398466. E: contact@nss.org.sg; W: www.nss.org.sg; Pub: *Nature News (newsletter); Nature Watch (magazine)*

Taiwan
Chinese Wild Bird Federation CWBF), 1F, No. 3, Lane 36 Jing-Long St., 116 Taipei. E: mail@bird.org.tw; W: www.bird.org.tw; Pub: *Flying Feather (newsletter)*

Thailand
Bird Conservation Society of Thailand (BCST), 221 Moo 2, Soi Ngamwongwan 2, Tambol Bangkhen, Ampur Meung, Nontaburi 11000. E: bcst@bcst.or.th; W: www.bcst.or.th; Pub: *BCST (bulletin)*

AFFILIATES

Indonesia
Burung Indonesia, Jl. Dadali 32, Bogor 16161. E: birdlife@burung.org; W: www.burung.org

Sri Lanka
Field Ornithology Group of Sri Lanka (FOGSL), Dept of Zoology, Univ of Colombo, Colombo 03. E: fogsl@cmb.ac.lk; W: http://fogsl.cmb.ac.lk

BIRDLIFE DIRECT ACTION PROGRAMMES

Cambodia
BirdLife International Cambodia Programme, House #32A, Street 494, Sangkat Phsar Daeum Thkov, Chamkarmon, Phnom Penh. E: admin@birdlifecambodia.org

Vietnam
BirdLife International in Vietnam, Viet Nature Conservation Centre, PO Box 89, 6 Dinh Le, Hanoi. E: birdlife@birdlife.org.vn

EUROPE & CENTRAL ASIA

PARTNERS

Austria
BirdLife Austria, Museumplatz 1/10/8, AT-1070 Wien. E: office@birdlife.at; W: www.birdlife.at; Pub: *VogelSchutz in Osterreich (magazine); Egretta (scientific)*

Belarus
BirdLife Belarus (APB), PO Box 306, Minsk, 220050. E: info@ptushki.org; W: www.ptushki.org; Pub: *Homeland Security birds (newsletter); Birds and Us (magazine); Subbuteo (newsletter)*

Belgium
(Flanders) Natuurpunt, Coxiestraat 11, Mechelen, BE-2800. E: info@natuurpunt.be; W: www.natuurpunt.be; Pub: *(various newsletters)*

(Wallonia) Natagora, Rue Nanon 98, Namur, BE-5000. E: info@natagora.be; W: www.natagora.be; Pub: *(newsletter); Natagora (magazine)*

Bulgaria
Bulgarian Society for the Protection of Birds (BSPB), PO Box 50, Sofia, BG-Sofia 1111. E: bspb_hq@bspb.org; W: www.bspb.org; Pub: *Living Nature (magazine/english)*

Cyprus
BirdLife Cyprus, PO Box 12026, Nicosia, CY-2340. E: birdlifecyprus@birdlifecyprus.org.cy; W: www.birdlifecyprus.org; Pub: *Annual Bird Report; (newsletter)*

Czech Republic
Czech Society for Ornithology (CSO), Na Belidle 252/34, Prague, CZ-150 00 Praha 5. E: cso@birdlife.cz; W: www.birdlife.cz; Pub: *Spolkové Zprávy (information journal); Ptaci Svet (magazine); Sylvia (scientific)*

Denmark
Dansk Ornitologisk Forening (DOF), Vesterbrogade 140, Copenhagen , DK-1620 Copenhagen V. E: dof@dof.dk; W: www.dof.dk; Pub: *Fuglearet (bird report); Fugle & Natur (magazine); Dansk Ornitologisk Forenings Tidsskrift (scientific)*

Estonia
Estonian Ornithological Society (EOS), Veski 4, Tartu, EE-51005. E: eoy@eoy.ee; W: www.eoy.ee; Pub: *Tiiutajat (newsletter); Hirundo (scientific)*

Finland
BirdLife Suomi, Annankatu 29 A 16, Helsinki, FI-00101. E: toimisto@birdlife.fi; W: www.birdlife.fi; Pub: *Tiira (newsletter); Linnut (magazine & yearbook); Ornis Fennica (scientific)*

France
Ligue pour la Protection des Oiseaux (LPO), Fonderies Royale, 8 rue de Docteur Pujos, BP 90263, FR-17305. E: lpo@lpo.fr; W: www.lpo.fr; Pub: *Ornithos (journal); L'Oiseau Magazine (magazine); L'Oiseau Mag junior (magazine for juniors); Rapaces de France (magazine)*

Georgia
Society for Nature Conservation (SABUKO), 11/13 Navtlughi street, 0190 Tbilisi. E: office@sabuko.ge; W: www.sabuko.ge; Pub: *(newsletter)*

Germany
Nature and Biodiversity Conservation Union (NABU), Charitestr. 3, Berlin, D-10117. E: nabu@nabu.de; W: www.nabu.de; Pub: *Naturschutz Heute (magazine)*

Gibraltar
Gibraltar Ornithological & Natural History Society (GONHS), The Gibraltar Natural History Field Centre, Jew's Gate, Upper Rock Nature Reserve, PO Box 843, Gibraltar. E: info@gonhs.org; W: www.gonhs.org; Pub: *Gibraltar Bird Report; Gibraltar Nature News (magazine)*

Greece
Hellenic Ornithological Society (HOS), Themistokleous 80, Athens, GR-10861. E: info@ornithologiki.gr; W: www.ornithologiki.gr; Pub: *(newsletter)*

Hungary
Magyar Madártani és Természetvédelmi Egyesület (MME), Kolto u. 21, Budapest, H-1121. E: mme@mme.hu; W: www.mme.hu; Pub: *(newsletter); Madártávlat (magazine); Ornis Hungarica (scientific)*

INTERNATIONAL/BIRDLIFE ORGANISATIONS

Ireland
BirdWatch Ireland, Unit 20, Block D, Bullford Business Campus, Kilcoole, Co Wicklow. E: info@birdwatchireland.org; W: www.birdwatchireland.ie; Pub: *eWings (newsletter); Wings (magazine); Bird Detectives (children's magazine); Irish Birds (scientific)*

Israel
Society for the Protection of Nature in Israel (SPNI), Hanagev 2, Tel-Aviv 66186. E: ioc@inter.net.il; W: www.natureisrael.org; Pub: *(newsletter)*

Italy
Lega Italiana Protezione Uccelli (LIPU), Via Udine 3/a, Parma, IT-43100. E: info@lipu.it; W: www.lipu.it; Pub: *(newsletter); Ali & Ali Junior (magazines)*

Kazakhstan
Association for the Conservation of Biodiversity of Kazakhstan (ACBK), Beibitshilik 18, Astana, 020000. E: acbk@acbk.kz; W: www.acbk.kz; Pub: *Saiga News (newsletter); Remez (newsletter); Selevinia (scientific)*

Latvia
Latvian Ornithological Society (LOB), A.k. 105, Riga, LV-1046. E: putni@lob.lv; W: www.lob.lv; Pub: *Putni Daba (magazine)*

Luxembourg
Natur&ëmwelt, Kraizhaff, 5 Route de Luxembourg, Kockelscheuer, L-1899. E: secretariat@naturewelt.lu; W: www.naturemwelt.lu; Pub: *(newsletter); Regulus (magazine)*

Malta
BirdLife Malta, 57 /28, Triq Abate Rigord, Ta' Xbiex, XBX 1120. E: info@birdlifemalta.org; W: www.birdlifemalta.org; Pub: *Bird's Eye View (magazine); Il-Huttafa (children's magazine); Il-Merill (scientific)*

Netherlands
Society for the Protection of Birds (VBN), PO Box 925, NL-3700 AX. E: info@vogelbescherming.nl; W: www.vogelbescherming.nl; Pub: *(newsletter); Vogels dichterbij (magazine)*

Norway
Norwegian Ornithological Society (NOF), Sandgata, Trondheim, N-7012. E: nof@birdlife.no; W: www.birdlife.no; Pub: *Var Fuglefauna (magazine); Fuglevennen (magazine); Ornis Norvegica (scientific)*

Poland
Polish Society for the Protection of Birds (OTOP), ul. Odrowaza 24, Marki 05-270. E: office@otop.org.pl; W: www.otop.org.pl; Pub: *(newsletter); Ptaki (magazine)*

Portugal
Portuguese Society for the Study of Birds (SPEA), Avenida Columbano Bordalo Pinheiro, 87, 3.° Andar, 11070-062, Lisboa. E: spea@spea.pt; W: www.spea.pt; Pub: *(newsletters); Pardela (magazine); AIRO (scientific)*

Romania
Romanian Ornithological Society (SOR)/BirdLife Romania, Bd. Hristo Botev, nr. 3, ap 6, Bucuresti, 030231. E: office@sor.ro; W: www.sor.ro; Pub: *(newsletter)*

Slovakia
SOS/BirdLife, Zelinarska 4, Bratislava, SK-821 08. E: vtaky@vtaky.sk; W: www.birdlife.sk; Pub: *Vtáky (magazine); Tichodroma (scientific)*

Slovenia
Birdlife Slovenia (DOPPS), Tržaška 2, p.p. 2990, Ljubljana, SI-1001. E: dopps@dopps.si; W: www.ptice.si; Pub: *Svet Ptic (magazine); Acrocephalus (scientific)*

Spain
SEO/BirdLife, Melquiades Biencinto 34, Madrid, ES-28053. E: seo@seo.org; W: www.seo.org; Pub: *Aves y Naturaleza (magazine); Ardeola (scientific)*

Sweden
Swedish Ornithological Society (SOF), Stenhusa Gard, Morbylanga, SE-380 62. E: info@birdlife.se; W: www.birdlife.se; Pub: *Vår Fågelvärld (magazine); Ornis Svecica (scientific)*

Switzerland
SVS/BirdLife Switzerland, PO Box Wiedingstrasse 78, Zurich, CH-8036. E: svs@birdlife.ch; W: www.birdlife.ch; Pub: *(newsletters); Ornis/Ornis Junior (magazines); Info BirdLife Suisse/Schweiz (magazines)*

Ukraine
Ukrainian Society for the Protection of Birds (USBP), PO Box 33, Kyivv, 01003. E: uspb@birdlife.org.ua; W: www.birdlife.org.ua; Pub: *'Bird' (magazine)*

United Kingdom (see National listing)
Royal Society for the Protection of Birds (RSPB), The Lodge, Sandy, Bedfordshire, SG19 2DL. W: www.rspb.org.uk

PARTNERS DESIGNATE

Azerbaijan
Azerbaijan Ornithological Society (AOS), M. Mushbig Street 4B, Ap. 60, Baku, AZ1021. E: info@aos.az; W: www.aos.az

Iceland
Fuglavernd - BirdLife Iceland (ISPB), Hverfisgata 105, 101 Reykjavik, IS, IS-101. E: fuglavernd@fuglavernd.is; W: www.fuglavernd.is; Pub: *Fuglar (magazine)*

Turkey
Doğa Derneği (DD), Mimar Sinan Mahallesi, Işılay Saygın Sokak, No:4 D:3 Konak / İzmir. E: doga@dogadernegi.org; W: www.dogadernegi.org; Pub: *(newsletter); Kuş Sesi (magazine)*

AFFILIATES

Croatia
Association BIOM, Preradoviceva 34, Zagreb, 10000. E: info@biom.hr; W: www.biom.hr; Pub: *Pogled U Divljinu (magazine)*

INTERNATIONAL/BIRDLIFE ORGANISATIONS

Faroe Islands
Faroese Orginithological Society (FOS), Postboks 1230,
FO-110 Torshavn. E: ffff@kallnet.fo; W: www.faroenature.net

Kyrgyzstan
Nature Kyrgyzstan, Ul, Tabatshnaja 24, Bishkek, 720011.
E: nabu-kirgistan@infotel.kg; W: www.wildlife.kg

Liechtenstein
Botanish-Zoologische Gesellschaft (BZG),
St.Markusgasse 19, FL-9490 Vaduz. E: bzg@bzg.li or
renat@renat.li; W: www.bzg.li

Lithuania
Lithuanian Ornithological Society (LOD),
Naugarduko St. 47-3, Vilnius, LT-03208.
E: lod@birdlife.lt; W: www.birdlife.lt;
Pub: *Paukščiai (magazine)*

Macedonia
Macedonian Ecological Society (MES), Bul. Boris
Trajkovski ul.7 br.9A, 1000 Skopje.
E: contact@mes.org.mk; W: www.mes.org.mk

Montenegro
Center for Protection & Research of Birds of
Montenegro (CZIP), Veliše Mugoše bb, Podgorica,
81 000. E: czip@czip.me; W: www.czip.me

Serbia
Bird Protection and Study Society of Serbia, Radnička
20a, Novi Sad, 21000. E: sekretar@pticesrbije.rs;
W: www.pticesrbije.rs; Pub: *Detlić (magazine); Ciconia
(scientific)*

Uzbekistan
Uzbekistan Society for the Protection of Birds (UzSPB),
Off. 501, Institute of Gene Pool of Plants & Animals of
Academy of Science, 32-Durmon-yuki Street, Tashkent
100125. E: roman.kashkarov@iba.uz; W: www.uzspb.uz;
Pub: *(newsletter)*

MIDDLE EAST

PARTNERS

Jordan
Royal Society of the Conservation of Nature (RSCN),
PO Box 6354, Jubeiha-Abu-Nusseir Circle 11183,
Amman. E: adminrscn@rscn.org.jo; W: www.rscn.org.jo

Lebanon
Society for the Protection of Nature in Lebanon (SPNL),
Awad Bldg, 6th Floor Abdel Aziz Street, PO Box: 11-5665,
Beirut. E: spnlorg@cyberia.net.lb; W: www.spnl.org;
Pub: *Wings & Waves (newsletter)*

Palestine
Palestine Wildlife Society (PWLS), PO Box 89, Beit
Sahour, Palestine. E: pwls@wildlife-pal.org;
W: www.wildlife-pal.org

AFFILIATES

Bahrain
Bahrain Natural History Society (BNHS), Box 1858,
Manama. E: saeed@alreem.com

Iraq
Nature Iraq, House 25, Street 27, Qtr 104 Ashti,
Sulaymaniyah. E: info@natureiraq.org;
W: www.natureiraq.org; Pub: *(newsletter)*

Kuwait
Kuwait Environment Protection Society (KEPS),
PO Box 1896, Safat 13019. E: info@keps.org.kw;
W: www.keps.org.kw

Qatar
Friends of the Environment Centre, Villa No 92, zone
52, Mekka St, Dohar. E: fec.org.qa@live.com;
W: www.fec.qa

Saudi Arabia
Saudi Wildlife Authority (SWA), Riyadh.
E: ncwcd@zajil.net; W: www.swa.gov.sa

Syria
Syrian Society for Conservation of Wildlife (SSCW),
Al-Mazza- Al-Sheikh Saad, Shabaan Building No. 20 - 1st
Floor, Damascus. E: sscw.syria@gmail.com

PACIFIC

PARTNERS

Australia
BirdLife Australia, Suite 2-05, 60 Leicester Street,
Carlton, VIC 3053. E: info@birdlife.org.au;
W: www.birdlife.org.au; Pub: *BirdLife (e-news);
Australian BirdLife (magazine); Australian Field
Ornithology (scientific); Emu - Austral Ornithology
(scientific)*

Cook Islands
Te Ipukarea Society (TIS), PO Box 649, Rarotonga.
E: 2tis@oyster.net.ck or info@tiscookislands.org;
W: www.tiscookislands.org; Pub: *(newsletter)*

French Polynesia
Société d'Ornithologie de Polynésie (MANU), Residence
du plateau Mitirapa, Lot 48, Impasse Des Acacias B.P.
7023, Taravao, 98719, Tahiti. E: sop@manu.pf;
W: www.manu.pf; Pub: *Te Manu (bulletin)*

New Zealand
Forest & Bird, 90 Ghunzee Street,
Wellington 6140.
E: office@forestandbird.org.nz;
W: www.forestandbird.org.nz;
Pub: *(newsletters); Forest & Bird
(magazine); Wild Things (magazine for
children)*

Palau
Palau Conservation Society (PSC), PO Box 1811, Koror,
96940. E: pcs@palaunet.com; W: www.palauconservation.org;
Pub: *(newsletter)*

PARTNERS DESIGNATE

New Caledonia (to France)
Société Calédonienne d'Ornithologie (SCO); BP 13641,
98803,Nouméa Cedex. E: president@sco.asso.nc;
W: www.sco.nc

AFFILIATES

Fiji
Nature Fiji, 14 Hamilton-Beattie
Street, Suva.
E: support@naturefiji.org;
W: www.naturefiji.org;
Pub: *(newsletter)*

312

Neil Gartshore

Birds at different sites may be roosting at high water or feeding on a rising/falling tide or may be miles out of view on a low tide. The tide tables in this section will help you sort out the high water times at coastal sites such as here on The Solent.

QUICK REFERENCE SECTION

SUNRISE & SUNSET TIMES FOR 2020

Predictions are given for the times of sunrise and sunset on every SUNDAY throughout the year. For places on the same latitude as the following, add FOUR minutes for each degree of longitude west (subtract if east).

These times are in GMT, except between 01:00 on Mar 29th and 01:00 on Oct 25th, when the times are in BST (one hour in advance of GMT).

		London Rise	London Set	Manchester Rise	Manchester Set	Edinburgh Rise	Edinburgh Set
January	5	08:06	16:06	08:24	16:04	08:42	15:54
	12	08:02	16:16	08:20	16:14	08:37	16:05
	19	07:56	16:27	08:13	16:26	08:30	16:18
	26	07:48	16:38	08:04	16:39	08:19	16:32
February	2	07:38	16:51	07:53	16:53	08:07	16:47
	9	07:27	17:04	07:41	17:06	07:52	17:02
	16	07:14	17:17	07:27	17:20	07:37	17:18
	23	07:00	17:29	07:12	17:34	07:21	17:33
March	1	06:45	17:42	06:56	17:48	07.03	17:48
	8	06:30	17:54	06:39	18:01	06:45	18:03
	15	06:14	18:06	06:23	18:14	06:27	18:17
	22	05:58	18:18	06:06	18:27	06:09	18:32
	29	06:42	19:30	06:49	19:40	06:50	19:46
April	5	06:26	19:41	06:32	19:52	06:32	20:00
	12	06:11	19:53	06:15	20:05	06:14	20:14
	19	05:56	20:05	05:59	20:18	05:57	20:29
	26	05:41	20:16	05:44	20:31	05:40	20:43
May	3	05:28	20:28	05:30	20:43	05:24	20:57
	10	05:16	20:39	05:16	20:55	05:09	21:11
	17	05:05	20:50	05:05	21:07	04:56	21:24
	24	04:57	20:59	04:55	21:18	04:45	21:36
	31	04:50	21:08	04:47	21:27	04:36	21:46
June	7	04:45	21:15	04:42	21:34	04:30	21:55
	14	04:43	21:19	04:39	21:39	04:26	22:00
	21	04:43	21:22	04:40	21:42	04:26	22:03
	28	04:46	21:22	04:43	21:42	04:30	22:02

SUNRISE & SUNSET TIMES FOR 2020

		London Rise	Set	Manchester Rise	Set	Edinburgh Rise	Set
July	5	04:51	21:19	04:48	21:39	04:36	21:59
	12	04:58	21:14	04:56	21:33	04:44	21:52
	19	05:07	21:07	05:05	21:25	04:55	21:42
	26	05:16	20:57	05:16	21:15	05:07	21:31
August	2	05:26	20:46	05:27	21:02	05:20	21:17
	9	05:37	20:34	05:39	20:49	05:33	21:02
	16	05:48	20:20	05:51	20:34	05:47	20:46
	23	05:59	20:06	06:03	20:19	06:00	20:29
	30	06:11	19:51	06:15	20:02	06:14	20:11
September	6	06:22	19:35	06:27	19:46	06:28	19:53
	13	06:33	19:19	06:40	19:29	06:41	19:35
	20	06:44	19:03	06:52	19:12	06:55	19:16
	27	06:55	18:47	07:04	18:54	07:09	18:58
October	4	07:07	18:31	07:17	18:37	07:22	18:39
	11	07:18	18:15	07:29	18:21	07:37	18:21
	18	07:30	18:00	07:42	18:05	07:51	18:04
	25	06:43	16:46	06:55	16:50	07:06	16:47
November	1	06:55	16:33	07:09	16:36	07:20	16:32
	8	07:07	16:21	07:22	16:23	07:35	16:17
	15	07:19	16:11	07:35	16:11	07:50	16:04
	22	07:31	16:02	07:48	16:02	08:04	15:54
	29	07:42	15:56	07:59	15:55	08:17	15:46
December	6	07:51	15:53	08:09	15:51	08:28	15:40
	13	07:58	15:52	08:17	15:49	08:36	15:38
	20	08:04	15:53	08:23	15:51	08:42	15:39
	27	08:06	15:58	08:25	15:56	08:44	15:44

QUICK REFERENCE

Reproduced with permission from HMNAO, UKHO and the Controller of Her Majesty's Stationery Office.

TIDE TABLES: USEFUL INFORMATION

BRITISH SUMMER TIME

In 2020 BST applies from 01:00 on March 29th to 01:00 on October 25th. Note that all the times in the following tide tables are GMT.

Shetland 42, 43
Orkney 44, 45

During British Summer Time one hour should be added. Predictions are given for the times of high water at Dover throughout the year.

The times of tides at the locations shown here may be obtained by adding or subtracting their 'tidal difference' as shown opposite (subtractions are indicated by a minus sign).

Tidal predictions for Dover have been computed by the National Oceanographic Centre. Copyright reserved.

Map showing locations for which tidal differences are given on facing page.

TIDE TABLES 2020

Example 1
To calculate the time of high water at Fraserburgh on January 25th, 2020:
1. Look up the time at Dover (11:24)*
   = 11:24 am
2. Add the tidal difference for Fraserburgh = plus 1 hour, 20 minutes
3. Therefore the time of high water at Fraserburgh = 12:44 pm

Example 2
To calculate the time of high water at Skomer Island on 9th September, 2020:
1. Look up the time at Dover (14:40)*
   = 14:40 pm
2. Add 1 hour for British Summer Time
   = 15:40 pm
3. Subtract the tidal difference for Skomer Island = minus 5 hours, 0 minutes
4. Therefore the time of high water at Skomer Island = 10:40 am

NB: *All Dover times are shown on the 24-hour clock.
Following the time of each high water, the height of the tide is given in metres. This height only applies to the high water level at Dover and may be different in other areas around the country.

TIDAL DIFFERENCES

#	Location			#	Location		
1	Dover	See pp 318-321		23	Morecambe	0	20
2	Dungeness	-0	12	24	Silloth	0	51
3	Selsey Bill	0	09	25	Girvan	0	54
4	Swanage (lst H.W.Springs)	-2	36	26	Lossiemouth	0	48
5	Portland	-4	23	27	Fraserburgh	1	20
6	Exmouth (Approaches)	-4	48	28	Aberdeen	2	30
7	Salcombe	-5	23	29	Montrose	3	30
8	Newlyn (Penzance)	5	59	30	Dunbar	3	42
9	Padstow	-5	47	31	Holy Island	3	58
10	Bideford	-5	17	32	Sunderland	4	38
11	Bridgwater	-4	23	33	Whitby	5	12
12	Sharpness Dock	-3	19	34	Bridlington	5	53
13	Cardiff (Penarth)	-4	16	35	Grimsby	-5	20
14	Swansea	-4	52	36	Skegness	-5	00
15	Skomer Island	-5	00	37	Blakeney	-4	07
16	Fishguard	-3	48	38	Gorleston	-2	08
17	Barmouth	-2	45	39	Aldeburgh	-0	13
18	Bardsey Island	-3	07	40	Bradwell Waterside	1	11
19	Caernarvon	-1	07	41	Herne Bay	1	28
20	Amlwch	-0	22	42	Sullom Voe	-1	34
21	Connahs Quay	0	20	43	Lerwick	0	01
22	Hilbre Island			44	Kirkwall	-0	26
	(Hoylake/West Kirby)	-0	05	45	Widewall Bay	-1	30

QUICK REFERENCE

NB. Care should be taken when making calculations at the beginning and end of British Summer Time. See worked examples above.

TIDE TABLES JANUARY-APRIL 2020

Time Zone: UT(GMT)

Tidal Predictions: HIGH WATERS 2020
Units: METRES

Datum of Predictions = Chart Datum: 3.67 metres below Ordnance Datum (Newlyn)
British Summer Time Dates for 2020: 29th March to 25th October (data not adjusted)

DOVER — January

Date	Morning time	m	Afternoon time	m
1 W	02:32	6.16	14:56	5.74
2 Th	03:15	5.92	15:44	5.48
3 F	04:03	5.67	16:42	5.27
4 Sa	05:02	5.46	17:48	5.17
5 Su	06:09	5.38	18:54	5.23
6 M	07:13	5.47	19:54	5.43
7 Tu	08:09	5.67	20:43	5.71
8 W	08:57	5.92	21:28	6.00
9 Th	09:40	6.17	22:10	6.27
10 F	10:22	6.40	22:53	6.50
11 Sa	11:06	6.58	23:38	6.67
12 Su	11:52	6.68		
13 M	00:24	6.78	12:41	6.70
14 Tu	01:12	6.79	13:31	6.63
15 W	02:00	6.73	14:23	6.48
16 Th	02:48	6.60	15:15	6.28
17 F	03:39	6.42	16:09	6.06
18 Sa	04:34	6.21	17:10	5.83
19 Su	05:38	6.00	18:20	5.68
20 M	06:49	5.89	19:33	5.68
21 Tu	08:00	5.92	20:42	5.83
22 W	09:04	6.05	21:38	6.05
23 Th	09:57	6.21	22:24	6.26
24 F	10:43	6.33	23:05	6.43
25 Sa	11:24	6.40	23:42	6.55
26 Su	00:19	6.59	12:02	6.42
27 M	00:54	6.58	12:38	6.38
28 Tu	01:29	6.50	13:12	6.29
29 W	02:01	6.36	13:48	6.16
30 Th	02:34	6.36	14:18	5.98
31 F	03:14	6.17	14:52	5.77

DOVER — February

Date	Morning time	m	Afternoon time	m
1 Sa	03:09	5.94	15:33	5.53
2 Su	03:54	5.68	16:27	5.31
3 M	04:52	5.44	17:34	5.17
4 Tu	06:04	5.32	18:52	5.21
5 W	07:20	5.41	20:06	5.46
6 Th	08:25	5.69	21:04	5.82
7 F	09:19	6.03	21:53	6.19
8 Sa	10:07	6.36	22:39	6.52
9 Su	10:54	6.63	23:24	6.78
10 M	11:40	6.81		
11 Tu	00:10	6.96	12:28	6.88
12 W	00:57	7.03	13:17	6.84
13 Th	01:42	6.99	14:04	6.70
14 F	02:26	6.85	14:50	6.47
15 Sa	03:11	6.61	15:38	6.18
16 Su	04:02	6.29	16:34	5.84
17 M	05:03	5.92	17:44	5.52
18 Tu	06:20	5.63	19:08	5.41
19 W	07:45	5.58	20:27	5.57
20 Th	08:57	5.75	21:26	5.85
21 F	09:51	5.98	22:11	6.13
22 Sa	10:34	6.16	22:48	6.35
23 Su	11:10	6.29	23:24	6.50
24 M	11:45	6.37	23:58	6.60
25 Tu			12:17	6.40
26 W	00:31	6.62	12:48	6.37
27 Th	01:02	6.57	13:15	6.28
28 F	01:28	6.46	13:41	6.15
29 Sa	01:53	6.31	14:08	6.01

DOVER — March

Date	Morning time	m	Afternoon time	m
1 Su	02:21	6.14	14:42	5.82
2 M	02:59	5.90	15:27	5.56
3 Tu	03:53	5.58	16:34	5.28
4 W	05:09	5.31	18:03	5.15
5 Th	06:42	5.28	19:34	5.34
6 F	08:02	5.57	20:42	5.76
7 Sa	09:02	5.99	21:35	6.20
8 Su	09:51	6.39	22:21	6.60
9 M	10:37	6.70	23:05	6.90
10 Tu	11:23	6.91	23:50	7.10
11 W			12:09	6.99
12 Th	00:34	7.17	12:55	6.95
13 F	01:18	7.11	13:39	6.79
14 Sa	02:00	6.93	14:22	6.54
15 Su	02:43	6.63	15:09	6.21
16 M	03:33	6.23	16:03	5.82
17 Tu	04:36	5.76	17:13	5.43
18 W	05:57	5.39	18:43	5.26
19 Th	07:31	5.36	20:07	5.44
20 F	08:46	5.59	21:06	5.76
21 Sa	09:39	5.86	21:51	6.06
22 Su	10:18	6.08	22:27	6.29
23 M	10:51	6.23	23:01	6.46
24 Tu	11:22	6.34	23:33	6.56
25 W	11:52	6.40		
26 Th	00:04	6.59	12:20	6.39
27 F	00:32	6.55	12:44	6.34
28 Sa	00:54	6.46	13:06	6.26
29 Su	01:17	6.35	13:33	6.16
30 M	01:45	6.22	14:06	6.00
31 Tu	02:22	6.01	14:51	5.75

DOVER — April

Date	Morning time	m	Afternoon time	m
1 W	03:15	5.67	15:57	5.42
2 Th	04:36	5.34	17:32	5.22
3 F	06:18	5.29	19:09	5.39
4 Sa	07:42	5.60	20:19	5.82
5 Su	08:43	6.03	21:12	6.28
6 M	09:32	6.43	21:58	6.67
7 Tu	10:17	6.73	22:42	6.96
8 W	11:01	6.92	23:25	7.13
9 Th	11:46	6.98		
10 F	00:09	7.17	12:31	6.93
11 Sa	00:52	7.07	13:15	6.77
12 Su	01:35	6.84	13:57	6.52
13 M	02:19	6.51	14:44	6.20
14 Tu	03:10	6.09	15:38	5.82
15 W	04:12	5.62	16:45	5.44
16 Th	05:33	5.27	18:11	5.25
17 F	07:09	5.26	19:35	5.40
18 Sa	08:21	5.49	20:35	5.69
19 Su	09:12	5.77	21:21	5.98
20 M	09:51	5.99	21:58	6.21
21 Tu	10:24	6.16	22:32	6.37
22 W	10:54	6.28	23:04	6.46
23 Th	11:23	6.35	23:33	6.48
24 F	11:49	6.37		
25 Sa	00:00	6.46	12:15	6.35
26 Su	00:24	6.40	12:41	6.30
27 M	00:50	6.32	13:11	6.21
28 Tu	01:22	6.20	13:48	6.06
29 W	02:03	5.99	14:36	5.83
30 Th	03:01	5.69	15:47	5.56

National Oceanography Centre (www.noc.ac.uk)

TIDE TABLES MAY-AUGUST 2020

Time Zone: UT(GMT)

Tidal Predictions : HIGH WATERS 2020

Units: METRES

Datum of Predictions = Chart Datum : 3.67 metres below Ordnance Datum (Newlyn)

British Summer Time Dates for 2020 : 29th March to 25th October (data not adjusted)

DOVER — May

Day	Morning time	m	Afternoon time	m
1 F	04:26	5.44	17:15	5.43
2 Sa	06:00	5.44	18:42	5.59
3 Su	07:19	5.72	19:51	5.95
4 M	08:19	6.09	20:45	6.34
5 Tu	09:09	6.42	21:31	6.68
6 W	09:54	6.66	22:15	6.91
7 Th	10:39	6.81	23:00	7.02
8 F	11:24	6.86	23:45	7.02
9 Sa			12:10	6.81
10 Su	00:30	6.89	12:55	6.68
11 M	01:15	6.66	13:39	6.47
12 Tu	02:01	6.34	14:24	6.21
13 W	02:51	5.98	15:15	5.90
14 Th	03:49	5.60	16:14	5.58
15 F	05:02	5.30	17:28	5.37
16 Sa	06:27	5.24	18:41	5.40
17 Su	07:37	5.39	19:51	5.60
18 M	08:30	5.62	20:41	5.84
19 Tu	09:13	5.84	21:22	6.05
20 W	09:49	6.02	21:59	6.20
21 Th	10:21	6.16	22:31	6.29
22 F	10:52	6.26	23:02	6.34
23 Sa	11:22	6.32	23:31	6.36
24 Su	11:53	6.35		
25 M	00:03	6.34	12:27	6.33
26 Tu	00:36	6.29	13:05	6.26
27 W	01:16	6.17	13:48	6.14
28 Th	02:05	6.00	14:42	5.98
29 F	03:07	5.81	15:46	5.83
30 Sa	04:21	5.68	16:57	5.76
31 Su	05:38	5.68	18:10	5.84

DOVER — June

Day	Morning time	m	Afternoon time	m
1 M	06:49	5.83	19:17	6.06
2 Tu	07:50	6.06	20:13	6.32
3 W	08:43	6.28	21:04	6.55
4 Th	09:33	6.47	21:53	6.71
5 F	10:21	6.60	22:41	6.79
6 Sa	11:09	6.67	23:29	6.77
7 Su	11:56	6.66		
8 M	00:16	6.66	12:40	6.59
9 Tu	01:01	6.47	13:22	6.45
10 W	01:45	6.24	14:05	6.28
11 Th	02:30	5.97	14:50	6.06
12 F	03:21	5.69	15:41	5.82
13 Sa	04:21	5.44	16:40	5.59
14 Su	05:31	5.29	17:49	5.46
15 M	06:41	5.29	18:57	5.50
16 Tu	07:40	5.42	19:53	5.63
17 W	08:30	5.61	20:41	5.81
18 Th	09:12	5.81	21:22	5.97
19 F	09:49	6.00	21:59	6.11
20 Sa	10:24	6.16	22:34	6.22
21 Su	11:00	6.29	23:10	6.31
22 M	11:39	6.39	23:49	6.37
23 Tu			12:20	6.45
24 W	00:32	6.37	13:05	6.45
25 Th	01:19	6.31	13:52	6.39
26 F	02:11	6.21	14:42	6.30
27 Sa	03:07	6.08	15:35	6.19
28 Su	04:06	5.96	16:33	6.10
29 M	05:09	5.88	17:36	6.06
30 Tu	06:15	5.86	18:41	6.08

DOVER — July

Day	Morning time	m	Afternoon time	m
1 W	07:19	5.92	19:44	6.17
2 Th	08:21	6.05	20:43	6.30
3 F	09:18	6.21	21:39	6.42
4 Sa	10:11	6.37	22:30	6.50
5 Su	10:59	6.49	23:18	6.53
6 M	11:43	6.56		
7 Tu	00:03	6.48	12:24	6.57
8 W	00:45	6.38	13:03	6.51
9 Th	01:26	6.24	13:42	6.41
10 F	02:06	6.07	14:22	6.27
11 Sa	02:48	5.87	15:05	6.07
12 Su	03:35	5.64	15:51	5.84
13 M	04:27	5.42	16:45	5.60
14 Tu	05:29	5.26	17:47	5.43
15 W	06:36	5.23	18:54	5.41
16 Th	07:39	5.35	19:54	5.53
17 F	08:33	5.57	20:46	5.73
18 Sa	09:19	5.84	21:30	5.96
19 Su	10:01	6.10	22:12	6.17
20 M	10:42	6.33	22:53	6.36
21 Tu	11:23	6.52	23:36	6.51
22 W			12:07	6.66
23 Th	00:22	6.59	12:53	6.73
24 F	01:11	6.58	13:40	6.72
25 Sa	02:01	6.50	14:26	6.64
26 Su	02:51	6.37	15:13	6.51
27 M	03:41	6.19	16:03	6.34
28 Tu	04:36	5.99	17:02	6.14
29 W	05:39	5.80	18:09	5.91
30 Th	06:52	5.71	19:23	5.79
31 F	08:07	5.79	20:33	6.00

DOVER — August

Day	Morning time	m	Afternoon time	m
1 Sa	09:12	5.99	21:34	6.15
2 Su	10:03	6.22	22:25	6.29
3 M	10:48	6.41	23:09	6.38
4 Tu	11:27	6.54	23:48	6.42
5 W			12:05	6.61
6 Th	00:26	6.40	12:41	6.62
7 F	01:02	6.33	13:16	6.56
8 Sa	01:36	6.22	13:51	6.45
9 Su	02:11	6.06	14:24	6.27
10 M	02:45	5.86	14:58	6.04
11 Tu	03:23	5.62	15:39	5.76
12 W	04:12	5.38	16:33	5.47
13 Th	05:16	5.18	17:45	5.27
14 F	06:38	5.16	19:06	5.29
15 Sa	07:55	5.38	20:15	5.54
16 Su	08:53	5.73	21:08	5.88
17 M	09:40	6.11	21:53	6.22
18 Tu	10:22	6.44	22:36	6.51
19 W	11:04	6.72	23:18	6.72
20 Th	11:47	6.92		
21 F	00:04	6.84	12:32	7.02
22 Sa	00:51	6.85	13:17	7.01
23 Su	01:38	6.75	14:00	6.90
24 M	02:24	6.56	14:45	6.70
25 Tu	03:11	6.31	15:33	6.42
26 W	04:04	6.00	16:31	6.07
27 Th	05:09	5.68	17:44	5.74
28 F	06:31	5.50	19:12	5.62
29 Sa	08:00	5.61	20:33	5.78
30 Su	09:05	5.89	21:33	6.02
31 M	09:53	6.19	22:18	6.22

QUICK REFERENCE

National Oceanography Centre (www.noc.ac.uk)

319

TIDE TABLES SEPTEMBER-DECEMBER 2020

Time Zone: UT(GMT)

Tidal Predictions : HIGH WATERS 2020

Datum of Predictions = Chart Datum : 3.67 metres below Ordnance Datum (Newlyn)

British Summer Time Dates for 2020 : 29th March to 25th October (data not adjusted)

Units: METRES

DOVER — September

Day	Morning time	m	Afternoon time	m
1 Tu	10:32	6.41	22:56	6.35
2 W	11:07	6.58	23:30	6.44
3 Th	11:42	6.68		
4 F	00:02	6.47	12:15	6.71
5 Sa	00:34	6.44	12:47	6.66
6 Su	01:03	6.36	13:15	6.55
7 M	01:30	6.23	13:41	6.38
8 Tu	01:56	6.06	14:07	6.18
9 W	02:27	5.86	14:40	5.92
10 Th	03:07	5.60	15:28	5.58
11 F	04:09	5.29	16:44	5.24
12 Sa	05:42	5.11	18:24	5.17
13 Su	07:20	5.29	19:49	5.46
14 M	08:27	5.72	20:47	5.90
15 Tu	09:17	6.18	21:33	6.33
16 W	10:00	6.59	22:15	6.67
17 Th	10:41	6.91	22:57	6.91
18 F	11:22	7.12	23:40	7.03
19 Sa	12:05	7.21		
20 Su	00:24	7.02	12:48	7.18
21 M	01:09	6.89	13:31	7.02
22 Tu	01:54	6.66	14:15	6.74
23 W	02:41	6.36	15:05	6.36
24 Th	03:35	5.98	16:06	5.91
25 F	04:42	5.59	17:25	5.51
26 Sa	06:12	5.37	19:09	5.43
27 Su	07:46	5.52	20:30	5.68
28 M	08:49	5.86	21:25	5.97
29 Tu	09:34	6.18	22:05	6.20
30 W	10:10	6.42	22:36	6.36

DOVER — October

Day	Morning time	m	Afternoon time	m
1 Th	10:44	6.59	23:06	6.46
2 F	11:16	6.69	23:36	6.52
3 Sa	11:47	6.72		
4 Su	00:04	6.52	12:15	6.67
5 M	00:30	6.45	12:39	6.55
6 Tu	00:54	6.35	13:02	6.42
7 W	01:18	6.22	13:27	6.25
8 Th	01:48	6.06	14:00	6.02
9 F	02:27	5.80	14:46	5.68
10 Sa	03:25	5.46	16:02	5.29
11 Su	05:02	5.21	17:52	5.19
12 M	06:45	5.34	19:22	5.96
13 Tu	07:57	5.77	20:23	5.96
14 W	08:49	6.26	21:09	6.41
15 Th	09:33	6.68	21:51	6.75
16 F	10:15	7.00	22:33	6.98
17 Sa	10:55	7.20	23:15	7.09
18 Su	11:38	7.27		
19 M	00:00	7.06	12:21	7.19
20 Tu	00:44	6.92	13:05	6.98
21 W	01:30	6.68	13:51	6.65
22 Th	02:18	6.37	14:42	6.23
23 F	03:11	5.99	15:45	5.77
24 Sa	04:15	5.61	17:04	5.39
25 Su	05:41	5.37	18:51	5.34
26 M	07:15	5.49	20:07	5.58
27 Tu	08:18	5.79	20:59	5.87
28 W	09:04	6.09	21:37	6.11
29 Th	09:42	6.33	22:09	6.28
30 F	10:15	6.50	22:39	6.41
31 Sa	10:48	6.59	23:09	6.48

DOVER — November

Day	Morning time	m	Afternoon time	m
1 Su	11:18	6.62	23:36	6.50
2 M	11:45	6.57		
3 Tu	00:03	6.47	12:09	6.48
4 W	00:27	6.40	12:34	6.38
5 Th	00:55	6.30	13:03	6.24
6 F	01:28	6.15	13:40	6.03
7 Sa	02:10	5.92	14:29	5.73
8 Su	03:10	5.64	15:45	5.43
9 M	04:36	5.45	17:24	5.36
10 Tu	06:06	5.53	18:48	5.59
11 W	07:20	5.86	19:51	5.98
12 Th	08:16	6.28	20:41	6.36
13 F	09:03	6.66	21:26	6.67
14 Sa	09:47	6.94	22:09	6.88
15 Su	10:30	7.11	22:54	6.98
16 M	11:15	7.15	23:41	6.97
17 Tu	12:01	7.05		
18 W	00:27	6.85	12:48	6.83
19 Th	01:13	6.66	13:35	6.52
20 F	02:00	6.40	14:26	6.15
21 Sa	02:50	6.09	15:23	5.76
22 Su	03:47	5.77	16:33	5.42
23 M	04:57	5.51	18:01	5.30
24 Tu	06:21	5.47	19:19	5.42
25 W	07:30	5.64	20:15	5.64
26 Th	08:24	5.87	21:00	5.87
27 F	09:07	6.09	21:38	6.07
28 Sa	09:45	6.26	22:12	6.22
29 Su	10:20	6.36	22:43	6.33
30 M	10:51	6.41	23:13	6.40

DOVER — December

Day	Morning time	m	Afternoon time	m
1 Tu	11:21	6.41	23:43	6.42
2 W	11:50	6.39		
3 Th	00:15	6.41	12:21	6.33
4 F	00:48	6.35	12:56	6.23
5 Sa	01:26	6.24	13:38	6.07
6 Su	02:12	6.08	14:30	5.87
7 M	03:07	5.92	15:36	5.69
8 Tu	04:14	5.79	16:51	5.62
9 W	05:26	5.80	18:06	5.70
10 Th	06:36	5.95	19:12	5.91
11 F	07:38	6.21	20:09	6.17
12 Sa	08:33	6.48	21:02	6.41
13 Su	09:23	6.69	21:52	6.60
14 M	10:12	6.83	22:42	6.73
15 Tu	11:02	6.87	23:31	6.78
16 W	11:51	6.81		
17 Th	00:17	6.75	12:38	6.66
18 F	01:01	6.64	13:23	6.43
19 Sa	01:44	6.47	14:09	6.16
20 Su	02:28	6.26	14:57	5.87
21 M	03:16	6.02	15:52	5.59
22 Tu	04:12	5.76	16:58	5.36
23 W	05:18	5.55	18:12	5.27
24 Th	06:29	5.49	19:19	5.34
25 F	07:33	5.57	20:15	5.51
26 Sa	08:27	5.73	21:03	5.72
27 Su	09:14	5.90	21:45	5.93
28 M	09:54	6.05	22:21	6.11
29 Tu	10:29	6.17	22:54	6.26
30 W	11:02	6.27	23:29	6.38
31 Th	11:37	6.35		

National Oceanography Centre (www.noc.ac.uk)

TIDE TABLES JANUARY-APRIL 2021

Time Zone: UT(GMT)

Tidal Predictions : HIGH WATERS 2021

Units: METRES

Datum of Predictions = Chart Datum : 3.67 metres below Ordnance Datum (Newlyn)

British Summer Time Dates for 2021 : 28th March to 31st October (data not adjusted)

DOVER — January

Day	Morning time	m	Afternoon time	m
1 F	00:05	6.46	12:15	6.38
2 Sa	00:45	6.50	12:55	6.36
3 Su	01:25	6.47	13:39	6.28
4 M	02:09	6.38	14:26	6.16
5 Tu	02:55	6.28	15:19	6.02
6 W	03:48	6.16	16:19	5.88
7 Th	04:48	6.06	17:24	5.79
8 F	05:54	6.00	18:32	5.77
9 Sa	07:02	6.03	19:41	5.87
10 Su	08:08	6.15	20:47	6.05
11 M	09:10	6.32	21:45	6.27
12 Tu	10:06	6.47	22:38	6.47
13 W	10:57	6.57	23:24	6.61
14 Th	11:45	6.60		
15 F	00:06	6.68	12:27	6.54
16 Sa	00:46	6.66	13:08	6.42
17 Su	01:24	6.59	13:47	6.25
18 M	02:03	6.46	14:27	6.05
19 Tu	02:44	6.27	15:11	5.81
20 W	03:27	6.01	15:59	5.54
21 Th	04:17	5.71	16:57	5.28
22 F	05:17	5.43	18:06	5.12
23 Sa	06:29	5.27	19:21	5.14
24 Su	07:41	5.32	20:25	5.34
25 M	08:40	5.51	21:16	5.62
26 Tu	09:28	5.75	21:58	5.91
27 W	10:07	5.99	22:35	6.17
28 Th	10:44	6.21	23:11	6.40
29 F	11:22	6.40	23:50	6.59
30 Sa			12:02	6.54
31 Su	00:30	6.71	12:44	6.60

DOVER — February

Day	Morning time	m	Afternoon time	m
1 M	01:12	6.75	13:27	6.57
2 Tu	01:53	6.71	14:11	6.45
3 W	02:35	6.60	14:57	6.28
4 Th	03:21	6.43	15:48	6.07
5 F	04:15	6.21	16:48	5.81
6 Sa	05:19	5.95	17:59	5.59
7 Su	06:35	5.77	19:22	5.55
8 M	07:57	5.79	20:42	5.74
9 Tu	09:09	5.98	21:43	6.04
10 W	10:07	6.20	22:31	6.32
11 Th	10:54	6.37	23:12	6.52
12 F	11:36	6.47	23:51	6.65
13 Sa			12:12	6.49
14 Su	00:27	6.70	12:48	6.45
15 M	01:02	6.68	13:22	6.35
16 Tu	01:36	6.58	13:55	6.21
17 W	02:09	6.41	14:28	6.00
18 Th	02:42	6.17	15:03	5.74
19 F	03:18	5.85	15:45	5.43
20 Sa	04:05	5.48	16:43	5.11
21 Su	05:12	5.14	18:09	4.93
22 M	06:45	5.02	19:40	5.06
23 Tu	08:05	5.21	20:44	5.40
24 W	09:01	5.56	21:31	5.79
25 Th	09:44	5.92	22:11	6.16
26 F	10:23	6.25	22:48	6.48
27 Sa	11:01	6.53	23:27	6.74
28 Su	11:42	6.72		

DOVER — March

Day	Morning time	m	Afternoon time	m
1 M	00:09	6.91	12:24	6.81
2 Tu	00:49	6.98	13:06	6.78
3 W	01:30	6.93	13:49	6.65
4 Th	02:11	6.79	14:33	6.44
5 F	02:56	6.55	15:22	6.14
6 Sa	03:49	6.20	16:22	5.77
7 Su	04:56	5.79	17:37	5.43
8 M	06:22	5.49	19:14	5.36
9 Tu	07:58	5.54	20:37	5.62
10 W	09:02	5.82	21:34	5.97
11 Th	10:05	6.09	22:18	6.26
12 F	10:45	6.28	22:54	6.48
13 Sa	11:19	6.40	23:30	6.62
14 Su	11:51	6.46		
15 M	00:03	6.69	12:24	6.46
16 Tu	00:36	6.68	12:54	6.41
17 W	01:06	6.59	13:22	6.29
18 Th	01:32	6.43	13:48	6.12
19 F	01:57	6.21	14:15	5.91
20 Sa	02:27	5.94	14:50	5.63
21 Su	03:07	5.57	15:42	5.28
22 M	04:11	5.16	17:05	4.97
23 Tu	05:51	4.93	18:51	4.98
24 W	07:27	5.11	20:06	5.34
25 Th	08:30	5.52	20:59	5.79
26 F	09:16	5.95	21:42	6.22
27 Sa	09:57	6.34	22:21	6.58
28 Su	10:36	6.64	23:00	6.86
29 M	11:17	6.84	23:41	7.04
30 Tu	11:59	6.93		
31 W	00:23	7.10	12:42	6.89

DOVER — April

Day	Morning time	m	Afternoon time	m
1 Th	01:05	7.02	13:27	6.73
2 F	01:48	6.82	14:12	6.48
3 Sa	02:36	6.50	15:03	6.14
4 Su	03:32	6.07	16:04	5.74
5 M	04:42	5.62	17:22	5.39
6 Tu	06:18	5.36	19:02	5.35
7 W	07:54	5.49	20:20	5.62
8 Th	09:00	5.77	21:13	5.95
9 F	09:48	6.03	21:54	6.22
10 Sa	10:24	6.20	22:30	6.42
11 Su	10:54	6.33	23:03	6.55
12 M	11:26	6.41	23:36	6.61
13 Tu	11:57	6.43		
14 W	00:08	6.58	12:26	6.39
15 Th	00:36	6.48	12:51	6.29
16 F	00:58	6.33	13:15	6.16
17 Sa	01:21	6.16	13:42	5.99
18 Su	01:51	5.94	14:17	5.76
19 M	02:32	5.63	15:07	5.45
20 Tu	03:35	5.26	16:28	5.16
21 W	05:15	5.05	18:06	5.14
22 Th	06:48	5.21	19:24	5.44
23 F	07:54	5.60	20:21	5.88
24 Sa	08:43	6.03	21:08	6.30
25 Su	09:26	6.40	21:49	6.66
26 M	10:08	6.68	22:30	6.92
27 Tu	10:50	6.86	23:13	7.06
28 W	11:35	6.92	23:57	7.08
29 Th			12:21	6.87
30 F	00:44	6.96	13:09	6.71

QUICK REFERENCE

National Oceanography Centre (www.noc.ac.uk)

MAP OF SEA AREAS

STATIONS WHOSE LATEST REPORTS ARE BROADCAST IN THE 5-MINUTE FORECASTS

Br Bridlington; C Channel Light-Vessel Automatic; F Fife Ness; G Greenwich Light-Vessel Automatic; J Jersey; L Lerwick; M Malin Head; R Ronaldsway; S Sandettie Light-Vessel Automatic; Sc Scilly Automatic; St Stornoway; T Tiree; V Valentia.

BEAUFORT WIND SCALE (SEA)

Scale	Description	MPH	Knots	State of the sea
0	Calm	<1	<1	Sea surface smooth and mirror-like.
1	Light Air	1-3	1-3	Scaly ripples/no crests.
2	Light Breeze	4-7	4-6	Small wavelets, crests glassy – no breaking.
3	Gentle Breeze	8-12	7-10	Large wavelets, crests begin to break, scattered whitecaps
4	Moderate Breeze	13-18	11-16	Small waves - becoming longer, fairly frequent whitecaps.
5	Fresh Breeze	19-24	17-21	Moderate waves taking longer form, many whitecaps, some spray.
6	Strong Breeze	25-31	22-27	Large waves, whitecap common, more spray.
7	Near Gale	32-38	28-33	Sea heaps up & white foam streaks off breaking waves.
8	Gale	39-46	34-40	Moderately high waves of greater length, edges of crests begin to break into spindrift, foam blown in streaks.
9	Strong Gale	47-54	41-47	High waves, dense streaks of foam, sea begins to roll, spray may reduce visibility.
10	Storm	55-63	48-55	Very high waves with overhanging crest, sea white with densely blown foam, heavy rolling, lowered visibility.
11	Violent Storm	64-72	56-63	Exceptionally high waves, foam patches cover sea, visibility more reduced.
12+	Hurricane	≥73	≥64	Air filled with foam, waves over 45ft, sea completely white with driving spray, visibility greatly reduced.

THE COUNTRYSIDE CODE

Launched on 12 July 2004, this Code for England has been produced through a partnership between the Countryside Agency and Countryside Council for Wales.

The Countryside Code has been revised and re-launched to reflect the introduction of new open access rights (Countryside & Rights of Way Act 2000) and changes in society over the last 20 years.

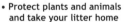

• **Be safe – plan ahead**
Follow any signs, even when going out locally, it's best to get the latest information about where and when you can go; for example, your rights to go onto some areas of open land may be restricted while work is carried out, for safety reasons or during breeding seasons. Follow advice and local signs, and be prepared for the unexpected.

• **Leave gates and property as you find them**
Please respect the working life of the countryside, as our actions can affect people's livelihoods, our heritage, and the safety and welfare of animals and ourselves.

• **Protect plants and animals and take your litter home**
We have a responsibility to protect our countryside now and for future generations, so make sure you don't harm animals, birds, plants, or trees.

• **Keep dogs under close control**
The countryside is a great place to exercise dogs, but it's every owner's duty to make sure their dog is not a danger or nuisance to farm animals, wildlife or other people.

• **Consider other people**
Showing consideration and respect for other people makes the countryside a pleasant Environment for everyone – at home, at work and at leisure.

BIRDS OF CONSERVATION CONCERN (BOCC) 4

The 4th list of the BOCC was published in December 2015 - the species under the 'Red', 'Yellow' and 'Green' categories are listed below. The full details of the assessment was published in *British Birds* 108, 708-746:

Eaton MA, Aebischer NJ, Brown AF, Hearn RD, Lock L, Musgrove AJ, Noble DG, Stroud DA and Gregory RD (2015). Birds of Conservation Concern 4: the population status of birds in the United Kingdom, Channel Islands and Isle of Man.

RED LIST
White-fronted Goose
Pochard
Scaup
Long-tailed Duck
Common Scoter
Velvet Scoter
Black Grouse
Capercaillie
Grey Partridge
Balearic Shearwater
Shag
Red-necked Grebe
Slavonian Grebe
White-tailed Eagle
Hen Harrier
Corncrake
Lapwing
Ringed Plover
Dotterel
Whimbrel
Curlew
Black-tailed Godwit
Ruff
Red-necked Phalarope
Woodcock
Arctic Skua
Puffin
Roseate Tern
Kittiwake
Herring Gull
Turtle Dove
Cuckoo
Lesser Spotted Woodpecker
Merlin
Golden Oriole
Red-backed Shrike
Willow Tit
Marsh Tit
Skylark
Wood Warbler
Grasshopper Warbler
Savi's Warbler
Aquatic Warbler
Marsh Warbler
Starling
Ring Ouzel
Fieldfare
Song Thrush
Redwing
Mistle Thrush
Spotted Flycatcher
Nightingale
Pied Flycatcher
Black Redstart
Whinchat

House Sparrow
Tree Sparrow
Yellow Wagtail
Grey Wagtail
Tree Pipit
Hawfinch
Linnet
Twite
Lesser Redpoll
Yellowhammer
Cirl Bunting
Corn Bunting

YELLOW LIST
Mute Swan
Bewick's Swan
Whooper Swan
Bean Goose
Pink-footed Goose
Greylag Goose
Barnacle Goose
Brent Goose
Shelduck
Wigeon
Gadwall
Teal
Mallard
Pintail
Garganey
Shoveler
Eider
Goldeneye
Smew
Quail
Red Grouse
Black-throated Diver
Great northern Diver
Fulmar
Manx Shearwater
Storm Petrel
Leach's Petrel
Gannet
Bittern
Spoonbill
Black-necked Grebe
Honey Buzzard
Marsh Harrier
Montagu's Harrier
Osprey
Spotted Crake
Crane
Stone Curlew
Avocet
Oystercatcher
Grey Plover
Bar-tailed Godwit

Turnstone
Knot
Curlew Sandpiper
Sanderling
Dunlin
Purple Sandpiper
Common Sandpiper
Green Sandpiper
Spotted Redshank
Greenshank
Wood Sandpiper
Redshank
Snipe
Great Skua
Black Guillemot
Razorbill
Guillemot
Little Tern
Sandwich Tern
Common Tern
Arctic Tern
Black-headed Gull
Mediterranean Gull
Common Gull
Lesser black-backed Gull
Yellow-legged Gull
Caspian Gull
Iceland Gull
Glaucous Gull
Great black-backed Gull
Stock Dove
Tawny Owl
Short-eared Owl
Nightjar
Swift
Kingfisher
Kestrel
Shorelark
House Martin
Willow Warbler
Dartford Warbler
Short-toed Treecreeper
Dipper
Redstart
Dunnock
Meadow Pipit
Water Pipit
Bullfinch
Mealy Redpoll
Scottish Crossbill
Parrot Crossbill
Snow Bunting
Lapland Bunting
Reed Bunting

BIRDS OF CONSERVATION CONCERN (BOCC) 4

GREEN LIST

Tufted Duck
Red-breasted Merganser
Goosander
Ptarmigan
Red-throated Diver
Great Shearwater
Sooty Shearwater
Great Cormorant
Little Egret
Grey Heron
Little Grebe
Great Crested Grebe
Red Kite
Goshawk
Sparrowhawk
Buzzard
Golden Eagle
Water Rail
Moorhen
Coot
Golden Plover
Little Ringed Plover
Little Stint
Jack Snipe
Pomarine Skua
Long-tailed Skua
Little Auk

Black Tern
Little Gull
Rock Dove
Wood Pigeon
Collared Dove
Barn Owl
Long-eared Owl
Green Woodpecker
Great Spotted Woodpecker
Hobby
Peregrine
Chough
Magpie
Jay
Jackdaw
Rook
Carrion Crow
Hooded Crow
Raven
Goldcrest
Firecrest
Blue Tit
Great Tit
Crested Tit
Coal Tit
Bearded Tit
Woodlark
Sand Martin

Swallow
Cetti's Warbler
Long-tailed Tit
Chiffchaff
Blackcap
Garden Warbler
Lesser Whitethroat
Whitethroat
Sedge Warbler
Reed Warbler
Waxwing
Nuthatch
Treecreeper
Wren
Blackbird
Robin
Stonechat
Wheatear
Pied Wagtail
Rock Pipit
Brambling
Chaffinch
Greenfinch
Crossbill
Goldfinch
Siskin

SCHEDULE 1 SPECIES

Under the provisions of the Wildlife and Countryside Act 1981 the following bird species (listed in Schedule 1 - Part I of the Act) are protected by special penalties at all times.

Avocet
Bee-eater
Bittern
Bittern, Little
Bluethroat
Brambling
Bunting, Cirl
Bunting, Lapland
Bunting, Snow
Buzzard, Honey
Chough
Corncrake
Crake, Spotted
Crossbills (all species)
Divers (all species)
Dotterel
Duck, Long-tailed
Eagle, Golden
Eagle, White-tailed

Falcon, Gyr
Fieldfare
Firecrest
Garganey
Godwit, Black-tailed
Goshawk
Grebe, Black-necked
Grebe, Slavonian
Greenshank
Gull, Little
Gull, Mediterranean
Harriers (all species)
Heron, Purple
Hobby
Hoopoe
Kingfisher
Kite, Red
Merlin
Oriole, Golden

Osprey
Owl, Barn
Owl, Snowy
Peregrine
Petrel, Leach's
Phalarope, Red-necked
Plover, Kentish
Plover, Little Ringed
Quail, Common
Redstart, Black
Redwing
Rosefinch, Scarlet
Ruff
Sandpiper, Green
Sandpiper, Purple
Sandpiper, Wood
Scaup
Scoter, Common
Scoter, Velvet
Serin

Shorelark
Shrike, Red-backed
Spoonbill
Stilt, Black-winged
Stint, Temminck's
Stone-curlew
Swan, Bewick's
Swan, Whooper
Tern, Black
Tern, Little
Tern, Roseate
Tit, Bearded
Tit, Crested
Treecreeper, Short-toed
Warbler, Cetti's
Warbler, Dartford
Warbler, Marsh
Warbler, Savi's
Whimbrel
Woodlark
Wryneck

The following birds and their eggs (listed in Schedule 1 - Part II of the Act) are protected by special penalties during the close season, which is Feb 1 to Aug 31 (Feb 21 to Aug 31 below high water mark), but may be killed outside this period - Goldeneye, Greylag Goose (in Outer Hebrides, Caithness, Sutherland, and Wester Ross only), Pintail.

Wetland Bird Survey (WeBS) Local Organisers Required

The BTO are looking for Local Organisers to co-ordinate counters in the areas listed below. Where someone is already in place, counters may still be required for individual sections - check out the County Directory for your nearest Local Organiser or contact the BTO (see below).

See page 305 for a short description about the work of WeBS.

> England
Buckinghamshire - South
Buckinghamshire - North
Derbyshire
Durham
Harrogate & Yorkshire Dales
Huddersfield/Halifax area (Yorkshire)
Kent – East
Kent - West (excl. north Kent estuaries, Sandwich & Dungeness)
Lancashire - West (inland) (excl. the Alt & Ribble estuaries)
Tamar Complex (Cornwall)

> Scotland
Angus (excl. Montrose Basin)
Isle of Cumbrae
Sutherland (excl. Moray Basin)

> Wales
Clwyd (inland)
Carmarthenshire

> Northern Ireland
Down (other sites) (excl. Strangford Lough, South Down Coast, Dundrum Bay
Loughs Neagh & Beg
Londonderry (other sites) (excl. Bann Estuary & Lough Foyle)
Outer Ards
South Down Coast
Tyrone (excl. Loughs Neagh & Beg)

> Channel Islands
Jersey (Inland)

For further information contact:
Gillian Birtles, BTO WeBS Office, The Nunnery, Thetford, Norfolk IP24 2PU
T: 01842 750 050
E: gillian.birtles@bto.org or webs@bto.org
W: www.bto.org/our-science/projects/webs

Looking out for birds

New Publications - in prep

We have started to 'dip our toe' into the water with some small publishing projects.

The two titles below will hopefully come to fruition in early 2020. If you are interested in further information about either of them please contact us (see page 6) and we will pass your enquiry on to the authors.

<><><><><><>

Avifaunas, Atlases & Authors: A Personal View of Local Ornithology in the United Kingdom, from the Earliest Times to 2019
David K. Ballance
A4 wire-bound, ca 280 pages

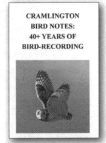

CRAMLINGTON
BIRD NOTES:
40+ YEARS OF
BIRD-RECORDING

Cramlington Bird Notes: 40+ Years of Bird-recording
Steve Holliday (ed)
A4 wire-bound, ca 190 pages

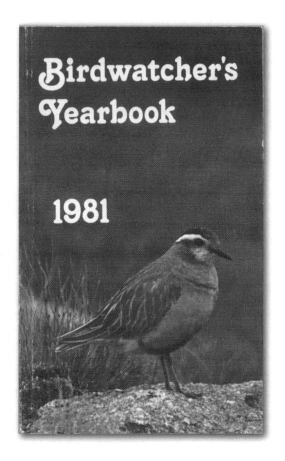

The editors & publishers

1981 to 2001 John E. Pemberton Buckingham Press

2002 to 2015 David & Hilary Cromack Buckingham Press

2016 to 2020 Neil Gartshore Calluna Books